The original and unique

Pets Welcome 2005

with

for more details see

www.winalot-dog.co.uk

including
Holidays with Horses
Pet's Products
Guide to
Pet Friendly Pubs

For Contents see page 3
For Index of towns/counties see back of book

FHG Publications
Paisley

Part of IPC Country and Leisure Media

CONTENTS

Pets Welcome! 2005

ENGLAND

SCOTLAND

WALES

Don’t let your dog’s behaviour spoil your holidays?

If you want to travel with your pet and make the most of the welcoming hotels, guest houses and holiday accommodation featured in ‘Pets Welcome’ then you need a dog whose behaviour won’t let you down. Royvon Dog Training Schools have an outstanding record of success in obedience training, reflecting over 45 year’s experience in pet care. Our 3 week residential training course, under the direction of training expert Darren James, is highly effective in enabling your dog to be under full control.

NO HARSH TRAINING METHODS ARE USED

Your dog will stay in our high quality accommodation and receive training from caring and experienced trainers, based on proven consistency and reward techniques. No harsh training methods are used. The Royvon Dog Training Programme is an intensive obedience course aimed at transforming your dog’s behaviour so you can make the most of your valued pet. Your dog will be taught to be under full control both on and off the lead and natural distractions are used to make the training as realistic as possible. At the end of the course we will give you a full demonstration of your dog’s new found abilities and we are confident that you will be satisfied with the behaviour of your dog.

The ideal holiday destinations for your pet, be assured of a warm and friendly reception, sit back, close your eyes and soak up the history and atmosphere.

Green Farm Hotel & Restaurant North Norfolk

For the past 21 years Philip and Dee Dee Lomax have been extending a warm welcome to guests at the Green Farm, to enjoy the relaxed and friendly atmosphere and the highest standards of hospitality.

Enjoy this tranquil backwater of North Norfolk. Green Farm is the ideal base to discover and dip into the hidden delights of Norfolk. The Glorious Norfolk Broads, beautiful beaches, footpaths and bridleways and many National Trust houses.

The charming 16th Century flint-faced Farmhouse Inn offers 14 antique style bedrooms, all en suite, including four-posters. The converted dairy ground floor accommodation is ideal for guests who find stairs difficult. The food enjoys an enviable reputation for quality, presentation and service.

★★ Please telephone for details of our special breaks available all year ★★

Green Farm Hotel and Restaurant
Thorpe Market, North Walsham, North Norfolk NR11 8TH
Tel: 01263 833602 ❖ Fax: 01263 833163
e-mail: grfarmh@aol.com
website: www.greenfarmhotel.co.uk

New Inn Hotel

Clapham – 'Jewel of the Dales'

A comfortable hotel in the Yorkshire Dales National Park. The New Inn has been lovingly and carefully refurbished during the 16 years of ownership by Keith & Barbara Mannion, with a fine blend of old and new to retain the characteristics of this fine 18th Century Coaching Inn where you can experience a warm and friendly welcome.

The beautiful old Dales village straggles either side of Clapham Beck, one half linked to the other by three bridges, the Church at the top, the New Inn at the bottom. This traditional Village Inn has 20 en suite bedrooms, including ground floor and disabled bedrooms. Resident lounges, Restaurant, two comfortable bars serving a selection of Yorkshire ales, fine wines and a large selection of malt whiskies. Our food offers a mix between traditional and modern cooking.

Truly a 'Yorkshire Inn run by Yorkshire Folk'

★★ Please telephone for details of our special breaks available all year ★★

New Inn Hotel
Clapham, Near Ingleton, North Yorkshire LA2 8HH
Tel: 015242 51203 ❖ Fax: 015242 51496
e-mail: info@newinn-clapham.co.uk
website: www.newinn-clapham.co.uk

ENGLAND and WALES
Counties
NORTH WALES
1. Denbighshire
2. Flintshire
3. Wrexham
SOUTH WALES
4. Swansea
5. Neath and Port Talbot
6. Bridgend
7. Rhondda Cynon Taff
8. Merthyr Tydfil
9. Vale of Glamorgan
10. Cardiff
11. Caerphilly
12. Blaenau Gwent
13. Torfaen
14. Newport
15. Monmouthshire
NORTHUMBERLAND
TYNE & WEAR
DURHAM
CUMBRIA
ISLE OF MAN
NORTH YORKSHIRE
LANCASHIRE
WEST YORKSHIRE
EAST RIDING OF YORKSHIRE
GREATER MANCHESTER
MERSEYSIDE
SOUTH YORKSHIRE
ISLE OF ANGLESEY
CONWY
CHESHIRE
DERBYSHIRE
LINCOLNSHIRE
NOTTINGHAMSHIRE
GWYNEDD
STAFFORDSHIRE
SHROPSHIRE
LEICESTERSHIRE
RUTLAND
NORFOLK
WEST MIDLANDS
POWYS
CAMBRIDGESHIRE
NORTHAMPTONSHIRE
CEREDIGION
WARWICKSHIRE
WORCESTERSHIRE
SUFFOLK
BEDFORDSHIRE
HEREFORDSHIRE
PEMBROKESHIRE
CARMARTHENSHIRE
BUCKINGHAMSHIRE
GLOUCESTERSHIRE
HERTFORDSHIRE
ESSEX
OXFORDSHIRE
BRISTOL
BERKSHIRE
GREATER LONDON
WILTSHIRE
SURREY
KENT
SOMERSET
HAMPSHIRE
WEST SUSSEX
E. SUSSEX
DORSET
DEVON
ISLE OF WIGHT
CORNWALL
SCILLY ISLES
©MAPS IN MINUTES™ 2004

Ratings You Can Trust

ENGLAND

The ***English Tourism Council*** (formerly the English Tourist Board) has joined with the ***AA*** and ***RAC*** to create a new, easily understood quality rating for serviced accommodation, giving a clear guide of what to expect.

HOTELS are given a rating from One to Five ***Stars*** – the more Stars, the higher the quality and the greater the range of facilities and level of services provided.

GUEST ACCOMMODATION, which includes guest houses, bed and breakfasts, inns and farmhouses, is rated from One to Five ***Diamonds***. Progressively higher levels of quality and customer care must be provided for each one of the One to Five Diamond ratings.

HOLIDAY PARKS, TOURING PARKS and CAMPING PARKS are now also assessed using ***Stars***. Standards of quality range from a One Star (acceptable) to a Five Star (exceptional) park.

Look out also for the new *SELF-CATERING* Star ratings. The more ***Stars*** (from One to Five) awarded to an establishment, the higher the levels of quality you can expect. Establishments at higher rating levels also have to meet some additional requirements for facilities.

NB Some self-catering properties had not been assessed at the time of going to press and in these cases the old-style ***KEY*** *symbols will still be shown.*

SCOTLAND

Star Quality Grades will reflect the most important aspects of a visit, such as the warmth of welcome, efficiency and friendliness of service, the quality of the food and the cleanliness and condition of the furnishings, fittings and decor.

THE MORE STARS, THE HIGHER THE STANDARDS.

The description, such as Hotel, Guest House, Bed and Breakfast, Lodge, Holiday Park, Self-catering etc tells you the type of property and style of operation.

WALES

Places which score highly will have an especially welcoming atmosphere and pleasing ambience, high levels of comfort and guest care, and attractive surroundings enhanced by thoughtful design and attention to detail

STAR QUALITY GUIDE FOR

HOTELS, GUEST HOUSES AND FARMHOUSES

SELF-CATERING ACCOMMODATION
(Cottages, Apartments, Houses)

CARAVAN HOLIDAY HOME PARKS
(Holiday Parks, Touring Parks, Camping Parks)

★★★★★	*Exceptional quality*
★★★★	*Excellent quality*
★★★	*Very good quality*
★★	*Good quality*
★	*Fair to good quality*

In England, Scotland and Wales, all graded properties are inspected annually by Tourist Authority trained Assessors.

People-friendly Cottages for Pets!

Lovely locations with superb walks in some of England's most picturesque countryside. From Windsor to the Welsh Borders, with lots to choose from in the Cotswolds and Shakespeare's Country. Small, friendly company with personal knowledge of the area - why not tell US what you are looking for and we'll do our best to find the right place for you to call 'home'!

e-mail: enquiries@cottageinthecountry.co.uk
www.cottageinthecountry.co.uk
Tel: 01993 831495
Fax: 01993 831095

Berkshire

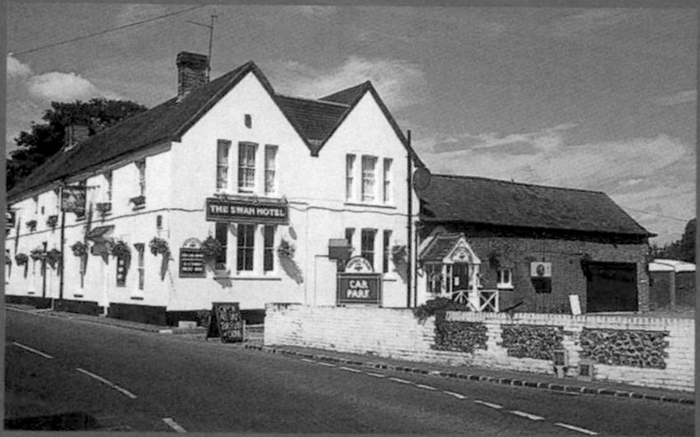

The Compton Swan Hotel

High Street, Compton, Near Newbury, Berkshire RG20 6NJ

Situated in the heart of the Berkshire Downlands. The Hotel has 6 en suite bedrooms with TV, radio alarms, hairdryers, beverage facilities, telephones and sauna. An extensive menu with traditional, exotic, vegetarian, and special diets catered for. Our home-cooked meals are a speciality. Downlands Healthy Eating Award winner. Large walled garden where we have *al fresco* eating; BBQs. Near the famous ancient Ridgeway National Trail and is an ideal base for walking, horse-riding, and golf. Stabling and horsebox available. Real Ales and Bar Meals available. Entry in CAMRA Good Beer Guide and Good Pub Guide.
A friendly reception by staff and our Jack Russells "Mushy & Bonnie".

Tel: 01635 578269 • Fax: 01635 578765
e-mail: info@comptonswan.co.uk • www.SmoothHound.co.uk

FHG

Visit the FHG website
www.holidayguides.com
for details of the wide choice of accommodation featured in the full range of FHG titles

Classy Cottages

Polperro – Fowey

Spectacular cottages just feet from beach... Along coast, isolated residence with sea views... Farm cottages in the 'Valley of the Foxes'
Open log fires. Pets Welcome. Dog friendly local beaches, and list of other beaches which welcome dogs. Local pubs which serve good food and allow dogs. Indoor Private Swimming Pool with sauna, spa etc.
We welcome you with a Cornish Cream Tea.

www.classycottages.co.uk • nicolle@classycottages.co.uk

Please telephone Fiona or Martin Nicolle on 07000 423000

TREMAINE GREEN

for MEMORABLE HOLIDAYS

"A beautiful private hamlet" of 11 award-winning traditional cosy **Cornish** craftsmen's cottages between **Looe** and **Polperro.** Clean, comfortable and well equipped, with a warm friendly atmosphere, for pets with 2 to 8 people. Set in lovely grounds, only 12 miles from the **Eden Project** with country and coastal walks nearby. Pets £16 pw; owners from only **£112:**

• Towels, Linen, Electricity & Central Heating included • Dishwashers in larger cottages • Power shower Baths • Launderette • Games Room • Tennis Court • TV/Videos • Cots & Highchairs available • Pubs & Restaurants in easy walking distance

Mr & Mrs J Spreckley, Tremaine Green Country Cottages, Pelynt, Near Looe, Cornwall PL13 2LT
Tel: 01503 220333 • e-mail: stay@tremainegreen.co.uk • web: www.tremainegreen.co.uk

Dalswinton

HOUSE

A Victorian stone built Cornish house of character in a glorious rural setting. Standing in 10 acres of formal gardens and meadowland, the house overlooks the Vale of Lanherne and the village of St Mawgan with views to the sea at the dog friendly beach of Mawgan Porth. Our Hotel offers a comfortable, friendly atmosphere and great food prepared with fresh local produce. Regret no children under 16.

- Dogs free of charge and allowed everywhere (except the dining room)
- 8 Acres of private meadowland for dog exercise
- Bed & Breakfast from £32.00 per person per night
- Short Break and weekly rates available
- Discounted Autumn and Spring rates
- Car parking and heated outdoor pool (in season)
- All rooms en suite, non-smoking, with tea/coffee and colour TV
- Licensed bar and a restaurant serving 3 course dinner
- Self catering Garden Chalet
- Easy access to Newquay airport and The Eden Project

Proprietors: Stuart and Sal Hope

Dalswinton House, St Mawgan-in-Pydar, Cornwall TR8 4EZ

Tel: 01637 860385

Visit us at www.dalswinton.com e-mail: dalswinton@bigwig.net

Paul & Barbie Higgins
Trewith, Duloe, near Liskeard
Cornwall PL14 4PR

TREWITH HOLIDAY COTTAGES

Self Catering Accommodation Open All Year

Tel: 01503 262184
mobile: 07968 262184

Situated in a superb elevated position of outstanding natural beauty. Just 1 1/2 miles from Looe. Choice of 4 refurbished cottages with 1-3 bedrooms. Fully-equipped and tastefully furnished with full central heating. Use of laundry room. Peaceful location with delightful walks. Many beaches, coves, fishing, shopping close by in Looe. Because of ponds young children need supervision. Well behaved dogs welcome.

E-mail: holiday-cottages@trewith.freeserve.co.uk
www.trewith.freeserve.co.uk

Friesian Valley Cottages

For Colour Brochure
Telephone 01209 890901

Luxury Cottages in peaceful rural hamlet on Atlantic coast between Newquay and St Ives, surrounded by fields, beautiful sandy beaches and National Trust Coastal path.

£130 to £620 per week.

Step onto The Coastal Path...

Escape the pressures of life. Relax! explore the Cornish Coast from Green Door Cottages in Port Gaverne.

8 comfortable, restored 18th Century cottages set around a sheltered courtyard, plus 2 prestigious apartments with panoramic sea views beside a picturesque cove, directly on the Coastal path, less than half a mile from Port Isaac.

An ideal location for your holiday and short breaks. Well behaved dogs are very welcome.

Call now for a brochure on:
01208 880293

Green Door Cottages
PORT GAVERNE
email: enquiries@greendoorcottages.co.uk
web: www.greendoorcottages.co.uk

Mawgan Porth Bay, Near Newquay, Cornwall TR8 4BN
Tel: 01637 860512

e-mail: adogfriendly@aol.com • web: www.dogfriendlyhotel.co.uk

GIVE YOURSELVES & YOUR DOGS A BREAK

at our family-run White Lodge Hotel overlooking beautiful Mawgan Porth Bay, near Newquay, Cornwall

- Dogs most welcome - FREE OF CHARGE
- Your dogs sleep with you in your bedroom
- Direct access to sandy beach and coastal path
- Dog loving proprietors with 20 years' experience in catering for dog owners on holiday with their dogs
- ALL bedrooms with colour TV, tea/coffee makers, alarm clocks, radios, heaters etc
- Fantastic sea views from most rooms
- Well-stocked residents' lounge bar, dining room & sun patio with outstanding sea views across the bay
- Large free car park within hotel grounds

SPECIAL 6 DAYS (5 NIGHTS) CHRISTMAS BREAK ONLY £305 Half Board	SPECIAL 6 DAYS (5 NIGHTS) NEW YEAR BREAK ONLY £260 Half Board	SPECIAL 6 DAYS (5 NIGHTS) BREAKS ONLY £205-£217.50 BB & Evening Meal	WEEKLY TERMS FROM £287-£304.50 FOR 5-COURSE EVENING DINNER, BED AND 4-COURSE BREAKFAST WITH CHOICE OF MENU

This Hotel is now open all year – Winter Break packages available

Phone for full colour brochure

ALL PRICES INCLUDE VAT AT $17\frac{1}{2}$%

TRENCREEK FARM
Self-Catering & Camping
with country views and within
easy reach of the sea. Tennis court,
heated swimming pool & fishing lakes etc
ONE OF CORNWALL'S
FAVOURITE FAMILY HOLIDAY PARKS
Trencreek Farm Holiday Park
Hewaswater, St Austell, Cornwall PL26 7JG
Tel: 01726 882540 • Website: www.trencreek.co.uk

The Rosevine Hotel

Porthcurnick Beach, Portscatho, St Mawes, Cornwall TR2 5EW

Tel: 01872 580206 • Fax: 01872 580230

e-mail: info@rosevine.co.uk • website: www.rosevine.co.uk

• Cornwall's "AA TOP 200" luxury hotel • De luxe bedrooms and suites • Award-winning cuisine • • Beautiful sub-tropical gardens facing directly over the safe, sandy beach fronting the National Trust coastline • • Warm heated indoor pool • • Children and pets most welcome •

CORNWALL'S ONLY RAC THREE DINING AWARDS AND BLUE RIBBON HOTEL

RAC ★★★ AA ★★★ 82%

Two comfortable, well-equipped cottages set in an Area of Outstanding Natural Beauty, each with its own charming garden. Individually furnished with co-ordinating furnishings. Full central heating and double glazed. Microwave, colour TV and video, telephone, washing machine, fridge and all bed linen. We also offer use of our boat during your stay, All these included in the price. Pets are welcome. Beautiful woodland walks for you to stroll through. Perfect for fishing and bird watching.

Tel: 01872 861915

E-mail: jean@kingharry.f9.co.uk

King Harry Ferry Cottages

High Quality Cottages to Let near Truro

www.kingharry-info.co.uk

Near Perranporth

Greenmeadow Cottages

Highly praised luxury cottages. Sleep 6. Superbly clean, comfortable and spacious. Open all year. Short Breaks out of season. Pets welcome in two of the cottages. Non-smoking available. Ample off-road parking.

For brochure and bookings

Tel: 01872 540483

Crantock Bay Hotel *a very special place, all year round...*

Crantock Bay Hotel is superbly located for a holiday with your dogs. Our gardens lead direct to the Cornish coastal path and within 10 minutes walk of the 'dogs welcome' beaches of Polly Joke and Crantock Bay. Facilities include: comfortable bedrooms – many with sea views, a quality restaurant, Indoor pool, Jacuzzi, gym and tennis court.

Crantock Bay Hotel
West Pentire, Crantock, Cornwall TR8 5SE
Tel: (01637) 830229 Fax: (01637) 831111
Email: stay@crantockbayhotel.co.uk
www.crantockbayhotel.co.uk

CORNWALL TOURISM AWARDS 2002 *HIGHLY COMMENDED*

AA 3 STAR GOOD HOTEL GUIDE ASHLEY COURTENEY

BOSINVER HOLIDAY COTTAGES

Nestling in a hidden valley near the sea, the Eden Project and Lost Gardens of Heligan, our small farm has friendly animals and ponies. Choose from our 16th Century thatched farmhouse or cottages privately set in their own gardens surrounded by wildflower meadows. Wander down to the fishing lake or village pub, swim in the pool, play tennis, or relax and listen to the birdsong. No pets during Summer school holidays please.

Brochure from: Mrs Pat Smith, Bosinver Farm,
Trelowth, St Austell, Cornwall PL26 7DT • Tel: 01726 72128
E-mail: reception@bosinver.co.uk • Website: www.bosinver.co.uk

- Caravan Holiday Homes
- Touring & Camping
- North coast 3 miles, Truro 5
- Families & couples
- Pets welcome
- Peace and quiet
- No club or bar
- Shop/Off-licence
- Laundry room • Games room
- Children's play area
- Electric hook-ups
- Satellite TV in all units

Set in the heart of glorious Cornish countryside, yet only a short distance from the A30, this spacious, well-run park offers peace and relaxation in a delightful 4-acre rural setting. Holiday homes are fully equipped (except linen, which may be hired)

Chiverton Park, Blackwater, Truro TR4 8HS • 01872 560667
info@chivertonpark.co.uk • www.chivertonpark.co.uk

Penmorvah Manor Hotel and Courtyard Cottages

Falmouth, Cornwall TR11 5ED

- 3 Star Country House Hotel and Self Catering Courtyard Cottages
- Situated in 6 acres of mature gardens and woodland
- Ideal for visiting Cornwall's superb gardens
- Close to Falmouth and Coastal Paths • Well-behaved dogs welcome
- Ground floor bedrooms for easy pet access • Ample car parking

Tel: 01326 250277 • Fax: 01326 250509
e-mail: reception@penmorvah.co.uk
website: www.penmorvah.co.uk

WILLAPARK MANOR HOTEL

Bossiney, Tintagel, Cornwall PL34 0BA
Tel: (01840) 770782

One of the most beautifully situated hotels in England

set in 14 acres of landscaped gardens and secluded woodland with spectacular views of Bossiney Bay and the rugged unspoilt coastline towards Boscastle. The lawns in front of this character country house sweep down to meet the cliffs where a hidden gate leads to the coast path and beach. This unique situation, well appointed en suite rooms, exceptional cuisine and friendly atmosphere, combined with the professionalism gained by years of experience make people return every year. A warm welcome and memorable holiday assured for you and your dog.

Tariff: En suite room, breakfast and 4 course dinner from £310 weekly or £48 daily inc. VAT.

English Tourism Council ★★ HOTEL

www.willapark.co.uk

Within the sound of the sea at Trevaunance Cove…

Delightful old inn with enormous beams

- Log fires
- Real Ale
- Malt Whisky
- Upstairs Eating Areas

The **Driftwood Spars** Hotel

Walkies Country

All bedrooms have excellent facilities, some with wonderful views

OPEN ALL YEAR • AMPLE PARKING

The Driftwood Spars Hotel, Trevaunance Cove, St Agnes, Cornwall TR5 0RT

Now Brewing Own Beer

Tel: 01872 552428 • www.driftwoodspars.com

www.foweyvacations.com
tel: 01726 814263
sarahfurniss@aol.com

Near Fowey

Fabulous Listed farmhouse and large, spacious barn with every comfort and convenience. Both set within their own gardens and grounds, with distant sea and spectacular countryside views in a tranquil setting. Great walks nearby. Close to the Eden Project, Lost Gardens of Heligan, the coast, beaches, and the harbour town of Fowey. Both properties are of an exceptionally high standard, mostly with en suite facilities and tasteful furnishings. Pets are very welcome, with their own 'Welcome Pack'. Both properties sleep 6.

Visit our website www.foweyvacations.com or telephone for a brochure 01726 814263

Creekside Cottages

offer a fine selection of individual water's edge, village and rural cottages, sleeping from 2-10, situated around the creeks of the Carrick Roads, near Falmouth, South Cornwall. Set in enchanting and picturesque positions, with many of the cottages offering panoramic creek views. Perfect locations for family holidays, all close to superb beaches, extensive sailing and boating facilities, Cornish gardens and excellent walks. The majority of the cottages are available throughout the year, and all offer peaceful, comfortable and fully equipped accommodation; most have open fires. Dogs welcome.

Just come and relax

**For a colour brochure please phone
01326 375972
www.creeksidecottages.co.uk**

The Coppermines & Coniston Lakes Cottages

ETC ★★ to ★★★★★

50 unique Lakeland cottages for 2-30 of quality and character in stunning mountain scenery. Log fires, exposed beams. Weekends and Short Breaks.

Book online: www.coppermines.co.uk

01539441765 **Pets very welcome!**

Rose Cottage

Lorton Road, Cockermouth CA13 0DX

Family run guest house on the outskirts of Cockermouth. Warm, friendly atmosphere. Ample off-road parking. All rooms en suite with colour TV, tea/coffee, central heating and most have double glazing.

Pets most welcome in the house (excluding dining room), and there are short walks nearby. Ideal base for visiting both Lakes and coast.

Tel & Fax: 01900 822189 **website: www.rosecottageguest.co.uk**

Midtown Cottages, High Lorton

These two cottages have both been awarded four stars and are electrically centrally heated for all year round use. Built around a courtyard area, they are 'upside down' – the bedrooms (one double, one twin) being downstairs with the lounge, dining area and small but well equipped kitchen with dishwasher and freezer upstairs to make the most of the views over the fells. Whilst the two cottages are not absolutely identical, they are both furnished to the same high standard. They are both non-smoking, but pets are very welcome. Cot & high chair available if required. Lorton lies at the northern end of Lorton Vale, a beautiful valley which runs from Cockermouth in the west to Buttermere in the east. The river Cocker runs the full length of the valley, and at the end of the 18th century its fast flowing streams that flow down from the fells, through the village were used as the motive power for flour and linen mills. Some of these mill buildings survive today, having later been used by the Jennings family as their brewery. The 'Yew Tree Hall', now the village hall, was once the brewery malt house. Jennings ales are still brewed in nearby Cockermouth.

Complete weeks £420(High Season), £360 (Mid Season), £240 (Low Season). Short breaks from £160

Please contact: Mr & Mrs M. Burrell • Tel: +44(0) 1264 710165
e-mail: info@midtown-cottages.com • website: www.midtown-cottages.com

015394 32330
www.smallwoodhotel.co.uk
smallwood house hotel
Compston Road, Ambleside, Cumbria. LA22 9DJ
..where quality and the customer come first
..try us

LONSDALE HOUSE HOTEL
11 Daltongate, Ulverston, Cumbria LA12 7BD

LONSDALE HOUSE HOTEL – situated right in the heart of Ulverston (South Lakes festival town). Offering friendly service, great food and comfortable accommodation. Dogs are most welcome, provided they are accompanied by well-behaved owners, and can stay in the rooms. A short walk from the hotel, on the edge of the National Park overlooking Ulverston, is Sir John Barrow's Monument on Hoad Hill. A popular place for walking with superb views of the Lake District peaks and panoramic view of Morecambe Bay. There are also some good walks along the bay coast a short drive from the hotel. Lonsdale House Hotel is an excellent base to explore the Lake District because we are only 15 minutes from Lake Windermere and about 30 minutes from Windermere Village, Coniston and Cartmel.

Phone **01229 582598** for a brochure and find out about our Special Breaks.
www.lonsdalehousehotel.co.uk

Greenhowe Caravan Park
Great Langdale, English Lakeland.

Greenhowe is a permanent Caravan Park with Self Contained Holiday Accommodation. Subject to availability Holiday Homes may be rented for short or long periods from 1st March until mid-November. The Park is situated in the heart of the Lake District some half a mile from Dungeon Ghyll at the foot of the Langdale Pikes. It is an ideal centre for Climbing, Fell Walking, Riding, Swimming, Water Skiing or just a lazy holiday.
Please ask about Short Breaks.

Greenhowe Caravan Park
Great Langdale, Ambleside
Cumbria LA22 9JU

For free colour brochure

Telephone: (015394) 37231
Fax: (015394) 37464
Freephone: 0800 0717231
www.greenhowe.com

Your Stepping Stone to the Cumbrian Lake District

Carrock Cottages are three recently renovated stone built cottages set on the fringe of the Lakeland Fells.
A quiet rural location near the lovely villages of Hesket Newmarket with its award winning brewery, Caldbeck and Greystoke.
Explore the beauty of the Lake District National Park or head North to historic Carlisle and on to Hadrians Wall.
Fell walking & other activities close to hand as well as excellent restaurants.
A warm welcome guaranteed.
Accommodation for 1 to 12 people.
On-site games room, home cooked meal service.
Spa facilities.

Carrock House, Hutton Roof, Penrith, Cumbria CA11 0XY
Tel: Malcolm or Gillian on 01768 484 111 or Fax: 017684 888 50

www.carrockcottages.co.uk • info@carrockcottages.co.uk

Quality Holiday Homes in England's Beautiful Lake District

Over 200 ETC inspected and graded properties throughout the southern and central Lake District.
Lakelovers are sure to have a property to meet your needs.

LAKELOVERS

Free Leisure Club membership with every booking

Tel: 015394 88855 • Fax: 015394 88857

e-mail: bookings@lakelovers.co.uk • www.lakelovers.co.uk ETC ★★★ – ★★★★★

Lakelovers, Belmont House, Lake Road, Bowness-on-Windermere, Cumbria LA23 3BJ

Publisher's Note

While every effort is made to ensure accuracy, we regret that FHG Publications cannot accept responsibility for errors, omissions or misrepresentations in our entries or any consequences thereof. Prices in particular should be checked because we go to press early. We will follow up complaints but cannot act as arbiters or agents for either party.

Tanglewood Caravan Park

CAUSEWAY HEAD, SILLOTH-ON-SOLWAY, CUMBRIA CA7 4PE

Tanglewood is a family-run park on the fringes of the Lake District National Park. It is tree-sheltered and situated one mile inland from the small port of Silloth on the Solway Firth, with a beautiful view of the Galloway Hills. Large modern holiday homes are available from March to January, with car parking beside each home. Fully equipped except for bed linen, with end bedroom, panel heaters in both bedrooms and the bathroom, electric lighting, hot and cold water, toilet, shower, gas fire, fridge and colour TV, all of which are included in the tariff. Touring pitches also available with electric hook-ups and water/drainage facilities, etc. Play area. Licensed lounge with adjoining children's play room. Pets welcome free but must be kept under control at all times. Full colour brochure available.

★★★ **TEL: 016973 31253**

e-mail: tanglewoodcaravanpark@hotmail.com
website: www.tanglewoodcaravanpark.co.uk

NEW HOUSE FARM

BUTTERMERE/LORTON VALLEY, COCKERMOUTH, CUMBRIA CA13 9UU
web: www.newhouse-farm.co.uk • e-mail: hazel@newhouse-farm.co.uk

Tel: 01900 85404
Fax: 01900 85478
(See Map 5 Ref C3)

SITUATED IN THE QUIETEST AND MOST BEAUTIFUL PART OF THE LAKES, NEW HOUSE FARM HAS 15 ACRES OF OPEN FIELDS, PONDS, STREAMS AND WOODS WHICH GUESTS AND DOGS MAY WANDER AROUND AT LEISURE AND THERE IS EASY ACCESS TO NEARBY LAKES AND FELLS. THERE ARE SIX LUXURIOUS EN SUITE BEDROOMS, ALL WITH SPECTACULAR VIEWS, AN ELEGANT DINING ROOM AND THREE SITTING ROOMS, ALL WITH OPEN FIRES. GOOD FOOD. WELCOMING HOSTS.

BED & BREAKFAST FROM £52, DINNER, BED & BREAKFAST FROM £74.

Good Hotel Guide — Which? Hotel Guide — **AA ◆◆◆◆◆**

"THE LORTON VALE — A PLACE FOR ALL SEASONS"

Toad Hall Cottages

Pets very welcome with well behaved humans!

250 outstanding and unusual quality cottages throughout Devon, Cornwall & Exmoor. Situated in fabulous walking countryside, with magical scenery, dog friendly beaches and pubs so your humans will enjoy their holiday too!

08700 777345

www.toadhallcottages.com

or email: thc@toadhallcottages.com

Holiday Homes & Cottages S.W.

www.swcottages.co.uk

Large selection of cottages in Devon & Cornwall. Pets welcomed. ETC rated. Coastal and Rural locations.

Tel: 01803 663650

Fax: 01803 664037

Watermill Cottages

Down a narrow lane lies a secret valley just over a mile inland from Slapton sands. There you will find the six delightful **Watermill Cottages** on the banks of a small river by an old mill house. A peaceful haven with wonderful walks and freedom for children to explore. Home cooking available. Winter breaks from **£95**.

Hansel, Dartmouth, South Devon TQ6 0LN

website: www.watermillcottages.co.uk

For our colour brochure call 01803 770 219 or e-mail: graham@hanselpg.freeserve.co.uk

Boswell Farm
Boswell Farm, Sidford, EX10 0PP
ETC ★★★★
Tel: 01395 514162 Fax: 01395 514162
Website: www.boswell-farm.co.uk
Email: dillon@boswell-farm.co.uk

17th Century Farmhouse with seven individual cottages, beautifully converted from period farm buildings, each with its own enclosed, delightful garden.

Cradled in 45 acres of peaceful valley amid glorious Devon countryside. Abundant wildlife. Art Studio facilities in restored historical Victorian building with stunning views. All weather tennis court, trout pond. Idyllic walks in Area of Outstanding Natural Beauty, two miles from beach and World Heritage Coastline.

14th Century Inn and amenities within walking distance. Open all year. ETC ★★★★

GET AWAY FROM IT ALL

There will always be times when you wish there was somewhere you could go to get away from it all, relax in beautiful surroundings, and sample delicious food.

THE CHERRYBROOK HOTEL

IS AN IDEAL CHOICE – WARMEST WELCOME

◆◆◆◆

Set in the heart of Dartmoor National Park, Cherrybrook is an excellent base for walking, touring or simply enjoying the breathtaking scenery.

To find out more, telephone or fax Margaret or Andy Duncan on:

01822 880260

CHERRYBROOK HOTEL, TWO BRIDGES, YELVERTON, DEVON PL20 6SP

e-mail: info@cherrybrook-hotel.co.uk www.cherrybrook-hotel.co.uk

CHICHESTER HOUSE HOLIDAY APARTMENTS

Quiet, relaxing, fully furnished apartments.

Opposite Barricane Shell Beach – central seafront position with outstanding sea and coastal views.

Watch the sun go down into the sea from your own balcony.

• Open all year • Free parking • Pets by arrangement.

SAE to resident proprietor, Joyce Bagnall.

Off-peak reductions. Short Break details on request.

The Esplanade, Woolacombe EX34 7DJ
Tel: 01271 870761

St Brannocks House

Come and see me sometime! Hi! I'm Sam the Daxi and my friends can come and stay here free. Look forward to seeing you. I've got:

- ★ Brilliant walks and beaches we can play on
- ★ A lovely relaxing home which is open all year
- ★ Great food and a cosy Bar where I can meet you
- ★ A mistress who likes us - and children too
- ★ A large dog-carriage park

Bed & Breakfast from £27.50 per night
7 nights Dinner, Bed & Breakfast from £250

Phone or write to Barbara Clarke

RAC ★★ ETC

Tel/Fax: 01271 863873
St Brannocks Road,
Ilfracombe EX34 8EQ
email: stbrannocks@aol.com
website: www.stbrannockshotel.co.uk

AMBER HOUSE HOTEL

6 Roundham Road, Paignton, Devon TQ4 6EZ • Tel: 01803 558372

✻ Family-run licensed Hotel. ✻ Colour TV and tea/coffee making facilities in all rooms. ✻ All en suite. ✻ Ground floor rooms. ✻ Non-smoking. ✻ Good food, highly recommended. ✻ Large car park. ✻ Spacious suntrap garden and patio. ✻ Park and beach 5 minutes' walk. ✻ We pride ourselves on our high standards. ✻ A warm welcome assured to pets and their families. ✻ B&B from £20 per night. ✻ PETS FREE.

Lisa & Aaron Linger

Write or telephone now for further details

Northcott Barton Farm Cottage

Beautifully equipped, spotlessly clean three bedroom cottage with large enclosed garden. A walker's and country lover's ideal: for a couple seeking peace and quiet or a family holiday. Very special rates for low season holidays, couples and short breaks. Near golf, riding, Tarka trail and R.H.S. Rosemoor. Character, comfort, beams, log fire, "*Perfick*". Pets Welcome, no charge.

For availability please contact Sandra Gay,
Northcott Barton, Ashreigney, Chulmleigh, Devon EX18 7PR
Tel/Fax: 01769 520259
e-mail: sandra@northcottbarton.co.uk
web: www.northcottbarton.co.uk

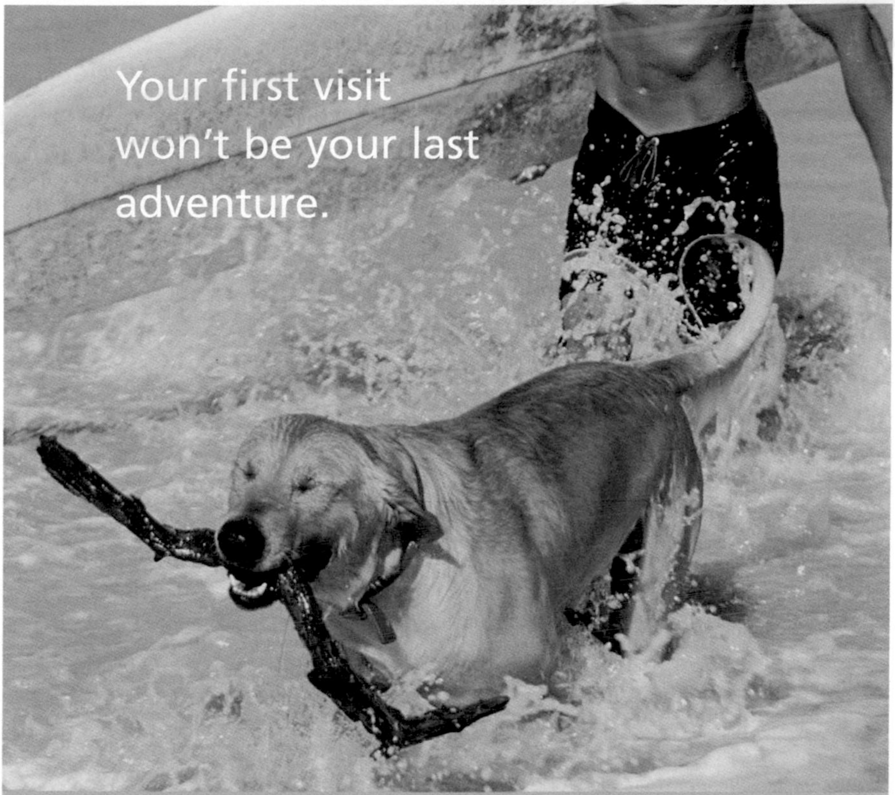
Your first visit
won't be your last
adventure.

WIDMOUTH FARM

Watermouth, Near Ilfracombe
Devon EX34 9RX

Tel: 01271 863743

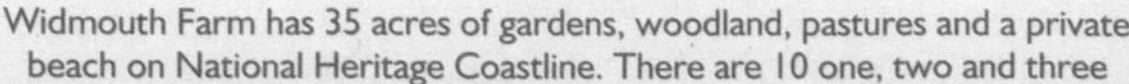
Widmouth Farm has 35 acres of gardens, woodland, pastures and a private beach on National Heritage Coastline. There are 10 one, two and three

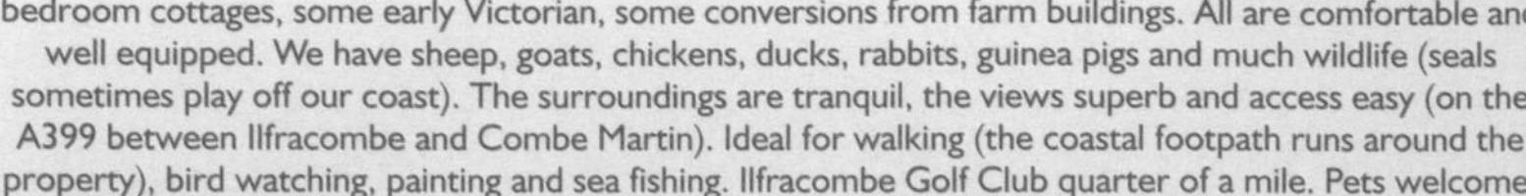
bedroom cottages, some early Victorian, some conversions from farm buildings. All are comfortable and well equipped. We have sheep, goats, chickens, ducks, rabbits, guinea pigs and much wildlife (seals sometimes play off our coast). The surroundings are tranquil, the views superb and access easy (on the A399 between Ilfracombe and Combe Martin). Ideal for walking (the coastal footpath runs around the property), bird watching, painting and sea fishing. Ilfracombe Golf Club quarter of a mile. Pets welcome.

e-mail: holiday@widmouthfarmcottages.co.uk **website: www.widmouthfarmcottages.co.uk**

Woolacombe holiday cottages

- Quality coastal cottages
- Seafront to Farmhouse • 1–5 bedrooms
- Woolacombe, Croyde, Georgeham, Willingcott, West Down ...

- **short breaks**
- **pets**
- **special offers**

Tel & Fax: 01271 870846

www.woolacombe-cottages.co.uk
e-mail: info@woolacombe-cottages.co.uk

The Port Light Hotel, Restaurant & Inn

Doggies' Heaven, Walkers' Paradise, Romantics' Dream

WE ARE REALLY TOTALLY PET-FRIENDLY

As featured in Times, Guardian, Mail, Telegraph, Express, Dogs Today, Your Dog and many pet-friendly internet sites

- **Luxury en suite rooms, easy access onto the gardens**
- **Close to secluded sandy cove (dogs permitted) 20 minutes' walk**
- **No charge for pets which are most welcome *throughout* the hotel and can dine with you.**
- **International award for outstanding food and service**
- **Outstanding reputation for superb home-cooked fayre specialising in fresh sea food**
- **Set alongside the famous National Trust Salcombe to Hope Cove coastal walk**
- **Fully licensed bar - log burner - real ale**
- **SPECIAL PET BREED BREAKS THROUGHOUT THE YEAR**
- **Large free car park • Open Christmas & New Year • Self-catering cottages**

A totally unique location, set amidst acres of National Trust coastal countryside with panoramic views towards Cornwall, Dartmoor and France.

Important advice: always check to ensure other so-called 'pet-friendly' hotels really are! Talk to us to find out more.

Bolberry Down, Malborough, Near Salcombe, South Devon TQ7 3DY
e-mail: info@portlight.co.uk • website: www.portlight.co.uk
Tel: (01548) 561384 or (07970) 859992 • Sean & Hazel Hassall

❖ Bolberry Farm Cottages ❖

Bolberry, Near Salcombe, Devon TQ7 3DY

Luxury two and three bedroom barn conversion cottages
• Private gardens • Shared orchard • Views across valley • Gas, coal, open fires
• Parking • Finished to a very high standard • Linen and towels included
• Central heating • Close to coastal path and pet friendly beaches
• No charge for pets • Dog wash • Short Breaks out of season • Special couples rate
• Discount on meals taken at our Hotel nearby – Port Light Hotel
Credit/Debit cards accepted

Tel: 01548 561384 • e-mail: info@bolberryfarmcottages.co.uk
www.bolberryfarmcottages.co.uk • Hazel & Sean Hassall

❖ The Pet Holiday Specialist ❖

THE LORD HALDON COUNTRY HOUSE HOTEL

Dunchideock, Near Exeter
Devon EX6 7YF
Tel: 01392 832483
Fax: 01392 833765
e-mail: enquiries@lordhaldonhotel.co.uk

The Lord Haldon Country House Hotel is the perfect venue for a quiet get-away break with your beloved pet. Acres of private grounds, mile of driveway for exercise and animals are welcome in guests' bedrooms by arrangement.The hotel stands in its own grounds, four miles south west of Exeter, set 400 feet above sea level above the Haldon Hills. It is a family Hotel run by the Preece family, owners for over 21 years. The hotel is AA*** recognised with two Red Rosettes for its restaurant, which is open seven days a week, lunch times and evenings. There is also an intimate Lounge Bar which serves bar food. The Lord Haldon is the only hotel in Devon that is a member of Relais du Silence, an independent hotel consortium dedicated to fine food, service, peace and quiet. For further information about how you can enjoy the finest part of Devon, please telephone for a free hotel brochure, or visit our website: **www.lordhaldonhotel.co.uk**

Torcross Apartments

Situated directly on the beach in the unspoilt countryside of the South Hams between the blue waters of Start Bay and the Slapton Ley Nature Reserve. Seven miles to Dartmouth. Half-price breaks. Central heating. Ground floor apartments and lift to all floors. In-house bar and restaurant; private car park. Lovely walks on coastal path.

Brochure with pleasure or visit our **website** on **www.torcross.com**
Torcross, South Devon TQ7 2TQ Tel: 01548 580206 • Fax: 01548 580996
e-mail: enquiries@torcross.com

YOUR PET STAYS FREE

ETC ★★★

Sandy Cove Hotel stands in 20 acres of cliff, coast and garden. The Hotel Restaurant overlooks the sea and cliffs with spectacular views of the bay. You will probably wonder how we can do it for the price when we offer a FIVE-COURSE MEAL including seafood platters with lobster, smoked salmon and steak. Every Saturday a Swedish Smorgasbord and Carvery carved by the Chef, and followed by dancing till late. Live entertainment weekly from Whitsun until September. All bedrooms have colour TV, telephone, teamaking and are en suite. The cocktail bar overlooks the bay and you have the use of the hotel's 80° heated indoor pool and recreation centre with sauna, sunbed, gym equipment and whirlpool, ALL FREE OF CHARGE.

Please return this advertisement to qualify for "Pets Stay Free" offer. Bargain Breaks and weekly rates available all year. Includes 5-course Evening Meal and coffee. Children – free accommodation. Please send for free brochure pack. Children under 5 years completely free, including meals.

Sandy Cove Hotel

Combe Martin Bay,
Devon EX34 9SR
Tel: (01271) 882243 & 882888
E-mail: rg14003483@aol.com

Indoor pool heated to 80°F with roll-back sides to enjoy the sun

Where else would your dog rather walk?
Well-behaved dogs welcome free of charge

Exmoor Sandpiper Inn

Countisbury, Lynmouth, Devon EX35 6NE
01598 741263
e-mail: info@exmoor-sandpiper.co.uk

The Exmoor Sandpiper

is a romantic Coaching Inn dating in part back to the 13th century.
On Exmoor, high above the twin villages of Lynmouth and Lynton, we are surrounded by rolling hills.

We have 16 en suite bedrooms, comfortable sofas in the bar and lounge areas, and five fireplaces, including a 13th century inglenook. Our extensive menus include local game and fish, particularly Lynmouth Lobster; specials are featured daily. Eat a hearty meal or choose from our Lite Bites. Good wines are available by the bottle or the glass.

Stay with us to relax, or to follow one of the seven circular walks through stunning countryside that start from the Inn. Horse riding for experienced riders or complete novices can be arranged. Plenty of parking. Dogs and children, and walkers with muddy boots are very welcome!

There is NO charge for dogs

Details and brochures on request

Blagdon Manor Hotel & Restaurant

AA Top 200 Hotel ★★ 2003-2004

86%

Ashwater,
North Devon EX21 5DF
Tel: 01409 211224
Fax: 01409 211634
stay@blagdon.com
www.blagdon.com

Liz and Steve along with our 2 Chocolate Labradors, Nutmeg and Cassia, look forward to welcoming you to Blagdon Manor

Restaurant: Enjoy excellent cuisine using locally sourced produce. Dinner available every night for residents. **Accommodation:** 7 en suite bedrooms *Panoramic views of the Devon countryside and Dartmoor. Beautifully restored Grade II Listed building. Enjoy a peaceful location halfway between Dartmoor and Exmoor and only 20 minutes from the North Cornish coast at Bude.*

3 acres of gardens and 17 acres of fields • Dogs welcome.
Children over the age of 12.
Double/twin rooms £100.00 per night, based on two sharing.
Single occupancy £72.00. Dogs £5.00 per night.

Caravan & Camping Park

ROSE AWARD · GOLD · AA DELUXE

A small country estate surrounded by forest in which deer roam.
Situated in an area of outstanding natural beauty.

Large, flat, sheltered camping/touring pitches
Modern facilities building, luxury 2/6 berth full service holiday homes, also self contained flat for 2 persons.

COLOUR BROCHURE ON REQUEST
Tel: (01404) 841381 (Evgs to 8pm)

CULLOMPTON
DEVON
EX15 2DT

Fax: (01404) 841593 • www.forest-glade.co.uk • email: enquiries@forest-glade.co.uk

Quality en suite accommodation in small, friendly hotel magnificently situated on cliff-side above secluded cove with spectacular sea views. Superb food, well-stocked licensed bar lounge. TV and tea-making facilities in all rooms. ***Please write or telephone for full details.***

AA ★★

Lundy House Hotel

Mortehoe, North Devon EX34 7DZ • Tel: 01271 870372

E-mail: info@lundyhousehotel.co.uk • Website: www.lundyhousehotel.co.uk

Peaceful woodland setting next to the River Walkham in the Dartmoor National Park. Ideally placed to explore the beauty of Devon. Purpose - built lodges available all year round, sleeping 2-7, tastefully blending into the surroundings. Interior specification and furnishings to a high standard - including fully-fitted kitchen with oven, microwave and dishwasher.

• 3 golf courses a short drive away. •Easy walk to village and shops • Scenic walks. •Fishing • Dogs accepted • Horse riding nearby • Small, select touring area for caravans, tents and motor caravans • Launderette • On A386 Plymouth-Tavistock road.

For Free Brochure:

Dept PW, Dartmoor Country Holidays, Magpie Leisure Park, Horrabridge, Yelverton, Devon PL20 7RY. Tel:01822 852651 or visit our website: www.dartmoorcountryholidays.co.uk

SELECTED SITE

Hedley Wood Caravan & Camping Park

Bridgerule (Near Bude), Holsworthy, Devon EX22 7ED

Tel: 01288 381404 • Fax: 01288 382011

16 acre woodland family-run site with outstanding views, where you can enjoy a totally relaxing holiday with a laid-back atmosphere, sheltered and open camping areas. Just 10 minutes' drive from the beaches, golf courses, riding stables and shops.

On site facilities include: Children's Adventure Areas, Bar, Clubroom, Shop, Laundry, Meals and all amenities. Free Hot Showers/Water. **Nice dogs/pets are very welcome. Daily kennelling facility. Dog walks/nature trail.**

Static caravans for hire. Caravan storage available. **Open all year.**

Visit our website: www.hedleywood.co.uk or write or phone for comprehensive brochure

The best of both worlds!...

★ *Indoor and Outdoor Swimming Pools* ★ *Spa Pool*
★ *Licensed Restaurant* ★ *Gym*
★ *Beauty Salon* ★ *Sauna*
★ *Launderette* ★ *Solarium*
★ *Indoor Recreation Room*

We've joined together the friendly service and facilities of the 2 star Red House Hotel for those wanting a traditional hotel atmosphere, with the privacy and freedom of Maxton Lodge's 24 self-contained holiday apartments. Two styles of accommodation sharing the same conveniently located grounds and superb range of facilities, so whether you're a working conference delegate or a fun loving family you'll find a style to suit you.

AA ★★

Red House Hotel, Rousdown Road, Chelston, Torquay TQ2 6PB
Tel: (01803) 607811
Fax: (01803) 605357
E-mail: Stay@redhouse-hotel.co.uk
Web: www.redhouse-hotel.co.uk

BLACKWELL PARK, LODDISWELL, KINGSBRIDGE

Bed, Breakfast and Evening Meal is offered in Blackwell Park, a 17th century farmhouse situated 5 miles from Kingsbridge. Seven bedrooms, some en suite, and all with washbasins and tea-making facilities. Games room; large garden, also adjoining 54 acres of woodland/Nature Reserve. Ample food with a choice of menu.

CHILDREN AND PETS ESPECIALLY WELCOME; babysitting, DOGSITTING. Pets welcome FREE of charge. Dartmoor, Plymouth, Torbay, Dartmouth and many beaches lie within easy reach.

Bed and Breakfast. Evening Meal optional.
Proprietress: Mrs B. Kelly Tel: 01548 821230
Blackwell Park, Loddiswell TQ7 4EA

Moorlands

Woody Bay, Devon EX31 4RA
www.moorlandshotel.co.uk
Where countryside and comfort combine
Tel: 01598 763224

Two self-contained apartments within a family-run guesthouse sleeping two or three persons. Our ground floor apartment is one bedroom, lounge, kitchen and bathroom and has its own entrance and private patio area.

The second apartment is on the first floor, comprising two bedrooms, lounge with screened kitchen and shower room. The house is set in six acres of garden surrounded by Exmoor countryside.

Guests are welcome to use all the hotel amenities, including the bar, dining room and outdoor swimming pool.

Telephone for brochure. Dogs welcome with well-behaved owners.

❖ WEST PUSEHILL FARM COTTAGES ❖

Nestling within the Kenwith Valley, our cottages are set along the beautiful North Devon Coast.

◆ 11 cottages, from farm buildings built from traditional local stone in 1854. ◆ 40 ft heated outdoor pool set amongst secluded, sheltered lawns. ◆ Perfectly situated to explore coast and countryside. ◆ Many "award winning" attractions close by. ◆ Pets and children welcome. ◆ Resident proprietors. ◆ Open all year. ◆ Walks, Golf, Riding & Fishing nearby.

West Pusehill Farm, Westward Ho!, North Devon EX39 5AH
Tel: 01237 475638/474622 ◆ www.wpfcottages.co.uk

Dogs Welcome • Peaceful valley setting
Close to dog-friendly beaches and great coastal walks
Six stone cottages with private gardens & country views
Private nature trail & wildlife watching
Silver medallist in Green Tourism Awards
Woodburners & Spa Baths
Romantic Breaks • Short Breaks • Open all year

For more information, prices and availability, please visit our website:

www.dittiscombe.co.uk

Colour Brochure: 01548 521272
Dittiscombe Holiday Cottages, Slapton
Near Kingsbridge, South Devon TQ7 2QF

SAND PEBBLES HOTEL & RESTAURANT

Hope Cove, near Salcombe. Friendly family-run Hotel 300 yards from delightful sandy beaches and coastal walks. Refurbished 2003. Relaxing restaurant renowned for excellent food and service. Come and stay with us and...

"Let Us Spoil You"

Telephone: 01548 561673

website: www.sandpebbleshotel.co.uk

SEE OUR ENTRY UNDER DEVON – SALCOMBE

• HOUSEBOAT HOLIDAYS •

SALCOMBE BOAT & MARINE Co. Ltd
Strand Court, Whitestrand, Salcombe, Devon TQ8 8ET

RELAX ON SALCOMBE'S BEAUTIFUL TRANQUIL ESTUARY
Well equipped Houseboats for self-catering
Motor boat & rowing dinghy included
CHILDREN AND PETS VERY WELCOME
For our Brochure please telephone: 01548 843730

- Gothic National Trust Hotel
- Set in 20 acres overlooking Studland Bay
- Superb food & rooms • Sea views & 4 posters • Log fires
- Tennis, golf, horse-riding • 2 minute walk to beach

The Manor House Hotel,
Studland Bay, Near Swanage, Dorset BH19 3AU
Tel/Fax: 01929 450288
www.themanorhousehotel.com

Cromwell House Hotel

Lulworth Cove, Dorset

Catriona and Alistair Miller welcome guests to their comfortable family-run hotel, set in secluded gardens with spectacular sea views. Situated 200 yards from Lulworth Cove, with direct access to the Dorset Coastal Footpath. A heated swimming pool is available for guests' use from May to October. Accommodation is in 17 en suite bedrooms, with TV, direct-dial telephone, and tea/coffee making facilities; most have spectacular sea views. Restaurant, bar wine list. Two nights dinner, bed and breakfast (fully en suite) from £90. Off peak mid week breaks available. Open all year except Christmas.

Cromwell House Hotel, Lulworth Cove, Dorset BH20 5RJ
Tel: 01929 400253/400332 • Fax: 01929 400566

ETC/AA/RAC ★★

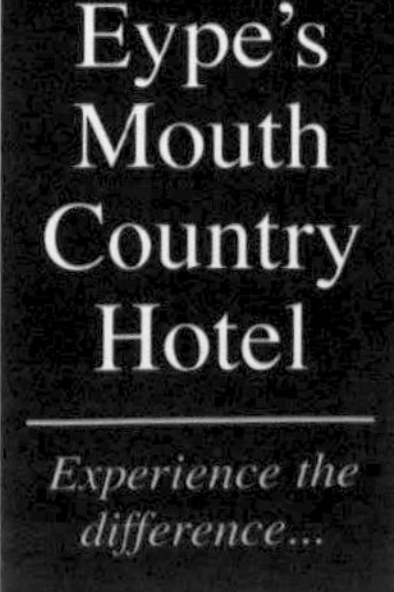

Set in the small Dorset village of Eype, **Eype's Mouth Country Hotel**, is a family run 18 bedroom hotel nestling between the downlands and clifftops at the end of a winding narrow lane. With superb sea views and only a few minutes walk to the beach, the hotel occupies a unique position on the Heritage Coastline. This stunning location provides the opportunity to walk along the Coastal Path with much to explore and observe in this area of unspoilt beauty.

Owners, Kevin and Glenis, are dedicated to providing a warm welcome, good food and the comfort and hospitality to the best possible standard. Creating a relaxed, friendly atmosphere is paramount, so you can be assured of a pleasant and enjoyable stay.

For bookings *or* more information telephone **01308 423300**
Email: info@eypesmouthhotel.co.uk **Web:** eypesmouthhotel.co.uk
Eype's Mouth Country Hotel, Eype, Bridport, Dorset DT6 6AL

THE KNOLL HOUSE

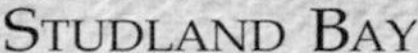

ESTABLISHED 1931

A peaceful and relaxing holiday for all ages.
An independent country-house hotel, in an unrivalled position above three miles of golden beach. Dogs are especially welcome and may sleep in your room. Special diets arranged. Our 100 acre grounds offer nice walks; squirrels and rabbits!

~

Good food and a sensible wine list.
Tennis courts; nine acre golf course and outdoor heated pool.
Health spa with Jacuzzi, sauna, Turkish room, plunge pool and gym.
Many ground-floor and single rooms for older guests.

~

Family suites, of connecting rooms with bathroom, separate young children's dining room.
Playrooms and fabulous SAFE adventure playground.

~

Daily half board terms: from £92. Children less, according to age.

~

Open Easter - end October

ONLY 2 HOURS FROM HEATHROW

STUDLAND BAY
DORSET
BH19 3AW
TEL 01929 · 450450 FAX 01929 · 450423
Email: info@knollhouse.co.uk
Website: www.knollhouse.co.uk

Guests enjoying the lounge

THE *REALLY* DOG-FRIENDLY PLACE

WHITE TOPPS

Small, friendly and catering only for guests with dogs. In a nice quiet position close to lovely walks on the beach (dogs allowed) and Hengistbury Head. Plus the New Forest isn't far away. There's no charge for pets, of course and the proprietor, MARJORIE TITCHEN, just loves dogs.

- DOG(S) ESSENTIAL - ANY SIZE, ANY NUMBER, ANYWHERE
- GROUND FLOOR ROOM FOR ELDERLY DOGS
- RESIDENTIAL LICENCE
- ADULTS ONLY (14yrs +)
- GENEROUS HOME COOKING
- VEGETARIANS WELCOME
- NOT SUITABLE FOR DISABLED
- CAR PARKING

WRITE (SAE APPRECIATED) OR PHONE FOR FACT SHEET.

WHITE TOPPS, 45 CHURCH ROAD, SOUTHBOURNE, BOURNEMOUTH, DORSET BH6 4BB
TEL: 01202 428868

e-mail: Thedogplace1@aol.com • www.whitetopps.co.uk
IF YOU DON'T LOVE DOGS YOU WON'T LIKE WHITE TOPPS

Little Hewish Barn

A 150 year old brick and flint barn, converted to provide comfortable accommodation of a very high standard, including oil-fired central heating. There are two double bedrooms (one converts to twin), both with en suite bath/shower facilities. Spacious open-plan living/dining area features a wood-burning stove, fully-equipped kitchen, dishwasher, washer/dryer, TV/video, stereo etc. Children and well-behaved pets are very welcome. Fully-enclosed patio garden and ample on-site parking. Prices are all inclusive – no hidden extras. 'Per person per night' pricing outside of peak periods.

Little Hewish Barn, Milton Abbas, Blandford Forum, Dorset DT11 0DP
Tel: 01258 881235 • Fax: 01258 881393 • E-mail: terry@littlehewish.co.uk

Langtry Manor

The Country House Hotel in Bournemouth

Built by Edward VII as a Lovenest for Lillie Langtry. A rare gem of a hotel where the building, food, service and history blend to form something quite exceptional. Four posters, Jacuzzi's, complimentary leisure club and award-winning restaurant. Midweek and weekend breaks. As featured on BBC Holiday Show. Pets welcome by arrangement.

"Best Hotel in Bournemouth" **- The Guardian**

Derby Road, East Cliff, Bournemouth BH1 3QB
Tel: (01202) 553887 www.langtrymanor.com

Country Inn set in the heart of lovely Piddle Valley. Within easy reach of all Dorset's attractions. All rooms en suite with colour TV, tea and coffee, telephone; swimming pool (May-September). Riverside garden, restaurant where Half Board guests choose from à la carte menu at no extra cost.

Telephone: 01300 348358; Fax: 01300 348153

e-mail: thepoachersinn@piddletrenthide.fsbusiness.co.uk website: www.thepoachersinn.co.uk

Bed and Breakfast
£30 per person per night.
Dinner, Bed and Breakfast
£45 per person per night.
10% discount for seven nights.
Low Season Breaks
two nights Dinner, Bed and Breakfast
£90 per person.
Third night Dinner, Bed and Breakfast – FREE. (OCT-APR)
(excluding Bank Holiday weekends)

Send for brochure

ETC/AA

◆◆◆◆

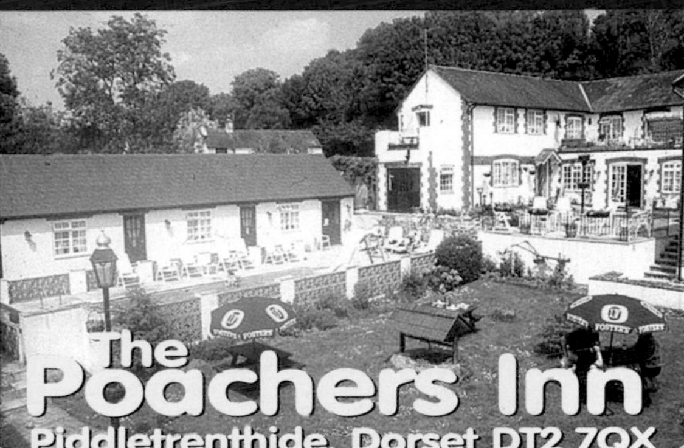

Gorselands Caravan Park

"Peaceful and Pretty"

ROSE AWARD
CARAVAN HOLIDAY PARK

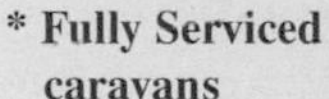

- **Fully Serviced caravans**
- **Shop**
- **Launderette**
- **Self contained flats**
- **Village Pub 100 yards**
- **Beach car park 3 mins by car**

Attractive secluded park set in coastal valley overlooking Chesil Beach, part of Dorset's World Heritage Jurassic Coastline. Tourist Board graded. Glorious sea views. Country and seaside walks. An ideal base for discovering Dorset's charming villages and Heritage coastline. The beach is a mile either by car or through the meadows, and the fishing is excellent. Pets are most welcome.

Colour brochure: Dept. PW
Gorselands Caravan Park
West Bexington-on-Sea, Dorset DT2 9DJ
Tel: 01308 897232 • Fax: 01308 897239

Superb detached holiday cottage on working farm, ideal for walking/touring in Weardale, the Yorkshire Dales and the Lake District. Village with pub and shop ½ mile.

•• open-plan lounge/kitchen/diner ••

•• one double and one twin bed bedrooms ••

•• bathroom with bath and shower ••

•• suitable for partially disabled ••

Large enclosed garden with patio, BBQ and garden furniture
PETS WELCOME

Low Mulberry Holiday Cottage

Details from Mrs Pauline Bowles, Marley Moor Farm, Ingleton, Darlington, Durham DL2 3HZ • 01833 660332

Low Lands Farm

Low Lands, Cockfield, Bishop Auckland, Co. Durham DL13 5AW
Tel 01388 718251 • Mobile: 07745 067754
e-mail: info@farmholidaysuk.com • website: www.farmholidaysuk.com

Two award-winning, beautifully renovated self-catering cottages on a working family farm. If you want peace and quiet in an area full of beautiful unspoilt countryside packed with things to see and do, then come and stay with us. Each cottage sleeps up to four people, plus cot. Beams, log fires, gas BBQ, own gardens and parking. Close to Durham City, the Lake District and Hadrian's Wall. Pets and children most welcome; childminding and equipment available. Terms from £150 to £340, inclusive of linen, towels, electricity and heating.

Please contact Alison or Keith Tallentire for a brochure.

Category 3 (one cottage)

The Cotswold Water Park is a peaceful and attractive location for a tranquil countryside break. Many properties are ETC ★★★★ standard, accept pets and sleep up to 8.

Mill Village a luxurious rural retreat. Heated outdoor pool, sauna, tennis, fishing, children's play area, trampoline, table tennis and cricket nets.

Isis Lakes relax and unwind on your own private sun deck or take advantage of the wide range of activities available, including fishing, tennis, children's play area, football net, golf practice net.

Spring Lake features a water-ski club catering for all levels of ability, plus a lakeside bar, gymnasium and children's play area.

Orion Holidays • 01285 861839 • Fax: 01285 869188
e-mail: bookings@orionholidays.com • www.orionholidays.com

ETC/AA◆◆◆

Dear Rover,

Well, we've just got back from our holidays – absolute bliss and what a lovely place the Downfield is – we got a really warm welcome from the owners. Great walks in the Cotswolds, comfy rooms, a bar, delicious food and the Joneses I brought with me were really pleased as well. I made lots of new friends – there were even some cats to chase! Why don't you come with me next year and bring your owners with you – Just call Nigel or Maura on the dog and bone on

Lots of licks, Toby

The Downfield Hotel

134 Cainscross Rd, Stroud, Gloucestershire GL5 4HN

01453 764496

e-mail: info@downfieldhotel.co.uk
www.downfieldhotel.co.uk

A historic country hotel whose heritage dates from the 13th Century, situated in the heart of the Forest of Dean, close to the Wye Valley. Tho hotol rotainc many of itc original foaturoc, including boamc, timbor panelling and oak spiral staircases. 22 en suite bedrooms are located throughout the hotel grounds, including Four-Poster rooms and a Cottage Suite. All bedrooms are en suite and have colour TV, direct dial telephones and tea and coffee making facilities. Our Red Rosette candlelit restaurant is renowned for its quality cuisine and friendliness of service. Tudor Farmhouse is the ideal retreat to relax and unwind.

Tudor Farmhouse Hotel & Restaurant

Clearwell, Near Coleford, Gloucestershire GL16 8JS
Freephone: 0800 7835935 • Fax: 01594 837093
e-mail: info@tudorfarmhousehotel.co.uk • website: www.tudorfarmhousehotel.co.uk

The Crown Hotel, New Forest

Tired of the same old walks? Enjoy forest, heath and the beach whilst staying at The Crown Hotel. 38 en suite rooms, all individual and recently refurbished.

Our Chef of thirty years, Stephen Greenhalgh, delights us with his imaginative menus using local produce wherever possible, either in the informal bar or the Restaurant overlooking our water-featured garden.

Dogs are welcome to bring their well-behaved owners!

High Street, Lyndhurst, Hampshire SO43 7NF • Tel: 023 8028 2922 • Fax: 023 8028 2751
E-mail: reception@crownhotel-lyndhurst.co.uk • Web: www.crownhotel-lyndhurst.co.uk

The Woodlands Lodge Hotel

Bartley Road, Woodlands, New Forest, Hampshire SO40 7GN
Reservations: (023) 80 292257 • Fax: (023) 80 293090
e-mail: reception@woodlands-lodge.co.uk www.woodlands-lodge.co.uk

The Woodlands Lodge Hotel is a luxuriously restored Georgian Country House, set within the beautiful New Forest, yet only 15 minutes from Southampton. Our attractive gardens have direct access to the forest and are ideal for romantic walks. Golf, fishing and horse riding are available nearby and the hotel is perfectly situated for touring the area. Come and unwind from the stress of everyday life and enjoy pure luxury without ostentation.

All bedrooms enjoy full en suite facilities of whirlpool bath and separate shower and have king sized beds and a full range of amenities. The quality four-course menu is changed seasonally to make use of local produce and is complemented by an interesting wine list. The service is friendly, efficient and informal.

Woodlands Lodge – where a warm welcome awaits you.

the Inn on the Wye
Kerne Bridge
Quality Food with Excellent Service!
A beautifully restored 18th century coaching inn with views of Goodrich Castle on the banks of the River Wye. All bedrooms en suite with colour TV, telephone and usual facilities. A la carte and bar snack menus offering home-cooked food using local produce where possible.
Peaceful country walks - ideal base for touring.
Families welcome. Children's play area and gardens.
Open all day, seven days a week. Large car park.
Pets welcome by arrangement.
Kerne Bridge, Goodrich,
Near Ross-on-Wye HR9 5QS
Tel: 01600 890872 • Fax: 01600 890594
e-mail: theinnonthewye@kernebridge.freeserve.co.uk
www.theinnonthewye.co.uk
RAC ♦♦♦ Guest Accommodation
AA Awaiting Grading

AA ★★

Ye Hostelrie Hotel

English Tourism Council ★★ HOTEL

GOODRICH, ROSS ON WYE,
HEREFORDSHIRE HR9 6HX

Tel: 01600 890241 • Fax: 01600 890838
e-mail: info@ye-hostelrie.co.uk
website: www.ye-hostelrie.co.uk

Enjoy comfort and good food at this fully centrally heated 17th Century Inn. Situated near to Goodrich Castle in a beautiful part of the Wye Valley, it affords easy access to the Forest of Dean, rural Herefordshire and Wales; although in a quiet village it is only a mile from the A40. Dine in the elegant surroundings of the restaurant, or the cosy atmosphere of the bar choosing from our extensive menu of home made dishes. A choice of real ales and fine wines, Morning Coffee and Afternoon Cream Tea is also available.

Prices: Bed and Breakfast in a double, twin bedded room or family room with en suite facilities, colour television, courtesy tray, clock radio, from: Double £55, Single £32.50; a cot can be provided.

• Pets are welcome in the bedrooms and garden. •

SENTRY MEAD HOTEL

Sentry Mead is a tranquil Country House set in its own spacious gardens where well-behaved dogs are welcome throughout the hotel (except in the dining room) and to sleep in guests' bedrooms; our own Labrador and Retriever always make our canine visitors feel at home as soon as they arrive. Personal care and attention to detail make this a very special 3 star hotel for both pets and people for either a short break or a longer stay.

RAC ★★★ Hotel

Mike & Julie Hodgson

Sentry Mead Hotel, Madeira Road, Totland Bay
Isle of Wight PO39 0BJ
Tel: 01983 753212 • Fax: 01983 754710
e-mail: pets@sentry-mead.co.uk • website: www.sentry-mead.co.uk

AA ★★★

"....a jewel in the crown of the West Wight"

The Country Garden Hotel

Church Hill, Totland Bay, Isle of Wight PO39 0ET

IOW Tourism's nominee Small Hotel of the Year 2003

A five minute stroll to the Solent, surrounded by lovely walks and hikes including Tennyson Downs and The Needles, and a short drive to the bustling port of Yarmouth. Set in lovely gardens this quiet and intimate hotel offers the best of all worlds for your holiday, including making your pet feel welcome! Excellent cuisine from our Chef of some thirteen years in our locally popular retaurant overlooking the gardens. Garden, sea view and ground floor rooms available, all en suite with colour TV, fridge, duvets, down pillows, bathrobes, phone, central heating, hairdryer, tea & coffee and ample off-street parking.

ANY DAY TO ANY DAY, B&B or HALF BOARD

ADULTS ONLY

Ferry inclusive rates October through April

B&B from £43pp/day; DB&B from £57pp/day, £364pp/week

For brochure, sample menu, tariff, and testimonials from recent guests, please

Phone/Fax: 01983 754 521

e-mail: countrygardeniow@aol.com

website: www.thecountrygardenhotel.co.uk

Fairhaven Holiday Cottages

Fairhaven offers a wide selection of holiday homes for 2 - 12 people as well as comprehensive local knowledge and a friendly service. We specialise in Kent and Sussex, but also offer two cottages on a Wiltshire farm. Our directors personally visit all of our properties to ensure quality and up-to-date information. Pets are welcome in many properties and short breaks are available out of season.

For full details of all our properties visit our website

www.fairhaven-holidays.co.uk

Alternatively request a colour brochure by telephone, fax or e-mail

Tel: 08452 304334 • Fax: 01634 570157 • e-mail: enquiries@fairhaven-holidays.co.uk

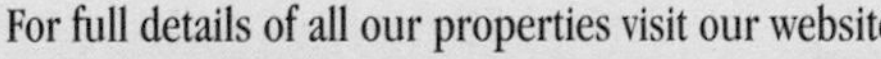

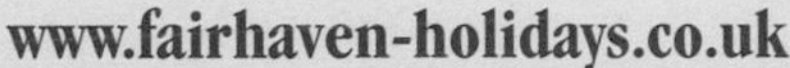

Looking for Holiday Accommodation?

for details of hundreds of properties throughout the UK including comprehensive coverage of all areas of Scotland try:

www.holidayguides.com

Set in the UK's most beautiful village of Burnham Market, this stylish, fabulous hotel provides a friendly atmosphere with attentive service. This privately owned inn offers individually designed bedrooms with a high degree of comfort, air-conditioned dining rooms in which modern British brasserie-style food is served, a traditional bar with log fire, which attracts many of the locals and is the sort of place where nice dogs like to meet, a sunny patio and garden in which to relax with dogs, and a conservatory which is tastefully furnished.

Amazing value midweek Dinner, Bed and Breakfast Breaks

Augustus and Sweep, affectionately known as "the boys"

Johansens Inn of the Year
Egon Ronay Inn of the Year
Good Hotel Guide Cesar Awards 'Inn of the Year'
Norfolk Dining Pub of the Year
Voted by The Times as their 2nd Favourite Hotel in England
Catey Award Winner
AA 2 Rosette Restaurant
The Sunday Times 'Golden Pillow Award'

The Hoste Arms, The Green, Burnham Market, Norfolk PE31 8HD
Tel: 01328 738777 • Fax: 01328 730103
E-mail: reception@hostearms.co.uk • Web: www.hostearms.co.uk

Short Breaks also available all season, except August from £60. 1st pet £5, 2nd pet free

Debit/Credit cards accepted

SUPERB VALUE FOR **2005** SEASON

Carefree HOLIDAYS

A warm welcome for you and your pets. Inexpensive, 'live-as-you-please' self-catering holidays in beautiful Norfolk. Chalets, Bungalows, and Cottages near Great Yarmouth & Norfolk Broads.

Booking Hotline
Tel: 01493 732176
All calls personally answered

Colour Brochure : Carefree Holidays, Chapel Briers, Yarmouth Road, Hemsby, Norfolk NR29 4NJ.
Find us on the internet: www.carefree-holidays.co.uk

4B&B STRENNETH **Country Bed and Breakfast**

Airfield Road, Fersfield, Diss, Norfolk IP22 2BP

STRENNETH is well-established and family-run, situated in unspoiled countryside just a short drive from Bressingham Gardens and the picturesque market town of Diss. Offering first-class accommodation, the original 17th Century building has been carefully renovated to a high standard with a wealth of exposed oak beams, with a newer single storey courtyard wing and two converted cottages. There is ample off-road parking and plenty of nice walks nearby. All seven bedrooms, including a Four-Poster and an Executive, are tastefully arranged with period furniture and distinctive beds. Each having remote-control colour television, hospitality trays, central heating and full en suite facilities. The establishment is smoke-free. Dinners are served by arrangement. There is an extensive breakfast menu using local produce. Ideal touring base. Pets most welcome at no extra charge. Outside kennels with runs if required. Bed and Breakfast from £25.00.

Telephone: 01379 688182 • Fax: 01379 688260
E-mail: pdavey@strenneth.co.uk • Website: www.strenneth.co.uk

The Lifeboat Inn

16th Century Smugglers' Ale House

Ship Lane,Thornham,
Norfolk PE36 6LT
Tel: 01485 512236 • Fax: 01485 512323
E-mail: reception@lifeboatinn.co.uk

THE LIFEBOAT INN has been a welcome sight for the weary traveller for centuries – roaring open fires on a frosty night, real ales and a hearty meal awaiting. The Summer brings its own charm – a cool beer, gazing over open meadows to the harbour, and rolling white horses gently breaking upon Thornham's sandy beach.

Dogs are welcome in all our bars and we provide the sort of breakfast that will enable you to keep up with your four-legged friend on the way to the beach!

Guests arriving at reception are greeted by our grand old fireplace in the lounge – ideal for toasting your feet after a day walking the coastal path – if you can coax your sleeping dog out of prime position!

The restaurant (AA rosette) opens every evening offering a varied selection of dishes to suit all tastes. Our extensive bar snack menu is also available if guests wish their pets to join them in the bar.

Bird watchers, walkers and nature lovers are spoilt for choice. A walk from our front door will take you to Thornham beach in no time at all and onto the Holme Nature Reserve. The Titchwell Marsh Nature Reserve is 2 miles away and Snettisham, Blakeney, Holkham and Cley Nature Reserves are all within short driving distance.

There are numerous and varied walks along miles of open beaches, across sweeping sand dunes, through pine woods or along chalk and sandstone cliff tops. It is truly a walker's paradise - especially if you're a dog.

We hope you will come and visit us. For our brochure and tariff which includes details of breaks please ring 01485 512236 or visit our website www.lifeboatinn.co.uk

Experience the great joy of Norfolk...

Idyllic Cottages @ Vere Lodge

We offer your pets 8 acres of lawns, paddock and woodland as a play area with Norfolk's vast beaches within a few minutes drive. We offer the rest of the family a choice of 14 superbly equipped cottages, leisure centre with heated indoor pool, sauna, solarium and games room. Animal farm, children's play area, enchanted wood, grass tennis court and croquet lawn.

Vere Lodge, South Raynham, Fakenham, Norfolk NR21 7HE
Tel: 01328 838261 (24 hour answering service)
Fax: 01328 838300 E-mail: major@verelodge.co.uk

www.idylliccottages.co.uk
for those who demand the very best

Kings Chalet Park Cromer, Norfolk

Sleep 2-4
Open March to October

Pet welcome free of charge

Comfortable, well-equipped chalets situated on beautiful, landscaped, quiet site. Ideally placed for walks to adjacent woods, cliffs and sandy beaches. 10 minutes' walk to town. Golf course and local shops nearby. Plenty of local places of interest to visit. One twin, one double room, bathroom, colour TV, microwave, well-equipped kitchenette. Children welcome.

Short Breaks in Spring/Autumn 2 nights or more from £70
Spring/Autumn £120-£185 per week
June-September £195-£275 per week

DETAILS FROM: MRS I. SCOLTOCK, SHANGRI-LA, LITTLE CAMBRIDGE, DUTON HILL, DUNMOW, ESSEX CM6 3QU • TEL: 01371 870482

The Mizen Head Hotel

Lucker Road, Bamburgh, Northumberland NE69 7BS

AA ★★

En suite bedrooms, a residents' conservatory lounge and non-smoking à la carte restaurant using local produce. Public bar offers good food and real ales with an open log fire in winter. Children welcome – family rooms are available with cots if required. Car park. Pets welcome in bedrooms and bar. Local attractions include Bamburgh Castle and Holy Isle. Three-and-a-half mile sandy beach five minutes away. Pets welcome. For golfers discounts can be arranged. Short break details on request.

Tel: 01668 214254 • Fax: 01668 214104
website: www.themizenheadhotel.co.uk
e-mail: Leadbitterk@vodaphone.net

NOTE

All the Information in this guide is given in good faith in the belief that it is correct. However, the publishers cannot guarantee the facts given in these pages, neither are they responsible for changes in ownership or facilities that may take place after the date of going to press.

Readers should always satisfy themselves that the facilities they require are available and that the terms, if quoted, still apply.

PETS WELCOME FREE

IN THE BEAUTIFUL EXMOOR NATIONAL PARK

The DUNKERY BEACON HOTEL

WOOTTON COURTENAY
WEST SOMERSET TA24 8RH

www.dunkerybeaconhotel.co.uk

Country house hotel in fabulous unrivalled setting.

The superb views can be absorbed at leisure from the terrace or lawns and gardens.

• Fully en suite rooms • Colour TV • Coffee and tea making facilities

• Hairdryers • Car park • Lots of lovely "walkies" • No single supplement

Complimentary tray of tea and biscuits on arrival

No restriction on dog access, apart from the main dining room (usual exceptions)

Special Breaks Spring/Summer/Autumn

For full information and brochure write or telephone Kenneth or Daphne Midwood

TELEPHONE 01643 841241 • E-mail: Dunkery.Beacon@virgin.net

YOU WILL BE WARMLY WELCOMED ON ARRIVAL,
BUT IT IS QUITE POSSIBLE THAT YOUR PET WILL GET EVEN MORE FUSS

Meet our two Old English sheepdogs Poppy and Sweet Pea

"I knew we were in the right place when the afternoon tea came with dog biscuits!

Edgcott House

Exford
Somerset
TA247QG
Tel: 01643 831 495

Marc Watts may have relocated from Cornwall's Trevaunance, but his blend of warm and mildly eccentric hospitality is unchanging.

Edgcott House is a 17th Century country house, in the village of Exford right in the heart of the magnificent Exmoor National Park.

Edgcott House is a country house of great charm and character set amidst mature, secluded gardens in beautiful lush countryside. Experience the sound of birdsong & bubbling brook, the comfort of open log fires, newly refurbished bedrooms - all with ensuite, and delicious full Exmoor breakfast.

The Castle Hotel

Porlock, Somerset TA24 8PY
Tel & Fax: 01643 862504
E-mail: castlehotel@btconnect.com

The Castle Hotel is a small, fully licensed family-run hotel in the centre of the lovely Exmoor village of Porlock. It is an ideal holiday location for those who wish to enjoy the grandeur of Exmoor on foot or by car. The beautiful villages of Selworthy and Dunster with its castle are only a short distance away. There are 13 en suite bedrooms, all fully heated, with colour TV and tea/coffee making facilities.The Castle Hotel has a well-stocked bar with Real Ale. Draught Guinness and Cider. A full range of Bar Meals is available at lunchtimes and evenings or dine in our Restaurant. Children and pets are most welcome. Dog walking field. Darts, pool and skittles.

✤ ✤ ***Special Breaks available*** ✤ ***Extremely low rates*** ✤✤

WENTWORTH HOTEL

WENTWORTH ROAD, ALDEBURGH, SUFFOLK IP15 5BD

Facing the sea, the Wentworth Hotel has the comfort and style of a country house. 37 bedrooms, many with sea views, two comfortable lounges with open fires and antique furniture, provide ample space to relax. The restaurant serves a variety of fresh produce, including local seafood, and a light lunch can be chosen from the bar menu and eaten "al fresco" in the terrace garden. There are many walks, some commencing from the Hotel. Aldeburgh is the perfect touring centre for East Anglia.

AA ★★★ Rosette 76%

For a reservation, please Telephone 01728 452312 or Fax: 01728 454343
E-mail: stay@wentworth-aldeburgh.co.uk Website: www.wentworth-aldeburgh.com

ETC Silver Award

Knights Holiday Homes

at Kessingland on the Suffolk Heritage Coast

THE BEST OF BRITISH SELF-CATERING HOLIDAYS

at the 'Seaview' and 'Alandale' Holiday Parks on the peaceful Suffolk Coast

CHILDREN AND PETS WELCOME
OPEN ALL YEAR

Welcome to a place where you can hear yourself think...

'Kessingland: Most easterly village in the United Kingdom. First to greet the sun. Once known as the richest village in England because of its prolific fishing. Now known for its peaceful, pleasant surroundings, its beautiful spacious beach and its Suffolk countryside, where you can relax in peace and watch the boats sail by on the North Sea's Herring Pond.'

Seaview Bungalows
These bungalows are situated on a quiet, attractive estate set in nine acres of lawns overlooking the sea. There is a made-up roadway round the estate and parking near your door. Your bungalow has three bedrooms, bathroom and toilet, kitchen and lounge with a sun door opening onto the lawns. A walkway leads immediately from the estate to the promenade and the beach.
SHOPS ARE APPROXIMATELY 450 YARDS AND BUS STOP 300 YARDS.

THE BUNGALOWS
- 1-6 persons
- Colour Television
- Bed linen supplied • Fully equipped kitchens
- Full size cookers and refrigerators
- Microwaves, video recorders
- Cots and Highchairs are available
- Electrically heated - no meters • Parking

THE VILLAGE
- Clean Beach Award
- Mother Hubbard's Cupboard – Kessingland Art Centre and Gift Shop
- Suffolk Wildlife Park
- Shops • Pubs
- Restaurants • Cafes • Bus Service

BROCHURE ◆ CALENDAR ◆ OFFER LETTER ◆ BOOKING FORM from
Knights Holiday Homes, 198 Church Road, Kessingland, Suffolk NR33 7SF Freephone 0800 269067

Gladwins Farm

Cottages in Constable Country

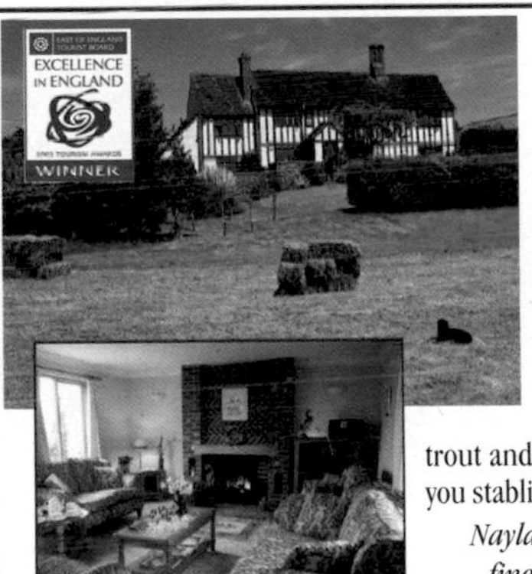

Set in 22 acres of the rolling countryside typical of the Stour Valley, made famous by John Constable, Gladwins Farm offers a selection of high quality accommodation. Guests staying in any of our 5★ or 4★ self-catering cottages, most of which accept pets, or farmhouse B&B, can use the heated indoor pool and sauna, the hard tennis court and children's play area. Our cottages sleep from 2 to 8 people and our two new 'sleeps 8' and 'sleeps 6' cottages are graded '5 Stars' by the English Tourism Council. There's a well-stocked fishing lake with trout and coarse fish, plus farm animals to entertain the children. We can offer you stabling for horses, an outdoor ménage and loads of space to walk your dogs.

Nayland is one of the famous cloth towns of Suffolk, having possibly the finest collection of medieval timber-framed buildings in the country. The other 'Heritage Villages' of the area – Lavenham, Long Melford and Sudbury – are all within a few minutes' drive and the coast is only half an hour away.

If a quiet holiday in a charming area of Olde England is on your agenda, call Pauline or Robert Dossor on 01206 262261 and arrange a memorable stay

see us on the Internet at www.gladwinsfarm.co.uk or call for our colour brochure.

Winners, Regional Self-Catering Holiday of the Year 2003

Fax: 01206 263001 • e-mail: GladwinsFarm@aol.com
Gladwins Farm, Harper's Hill, Nayland, Suffolk CO6 4NU

- Spacious standard and executive accommodation
- Delicious cuisine – from bread to ice-cream made by our chefs
- 40 acres of gardens & meadows plus country walks
- Ideal for Southwold, the Norfolk Broads, Norwich, Suffolk Heritage Coast
- Cheerful and helpful staff who look forward to welcoming you and your four-legged friends

AA ★★★77% Silver Award

Ivy House Country Hotel

'Oulton Broad's hidden oasis'

Tel: 01502 501353 / 588144

Ivy House Country Hotel, Ivy Lane, Oulton Broad, Lowestoft, Suffolk NR33 8HY

e-mail:pets@ivyhousefarm.co.uk

website: www.ivyhousefarm.co.uk

photos © Dougal Waters Photography

The Crown and Castle

Orford, Woodbridge, Suffolk IP12 2LJ

Tel: 01394 450205

e-mail: info@crownandcastle.co.uk

website: www.crowncastle.co.uk

Suffolk Heritage Coast

Now owned by the ex-proprietors of Hintlesham Hall, this comfortable and very dog-friendly hotel is situated close to the 12th century castle in this historic and unspoilt village. Honest good food served in the acclaimed award-winning Trinity Restaurant.

AA *** Les Routiers RAC ***

Chase Lodge Hotel

An Award Winning Hotel

with style & elegance, set in tranquil surroundings at affordable prices.

10 Park Road Hampton Wick Kingston-Upon-Thames KT1 4AS

Tel: 020 8943 1862 . Fax: 020 8943 9363

E-mail: info@chaselodgehotel.com Web: www.chaselodgehotel.com & www.surreyhotels.com

Quality en suite bedrooms
Close to Bushy Park
Full English Breakfast
A la carte menu
Licensed bar
Wedding Receptions
Honeymoon suite available with jacuzzi & steam area
20 minutes from Heathrow Airport
Close to Kingston town centre & all major transport links.

Pets welcome

All Major Credit Cards Accepted

JEAKE'S HOUSE

Mermaid Street, Rye, East Sussex TN31 7ET
Telephone: 01797 222828 Fax: 01797 222623
E-mail: stay@jeakeshouse.com • Website: www.jeakeshouse.com

Dating from 1689, this beautiful Listed Building stands in one of England's most famous streets. Oak-beamed and panelled bedrooms overlook the marsh to the sea. Brass, mahogany or four-poster beds with linen sheets and lace; honeymoon suite; TV, radio, telephone. Book-lined bar. Residential licence. Traditional and vegetarian breakfast served. £39.00–£59.00pp. Private car park. Visa and Mastercard accepted.

AA PREMIER SELECTED ◆◆◆◆◆ RAC ◆◆◆◆◆ Sparkling Diamond & Warm Welcome Award Good Hotel Guide César Award

LITTLE HEMINGFOLD HOTEL

★ **Relax** and enjoy the friendly and tranquil atmosphere of our part 17th century and early Victorian farmhouse.

★ **Meander** through our 40 acres of farm and woodland with endless walks in the adjoining countryside.

★ **Treat** your pets to one of our courtyard garden rooms, all en suite and some with log-burning stoves.

★ **Fish,** row and swim in our two-acre trout lake or take up a challenge on our grass tennis court.

Discounts for children 7-14 years old. and FREE accommodation for pets. Weekly Dinner, Bed and Breakfast from £60 per person per night. Two day breaks from £64 per person per night.

Please ring or write to Paul and Alison Slater

LITTLE HEMINGFOLD HOTEL, TELHAM, BATTLE, EAST SUSSEX TN33 0TT

Tel: 01424 774338 • Fax: 01424 775351

E-mail: littlehemingfoldhote@tiscali.co.uk • Website: www.littlehemingfoldhotel.co.uk

'Special Places to Stay' **ETC ◆◆◆** **Charming Small Hotels**

Little Oaks

Farley Way, Fairlight East Sussex

Luxury bungalow on one level set in quiet coastal village with clifftop parklands, close to ancient towns of Rye, Battle and Hastings. Furnished to a very high standard, the spacious accommodation comprises double bedroom with en suite shower, twin bedroom, lounge with TV, dining room, fully equipped kitchen/diner, bathroom, conservatory and balcony overlooking beautiful secluded garden and garage. No smoking in bungalow. Pets welcome. Rates on application, which include central heating, electricity, bed linen and towels.

Contact: Ray and Janet Adams, Fairlight Cottage, Warren Road, Fairlight, East Sussex TN35 4AG • Tel/Fax: 01424 812545

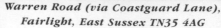

FAIRLIGHT COTTAGE

Warren Road (via Coastguard Lane), Fairlight, East Sussex TN35 4AG

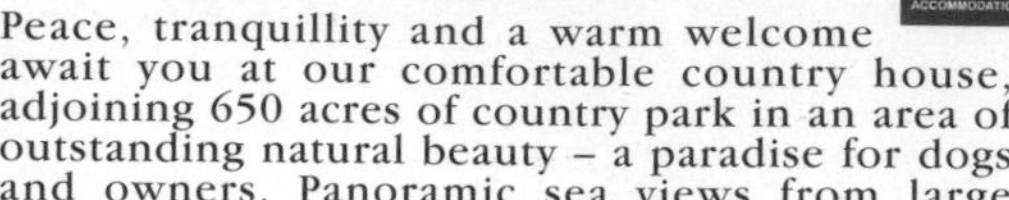

Peace, tranquillity and a warm welcome await you at our comfortable country house, adjoining 650 acres of country park in an area of outstanding natural beauty – a paradise for dogs and owners. Panoramic sea views from large balcony. Centrally heated en suite bedrooms with beverage trays and colour TV. Comfortable guest lounge. Delicious breakfasts. No smoking. Ample parking. Pets stay with owners (free of charge).

B&B from £27.50 pppn. • Single supplement
Janet & Ray Adams • 01424 812545

ST ANDREWS LODGE

Chichester Road, Selsey, West Sussex PO20 0LX
Tel: 01243 606899 • Fax: 01243 607826
e-mail: info@standrewslodge.co.uk
web: www.standrewslodge.co.uk

Welcoming, family-run hotel with a reputation for an excellent hearty breakfast. Situated on the Manhood peninsula just south of Chichester, close to unspoilt beaches and countryside. Ten bedrooms, all en suite, with direct-dial telephones, TV, fridge and tea-making facilities; some on ground floor. Spacious lounges with log fire; licensed bar for residents only. Wheelchair accessible room. Large car park. Dogs welcome in rooms overlooking large garden. Apply for brochure, prices and details of special winter offers October to February.

St Andrews Lodge
Tel: 01243 606899
ETC/AA ◆◆◆◆

Willersey Hill, Broadway,Worcestershire WR12 7LF

Telephone: Broadway (01386) 852711 Telefax: (01386) 858636
e-mail: reservations@dormyhouse.co.uk
website: www.dormyhouse.co.uk

DORMY HOUSE

The 17th century Dormy House Hotel is set high in the rolling Cotswold countryside between the picturesque villages of Broadway and Chipping Campden, with Stratford-upon-Avon only a short drive away. Adjacent to Broadway Golf Course, it is a really lovely place in which to relax with your dog(s) and enjoy a one night stay, or classic Dormy Break for two or more nights. Telephone for brochure or booking, or visit our website.

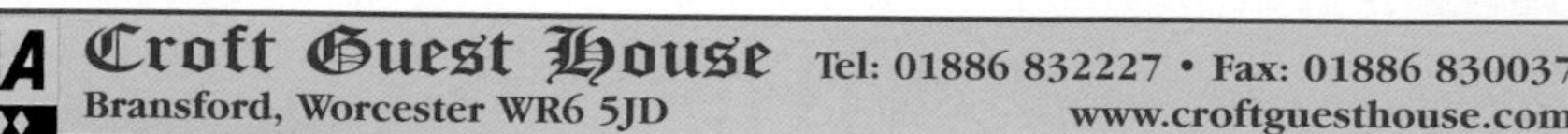

Croft Guest House

Bransford, Worcester WR6 5JD
Tel: 01886 832227 • Fax: 01886 830037
www.croftguesthouse.com

16th-18th century part black-and-white cottage-style country house situated in the Teme Valley, four miles from Worcester and Malvern. Croft House is central for visiting numerous attractions in Worcester, Hereford, the Severn Valley and surrounding countryside. River and lake fishing are close by, and an 18-hole golf course is opposite. Three en suite guest rooms (two double, one family) and two with washbasins are available. All bedrooms are no-smoking. Rooms are double glazed and have colour TV, radio alarm and courtesy tray. TV lounge, residential licence. Dogs welcome by arrangement. Full English breakfast and evening meals are prepared from home-grown/made or locally sourced produce.

Visit our website for full details of Croft Guest House

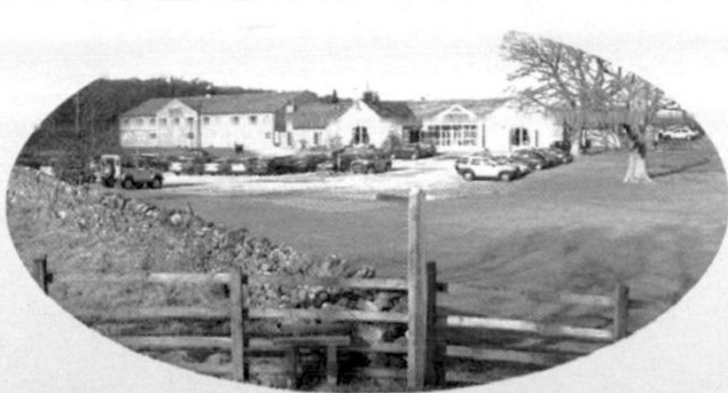

Situated beside the A65, the Hotel offers an ideal base for business or leisure guests looking for peace and relaxation. The estate comprises the Hall and 1200 acres around a 24-acre lake. There are 40 en suite bedrooms, each with bath and shower, direct-dial telephone, satellite TV, hairdryer, trouser press and tea/coffee facilities. The relaxed yet sophisticated ambience of the hotel ensures that many of our visitors return time and time again.

An in-house co-ordinator can take care of every detail for conferences, corporate events, weddings and private functions. Special rates are available for Leisure Breaks and for family rooms.

THE CONISTON HOTEL

Coniston Cold, Skipton, North Yorkshire BD23 4EB

Tel: 01756 748080 • Fax: 01756 749487 • E-mail: info@theconistonhotel.com • Website: www.theconistonhotel.com

Summerwine Cottages

Cottages of Distinction

Close to 'Last of the Summer Wine' country are three comfortable, well equipped English country-style Cottages, each with unique character and beauty. Each cottage has French doors leading from the lounge into a beautiful walled cottage garden. The cottages are set within six acres of beautiful countryside, giving the ideal location for relaxation and seasonal breaks for family and friends. All cottages have the added tranquillity of an indoor heated swimming pool, located literally a stone's throw away. Summerwine Cottages give you the freedom and independence of a self-catering holiday with the added convenience of local pubs and restaurants within walking distance. We also welcome cats and dogs, and offer DIY livery for your horse within our on-site modern stable yard.

YORKSHIRE TOURIST BOARD MEMBER

Pet Friendly Accommodation

Contact Mr & Mrs Halstead, West Royd Farm, Marsh Lane, Shepley, Near Holmfirth, Huddersfield HD8 8AY

Tel: 01484 602147 • Fax: 01484 609427 • www.summerwinecottages.co.uk • e mail: summerwinecottages@lineone.net

FHG

Publisher's Note

While every effort is made to ensure accuracy, we regret that FHG Publications cannot accept responsibility for errors, omissions or misrepresentations in our entries or any consequences thereof. Prices in particular should be checked because we go to press early. We will follow up complaints but cannot act as arbiters or agents for either party.

FHG

Visit the FHG website

www.holidayguides.com

for details of the wide choice of accommodation featured in the full range of FHG titles

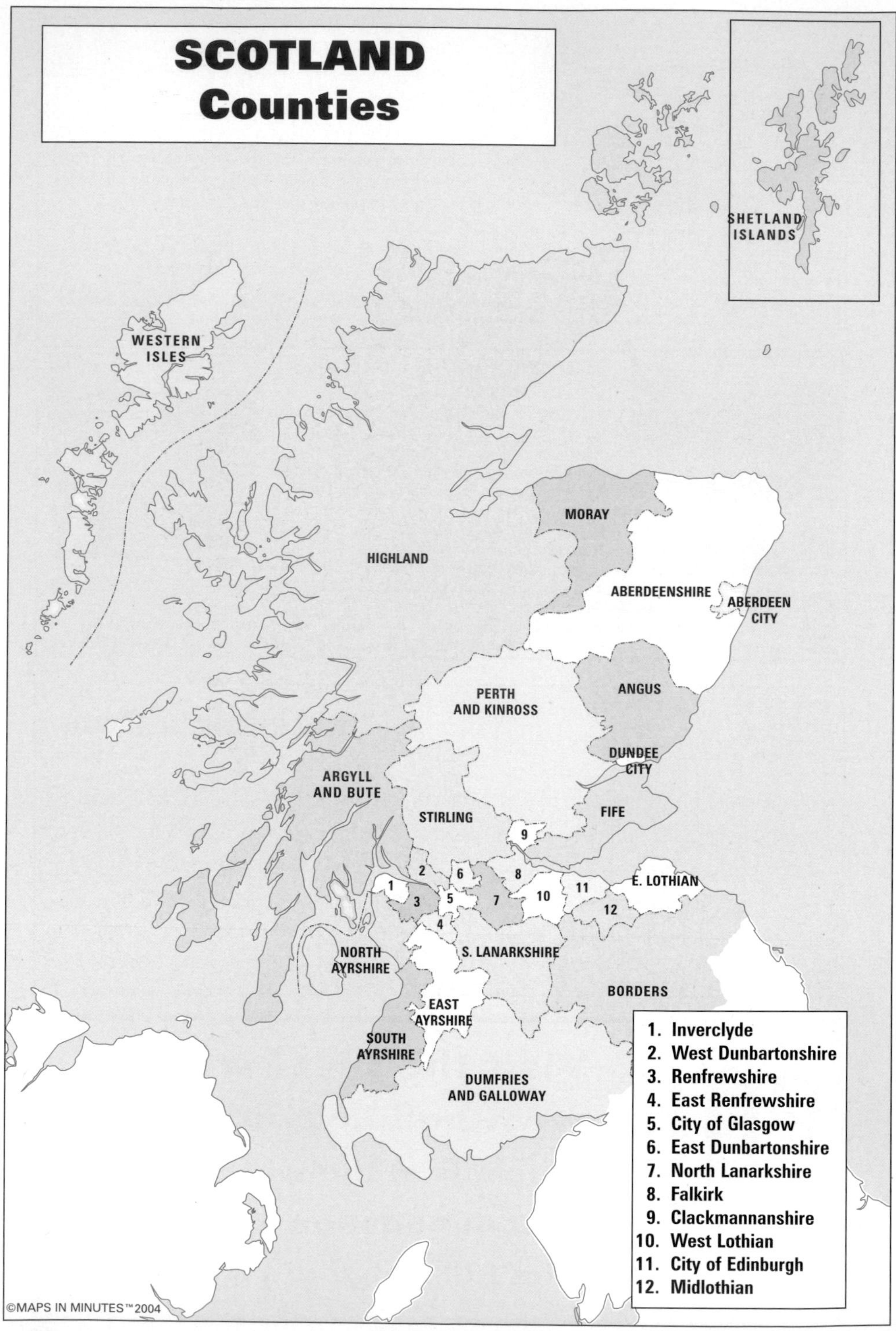
SCOTLAND
Counties
SHETLAND ISLANDS
WESTERN ISLES
HIGHLAND
MORAY
ABERDEENSHIRE
ABERDEEN CITY
ANGUS
PERTH AND KINROSS
DUNDEE CITY
ARGYLL AND BUTE
STIRLING
FIFE
9
2
6
8
1
3
5
7
10
11
12
4
E. LOTHIAN
NORTH AYRSHIRE
S. LANARKSHIRE
BORDERS
EAST AYRSHIRE
SOUTH AYRSHIRE
DUMFRIES AND GALLOWAY
1. Inverclyde
2. West Dunbartonshire
3. Renfrewshire
4. East Renfrewshire
5. City of Glasgow
6. East Dunbartonshire
7. North Lanarkshire
8. Falkirk
9. Clackmannanshire
10. West Lothian
11. City of Edinburgh
12. Midlothian
©MAPS IN MINUTES™2004

Aberdeen, Banff & Moray

ABBOT'S BRAE HOTEL

West Bay, Dunoon, Argyll PA23 7QJ

Tel: 01369 705021 • Fax: 01369 701191

e-mail: info@abbotsbrae.co.uk • website: www.abbotsbrae.co.uk

Award-winning, small Country House Hotel set in its own secluded woodland garden with breathtaking views of the sea and hills. Very spacious en suite bedrooms including four-poster, king-size and twin rooms. The welcoming, homely atmosphere, peaceful surroundings and appetising menus will ensure a memorable stay. Special offers in spring and autumn. Pets stay free. Ideal base to explore the Western Highlands, situated at the Gateway to Scotland's first National Park.

For further details contact either Helen or Gavin.

CAIRNDOW, ARGYLL.

AT THE HEAD OF LOCH FYNE

Two comfortable holiday cottages at the head of the longest sea loch in Scotland. **INVERFYNE** (pictured left), a very spacious cottage with 4 twin bedded rooms, overlooks the estuary. There is a piano in the 32 foot living room and a large utility/drying room.

BRIDGE COTTAGE (pictured right), is a traditional stone cottage and sleeps four, overlooks the bottom pool of the river Fyne. Linen and electricity are included. Achadunan Estate is set amidst lovely walking country. Golden eagles and deer are your neighbours. Achadunan is home to Fyne Ales micro brewery. Brochures available from:

Scottish Tourist Board ★★★ Self Catering

Mrs Delap, Achadunan, Cairndow, Argyll PA26 8BJ
Tel & Fax: +44 (0) 1499 600 238
Web: www.argyllholidaycottages.com

Top Graded 5 Star, Tralee Bay Holidays has been a David Bellamy Gold Award Park for the last 5 years. Located on the West Coast of Scotland near Oban, overlooking Ardmucknish Bay, the wooded surroundings and sandy beach make Tralee the ideal destination for a self-catering lodge or caravan holiday at any time of the year. The Park offers something for everyone with play area, mini golf, fly fishing, nature walks and boat slipway. Set in breathtaking Highland countryside, the gateway to the Isles. The choice of self-catering accommodation ranges from 2003 model 2 and 3 bedroom caravans to brand new lavishly furnished lodges. Pets welcome.

Scottish Thistle Awards 2003 Winner

TRALEE BAY HOLIDAYS

Tel: 01631 720255/217

Tralee Bay Holidays, Benderloch, by Oban, Argyll PA37 1QR
E-mail: tralee@easynet.co.uk Web: www.tralee.com

SKIPNESS ESTATE, By Tarbert, Argyll PA29 6XU

Tel: 01880 760207 • Fax: 01880 760208 • e-mail: sophie@skipness.freeserve.co.uk

This unspoilt, peaceful, West Highland estate with its own historic castle, mediaeval chapel and way-marked walks has traditional cottages to let all year round. Each cottage has an open fire and television; some cottages have a rowing dinghy in summer. Laundry facilities are available alongside the Seafood Cabin at Skipness Castle. Properties sleep 4-10. All cottages have magnificent views and beautiful surrounding countryside and coastline. Safe, sandy beaches can be enjoyed on the estate, with fishing, pony trekking and golf nearby. Local ferries to Arran, Gigha, Islay and Jura.

PETS WELCOME. Apply for rates and further details: Sophie James.

FARM HOLIDAY GUIDE DIPLOMA • STB ★★/★★★ SELF-CATERING

Willowburn Hotel and Restaurant

The Willowburn Hotel garden reaches down to the peaceful waters of Clachan Sound. Inside, the lounge, dining room and most of our comfortable en suite bedrooms enjoy this wonderful view – we see otters, seals, deer and a huge variety of birds.

We are informal and relaxed and take pride in what we offer – in particular our food, which is imaginative and varied, as is our wine list. There's some wonderful walking in the area, wildlife, wild flowers, gardens, boat trips, and places and opportunities just to sit and ponder.

We are non-smoking, pet-friendly and we just want you to relax and enjoy yourselves.

Seil Island, by Oban, Argyll P34 4TJ
Telephone: 01852 300276
Web page: www.willowburn.co.uk
Personally run and managed by Jan and Chris Wolfe.

Slipperfield House

West Linton EH46 7AA

America Cottage

Two well-equipped cottages a mile from West Linton at the foot of the Pentland Hills, set in 100 acres of lochs and woodlands. Only 19 miles from Edinburgh City Centre. Both cottages have sittingrooms with central heating and open fires, digital TV, modern bathrooms and kitchens, microwave ovens and telephones etc.

Loch Cottage

Details from Mrs C.M. Kilpatrick

• Dogs welcome • Ample parking
• Car essential • Central Edinburgh 19 miles
• Golf and private fishing • Available all year.

This is an ideal dog-friendly location for a family holiday near Edinburgh.

Tel and Fax: 01968 660401 e-mail: cottages@slipperfield.com website: www.slipperfield.com

Westwood House – Kelso

Overlooking Scotland's famous River Tweed

TOTAL "OFF LEAD" FREEDOM FOR DOGS IN ENCLOSED AND SECLUDED GROUNDS

Renovated riverside cottage with 12 acres of paths, through walled gardens and on own private island. 4 bedrooms sleeping 2 - 8 (+ child), 2 bathrooms, period features, cosy log fire and centrally heated.
• ½ mile Kelso town • one hour Edinburgh/Newcastle • ½ hour Berwick (station) and Northumberland coast

DOGS WELCOME FREE

For Brochure and tariff, from £325 per week fully inclusive of all linen and towels, electricity and heating. 2-person discounts available. Trout fishing also included.

Debbie Crawford, Tel: 07788 134 832
Pippin Heath Farm, Holt, Norfolk NR25 6SS
e-mail: westwood.house@btinternet.com

ACHIEVING GOLD IN GREEN TOURISM AND 'HIGHLY COMMENDED' IN SCOTTISH THISTLE AWARDS

THE Urr Valley HOTEL

A privately owned hotel set in 14 acres of mature woodland and gardens within walking distance of Castle Douglas. Galloway is one of the most beautiful and diverse areas of countryside in Britain - offering everything from golden sandy beaches to grouse moors, and picturesque harbour villages to forest walks. Panelled walls, log fires and a cosy Sportsman's Bar with over 50 whiskies to offer. 17 en suite rooms, with colour TV, tea & coffee making facilities, hairdryer, trouser press and direct dial telephone.

The Urr Valley Hotel is delighted to welcome dogs and the intimate atmosphere of the building is increased by the presence of two 'in house' golden retrievers and one basset hound. We allow dogs into all areas except those where food is served and we have excellent outdoor watering facilities. The grounds are perfect for exercising pets and their owners, and we look forward to welcoming you in the near future. AA ★★

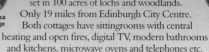

The Urr Valley Hotel,
Ernespie Road, Castle Douglas,
Dumfries & Galloway, Scotland DG7 3JG
Tel: 01556 502188 Fax: 01556 504055

e-mail: info@urrvalleyhotel.co.uk website: www.urrvalleyhotel.co.uk

Spacious, beautiful farmhouse and charming, cosy cottages set amid stunning Scottish scenery near beaches (dogs allowed), hills, forests, castles, gardens and golf course. Loch and river fishing with tuition, free tennis, wonderful walking, cycling and riding country.

Sleep 2-12 • Rates £189 - £1155 • Short breaks available.

Pets, including horses, welcome.

info@ruskoholidays.co.uk • www.ruskoholidays.co.uk

Rusko Holidays

Gatehouse of Fleet, Castle Douglas DG7 2BS
Tel: 01557 814215 • Fax: 01557 814679

Buccleuch Arms Hotel

High Street, Moffat DG10 9ET

We are genuinely dog friendly, not just dog tolerant.

Add to this the best food and service available in Southern Scotland. Shortlisted "Best New Restaurant 2004" by the Scottish Chefs Association.

Tel: 01683 220003 • Fax: 01683 221291
e-mail: enquiries@buccleucharmshotel.com
website: www.buccleucharmshotel.com

The Buccleuch Team welcomes you
Wine, Dine and Explore

• LOCH NESS •

Exceptional riverside lodges close to the spectacular Loch Ness. Mountains, lochs, waterfalls and wildlife abound.

• Charming riverside lodges with private lawns, some with log fires, up to 6 persons. • Cosy studio lodges just for two.• All enjoy magnificent views. • Quiet location with excellent walks from your lodge. • Heating, linen and towels included. • Short Breaks welcome. • Pets welcome. • Free Fishing. • Country pub and restaurant nearby. • Colour brochure / website.

Wildside, Whitebridge, Inverness IV2 6UN
Tel: 01456 486 373 • Fax: 01456 486 371
e-mail: info@wildsidelodges.com • web: www.wildsidelodges.com

Cairngorm Highland Bungalows

Glen Einich, 29 Grampian View,
Aviemore, Inverness-shire PH22 1TF

Tel: 01479 810653 • Fax: 01479 810262
e-mail: linda.murray@virgin.net
website: www.cairngorm-bungalows.co.uk

Beautifully furnished and well-equipped bungalows ranging from one to four bedrooms. All have colour TV, video, microwave, cooker, washer-dryer, fridge and patio furniture. Some have log fires. Leisure facilities nearby include golf, fishing on the River Spey, swimming, sauna, jacuzzi, tennis, skating and skiing. Within walking distance of Aviemore. Ideal touring base. Children and pets welcome. Phone for colour brochure. Open all year.

See advertisement under Perth & Kinross

Aberdovey Hillside Village

Tel: 01654 767522 • Fax: 01654 767069

A cluster of specially designed houses and apartments which blend naturally into south-facing hillside, with the seaside town of Aberdovey nestling below. Shops and beaches are within 300 yards.

- Well equipped kitchen • Bathroom with bath and shower
- Comfortably furnished lounge with colour TV
- Magnificent views • Properties sleep 4/6/8
- Short breaks available outside peak times
- Dogs welcome • Ideal for family holidays

Terms inclusive of heating (Oct - June) and electricity - no coin meters.

Colour Brochure from

Aberdovey Hillside Village, Aberdovey, Gwynedd LL35 0ND

www.hillsidevillage.co.uk • info@hillsidevillage.co.uk

Parc Wernol Park Chwilog, Pwllheli, Gwynedd LL53 6SW

Telephone: 01766 810506

- Panoramic views • Peaceful and quiet
- Ideal for touring Lleyn and Snowdonia
- 4 miles Criccieth and Pwllheli
- 3 miles beach • Cycle route
- Free coarse fishing lake
- Safe children's play area
- Games room
- Footpaths • Dog exercise field

- Self-catering holidays
- 3 bedroom farmhouse
- 2 and 3 bedroom caravans and chalets
- Colour brochure
- Personal attention at all times
- A truly Welsh welcome.

www.wernol.com

The Golden Pheasant is an 18th Century country hotel and inn ideally situated to welcome all pets, especially dogs. Dogs can take their mistress or master for quiet country walks along the country lanes in the summer and on their return enjoy a refreshing drink or sit outside in our garden. If their owners are well-behaved they can enjoy a relaxing drink too! In winter you can warm in front of our old range fire in our 'olde worlde' bar. Ted & Fred, our two Labradors love making new friends. They will wait for the phone to ring or chase the postman for your enquiries, as they have not yet mastered surfing the web. So please ask your mistress or master to bring you for a break – they would be barking mad not to come and stay with us all at The Golden Pheasant where Ted & Fred will be waiting to greet you!!

2 nights D,B&B from £120 pp. B&B from £85, two sharing. Pets from £5 per night.

Llwynmawr, Glyn Ceiriog, Near Llangollen LL20 7BB

Tel: 01691 718281 • Fax: 01691 718479

e-mail: goldenpheasant@micro-plus-web.net website: www.goldenpheasanthotel.co.uk

Don't Delay, Send, phone or fax for free colour brochure.

TYGLYN HOLIDAY ESTATE

A chance to spend a relaxing time amidst beautiful, unspoilt Welsh countryside yet within easy reach of the renowned coastal towns and beaches of New Quay and Aberystwyth with the nearest being the picturesque Aberaeron.

The bungalows are set within seventeen acres of the awe-inspiring Aeron Valley which is home to some magnificent wildlife with Buzzards, Kestrels and the re-established Red Kites being a main attraction, with fishing available on the River Aeron which runs through the estate.

Each bungalow is semi-detached, self-catering, ideal for four people but will accommodate six, with two bedrooms, lounge, kitchen and bathroom.

Bed linen and Electricity are provided.

Your evenings can be spent happily at the adjacent Tyglyn Aeron Hotel, whose bars and restaurants are available to all our visitors.

Don't forget your dogs are always welcome with a nine acre field for their exercise and freedom.

Bookings taken March to January, Short breaks available on request.

**CILIAU AERON,
NEAR LAMPETER,
CEREDIGION,
WALES SA48 8DD
TEL: 01570 470625
FAX: 01570 471435
E-mail:**
look@tyglyn.com

FOR THE MORE ACTIVE HOLIDAYMAKER

- horseriding
- golf
- tennis
- bowls
- walking
- swimming
- ten-pin bowling
- cycling
- quad-biking

a number of leisure centres are all within easy reach.

www.tyglyn.com

Welcome to Ivybridge, where your pet is as welcome as you are!

- Situated down a leafy lane, Ivybridge is a modern guesthouse waiting to welcome you.
- All rooms en suite with TV/hot drinks tray.
- Swim in our indoor pool, relax in our lounge/bar.
- Good home cooking. • Ample off-road parking.
- Close by are quiet walks to the sea which you and your pet will enjoy.

Ivybridge, Drim Mill, Dyffryn, Goodwick SA64 0JT • Tel: 01348 875366
Fax: 01348 872338 • e-mail: ivybridge@cwcom.net • website: www.ivybridge.cwc.net

Conveniently situated on outskirts of picturesque coastal village with shops, beaches and restaurants.
We have large gardens and paddock for pets and owners' relaxation and exercise.
Private parking for guests.
Warm hospitality in relaxed atmosphere.
Non-smoking throughout. All rooms en suite with central heating, clock-radio, colour TV, hairdryer and hospitality tray. Children 6 to 16 years, half price when sharing with two adults. £1 per day per dog.
Brochure and pet guidelines on request.

*** GUEST HOUSE AA ♦♦♦♦

Telephone: 01834 814422
E-mail: enquiries@vinecottageguesthouse.co.uk
Website: www.vinecottageguesthouse.co.uk

VINE COTTAGE

David & Helen Trimmings
The Ridgeway, Saundersfoot
Pembrokeshire SA69 9LA

St Bride's Bay COTTAGES

Cosy cottages and farmhouses near superb beaches and coastal path, around beautiful St.Brides Bay in Pembrokeshire. WTB graded. Sleeps 2-11. Pet welcome.

www.stbridesbaycottages.com

Tel: 0870 7572270

Gwarmacwydd

Gwarmacwydd is a country estate of over 450 acres, including two miles of riverbank. See a real farm in action, the hustle and bustle of harvest, newborn calves and lambs. Children are welcomed. On the estate are six character stone cottages. Each cottage has been lovingly converted from traditional farm buildings, parts of which are over 200 years old. Each cottage is fully furnished and equipped. All electricity and linen included. All cottages are heated for year-round use. Colour brochure available.

Tel: 01437 563260 Fax: 01437 563839
e-mail: info@a-farm-holiday.org
website: www.a-farm-holiday.org
Cottages 1-5 WTB ★★★★ SELF CATERING

Mrs Angela Colledge,
Llanfallteg, Whitland,
Pembrokeshire SA34 0XH

Tel: 01348 837724
Fax: 01348 837622
E-mail: stay@lochmeyler.co.uk
Web: www.lochmeyler.co.uk

Mrs Morfydd Jones
Llandeloy,
Pen-y-Cwm,
Near Solva,
St. Davids,
Pembrokeshire
SA62 6LL

A warm welcome awaits you at Lochmeyler, a 220 acre dairy farm in the centre of the St David's Peninsula. It is an ideal location for exploring the beauty of the coast and countryside.

There are 15 bedrooms, eight of them in the adjacent cottage suites. All are en-suite, non-smoking, luxury rooms with colour TV, video and refreshment facilities. Rooms serviced daily. Children are welcome and there is a children's play area. Well behaved dogs are welcome in some of our rooms. Dogs are not permitted to be left unattended in the rooms. There are kennel facilities for owners wishing to leave their dogs during the day. We do not charge for dogs or the kennel facilities.

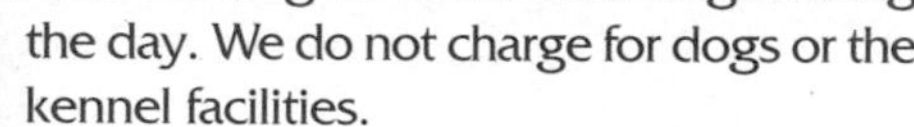

Closed Christmas & New Year
Credit cards accepted.
Colour brochure on request.

AA/RAC ♦♦♦♦♦

DAILY RATES

Bed & Breakfast per person per night £25-£30
Children half price sharing family room
Optional Dinner every night @ £15 per person
10% discount on Bed & Breakfast and Evening Meal bookings of 7 nights or more

Nolton Haven Farm Cottages

Nolton Haven, Haverfordwest,
Pembrokeshire SA62 3NH
Tel: 01437 710200
e-mail: info@havencottages.co.uk
www.havencottages.co.uk

In an Area of Outstanding Natural Beauty, with excellent bathing, boating and surfing. Golf and fishing locally; ideal for walking.

Sympathetically converted cottages situated on a grass bank overlooking Nolton Haven's sandy beach.

- *Primrose Cottage sleeps 5*
- *Bluebell Cottage sleeps 6*
- *Thrift Cottage sleeps 2+2*
- *Honeysuckle & Buttercup Cottages sleep 5*
- *Rose Cottage sleeps 6.*

All are fully equipped, with colour TV, fridge/freezer, microwave etc. Duvets supplied, but no linen. Coin meters for cooking and hot water. Children and pets welcome

OAK WOOD LODGES
Llwynbaedd, Rhayader, Powys LD6 5NT

SELF CATERING LOG CABINS

Luxurious Norwegian log cabins situated at approximately 1000ft above sea level with spectacular views of the Elan Valley and Cambrian Mountains. Enjoy pursuits such as walking, pony trekking, mountain biking, fishing, and bird watching in the most idyllic of surroundings. Excellent touring centre. Dogs welcome. Short breaks as well as full weeks. Open all year round.

For more information and brochure call
01597 811422

AA ★★★

This distinguished country house boasts a wealth of fine antiques, porcelain and paintings. Dating from the 17th century, it has been magnificently preserved, with beautifully restored Edwardian bathrooms, open fireplaces, and mahogany and oak panelling. Guests are served traditional country house recipes on elegant china, and the superb cuisine is featured in many guides. Bedrooms, all individually decorated, provide every thoughtful detail.

Set in seven acres of lush gardens in a peaceful and secluded valley just ten miles west of Cardiff, the hotel is perfectly located for touring South Wales, the Gower Peninsula and the Brecon Beacons.

Egerton Grey
COUNTRY HOUSE HOTEL

Porthkerry, Barry, South Glamorgan CF62 3BZ • Tel: 01446 711666
Fax: 01446 711690 • info@egertongrey.co.uk • www.egertongrey.co.uk

Hosts, Richard Morgan-Price and Huw Thomas, will ensure you have a comfortable and enjoyable stay.

FHG

Visit the FHG website
www.holidayguides.com
for details of the wide choice of accommodation featured in the full range of FHG titles

Portable homes from home for discerning pets!

Dog Bag - GLEE "New Product Award" winner

Dog Bag is an award winning ‘pop up’ fabric kennel, a portable ‘home from home’ which provides an appropriate combination of strength, privacy and air circulation, as well as good sun protection when used in the car or in the garden. Dog Bag even packs into its own rucksack for storage and convenience.

As well as the Dog Bags, Pet Tubes (particularly suitable for use on rear car seats) and the USB small animal carrier, a wide range of accessories is available - from a waterproof cover to a full tent, ideal for those who take their pets camping or caravanning.

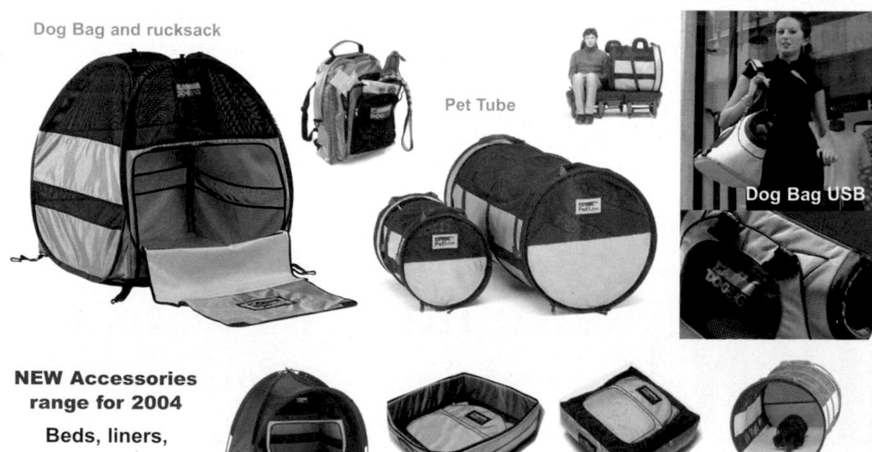

NEW Accessories range for 2004

Beds, liners, even a tent!

0845 230 8228 www.dog-bag.co.uk

BOARDING YOUR PET by Kenn Oultram

THE remarkable growth of travel and tourism has provided satellite industries like **Animal Boarding Establishments (ABE)** with year-round financial benefits, though ABE owners will reveal they were never entirely dependent on the holiday-maker. For this is very much a service industry in its own right; greatly appreciated by, for example, pet owners who may be moving house...entering hospital...taking a work assignment abroad...having the builders in...throwing a fireworks party...coping with a bitch in season or, perhaps, a cat recuperating from surgery. As looking after pets is an awesome responsibility and a job for the professional, is it reasonable to expect a neighbour or pet-sitter to take this on?

Staff at an ABE must be alert for blood, constipation, diarrhoea, lethargy, coughing, fleas, incontinence, sneezing, worms and vomit! It is taken for granted that an ABE will accept the allergic, the arthritic, the diabetic, the epileptic, the hyper-active and the neurotic...and administer pills, drops and injections. Most of all they will be expected to guarantee the safe-keeping of your pet during your absence. Postmen may claim they face the risk of dog bites, but try opening the kennel door of an outsize hound with a 30 inch neck and two cute rows of flashing stained teeth.

Early advance booking at an ABE for your pet's boarding card is now essential as the equation of 5,000 kennels/catteries to cope with a potential 11 million UK dogs and cats simply doesn't balance and, at peak times, you'll discover there's no room at the inn.

All ABEs are inspected annually by an officer from the Environmental Health Department of the Local Authority which issues a licence to operate. It is illegal to run an ABE without a licence and this must be displayed for all to see (usually in the reception area).

Some general guidelines:

- A brochure indicates a professional approach. Ring round requesting these.
- Do NOT book if the ABE will not permit you to inspect the facilities. On arrival ask to see the exercise area for dogs (leaving dogs to their own devices all day in outside runs is NOT exercise). In catteries check that sneeze barriers are installed.
- If vaccinations are not necessary do NOT book; especially if dogs are not required to be vaccinated against kennel cough.
- Ask if the ABE's insurance covers your pet's stay; otherwise a nasty vet's bill could be awaiting your return.
- Many pet owners have more than one dog or cat. Look for family-sized units and check heating facilities (after all, our winters are twice the duration of our summers...and the ABE staff need to be kept warm too!)

- Check that your pet will not come into contact with another client's pet.
- On arrival – your ears, eyes and nose will tell all! You are looking for cleanliness, contented boarders and an experienced, caring staff. If apprehensive ask if you may send someone to visit your pet during its stay. You could also try your pet for a day (or a night) prior to the planned lengthy stay.
- If your pet is taken ill, ensure that the ABE is advised whether to call its own veterinarian or your own. Leave a contact number.
- If the ABE does not stock your pet's favourite food, offer to supply this, though there may not be any discount off your bill by doing so.
- Ask if a grooming service is offered. Some ABEs do. Others provide a collection and delivery service.

Finally, the time has surely come for an exhaustive, independent survey of British kennels and catteries with a one-to-four star ratings assessment. Perhaps one of the major motoring organisations should attempt this.... after all, 99% of ABE clients arrive on four wheels.

For free advice and addresses call the Animal Boarding Advisory Bureau on 01606 891303 or the Feline Advisory Bureau on 01747 871872 during office hours. For the boarding of house rabbits write to The British House Rabbit Association, Box 346, Newcastle-upon-Tyne NE99 1FA. You may even wish to recommend your own Animal Boarding Establishment.

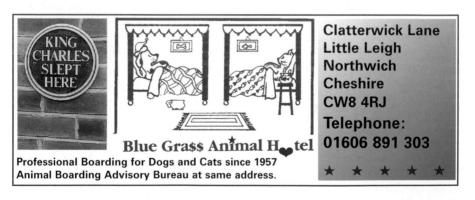

Preparing your Dogs and Cats for travel abroad

How can my pet travel? Because of stringent requirements, dogs and cats travelling under the so-called pet passport scheme cannot make last minute reservations; in general, six-month advance planning is required. Veterinarians must implant a microchip in the animal, inoculate it against rabies, have a laboratory recognized by the Department for Environment, Food and Rural Affairs (DEFRA) confirm by blood sample that the vaccine is active, and issue a PETS certificate. Certificates are valid from six months after obtaining the blood sample results until the date of the animal's next rabies booster shot. (Dogs and cats resident in Britain whose blood sample was drawn before Feb 29, 2000 are exempt from this six month rule). Dogs and cats must also be treated against ticks and tapeworms no less than 24 nor more than 48 hours before check-in (when the animal enters carrier's custody). Animals travelling by air are placed in containers bearing an official seal (the number of which is also inscribed on the PETS certificate) to ensure animals are not exposed to disease en route. Sealing requirements do not apply to Cyprus or Malta. Owners must also sign a certificate attesting that the animal has not been outside participating territories in the last six months. Travellers are cautioned that Britain will enforce its rules rigorously.

Your pet must be injected with a harmless identification ISO (International Standards Organisation) approved microchip. This chip will be read by a handheld scanning device.

From and back to the UK.

Ask your vet to implant an ISO (International Standards Organisation) approved microchip - then to vaccinate against rabies recording the batch number of the vaccine on a veterinary certificate together with the microchip number.

Approximately 30 days later your vet should take a blood sample and send it to one of the DEFRA approved laboratories to check that the vaccine has provided the correct level of protection.

Your vet will then issue you with a certificate confirming all the above – in the UK this is called The Pet Travel Scheme Re-Entry Certificate. It is valid for the life of the rabies vaccine, so keep your rabies vaccine up to date and a new certificate will be issued without the need for further blood tests.

Six months from the taking of a successful blood test you will be able to enter or re-enter the UK from Western Europe and 28 other countries including Australia, Japan and Singapore.

Pets must be treated for ticks and for the echinococcus parasite by a qualified vet who will record this on an official UK certificate not less than 24 hours and not more than 48 hours before entry into the UK. We are trying to secure changes in this very awkward timetable, which is being rigidly enforced.

On entering the UK you must therefore have two official certificates; one for the microchip, rabies vaccine and blood test; the second for treatment against ticks and parasites. You will also have to sign a residence declaration form - provided by the travel operator who is carrying out the checking. It simply confirms that the pet has not been outside the approved countries in the previous six months.

From Europe to the UK

As above, you must microchip your pet, vaccinate against rabies and approximately 30 days later your vet will take a blood test sending it to one of the laboratories from the list of those approved by MAFF. SIX MONTHS after a successful blood test your pet will be allowed to travel to the UK providing it has been treated against ticks and worms.

Costs:

- Microchip: Should be in the region of £25.00
- Vaccine: Varies according to vet but again approximately £30.00
- Blood test: We know that the blood testing laboratory at Weybridge (VLA) charge £49.50 per test.

Therefore anything in addition is that levied by the vet. Providing the rabies vaccination is kept up to date the blood test will not have to be repeated. Should there be a break between rabies vaccines a further blood test would have to be taken and then a period of 6 months allowed before re-entry to the UK would be permitted.

Therefore: Microchip and blood-test are one-off costs but the rabies vaccination is a yearly or 2 yearly cost depending on the vaccine used.

DEFRA Help line Telephone Number is: 0870 241 17110

Current ports of entry are Dover (from Calais by ferry), Portsmouth (from Caen, Cherbourg, Le Havre or St Malo by ferry) and Folkestone (from Calais or Cheriton by Eurotunnel). London Heathrow is the authorised port-of-entry for : British Midland Airlines from Amsterdam-Schiphol, Brussels, Madrid, Palma Majorca, and Paris (Paris for guide dogs only); Finnair from Helsinki; and Lufthansa from Frankfurt.

The laboratories approved by MAFF for blood testing:

Veterinary Laboratory Agency New Haw, Addlestone Surrey KT15 3NB UNITED KINGDOM	Tel: (+44) 01932 357 345 Fax:(+44) 01 932 357 856 Costs: £49.50
BioBest Bush Loan - Paul Burns, Vet Penicuick Midlothian EH26 0PZ SCOTLAND	Tel: (+44) 0131 445 6101 Fax: (+44) 0131 445 6102 Costs: £32.50
Agence Francaise De Securite Sanitaire des Aliments Nancy Domaine de Pixerecourt B.P. 9F-54220 Maizeville, FRANCE	Tel: (+33) 3 83 298950 Fax:(+33) 3 83 298959 Costs: 425ff = approx £42
National Veterinary Institute Commission of Diagnosites Section of Diagnostic Department of Virology P.O. Box 585, BMCS-751 23 Uppsala SWEDEN	Tel: (+46) 1867 4000 Fax:(+46) 1847 14517 Costs: 500K=approx £40
Danish Veterinary Institute for Virus Research Lindholm DK-4771 Kalvehave DENMARK	Tel: (+45) 55 8602 00 Fax:(+45) 55 8603 00 Costs: 252K=approx £25
National Veterinary and Food Research Institute PL 368 (Heimmeentie 57) 00231 Helsinki FINLAND	Tel: (+35) 89393 1901 Fax:(+35) 89393 1811 Costs: 396.50 Fmark = approx £26.00
Institut fur Virologie Frankfurter Strasse 107 D35392 Giessen GERMANY	Tel: (+49) 641 99 38350 Fax: (+49) 641 99 38359 Costs: 72.60DM= approx £25
Dept. for Equine, Pets and Vaccine Control Virology Unit Federal Institute for the Control of Viral Infection in Animals Robert Kochgasse 17 2340 Modling AUSTRIA	Tel: (+43) 2236 46 640 902 or 906 Fax:(+43) 2236 46 640 941 Costs: 600 schillings= approx £30

Instituto Zooprotilattico Sperimentale delle Venezie Via Romea 14/A 1-35020 Legonaro (PD) ITALY	Tel: (+39) 04980 70 306 Fax:(+39) 04988 30 Costs: Price Unknown
Direccion General de Sanidad de la Produccion Agaria, Laboratono de Sanidad y Produccion Animal del Estado, Camino del Jau, S/N E-18320 Santa Fe (Granada) SPAIN	Tel: (+34) 958 44 03 75 Fax:(+34) 958 44 12 00 Costs: FREE
Institute Pasteur of Brussels Rue Engeland 642 B-i 180 Brussels BELGIUM	Tel: (+32) 2 373 31 58 Fax:(+32) 2 373 31 74 Costs: 1,500BF- approx £25
Institute of Veterinary Virology Schweizerische Tollwutzentrale Langgass-Strasse 122 CH-3012 Bern SWITZERLAND	Tel: (+41) 31 631 2378 Fax:(+41) 31 631 2534 Costs: 96.75 SF= approx £40

You can e-mail us at passports.forpets@virgin.net
or write to our London address: PASSPORTS FOR PETS

What we musn't forget?

Medicine, if needed

Toys

Health certificates

Food and drink dishes

The dog's basket or blanket – it is extremely important that your dog has something to make him feel at home

A thermometer

A bell to hang around the dog's collar.

A can opener if you have canned food

A deodorant for the hotel room

Paper towels

Brushes to brush your dog

A towel to dry the dog in case of rain or when you get back to the hotel room

0906 500 1099
0906 500 1099

Have your pet's photo featured in

Pets Welcome!

As the sponsor of

Pets Welcome! 2005

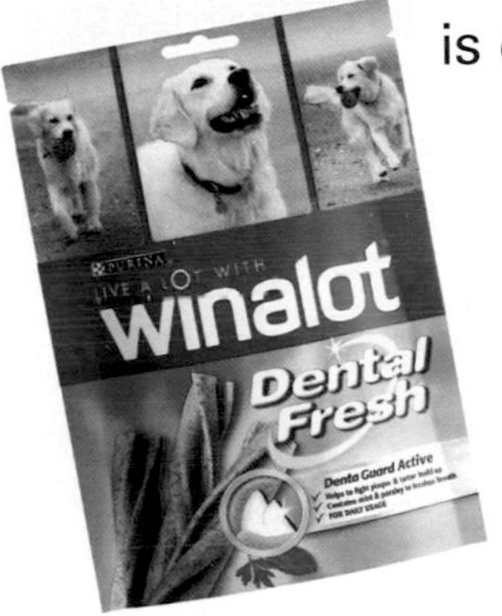

is offering readers a free packet of

Winalot Dental Fresh

for every photo featured – the perfect way to reward your best friend.

Live a lot with your dog at

www.winalot-dog.co.uk

Send us your favourite Pet Photo!

On the following pages are a selection of Pets photos sent in by readers of **Pets Welcome!**

If you would like to have a photo of your pet included in the next edition (published in APRIL 2005), send it along with a brief note of the pet's name and any interesting anecdotes about them. Please remember to include your own name and address and let us know if you would like the pictures returned.

Everyone sending a photo can select a **FREE** copy of any of FHG's year 2005 guides from the list shown at the back of this book. If your picture is featured in the next issue we will also pay £10.

We will be happy to receive prints, transparencies or pictures on disk or by e-mail to **fhg@ipcmedia.com** All pictures should be forwarded by the end of January 2005.

Thanks to everyone who sent in pictures of their pets and regret that we were unable to include all of them. ***See page 84 for this year's selection***

Send your Pet photo to: FHG Publications, Abbey Mill Business Centre, Seedhill, Paisley PA1 1TJ.

Readers' Pets Pictures

Where have all the birds gone?
sent by Elaine Brookes of Leeds

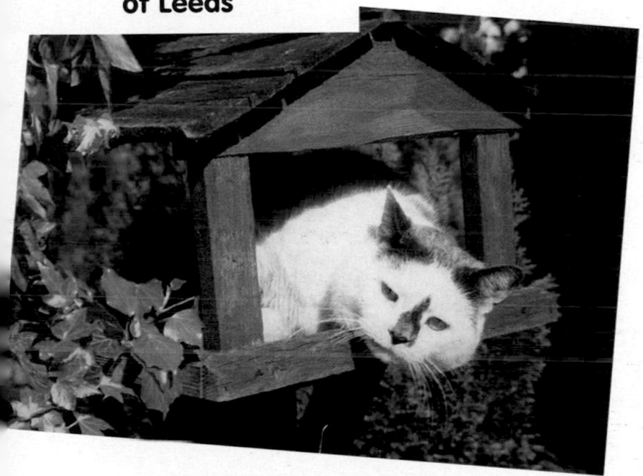

We would like to thank readers for their response to our request for pictures in this issue, and are pleased to present the following selection.

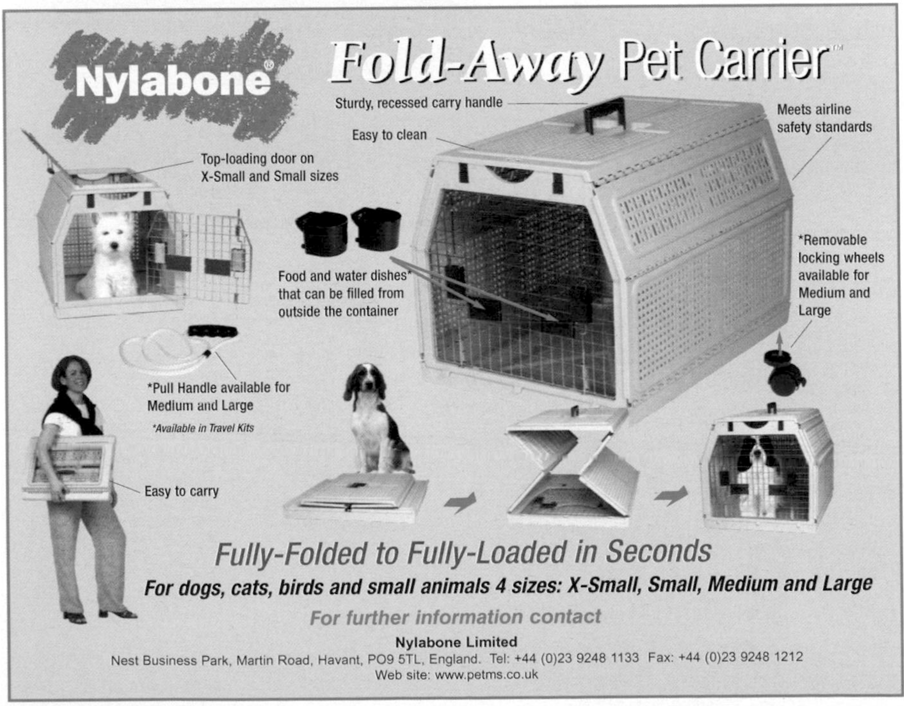

Does my head look big in this? says MICKEY from Mrs Langton of Devon

KASHKA's a back seat driver sent by Katrina Anderson of Hertfordshire

DALLY's dressed for hill climbing from Ms Sue Lloyd of Worcestershire

Looks can be deceiving, KA CEE's no angel from Mrs Margaret Dawson of Powys

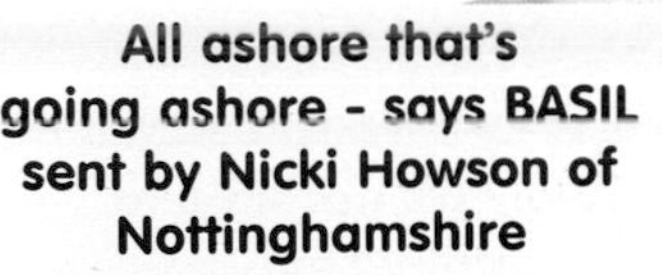

All ashore that's going ashore - says BASIL sent by Nicki Howson of Nottinghamshire

KATIE, BILLIE & MOLLY relax amongst the sand dunes from Ms Thomson of Lincolnshire

"THE BOYS" at home, sent by Ms Jackie Mulcair of Nottinghamshire

Surely it's not time to get up yet, say HOLLIE and SPICE from Miss Flintoft, Lincolnshire

We are not amused, says JADE PRINCESS from Clive Hockley

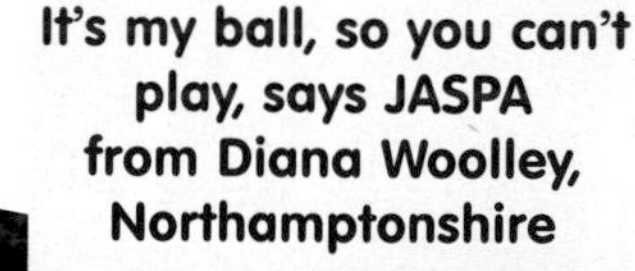

It's my ball, so you can't play, says JASPA from Diana Woolley, Northamptonshire

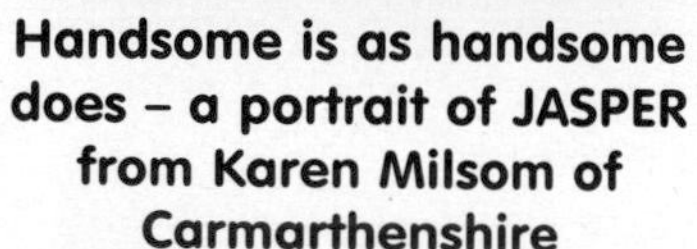

Handsome is as handsome does – a portrait of JASPER from Karen Milsom of Carmarthenshire

Don't forget to pack my favourite toy, says FRED from Mrs Baker of West Midlands

FLEUR, BUFFEE and MOLLEE in holiday mode, from Ms Jackie Mulcair of Nottinghamshire

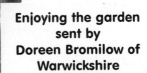

Enjoying the garden sent by Doreen Bromilow of Warwickshire

The Happy Gang – CASSIE, ROSIE, ANNABELLE, JODIE, HOLLY and JONTY chill out on the beach from Steve Jardine

**MARMITE,
"Princess for a Day"
sent by Mrs Thatcher
of Peterborough**

**Is that a whale our
there? asks MILLY
from Carolyn Custerson
of Devon**

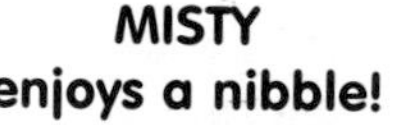

**MISTY
enjoys a nibble!**

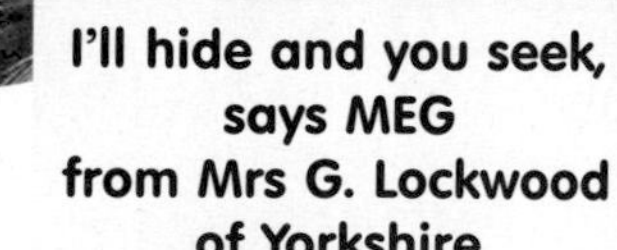

**I'll hide and you seek,
says MEG
from Mrs G. Lockwood
of Yorkshire**

KANE enjoys his daily swim
sent by Mrs De Wolfreys of Cornwall

DYLAN is wrapped up
warmly for the snow
from Mrs Lloyd of
Worcestershire

Kiss me quick -
MICKEY & BONNIE
at the seaside from
Mrs Langton of Devon

KOSHKA, The Copy Cat
from Ms Sue Lloyd of
Worcestershire

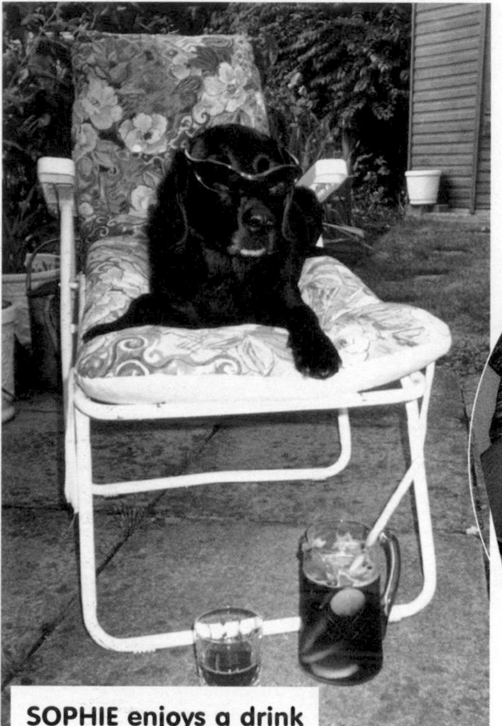

SOPHIE enjoys a drink
on the patio
from Miss Thomson
of Middlesex

POPPY loves to help
from Mrs Cade
of South Humberside

HAMLET hides
amongst the rocks
from Sally Towle
of Devon

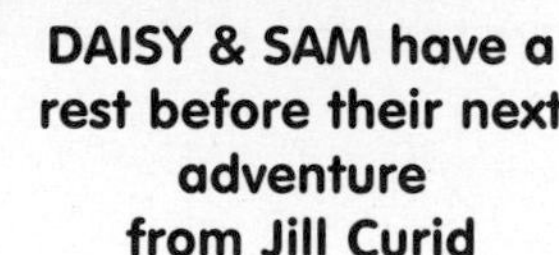

DAISY & SAM have a
rest before their next
adventure
from Jill Curid

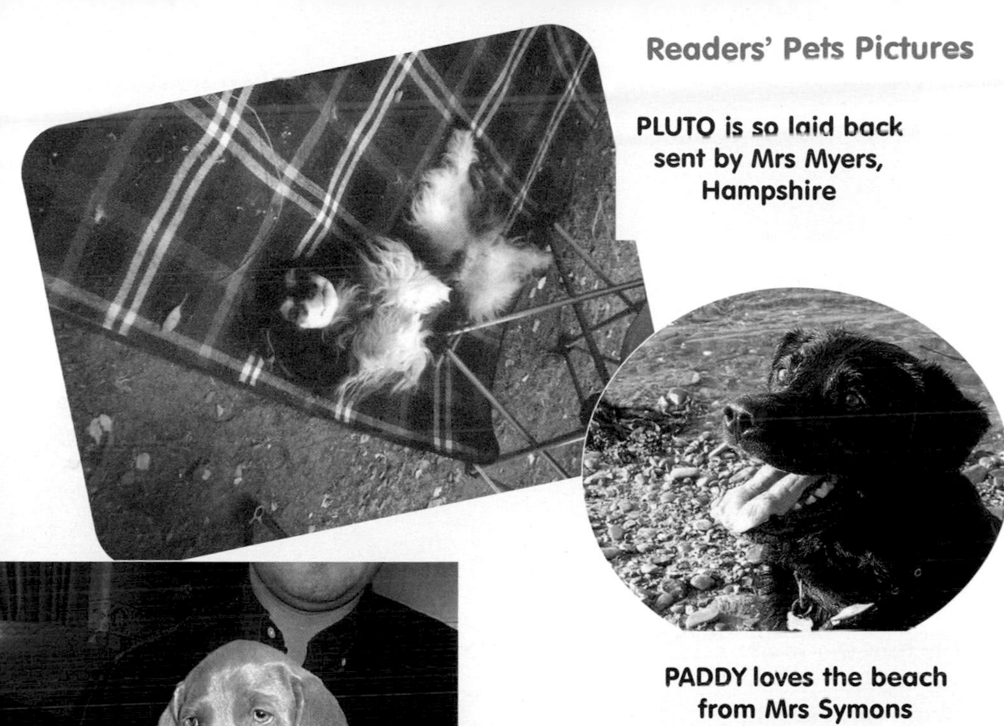

PLUTO is so laid back
sent by Mrs Myers,
Hampshire

PADDY loves the beach
from Mrs Symons
of Cornwall

MILLI is a proper little
handful
sent by Clare Mansfield
of West Yorkshire

PETER & SMARTIE
take a well earned rest
from Carol Rowland
of Farndon

Just smell that fresh air
says MOJO
sent by Ms Mel Hannam
of North Lancashire

This is no time for resting – YASSKO tells CERYS from Mrs Halling of Bedfordshire

Is that the taxi? ask YASSKO & CERYS from Mrs Halling of Bedfordshire

Mind your feet, these rocks are slippery, says YASSKO from Mrs Halling of Bedfordshire

SWEEP takes a breather from Nina Major of Cheshire

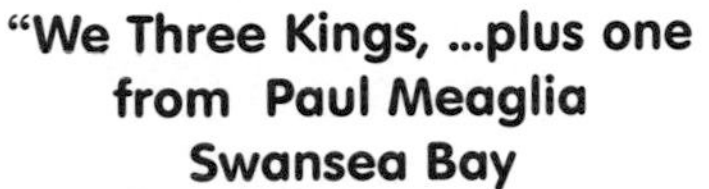

"We Three Kings, ...plus one
from Paul Meaglia
Swansea Bay

FLYNN
enjoys the
creature comforts
from Polly & Ian
Price
Cheshire

JADE & friend
enjoy a spot of relaxation
sent by Paul & Julie Lewis, Kent

"Surely we can't be twins"
say RUPERT & ARNIE
sent by Mr T. Addis,
Walsall

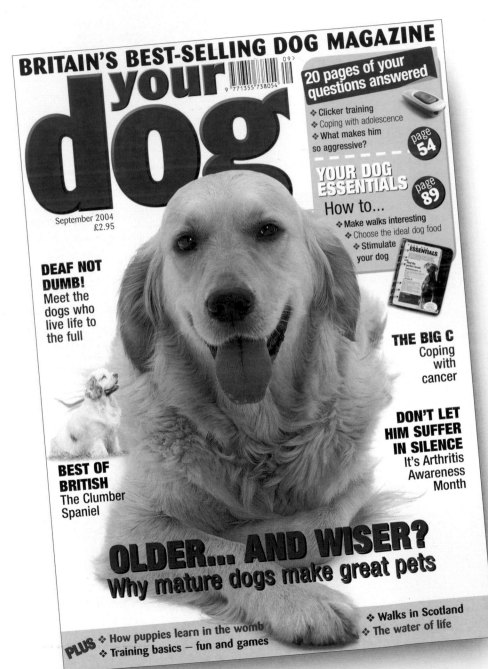

DogsTrust: A Dog is For Life

Are you thinking of going on holiday in the UK with your dog?

If so, the Dogs Trust has a free factsheet which will be of particular interest.

"Safe travel and happy holidays with your hound in the UK"

For this and any other of our free Dogs Trust factsheets please contact us at:

Dogs Trust,
17 Wakley St. London EC1V 7RQ.
Tel: 020 7837 0006
Website: www.dogstrust.org.uk
or e-mail us, info@dogstrust.org.uk

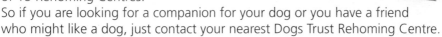

Last year Dogs Trust cared for over 11,500 stray and abandoned dogs at our network of 15 Rehoming Centres.
So if you are looking for a companion for your dog or you have a friend who might like a dog, just contact your nearest Dogs Trust Rehoming Centre.

We care for around 1,600 dogs on any given day, so we are sure we will be able to find your perfect partner. The Dogs Trust never destroys a healthy dog.
For details of our Sponsor-a-Dog scheme please call 020 7837 0006 or visit www.sponsoradog.org.uk

Dogs Trust Rehoming Centres

ENGLAND

Dogs Trust Canterbury
01227 792 505

Dogs Trust Darlington
01325 333 114

Dogs Trust Evesham
01386 830 613

Dogs Trust Ilfracombe
01271 812 709

Dogs Trust Kenilworth
01926 484 398

Dogs Trust Leeds
01132 613 194

Dogs Trust Merseyside
0151 480 0660

Dogs Trust Newbury
01488 658 391

Dogs Trust Roden
01952 770 225

Dogs Trust Salisbury
01980 629 634

Dogs Trust Shoreham
01273 452 576

Dogs Trust Snetterton
01953 498 377

WALES

Dogs Trust Bridgend
01656 725 219

SCOTLAND

Dogs Trust West Calder
01506 873 459

NORTHERN IRELAND

Dogs Trust Ballymena
028 2565 2977

Registered Charity No. 227523

The original and unique

Pets Welcome 2005

Foreword

Because your dog is important to you and your family, you want him to share all the special times in your life, including holidays. The 44th edition of Pets Welcome! is packed full of holiday ideas, from luxury pet-friendly accommodation, to caravan parks and B&B stopovers, so taking your dog on holiday has never been easier.

We all like to relax and let our hair down when we are on holiday, but while we are having fun we should also remember that dogs are used to a certain daily routine, and we should therefore try to stick as closely as possible to their usual times for feeding, walks and playtime.

All of our proprietors welcome pets, but they do expect owners to be responsible. Pets should be kept under control at all times and discouraged from jumping up on furniture or people. They should never be left unattended, especially in a strange environment – a lonely or unhappy pet is very likely to get into mischief. Grooming is also important – muddy paws and sandy coats are not too welcome indoors! Remember that a little consideration now will ensure that you and your pets are welcome to return another time.

Most of our entries are of long standing and are tried and tested favourites with animal lovers. However as publishers we do not inspect the accommodation advertised in Pets Welcome! and an entry does not imply our recommendation. Some proprietors offer fuller facilities for pets than others, and in the classified entry which we give each advertiser we try to indicate by symbols whether or not there are any special facilities and if additional charges are involved. However, we suggest that you raise any queries or particular requirements when you make enquiries and bookings.

If you have any problems or complaints, please raise them on the spot with the owner or his representative in the first place. We will follow up complaints if necessary, but we regret that we cannot act as intermediaries nor can we accept responsibility for details of accommodation and/or services described here. Happily, serious complaints are few. Finally, if you have to cancel or postpone a holiday booking, please give as much notice as possible. This courtesy will be appreciated and it could save later difficulties.

Boarding your Pet (Page 73), Preparing your Dogs and Cats for Travel Abroad (Page 75), Holidays with Horses (Page 406), and The Guide to Pet Friendly Pubs (Page 412) are now regular features, and on page 99 you will find some useful information on keeping your pet happy in warm weather. Our latest selection of Pets Pictures starts on page 84.

We would be happy to receive readers' suggestions on any other useful features. Please also let us know if you have had any unusual or humorous experiences with your pet on holiday. This always makes interesting reading! And we hope that you will mention ***Pets Welcome!*** when you make your holiday inquiries or bookings.

Anne Cuthbertson, Editor

44th Edition © IPC Media Ltd 2004
ISBN 1 85055 359 9

Cover design: Focus Network
Cover Pictures: BananaStock at Alamy

Maps: ©MAPS IN MINUTES™ 2004. ©Crown Copyright, Ordnance Survey 2004.

Typeset by FHG Publications Ltd, Paisley.
Printed and bound in Great Britain by William Clowes, Beccles, Suffolk.

Distribution. Book Trade: ORCA Book Services, Stanley House,
3 Fleets Lane, Poole, Dorset BH15 3AJ
(Tel: 01202 665432; Fax: 01202 666219)
e-mail: mail@orcabookservices.co.uk
News Trade: Market Force (UK) Ltd, 5th Floor Low Rise, Kings Reach Tower
Stamford Street, London SE1 9LS
(Tel: 0207 633 3450; Fax: 0207 633 3572).

Published by FHG Publications Ltd., Abbey Mill Business Centre,
Seedhill, Paisley PA1 lTJ (Tel: 0141-887 0428 Fax: 0141-889 7204).
e-mail: fhg@ipcmedia.com

Pets Welcome! is an FHG publication, published by
IPC Country & Leisure Media Ltd, part of IPC Media Group of Companies.

All the advertisers in PETS WELCOME! have an entry in the appropriate classified section and each classified entry may carry one or more of the following symbols:

- 🐕 This symbol indicates that pets are welcome free of charge.
- **£** The £ indicates that a charge is made for pets. We quote the amount where possible, either per night or per week.
- **pw!** This symbol shows that the establishment has some special provision for pets; perhaps an exercise facility or some special feeding or accommodation arrangements.
- ⌂ Indicates separate pets' accommodation.

PLEASE NOTE that all the advertisers in PETS WELCOME! extend a welcome to pets and their owners but they may attach conditions. The interests of other guests have to be considered and it is usually assumed that pets will be well trained, obedient and under the control of their owner.

Live a lot with your dog at www.winalot-dog.co.uk

For many of us enjoying a country holiday also means taking our dogs on scenic walks, or for a journey in the car - often in warm weather, and at these times they may need a little extra care and attention. The following tips could make your pet's life on hot days considerably more comfortable:

WATER!

A normal 20kg dog will drink about one and a half pints of water a day. In the heat this can increase by 200 to 300%. Water should always be available. Make sure you take plenty for your pet, as well for yourself when out walking and in the car. Stabilising non-spill water bowls are great for travel, while handy inflatable bowls are ideal for stowing in your knapsack. You can even buy water bottles that your dog can carry.

SHADE

Encourage your dog to favour shady, cool spots when you stop for a rest - rather than sunbathe with the rest of the family!

CAR

NEVER leave your dog in the car unattended. Placing a dog in the back of any car even with an open rear window is undesirable and may be fatal. Remember - even a car parked in shade in the morning when it's cool could reach over 100 degrees very quickly as the sun moves. Heat stroke can occur within minutes.

EXERCISE

Plan your walk so you avoid strenuous exercise during the hottest part of the day. Some dogs like to paddle or swim - if there is no water around and your dog seems uncomfortably hot, seek a shady spot and provide water.

HEALTH

A dog's heat loss system is dependent on overall health. If your dog is fit, supple and active then walking will be a pleasurable experience, however, if there is any indication of heart or respiratory problems arising, controlled exercise in the cool is recommended. Veterinary advice should be sought if problems persist during heat stressful times.

HEAT STROKE

This is an emergency and potentially life threatening situation. If in doubt take the following action, then seek advice. A chilled dog is better than an overheated one.

- Cease any form of exercise.
- Move the dog into a cool place.
- Sponge the dog with cold water - all over, avoiding water round the mouth or nose.
- Do not offer food or fluids until evident recovery.
- Seek veterinary advice if in doubt.

THE FHG DIPLOMA

HELP IMPROVE BRITISH TOURIST STANDARDS

You are choosing holiday accommodation from our very popular FHG Publications. Whether it be a hotel, guest house, farmhouse or self-catering accommodation, we think you will find it hospitable, comfortable and clean, and your host and hostess friendly and helpful.

Why not write and tell us about it?

As a recognition of the generally well-run and excellent holiday accommodation reviewed in our publications, we at FHG Publications Ltd. present a diploma to proprietors who receive the highest recommendation from their guests who are also readers of our Guides. If you care to write to us praising the holiday you have booked through FHG Publications Ltd. – whether this be board, self-catering accommodation, a sporting or a caravan holiday, what you say will be evaluated and the proprietors who reach our final list will be contacted.

The winning proprietor will receive an attractive framed diploma to display on his premises as recognition of a high standard of comfort, amenity and hospitality. FHG Publications Ltd. offer this diploma as a contribution towards the improvement of standards in tourist accommodation in Britain. Help your excellent host or hostess to win it!

FHG DIPLOMA

We nominate

Because

Name ....

Address...

....

Telephone No...

FHG READERS' OFFER 2005

Leighton Buzzard Railway

Page's Park Station, Billington Road,
Leighton Buzzard, Bedfordshire LU7 4TN
Tel: 01525 373888
e-mail: info@buzzrail.co.uk • website: www.buzzrail.co.uk

One free adult/child with full-fare adult ticket

valid from 20/3/05 – 30/10/05

NOT TO BE USED IN CONJUNCTION WITH ANY OTHER OFFER

FHG READERS' OFFER 2005

Buckinghamshire Railway Centre

Quainton Road Station, Quainton, Aylesbury HP22 4BY
Tel & Fax: 01296 655720
e-mail: bucksrailcentre@btopenworld.com
website: www.bucksrailcentre.org

One child FREE with each full-paying adult

not valid for for special events

NOT TO BE USED IN CONJUNCTION WITH ANY OTHER OFFER

FHG READERS' OFFER 2005

Sacrewell Farm & Country Centre

Sacrewell, Thornhaugh, Peterborough PE8 6HJ
Tel & Fax: 01780 782254
e-mail: info@sacrewell.fsnet.co.uk
website: www.sacrewell.org.uk

One child FREE with one full paying adult

valid from March 1st to October 1st 2005

NOT TO BE USED IN CONJUNCTION WITH ANY OTHER OFFER

FHG READERS' OFFER 2005

The Salt Museum

162 London Road, Northwich, Cheshire CW9 8AB
Tel: 01606 41331
e-mail: cheshiremuseums@cheshire.gov.uk
website: www.saltmuseum.org.uk

one FREE entry with one paying adult

valid until October 2005

NOT TO BE USED IN CONJUNCTION WITH ANY OTHER OFFER

FHG READERS' OFFER 2005

Stretton Watermill

contact: Cheshire Museums Service, 162 London Road, Northwich CW9 8AB
Tel: 01606 41331
e-mail: cheshiremuseums@cheshire.gov.uk

one FREE entry with one paying adult

valid until October 2005

NOT TO BE USED IN CONJUNCTION WITH ANY OTHER OFFER

A 70-minute journey into the lost world of the English narrow gauge light railway. Features historic steam locomotives from many countries.

PETS MUST BE KEPT UNDER CONTROL AND NOT ALLOWED ON TRACKS

Open: Sundays and Bank Holiday weekends 13 March to 30 October. Additional days in summer.

Directions: on A4146 towards Hemel Hempstead, close to roundabout junction with A505.

FHG PUBLICATIONS, ABBEY MILL BUSINESS CENTRE, PAISLEY PA1 1TJ

A working steam railway centre. Steam train rides, miniature railway rides, large collection of historic preserved steam locomotives, carriages and wagons.

Open: Sundays and Bank Holidays April to October, plus Wednesdays in June, July and August 10.30am to 5.30pm.

Directions: off A41 Aylesbury to Bicester Road, 6 miles north west of Aylesbury.

FHG PUBLICATIONS, ABBEY MILL BUSINESS CENTRE, PAISLEY PA1 1TJ

Farm animals, 18th century watermill and farmhouse, farm artifacts, caravan and camping, children's play areas. Restaurant and gift shop.

Open: all year 9.30am to 5pm.

Directions: signposted off both A47 and A1.

FHG PUBLICATIONS, ABBEY MILL BUSINESS CENTRE, PAISLEY PA1 1TJ

The unique story of the salt industry and the local history of the area. With temporary exhibitions and special events throughout the year, there is something for everyone.

Open: Tuesday to Friday (+ Mondays in August and Bank Holiday Mondays) 10am to 5pm
Saturday and Sunday 2-5pm
(12 noon-5pm in August)

Directions: on A533 ½ mile from town centre. Approx. 30 mins from Chester.

FHG PUBLICATIONS, ABBEY MILL BUSINESS CENTRE, PAISLEY PA1 1TJ

This delightful cornmill dates back to 1351. A guided tour of the working mill is included in the admission price.

Open: April and September weekends: 1-5pm.
May to August
Tuesday to Sunday 1-5pm
+ Bank Holiday Mondays

Directions: 10 miles from Chester, well signposted from the A534

FHG PUBLICATIONS, ABBEY MILL BUSINESS CENTRE, PAISLEY PA1 1TJ

FHG READERS' OFFER 2005

Cars of the Stars Motor Museum

Standish Street, Keswick, Cumbria CA12 5HH

Tel: 017687 73757

e-mail: cotsmm@aol.com • website: www.carsofthestars.com

One child free with two paying adults

Valid 2005

NOT TO BE USED IN CONJUNCTION WITH ANY OTHER OFFER

FHG READERS' OFFER 2005

Windermere Steamboats & Museum

Rayrigg Road, Windermere, Cumbria LA23 1BN

Tel: 015394 45565 • e-mail:steamboat@ecosse.net

website: www.steamboat.co.uk

Two for the price of one (adults)

valid March to October 2005

NOT TO BE USED IN CONJUNCTION WITH ANY OTHER OFFER

FHG READERS' OFFER 2005

Blue-John Cavern

Castleton, Hope Valley, Derbyshire S33 8WP

Tel: 01433 620642 • e-mail: lesley@bluejohn.gemsoft.co.uk

website: www.bluejohn-cavern.co.uk

One child free with every paying adult

Valid until end 2005

NOT TO BE USED IN CONJUNCTION WITH ANY OTHER OFFER

FHG READERS' OFFER 2005

Crich Tramway Village

Crich, Matlock, Derbyshire DE4 5DP

Tel: 0870 758 7267 • Fax: 0870 753 4321

e-mail:enquiry@tramway.co.uk • website: www.tramway.co.uk

One child FREE with every full paying adult

valid during 2005

NOT TO BE USED IN CONJUNCTION WITH ANY OTHER OFFER

FHG READERS' OFFER 2005

Treak Cliff Cavern

HOME OF BLUE JOHN STONE

Castleton, Hope Valley, Derbyshire S33 8WP

Tel: 01433 620571

e-mail: treakcliff@bluejohnstone.com • website: www.bluejohnstone.com

10% discount (not valid on Special Events days)

valid during 2005

NOT TO BE USED IN CONJUNCTION WITH ANY OTHER OFFER

A collection of cars from film and TV, including Chitty Chitty Bang Bang, James Bond's Aston Martin, Del Boy's van, Fab1 and many more.

PETS MUST BE KEPT ON LEAD

Open: daily 10am-5pm. Closed February half term. Weekends only in December.

Directions: in centre of Keswick close to car park.

FHG PUBLICATIONS, ABBEY MILL BUSINESS CENTRE, PAISLEY PA1 1TJ

World's finest steamboat collection and premier all-weather attraction. Swallows and Amazons exhibition, model boat pond, tea shop, souvenir shop. Free guided tours. Model boat exhibition.

Open: 10am to 5pm 3rd weekend in March to last weekend October.

Directions: on A592 half-a-mile north of Bowness-on-Windermere.

FHG PUBLICATIONS, ABBEY MILL BUSINESS CENTRE, PAISLEY PA1 1TJ

Large range of natural water-worn caverns featuring mining equipment, stalactites and stalagmites, and fine deposits of Blue-John stone, Britain's rarest semi-precious stone.

DOGS MUST BE KEPT ON LEAD

Open: 9.30am to 5.30pm.

Directions: situated 2 miles west of Castleton; follow brown tourist signs.

FHG PUBLICATIONS, ABBEY MILL BUSINESS CENTRE, PAISLEY PA1 1TJ

A superb family day out in the atmosphere of a bygone era. Explore the recreated period street and fascinating exhibitions. Unlimited tram rides are free with entry. Play areas, shops, tea rooms, pub, restaurant and lots more.

Open: daily April to October 10 am to 5.30pm, weekends in winter.

Directions: eight miles from M1 Junction 28, follow brown and white signs for "Tramway Museum".

FHG PUBLICATIONS, ABBEY MILL BUSINESS CENTRE, PAISLEY PA1 1TJ

An underground wonderland of stalactites, stalagmites, rocks, minerals and fossils. Home of the unique Blue John stone – see the largest single piece ever found. Suitable for all ages.

Open: opens 10am. Enquire for last tour of day and closed days.

Directions: half-a-mile west of Castleton on A6187 (old A625)

FHG PUBLICATIONS, ABBEY MILL BUSINESS CENTRE, PAISLEY PA1 1TJ

FHG READERS' OFFER 2005

Crealy Adventure Park

Sidmouth Road, Clyst St Mary, Exeter, Devon EX5 1DR

Tel: 0870 116 3333 • Fax: 01395 233211

website: www.crealy.co.uk

FREE superkart race or panning for gold. Height restrictions apply

valid until 31/10/05

NOT TO BE USED IN CONJUNCTION WITH ANY OTHER OFFER

FHG READERS' OFFER 2005

The Gnome Reserve & Wild Flower Garden

West Putford, Near Bradworthy, Devon EX22 7XE

Tel: 0870 845 9012 • e-mail: info@gnomereserve.co.uk
website: www.gnomereserve.co.uk

One FREE child with full paying adult

Valid during 2005

NOT TO BE USED IN CONJUNCTION WITH ANY OTHER OFFER

FHG READERS' OFFER 2005

Killhope Lead Mining Museum

Cowshill, Upper Weardale, Co. Durham DL13 1AR

Tel: 01388 537505

e-mail: killhope@durham.gov.uk • website: www.durham.gov.uk/killhope

One child FREE with full-paying adult (not valid for Park Level Mine)

valid April to October 2005

NOT TO BE USED IN CONJUNCTION WITH ANY OTHER OFFER

FHG READERS' OFFER 2005

Barleylands Farm

Barleylands Road, Billericay, Essex CM11 2UD

Tel: 01268 290229 • e-mail: info@barleylands.co.uk
website: www.barleylands.co.uk

FREE adult ticket when accompanied by one child

Valid 1st March to 31st October. Not special event days

NOT TO BE USED IN CONJUNCTION WITH ANY OTHER OFFER

FHG READERS' OFFER 2005

Chislehurst Caves

Old Hill, Chislehurst, Kent BR7 5NB

Tel: 020 8467 3264 • Fax: 020 8295 0407

e-mail: info@chislehurstcaves.co.uk • website: www.chislehurstcaves.co.uk

one FREE entry with one full-paying adult

valid until 31st December 2005

NOT TO BE USED IN CONJUNCTION WITH ANY OTHER OFFER

Maximum fun, magic and adventure. An unforgettable family experience, with Tidal Wave log flume, rollercoaster, Queen Bess pirate ship, techno race karts, bumper boats, Vicorian carousel, animal handling, and huge indoor and outdoor play areas. The South-West's favourite family attraction!

Open:
Summer – daily 10am to 5pm
Holiday season – daily 10am to 6pm
Winter (Nov-March) – Wed-Sun 10am-5pm

Directions: minutes from M5 Junction 30 on the A3052 Sidmouth road, near Exeter

Visit 1000+ gnomes and pixies in two-acre beech wood. Gnome hats are loaned free of charge - so the gnomes think you are one of them - don't forget your camera! Also 2-acre wild flower garden with 250 labelled species.

Open: daily 10am to 6pm 21st March to 31st October.

Directions: between Bideford and Bude; follow brown tourist signs from A39/A388/A386.

Voted 'Most Family-Friendly Museum 2004', Killhope is Britain's best preserved lead mining site, with lots to see and do. Underground Experience is something not to be missed.

Open: March 19th to October 31st 10.30am to 5pm daily.

Directions: alongside A689, midway between Stanhope and Alston in the heart of the North Pennines.

Craft Village with animals, museum, blacksmith, glassblowing, miniature railway (Sundays and August), craft shops, tea room and licensed restaurant.

DOGS MUST BE KEPT ON LEAD

Open: Craft Village open all year. Farm open 1st March to 31st October.

Directions: M25, A127 towards Southend. Take A176 junction off A127, 3rd exit Wash Road, 2nd left Barleylands Road.

Miles of mystery and history beneath your feet! Grab a lantern and get ready for an amazing underground adventure. Your whole family can travel back in time as you explore this labyrinth of dark mysterious passageways. See the caves church, Druid altar and more. Under 16s must be accompanied by an adult.

Open: Wednesday to Sunday from 10am. Last tour 4pm. Open daily during local school holidays.

Directions: take A222 between A20 and A21; at Chislehurst railway bridge turn into station approach; turn right at end, then right again.

FHG READERS' OFFER 2005

Museum of Kent Life

Lock Lane, Sandling, Maidstone, Kent ME14 3AU

Tel: 01622 763936 • Fax: 01622 662024

e-mail: enquiries@museum-kentlife.co.uk • website: www.museum-kentlife.co.uk

Two tickets for the price of one (cheapest ticket FREE)

valid from March to November 2005

NOT TO BE USED IN CONJUNCTION WITH ANY OTHER OFFER

FHG READERS' OFFER 2005

Docker Park Farm

Arkholme, Carnforth, Lancashire LA6 1AR

Tel & Fax: 015242 21331

e-mail: info@dockerparkfarm.co.uk • website: www.dockerparkfarm.co.uk

One FREE child per one paying adult (one voucher per child)

valid from January to December 2005

NOT TO BE USED IN CONJUNCTION WITH ANY OTHER OFFER

FHG READERS' OFFER 2005

Snibston Discovery Park

Ashby Road, Coalville, Leicestershire LE67 3LN

Tel: 01530 278444 • Fax: 01530 813301

e-mail: snibston@leics.gov.uk • website: www.leics.gov.uk/museums

One FREE child with every full paying adult

valid until June 2005

NOT TO BE USED IN CONJUNCTION WITH ANY OTHER OFFER

FHG READERS' OFFER 2005

Skegness Natureland Seal Sanctuary

North Parade, Skegness, Lincolnshire PE25 1DB

Tel: 01754 764345

e-mail: natureland@fsbdial.co.uk • website: www.skegnessnatureland.co.uk

Free entry for one child when accompanied by full-paying adult.

Valid during 2005

NOT TO BE USED IN CONJUNCTION WITH ANY OTHER OFFER

FHG READERS' OFFER 2005

The Collectors World of Eric St John-Foti

Hermitage Hall, Downham Market, Norfolk PE38 0AU

Tel: 01366 383185 • Fax: 01366 386519

website: www.collectors-world.org

50p off adult admission - 25p off child admission

valid during 2005

NOT TO BE USED IN CONJUNCTION WITH ANY OTHER OFFER

Kent's award-winning open air museum is home to a collection of historic buildings which house interactive exhibitions on life over the last 150 years.

Open: seven days a week from March to November. 10am to 5.30pm.

Directions: Junction 6 off M20, follow signs to Aylesford.

FHG PUBLICATIONS, ABBEY MILL BUSINESS CENTRE, PAISLEY PA1 1TJ

We are a working farm, with lots of animals to see and touch. Enjoy a walk round the Nature Trail or refreshments in the tearoom. Lots of activities during school holidays.

Open: Summer: daily 10.30am to 5pm
Winter: weekends only 10.30am to 4pm.

Directions: Junction 35 off M6, take B6254 towards Kirkby Lonsdale, then follow the brown signs.

FHG PUBLICATIONS, ABBEY MILL BUSINESS CENTRE, PAISLEY PA1 1TJ

Located in 100 acres of landscaped grounds, Snibston is a unique mixture, with historic mine buildings, outdoor science play areas, wildlife habitats and an exhibition hall housing five hands-on galleries. Cafe and gift shop. Plus new Toy Box gallery for under 5s & 8s.

Open: seven days a week 10am to 5pm.

Directions: Junction 22 from M1, Junction 13 from M42. Follow brown Heritage signs.

FHG PUBLICATIONS, ABBEY MILL BUSINESS CENTRE, PAISLEY PA1 1TJ

Well known for rescuing and rehabilitating orphaned and injured seal pups found washed ashore on Lincolnshire beaches. Also: penguins, aquarium, pets' corner, reptiles, Floral Palace (tropical birds and butterflies etc).

Open: daily from 10am. Closed Christmas/Boxing/New Year's Days.

Directions: at the north end of Skegness seafront.

FHG PUBLICATIONS, ABBEY MILL BUSINESS CENTRE, PAISLEY PA1 1TJ

Eric St John-Foti invites you to visit his vast collections, from a Concorde engine to Barbara Cartland memorabilia and the the Magical Dickens Experience. Two amazing attractions for the price of one. Somewhere totally different, unique and interesting.

Open: 11am to 5pm (last entry 4pm)
Open all year.

Directions: one mile from town centre on the A1122 Downham/Wisbech Road.

FHG PUBLICATIONS, ABBEY MILL BUSINESS CENTRE, PAISLEY PA1 1TJ

FHG READERS' OFFER 2005

Galleries of Justice

Shire Hall, High Pavement, Lace Market, Nottingham NG1 1HN

Tel: 0115 9520555 • e-mail: info@galleriesofjustice.org.uk
Fax: 0115 9939828 • website: www.galleries of justice.org.uk

TWO for ONE with full paying adult one free visit per voucher

Valid from Jan to Dec 2005, not Bank Holidays

NOT TO BE USED IN CONJUNCTION WITH ANY OTHER OFFER

FHG READERS' OFFER 2005

Newark Air Museum

The Airfield, Winthorpe, Newark, Nottinghamshire NG24 2NY

Tel: 01636 707170

e-mail: newarkair@onetel.com • website: www.newarkairmuseum.co.uk

Party rate discount for every voucher (50p per person off normal admission)

Valid during 2005

NOT TO BE USED IN CONJUNCTION WITH ANY OTHER OFFER

FHG READERS' OFFER 2005

The Tales of Robin Hood

30 - 38 Maid Marian Way, Nottingham NG1 6GF

Tel: 0115 9483284 • Fax: 0115 9501536

e-mail: robinhoodcentre@mail.com • website: www.robinhood.uk.com

One FREE child with full paying adult per voucher

valid from January to December 2005

NOT TO BE USED IN CONJUNCTION WITH ANY OTHER OFFER

FHG READERS' OFFER 2005

The Helicopter Museum

The Heliport, Locking Moor Road, Weston-Super-Mare BS24 8PP

Tel: 01934 635227• Fax: 01934 645230

e-mail: office@helimuseum.fsnet.co.uk • website: www.helicoptermuseum.co.uk

One child FREE with two full-paying adults

valid from April to October 2005

NOT TO BE USED IN CONJUNCTION WITH ANY OTHER OFFER

FHG READERS' OFFER 2005

Easton Farm Park

Easton, Woodbridge, Suffolk IP13 0EQ

Tel: 01728 746475 • e-mail: easton@eastonfarmpark.co.uk
website: www.eastonfarmpark.co.uk

£1 per person OFF for up to 4 full paying admissions

Valid until end 2005

NOT TO BE USED IN CONJUNCTION WITH ANY OTHER OFFER

Journey with us through 300 years of Crime and Punishment on this unique atmospheric site. Witness a real trial in the authentic Victorian courtroom. Prisoners and gaolers act as guides as you become part of history.

Open: Tuesday to Sunday
10am to 5pm peak season
10am to 4pm off-peak.

Directions: from Nottingham city centre follow the brown tourist signs.

FHG PUBLICATIONS, ABBEY MILL BUSINESS CENTRE, PAISLEY PA1 1TJ

A collection of 65 aircraft and cockpit sections from across the history of aviation. Extensive aero engine and artefact displays.

Open: daily from 10am
(closed Christmas period).

Directions: follow brown and white signs from A1, A46, A17 and A1133.

FHG PUBLICATIONS, ABBEY MILL BUSINESS CENTRE, PAISLEY PA1 1TJ

Travel back in time to the dark and dangerous world of intrigue and adventure of Medieval England's most endearing outlaw - Robin Hood. Story boards, exhibitions and a film show all add interest to the story.

Open: 10am -6pm,
last admission 4.30pm.

Directions: follow the brown and white tourist information signs whilst heading towards the city centre.

FHG PUBLICATIONS, ABBEY MILL BUSINESS CENTRE, PAISLEY PA1 1TJ

The world's largest helicopter collection - over 70 exhibits, includes two royal helicopters, Russian Gunship and Vietnam veterans plus many award-winning exhibits. Cafe, shop. Flights.

PETS MUST BE KEPT UNDER CONTROL

Open: Wednesday to Sunday
10am to 5.30pm. Daily during school Easter and Summer holidays and Bank Holiday Mondays.
(10am to 4.30pm November to March)

Directions: Junction 21 off M5 then follow the propellor signs.

FHG PUBLICATIONS, ABBEY MILL BUSINESS CENTRE, PAISLEY PA1 1TJ

Come and meet the farm animals. Pony rides, pat-a-pet, indoor and outdoor play areas, woodland and river walks. Gift shop, tearoom. Monthly farmers' market.

DOGS MUST BE KEPT ON LEADS

Open: March to September
10.30am to 6pm

Directions: follow brown tourist signs off A12 and other roads

FHG PUBLICATIONS, ABBEY MILL BUSINESS CENTRE, PAISLEY PA1 1TJ

FHG READERS' OFFER 2005

Buckleys Yesterday's World

High Street, Battle, East Sussex TN33 0AQ

Tel: 01424 775378 • e-mail: info@yesterdaysworld.co.uk

website: www.yesterdaysworld.co.uk

50p OFF each admission

Valid until end 2005

NOT TO BE USED IN CONJUNCTION WITH ANY OTHER OFFER

FHG READERS' OFFER 2005

Wilderness Wood

Hadlow Down, Near Uckfield, East Sussex TN22 4HJ

Tel: 01825 830509 • Fax: 01825 830977

e-mail: enquiries@wildernesswood.co.uk • website: www.wildernesswood.co.uk

one FREE admission with a full-paying adult

valid during 2005

NOT TO BE USED IN CONJUNCTION WITH ANY OTHER OFFER

FHG READERS' OFFER 2005

World of James Herriot

23 Kirkgate, Thirsk, North Yorkshire YO7 1PL

Tel: 01845 524234 • Fax: 01845 525333

website: www.worldofjamesherriot.org

admit TWO for the price of ONE (one voucher per transaction only)

valid until October 2005

NOT TO BE USED IN CONJUNCTION WITH ANY OTHER OFFER

FHG READERS' OFFER 2005

Museum of Rail Travel

Ingrow Railway Centre, Near Keighley, West Yorkshire BD22 8NJ

Tel: 01535 680425 • e-mail: admin@vintagecarriagestrust.org

website: www.vintagecarriagestrust.org

"ONE for ONE" free admission

Valid during 2005 except during special events (ring to check)

NOT TO BE USED IN CONJUNCTION WITH ANY OTHER OFFER

FHG READERS' OFFER 2005

Oban Rare Breeds Farm Park

Glencruitten, Oban, Argyll PA34 4QB

Tel: 01631 770608

e-mail: info@obanrarebreeds.com • website: www.obanrarebreeds.com

20% DISCOUNT on all admissions

valid during 2005

NOT TO BE USED IN CONJUNCTION WITH ANY OTHER OFFER

The past is brought to life at one of the best loved family attractions in the South East. Step back in time and wander through over 30 shop and room settings.

PETS NOT ALLOWED IN CHILDREN'S PLAY AREA

Open: 9.30am to 6pm (last admission 4.45pm, one hour earlier in winter).

Directions: just off A21 in Battle High Street opposite the Abbey.

FHG PUBLICATIONS, ABBEY MILL BUSINESS CENTRE, PAISLEY PA1 1TJ

Wilderness Wood is a unique family-run working woodland in the Sussex High Weald. Explore trails and footpaths, enjoy local cakes and ices, try the adventure playground. Many special events and activities. Parties catered for.

Open: daily 10am to 5.30pm or dusk if earlier.

Directions: on the south side of the A272 in the village of Hadlow Down. Signposted with a brown tourist sign.

FHG PUBLICATIONS, ABBEY MILL BUSINESS CENTRE, PAISLEY PA1 1TJ

Visit James Herriot's original house recreated as it was in the 1940s. Television sets used in the series 'All Creatures Great and Small'. A new children's interactive gallery with life-size model farm animals and three rooms dedicated to the history of veterinary medicine.

Open: daily.
April to October 10am-6pm
November to March 11am to 4pm

Directions: follow signs off A1 or A19 to Thirsk, then A168, off Thirsk market place

FHG PUBLICATIONS, ABBEY MILL BUSINESS CENTRE, PAISLEY PA1 1TJ

A fascinating display of railway carriages and a wide range of railway items telling the story of rail travel over the years.

ALL PETS MUST BE KEPT ON LEADS

Open: daily 11am to 4.30pm

Directions: approximately one mile from Keighley on A629 Halifax road. Follow brown tourist signs

FHG PUBLICATIONS, ABBEY MILL BUSINESS CENTRE, PAISLEY PA1 1TJ

Rare breeds of farm animals, pets' corner, conservation groups, tea room, woodland walk in beautiful location

Open: 10am to 6pm mid-March to end October

Directions: two-and-a-half miles from Oban along Glencruitten road

FHG PUBLICATIONS, ABBEY MILL BUSINESS CENTRE, PAISLEY PA1 1TJ

FHG READERS' OFFER 2005

Inveraray Jail

Church Square, Inveraray, Argyll PA32 8TX

Tel: 01499 302381 • Fax: 01499 302195

e-mail: inverarayjail@btclick.com • website: www.inverarayjail.co.uk

one child FREE with one full-paying adult

valid until end 2005

NOT TO BE USED IN CONJUNCTION WITH ANY OTHER OFFER

FHG READERS' OFFER 2005

Kelburn Castle & Country Centre

Fairlie, Near Largs, Ayrshire KA29 0BE

Tel: 01475 568685 • e-mail: admin@kelburncountrycentre.com
website: www.kelburncountrycentre.com

One child FREE for each full paying adult

Valid until October 2005

NOT TO BE USED IN CONJUNCTION WITH ANY OTHER OFFER

FHG READERS' OFFER 2005

Scottish Maritime Museum

Harbourside, Irvine, Ayrshire KA12 8QE

Tel: 01294 278283 • e-mail: smm@tildesley.fsbusiness.co.uk
website: www.scottishmaritimemuseum.org • Fax: 01294 313211

TWO for the price of ONE

Valid from January to December 2005

NOT TO BE USED IN CONJUNCTION WITH ANY OTHER OFFER

FHG READERS' OFFER 2005

MYRETON MOTOR MUSEUM

Aberlady, East Lothian EH32 0PZ

Tel: 01875 870288

One child FREE with each paying adult

valid during 2005

NOT TO BE USED IN CONJUNCTION WITH ANY OTHER OFFER

FHG READERS' OFFER 2005

Landmark Forest Theme Park

Carrbridge, Inverness-shire PH23 3AJ

Tel: 01479 841613 • Freephone 0800 731 3446

e-mail: landmarkcentre@btconnect.com • website: www.landmark-centre.co.uk

10% DISCOUNT for pet owners. Free admission for pets!
Maximum of four persons per voucher

Valid during 2005

NOT TO BE USED IN CONJUNCTION WITH ANY OTHER OFFER

19th century prison with fully restored 1820 courtroom and two prisons. Guides in uniform as warders, prisoners and matron. Remember your camera!

Open:
April to October 9.30am - 6pm
(last admission 5pm)
November to March 10am - 5pm
(last admission 4pm)
Directions: A83 to Campbeltown

The historic home of the Earls of Glasgow. Waterfalls, gardens, famous Glen, unusual trees. Riding school, stockade, play areas, exhibitions, shop, cafe and The Secret Forest. Falconry Centre.

PETS MUST BE KEPT ON LEAD

Open: daily 10am to 6pm
Easter to October.

Directions: on A78 between Largs and Fairlie,
45 minutes' drive from Glasgow.

Scotland's seafaring heritage is among the world's richest and you can relive the heyday of Scottish shipping at the Maritime Museum.

Open: all year except Christmas and New Year Holidays.
10am - 5pm
Directions: Situated on Irvine harbourside and only a 10 minute walk from Irvine train station.

On show is a large collection, from 1899, of cars, bicycles, motor cycles and commercials. There is also a large collection of period advertising, posters and enamel signs.

Open: daily April to October
11am to 4pm
November to March:
weekends 11am to 3pm or
by special appointment.

Directions: off A198 near Aberlady.
Two miles from A1.

Great day out for all the family. Wild Water Coaster, Microworld exhibition, Forest Trails, Viewing Tower, Climbing Wall*, Tree Top Trail, Steam powered Sawmill*, Clydesdale Horse*. Shop, restaurant and snackbar. (* Easter to October)*

DOGS MUST BE KEPT ON LEADS

Open: daily (except Christmas Day and attractions marked*).

Directions: 23 miles south of Inverness at Carrbridge, just off the A9.

FHG READERS' OFFER 2005

Speyside Heather Garden & Visitor Centre

Speyside Heather Centre, Dulnain Bridge, Inverness-shire PH26 3PA

Tel: 01479 851359 • Fax: 01479 851396

e-mail: enquiries@heathercentre.com • website: www.heathercentre.com

FREE entry to 'Heather Story' exhibition

valid during 2005

NOT TO BE USED IN CONJUNCTION WITH ANY OTHER OFFER

FHG READERS' OFFER 2005

Finlaystone Country Estate

Langbank, Renfrewshire PA14 6TJ

Tel & Fax: 01475 540505

e-mail: info@finlaystone.co.uk • website: www.finlaystone.co.uk

TWO for the price of ONE

valid until April 2005

NOT TO BE USED IN CONJUNCTION WITH ANY OTHER OFFER

FHG READERS' OFFER 2005

Llanberis Lake Railway

Gilfach Ddu, Llanberis, Gwynedd LL55 4TY

Tel: 01286 870549 • e-mail: info@lake-railway.co.uk

website: www.lake-railway.co.uk

One pet travels FREE with each full fare paying adult

Valid Easter to October 2005

NOT TO BE USED IN CONJUNCTION WITH ANY OTHER OFFER

FHG READERS' OFFER 2005

Felinwynt RAINFOREST & BUTTERFLY CENTRE

Felinwynt, Cardigan, Ceredigion SA43 1RT

Tel: 01239 810882

website: www.butterflycentre.co.uk

TWO for the price of ONE (one voucher per party only)

valid until end October 2005

NOT TO BE USED IN CONJUNCTION WITH ANY OTHER OFFER

FHG READERS' OFFER 2005

National Cycle Collection

Automobile Palace, Temple Street, Llandrindod Wells, Powys LD1 5DL

Tel: 01597 825531

e-mail: cycle.museum@care4free.net • website: www.cyclemuseum.org.uk

TWO for the price of ONE

Valid during 2005 except Special Event days

NOT TO BE USED IN CONJUNCTION WITH ANY OTHER OFFER

Award-winning attraction with unique 'Heather Story' exhibition, gallery, giftshop, large garden centre selling 300 different heathers, antique shop, children's play area and famous Clootie Dumpling restaurant.

Open: all year except Christmas Day.

Directions: just off A95 between Aviemore and Grantown-on-Spey.

FHG PUBLICATIONS, ABBEY MILL BUSINESS CENTRE, PAISLEY PA1 1TJ

Colourful gardens, imaginative woodland play areas and tumbling waterfalls. The Estate combines history with adventure in a fun day out for all the family, where your dog can run freely. Step back in time and uncover its secrets.

Open: daily 10.30am to 5pm

Directions: off A8 west of Langbank, 20 minutes west of Glasgow Airport.

FHG PUBLICATIONS, ABBEY MILL BUSINESS CENTRE, PAISLEY PA1 1TJ

A 60-minute ride along the shores of beautiful Padarn Lake behind a quaint historic steam engine. Magnificent views of the mountains from lakeside picnic spots.

DOGS MUST BE KEPT ON LEAD AT ALL TIMES ON TRAIN

Open: most days Easter to October. Free timetable leaflet on request.

Directions: just off A4086 Caernarfon to Capel Curig road at Llanberis; follow 'Country Park' signs.

FHG PUBLICATIONS, ABBEY MILL BUSINESS CENTRE, PAISLEY PA1 1TJ

Mini-rainforest full of tropical plants and exotic butterflies. Personal attention of the owner, Mr John Devereux. Gift shop, cafe, video room, exhibition. Suitable for disabled visitors. WTB Quality Assured Visitor Attraction.

PETS NOT ALLOWED IN TROPICAL HOUSE ONLY

Open: daily Easter to end October 10.30am to 5pm

Directions: 7 miles north of Cardigan on Aberystwyth road. Follow brown tourist signs on A487.

FHG PUBLICATIONS, ABBEY MILL BUSINESS CENTRE, PAISLEY PA1 1TJ

Journey through the lanes of cycle history and see bicycles from Boneshakers and Penny Farthings up to modern Raleigh cycles. Over 250 machines on display

PETS MUST BE KEPT ON LEADS

Open: 1st March to 1st November daily 10am onwards.

Directions: brown signs to car park. Town centre attraction.

FHG PUBLICATIONS, ABBEY MILL BUSINESS CENTRE, PAISLEY PA1 1TJ

The ideal holiday destinations for your pet, be assured of a warm and friendly reception, sit back, close your eyes and soak up the history and atmosphere.

Green Farm Hotel & Restaurant **North Norfolk**

For the past 21 years Philip and Dee Dee Lomax have been extending a warm welcome to guests at the Green Farm, to enjoy the relaxed and friendly atmosphere and the highest standards of hospitality.

Enjoy this tranquil backwater of North Norfolk. Green Farm is the ideal base to discover and dip into the hidden delights of Norfolk. The Glorious Norfolk Broads, beautiful beaches, footpaths and bridleways and many National Trust houses.

The charming 16th Century flint-faced Farmhouse Inn offers 14 antique style bedrooms, all en suite, including four-posters. The converted dairy ground floor accommodation is ideal for guests who find stairs difficult. The food enjoys an enviable reputation for quality, presentation and service.

★★ Please telephone for details of our special breaks available all year ★★

Green Farm Hotel and Restaurant

Thorpe Market, North Walsham, North Norfolk NR11 8TH
Tel: 01263 833602 ❖ Fax: 01263 833163
e-mail: grfarmh@aol.com
website: www.greenfarmhotel.co.uk

New Inn Hotel

Clapham – 'Jewel of the Dales'

A comfortable hotel in the Yorkshire Dales National Park. The New Inn has been lovingly and carefully refurbished during the 16 years of ownership by Keith & Barbara Mannion, with a fine blend of old and new to retain the characteristics of this fine 18th Century Coaching Inn where you can experience a warm and friendly welcome.

The beautiful old Dales village straggles either side of Clapham Beck, one half linked to the other by three bridges, the Church at the top, the New Inn at the bottom. This traditional Village Inn has 20 en suite bedrooms, including ground floor and disabled bedrooms. Resident lounges, Restaurant, two comfortable bars serving a selection of Yorkshire ales, fine wines and a large selection of malt whiskies. Our food offers a mix between traditional and modern cooking.

Truly a 'Yorkshire Inn run by Yorkshire Folk'

★★ Please telephone for details of our special breaks available all year ★★

New Inn Hotel

Clapham, Near Ingleton, North Yorkshire LA2 8HH
Tel: 015242 51203 ❖ Fax: 015242 51496
e-mail: info@newinn-clapham.co.uk
website: www.newinn-clapham.co.uk

See also Colour Advertisement on page 6

See also Colour Advertisement on page 2

MR P.W. REES, "QUALITY COTTAGES', CERBID, SOLVA, HAVERFORDWEST, PEMBROKESHIRE SA62 6YE (01348 837871). Cottages set in all coastal areas, unashamed luxury, highest residential standards. Dishwashers, microwaves, washing machines. Log fires. Linen supplied. Pets welcome. [pw! 🐕]
website: www.qualitycottages.co.uk

RECOMMENDED COTTAGE HOLIDAYS. 1st choice for dream cottages at very competitive prices in all holiday regions of beautiful Britain. All properties inspected. Many accept pets at no extra charge. Full details in our brochure - call 08700 718718.
website: www.recommended-cottages.co.uk

COUNTRY HOLIDAYS BROCHURE LINE: 0870 3367229. Many properties welcome pets. (£20 per pet per week/Short Break).
website: www.country-holidays.co.uk

HOSEASONS. Tailwagging holidays at over 200 locations where your pet is as welcome as you are. Pine lodges surrounded by picturesque countryside. Or seaside holiday parks with miles of coastline to explore. Mid-week and weekend short breaks available. Many open all year round. Call for your free brochure on 0870 900 9011 Quote H0004 or book on-line.
website: www.hoseasons.co.uk

The Compton Swan Hotel, High Street, Compton, Near Newbury, Berkshire RG20 6NJ

In the Berkshire Downlands, the Hotel has 5 en suite bedrooms, TV, beverages and telephones. An extensive menu with traditional, exotic, vegetarian and special diets catered for. Home-cooked meals a speciality. Downlands Healthy Eating Award winner. Walled garden where we have *al fresco* eating; BBQs. Near the Ridgeway National Trail, an ideal base for walking, horse-riding and golf. Stabling and horsebox. Real Ales, Bar Meals available. CAMRA Good Beer Guide and Good Pub Guide. **01635 578269 • Fax: 01635 578765**

e-mail: info@comptonswan.co.uk • www.SmoothHound.co.uk

See also Colour Advertisement on page 10

Compton

Village 5 miles/7 km west of Streatley where Georgian houses are one of the notable sights on the banks of the Thames.

COMPTON SWAN HOTEL, HIGH STREET, COMPTON, NEAR NEWBURY RG20 6NJ (01635 578269; Fax: 01635 578765). Situated in the heart of the Berkshire Downlands; 5 rooms en suite with TV, beverage facilities and telephones. Extensive menu with special diets catered for. Large walled garden. [🐕]
e-mail: info@comptonswan.co.uk website: www.SmoothHound.co.uk

BUCKINGHAMSHIRE

Chesham

Town on south side of Chiltern Hills. Ideal walking area.

PAT & GEORGE ORME, 49 LOWNDES AVENUE, CHESHAM HP5 2HH (01494 792647). B&B detached house. 10 minutes from underground. Private bathroom, Tea/coffee. TV. Good walking country - Chiltern Hills (3 minutes). ETC ◆◆◆ [🐕]
e-mail: bbormelowndes@tiscali.co.uk

CAMBRIDGESHIRE

Wood Walton

The Elephant & Castle Motel & Free House

The Green, Wood Walton, Huntingdon, Cambs PE28 5YN

Family-run establishment in tranquil surroundings yet close to all major routes. 13 en suite motel rooms with TV, tea/coffee making, electric heating, radio and showers. Eight electric hook-ups for touring caravans. Ample parking space. Pets welcome. Full English breakfast served. Bar meals available.

Tel & Fax: 01487 773337

Ely

Magnificent Norman Cathedral dating from 1083. Ideal base for touring the fen country of East Anglia.

MRS C. H. BENNETT, STOCKYARD FARM, WISBECH ROAD, WELNEY PE14 9RQ (01354 610433; Fax: 01354 610422). Comfortable converted farmhouse, rurally situated between Ely and Wisbech. Conservatory breakfast room, TV lounge. Free range produce. Miles of riverside walks. No smoking. B&B from £20. [🐕 pw!]

St Ives

Town on the River Ouse 5 miles east of Huntingdon.

ST IVES MOTEL, LONDON ROAD, ST IVES, HUNTINGDON PE27 5EX (Tel & Fax: 01480 463857). 16 rooms, all en suite, overlooking orchards and garden. Close to Cambridge and A14. Licensed bar and restaurant. AA/RAC ★★[Pets £2-£5 per night depending on type of animal].
e-mail: mail@stives-motel.co.uk website: www.stives-motel.co.uk

Wood Walton

Village 6 miles north of Huntingdon. Wood Walton Fen Nature Reserve to north east.

ELEPHANT & CASTLE MOTEL AND FREEHOUSE, THE GREEN, WOOD WALTON, HUNTINGDON PE28 5YN (Tel & Fax: 01487 773337). Family-run establishment in tranquil surroundings. 13 en suite motel rooms with shower, TV, tea/coffee making, electric heating and radio. Caravan hook-ups. Bar meals available. Large garden, close to country walks. [Pets £3 per night].

CHESHIRE

Balterley, Chester

Balterley

Small village two miles west of Audley.

MR & MRS HOLLINS, BALTERLEY GREEN FARM, DEANS LANE, BALTERLEY, NEAR CREWE CW2 5QJ (01270 820214). 145-acre dairy farm in quiet and peaceful surroundings. Within easy reach of Junction 16 on the M6. Bed and Breakfast from £24pp. ETC ◆◆◆◆. Caravans and tents welcome. [pw! Pets £2 per night]

Chester

Former Roman city on the River Dee, with well-preserved walls and beautiful 14th century Cathedral. Liverpool 25 miles

THE EATON HOTEL, CITY ROAD, CHESTER CH1 3AE (01244 320840; Fax: 01244 320850). In a perfect central location. All rooms have bath or shower, colour TV, radio, telephone, hair dryer and tea making facilities. Pets allowed in rooms only. [🐕]
website: www.eatonhotelchester.co.uk

Toad Hall Cottages
250 outstanding waterside and rural properties in truly beautiful locations in Devon, Cornwall & Exmoor.
PETS WELCOME
For our full colour brochure please call
08700 777345
www.toadhallcottages.com
email: thc@toadhallcottages.com

See also Colour Advertisement on page 11

400 carefully selected cottages throughout Cornwall, Devon, Pembrokeshire, Gower and Cotswolds...

...chosen with you and your pet in mind.

Powells COTTAGE HOLIDAYS

Powells Cottage Holidays
www.powells.co.uk
0800 378771

Classy Cottages

Polperro – Fowey

Spectacular cottages just feet from beach... Along coast, isolated residence with sea views... Farm cottages in the 'Valley of the Foxes'
Open log fires. Pets Welcome. Dog friendly local beaches, and list of other beaches which welcome dogs. Local pubs which serve good food and allow dogs. Indoor Private Swimming Pool with sauna, spa etc.
We welcome you with a Cornish Cream Tea.

www.classycottages.co.uk • nicolle@classycottages.co.uk•
Please telephone Fiona or Martin Nicolle on 07000 423000

See also Colour Advertisement on page 12

Readers are requested to mention this guidebook when seeking accommodation (and please enclose a stamped addressed envelope).

Penrose Burden Holiday Cottages

St Breward, Bodmin, Cornwall PL30 4LZ

Tel: 01208 850277 & 850617 • Fax: 01208 850915 • Web: www.penroseburden.co.uk

Set in an area of outstanding natural beauty, sits 'Penrose Burden' surrounded by its 250 acres with breathtaking views overlooking the protected Camel Valley, on the edge of Bodmin Moor. Penrose Burden is a settlement of attractive stone cottages, varying in size, catering for two to seven persons, that have been beautifully converted into holiday homes. Also nestling beside Wenford Bridge are two riverside character cottages, idyllic for the free estate salmon and trout fishing!

NEW IN 2002: "TOAD HALL" a creative concept for today's open-plan living. All bedrooms en suite, enjoy 'patio dining' perched among stunning views, in your own grounds. With the ever-changing seasons, this all year round accommodation is geared to meet all seasonal requirements, including wood burners. All accommodation is suitable for disabled guests.

Paradise for dogs and their owners! Situated midway between north and south coasts, easy access to the new 'Eden Project', 'The Lost Gardens' and 'National Trust' properties. Why not walk or cycle the 'Camel Trail' and end up at "Rick Stein's"? Our 'Patsy' provides delicious home-cooked Cornish food, and will have a meal waiting on your arrival, at your request. Penrose Burden has received much acclaim including being featured on television and in the national press!

Please ring for a brochure

Spacious house, centrally situated. Three double bedrooms. Optional evening meal. The surrounding area is breathtakingly beautiful, especially in springtime. Short walks from the house will take you to some of the county's best beauty spots like Cardinham Woods which is ideal for dog walking. B&B £18, £15 for stays of more than one night. Stannah Stair Lift.

MRS JOAN HARRISON, WILBURY, SUNNYBANKS LANE, FLETCHERS BRIDGE, BODMIN PL30 4AN Tel: 01208 74001

Darrynane Cottages **Darrynane, St Breward, Bodmin Moor PL30 4LZ**

Tel/Fax: 01208 850885 * www.darrynane.co.uk * enquiries@darrynane.co.uk

3 detached cottages all with private, fenced gardens. Situated in a unique moorland valley, with oak woods, waterfalls and the river. The cottages provide a homely base for walking, relaxing or touring Cornwall. Woodburning stoves, four-poster beds. Open all year.

'PENVENTON' **Boscastle/Crackington-Haven Area**

Modern bungalow sleeping 2-6, heating; microwave; TV. Near sandy beaches, spectacular coastal path. Beautiful scenery, walking distance local store and Inn. Just off A39 and central to most tourist attractions.

Spring and Autumn £90-£200 per week • Pets welcome • 01840 250289

FREE or REDUCED RATE entry to Holiday Visits and Attractions – see our READERS' OFFER VOUCHERS on pages 101-116

PLEASE NOTE

All the information in this book is given in good faith in the belief that it is correct. However, the publishers cannot guarantee the facts given in these pages, neither are they responsible for changes in policy, ownership or terms that may take place after the date of going to press. Readers should always satisfy themselves that the facilities they require are available and that the terms, if quoted, still apply.

A 14th Century Country Hotel

Crafthole, Near Torpoint, Cornwall PL11 3BD

Tel: 01503 230863 • Fax: 01503 230675

e-mail: enquiries@liscawn.co.uk • website: www.liscawn.co.uk

Charming, family-run 14th Century Hotel in 'The Forgotten Corner of Cornwall'.

A few minutes' walk from the Cornish Coastal Path.
The perfect site for Fishing and Bird-watching.

Central to 3 golf courses, Whitsand Bay, Looe and St Mellion.

En suite accommodation with colour TV and coffee and tea making facilities in every room.

Self-Catering Suites available. Family and Pets welcome.

Bar meals available and cask ales a speciality.

Extensive Grounds and Beer garden with beautiful views over to Dartmoor.

Crantock Bay Hotel a very special place, all year round...

CORNWALL TOURISM AWARDS 2002 *HIGHLY COMMENDED*

AA 3 STAR GOOD HOTEL GUIDE ASHLEY COURTENEY

Crantock Bay Hotel is superbly located for a holiday with your dogs. Our gardens lead direct to the Cornish coastal path and within 10 minutes walk of the 'dogs welcome' beaches of Polly Joke and Crantock Bay. Facilities include: comfortable bedrooms – many with sea views, a quality restaurant, Indoor pool, Jacuzzi, gym and tennis court.

Crantock Bay Hotel
West Pentire, Crantock, Cornwall TR8 5SE

Tel: (01637) 830229 Fax: (01637) 831111
Email: stay@crantockbayhotel.co.uk
www.crantockbayhotel.co.uk

See also Colour Advertisement on page 17

Cusgarne (near Truro)

Sleeps 2. A cosy, clean, detached dwelling within grounds of Saffron Meadow. In a quiet hamlet five miles west of Truro. Own enclosed garden, secluded and surrounded by wooded pastureland. Bedroom (double bed) with twin vanity unit. Fully tiled shower/WC and L.B. Comprehensively equipped kitchen/diner. Compact TV room. Storage room. Hot water galore and gas included. Metered electricity. Automatic external safety lighting. Your own ample parking space. Inn, good food, a short walk. Central to Truro, Falmouth and North and South Coast. £150 - £240 per week.

Joyce and George Clench, Saffron Meadow, Cusgarne, Truro TR4 8RW Tel: 01872 863171

Creekside Cottages offer a fine selection of individual water's edge, village and rural cottages, sleeping from 2-10, situated around the creeks of the Carrick Roads, near Falmouth, South Cornwall. Set in enchanting and picturesque positions, with many of the cottages offering panoramic creek views. Perfect locations for family holidays, all close to superb beaches, extensive sailing and boating facilities, Cornish gardens and excellent walks. The majority of the cottages are available throughout the year, and all offer peaceful, comfortable and fully equipped accommodation; most have open fires. Dogs welcome.

Just come and relax • colour brochure 01326 375972 • www.creeksidecottages.co.uk

See also Colour Advertisement on page 19

AA ★★★

Penmorvah Manor Hotel & Courtyard Cottages

• 3 Star Country House Hotel and self-catering courtyard cottages
• Situated in 6 acres of mature gardens and woodland • Ideal for visiting Cornwall's superb gardens • Well behaved dogs welcome • Close to Falmouth and Coastal Paths
• Ground floor bedrooms for easy pet access • Ample car parking

Budock Water, Near Falmouth, Cornwall TR11 5ED • Tel: 01326 250277 • Fax: 01326 250509
e-mail: reception@penmorvah.co.uk • web: www.penmorvah.co.uk

See also Colour Advertisement on page 17

The Old Ferry Inn

Bodinnick-by-Fowey, Cornwall PL23 1LX

Telephone: (01726) 870237 Fax: (01726) 870116

Website: www.oldferryinn.com

Email: ferryinn@bodinnick.fsnet.co.uk

Why not bring your dog for its well deserved holiday to the family-run Old Ferry Inn, close to the edge of the beautiful River Fowey.

There are many varied walks from country and riverside to breathtaking views along the Cornwall Coastal Path.

The 400-year-old hotel has an excellent à la carte restaurant for evening meals and a comprehensive bar menu for lunch and evening. The Inn has 12 letting rooms with tea and coffee making facilities, colour TVs and telephones, most rooms being en suite, some with views of the Fowey river.

Prices are from £60-£85 per person, per night for two people sharing.

Near Fowey Fabulous Listed farmhouse and large, spacious barn with every comfort and convenience. Both set within their own gardens and grounds, with distant sea and spectacular countryside views in a tranquil setting. Great walks nearby. Close to the Eden Project, Lost Gardens of Heligan, the coast, beaches, and the harbour town of Fowey. Both properties are of an exceptionally high standard, mostly with en suite facilities and tasteful furnishings. Pets are very welcome, with their own 'Welcome Pack'. Both properties sleep 6. Brochure on request.

www.foweyvacations.com • 01726 814263 • sarahfurniss@aol.com

See also Colour Advertisement on page 19

When making enquiries or bookings,
a stamped addressed envelope is always appreciated

BOSCREGE CAMPING & CARAVAN PARK
ASHTON, HELSTON, CORNWALL, TR13 9TG

★ Award winning quiet family rural park close to local beaches and attractions with no bar or clubs
★ Free showers ★ Microwave facilities ★ Games room ★ Childs play area ★ Laundry ★ Pets welcome

Phone/Fax 01736 762231 for colour brochure

www.caravanparkcornwall.com - enquires@caravanparkcornwall.com

Holiday Accommodation - Lerryn

Sleeps up to 4 people. Characterful, well appointed accommodation in the beautiful riverside village of Lerryn. Excellent dog walking area and in a central village location. River views. Open all year with short breaks available in winter. Dogs welcome at £10 a week and bring your owner too from £200. No smokers.

*More information and photos at **www.lerrynvillage.co.uk/greenview***
*or phone **Sue Smith (01208 872375)***

Mrs Northcott, Pendower House, East Taphouse, Liskeard, Cornwall PL14 4NH. Tel: 01579 320332

Bed and Breakfast ***Central for Cornwall***

H/C in all rooms. Good touring area. Television. All comforts. Central heating. Ground floor single suite. Good food. Main Road. Open all year. Moderate terms.

CUTKIVE WOOD HOLIDAY LODGES

Nestling in the heart of a peaceful and lovely 41-acre family-owned country estate, there are six well-equipped cedar-clad lodges. Set on the edge of bluebell woods with wonderful rural views, you can relax and enjoy yourself in a tranquil and idyllic setting. Ideally situated to enjoy year-round holidays. Children can help to feed the animals, milk the goats, explore the woods and fields. Big play area. So much to see and do, including The Eden Project, lovely beaches, walks on the moors, theme parks, sporting activities. Dogs welcome. Short breaks. Open all year.

St Ive, Liskeard, Cornwall PL14 3ND • Tel: 01579 362216
www.cutkivewood.co.uk • e-mail: holidays@cutkivewood.co.uk

Country Caradon Cottages

Luxury cottages in the heart of the Cornish countryside. Ideal centre for exploring Devon and Cornwall, coast and moor. Just east of the Eden Project. Central heating and log burners for cosy off-season breaks. Every comfort for you and your pets.

Celia Hutchinson, Caradon Country Cottages
East Taphouse, Near Liskeard, Cornwall PL14 4NH
Telephone & Fax: 01579 320355
Website: www.caradoncottages.co.uk

ROSECRADDOC HOLIDAYS, Rosecraddoc Lodge, Cornwall
"Ducks Ditty", "Mallards" and "Watery Fowls". Three comfortable and well-equipped bungalows on a purpose built holiday estate with beautiful, peaceful open gardens in a woodland setting on the outskirts of Liskeard. One bungalow specially adapted for wheelchairs. PETS VERY WELCOME. Ideal centre for touring North and South coasts, visiting Eden, National Maritime Museum and the Tate Gallery St Ives.
Mrs N. Arthur, Rosecraddoc Lodge, Liskeard PL14 5BU • Tel or Fax: 01579 346768

RIVERMEAD FARM

Twowatersfoot, Liskeard, Cornwall PL14 6HT

Telephone: 01208 821 464

Self Catering Apartments and Farm Cottage

Set in beautiful wooded Glynn Valley, amidst 30 acres of meadows and water meadows.

- River and lakeside walks.
- Convenient for both Coasts and Moors.
- A mile of Sea Trout and Salmon fishing on the River Fowey.
- Pets welcome.

Brochure on request to Alan & Kathleen Hunstone at Rivermead Farm.
Website: www.rivermeadfarm.co.uk

An award winning Holiday Park near Helston, in an area of outstanding natural beauty and close to safe sandy beaches. Dogs welcome!

Weststar HOLIDAY PARKS

Quote: WP

0870 444 0080

book online: **www.weststarholidays.co.uk/pw**

TREMAINE GREEN "A beautiful hamlet" of 11 award-winning traditional cosy craftsmen's cottages, between Polperro & Looe. Clean, comfortable and well equipped, for pets with 2 to 8 people. Set in lovely grounds with country/coastal walks and The Eden Project nearby. Pets £16 pw. Owners from only £112.
- **Tel: 01503 220333 • e-mail: stay@tremainegreen.co.uk**
- **website: www.tremainegreen.co.uk** **ETC ★★★**

See also Colour Advertisement on page 12

TREWITH HOLIDAY COTTAGES • Self Catering Accommodation Open All Year

Situated in a superb elevated position of outstanding natural beauty. Just 1½ miles from Looe. Choice of 4 refurbished cottages with 1-3 bedrooms. Fully equipped and tastefully furnished with full central heating. Use of laundry room. Peaceful location with delightful walks. Many beaches, coves, fishing, shopping close by.. Because of ponds young children need supervision. Well behaved dogs welcome.

Paul & Barbie Higgins, Trewith, Duloe, near Liskeard, Cornwall PL14 4PR • Tel: 01503 262184
mobile: 07968 262184 • E-mail: holiday-cottages@trewith.freeserve.co.uk • www.trewith.freeserve.co.uk

See also Colour Advertisement on page 14

An award winning Holiday Park near Looe, in an area of outstanding natural beauty and close to safe sandy beaches. Dogs most welcome!

Quote: WP

0870 444 0080

book online:

Valleybrook

Peakswater, Lansallos, Looe, Cornwall PL13 2QE

LODGES • COTTAGES • CARAVANS

Small peaceful secluded country site near Looe & Polperro, just 10 miles from the Eden Project.

• High quality scandinavian pine lodges
• Olde - worlde charm cottages
• Short Breaks Available • Dogs Welcome
• Open all year • No club or swimming pool

Contact Denise, Keith & Brian Holder

www.valleybrookholidays.co.uk **01503 220493**

POLPERRO CORNWALL

Spectacularly situated holiday cottages in picturesque Cornish fishing village.

Sleeping from 2 to 8 persons - £175 to £475 per cottage per week.

With terraced gardens and fabulous outlook over harbour, encompassing 15 mile sea views. Private parking, two minutes shops, beach, quay and National Trust cliff walks. Open all year. Children and pets most welcome. All cottages are fully furnished and equipped to include a colour television, microwave, electric oven, refrigerator, duvets and pillows. **Graham Wright, Guardian House, Liskeard, PL14 6AD**

01579 344080

COLDRINNICK COTTAGES **Duloe, Near Looe PL14 4QF**

Rose and Well Meadow Cottages are attractively converted barns, set in their own large secure, secluded garden on a working dairy farm. Oustanding views, woodland walks to west Looe valley, close to moors and coast. Excellent locality for walking and relaxing. Well Meadow sleeps 2/4, Rose 2/6 people. Heating, electricity, bed linen etc all inclusive. An ideal place for families and dogs alike.

For a brochure or any information please contact:

Bill and Kaye Chapman on 01503 220251

web: www.cornishcottage.net ETC ★★★★

Talehay Holiday Cottages

Pelynt, Near Looe PL13 2LT

A Quiet Haven in the Countryside near the sea

Cosy, traditional cottages with many original features retained provide superb holiday accommodation on 17C non-working farmstead. Set in 4 acres of unspoilt countryside offering peace and tranquillity with breathtaking coastal and country walks on your doorstep. This is an ideal location for dogs and their owners alike. C.T.B. approved. Close to the Eden Project.

Let our brochure convince you – Tel/Fax Mrs Ann Brumpton 01503 220252

E-mail: paul@talehay.co.uk Website: www.talehay.co.uk

TALLAND CARAVAN PARK
Talland Bay, Looe, Cornwall PL13 2JA

Now under new ownership, this small family site is situated in secluded Talland Bay between Looe and Polperro and adjacent to the Coastal Heritage Path. We have a wide range of fully equipped caravans from luxury to economy, with both two or three beds. The camping area overlooks the bay with direct access down to the shore. The site has a shop, licensed bar with bar meals and takeaways, laundry, play area and swimming pool. An ideal site for families and as touring centre *Pets are welcome, with coastal walks at your doorstep.*

For colour brochure – SAE appreciated or ring (01503) 272715

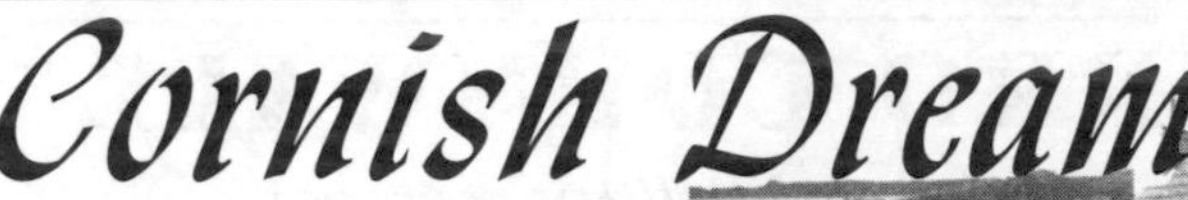

"For those who enjoy the comfort of a high quality hotel but prefer the freedom of a cottage"

...The Good Holiday Cottage Guide

Idyllic 18th Century Country Cottages for romantics and animal lovers, near the sea in the beautiful Looe River valley. Your own delightful private garden with roses around the door and breathtaking views.

Exclusively furnished, antiques, crackling log fires, candlelit meals, dishwashers, videos, four-poster beds, crisp white linen and towels. Riding, heated swimming pool & tennis court. Wonderful walks from your cottage gate.

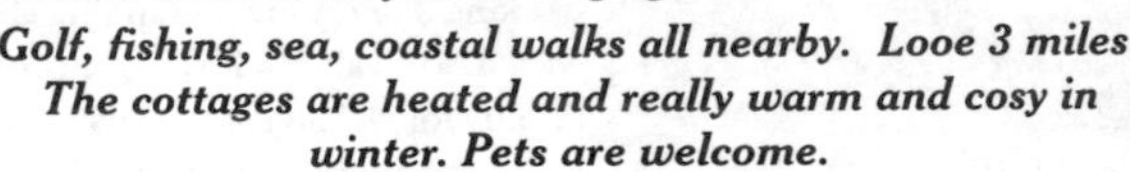

English Tourism Council ★★★★★ SELF CATERING

Personal attention and colour brochure from:

B.Wright, Treworgey Cottages, Duloe, Liskeard, Cornwall PL14 4PP

Tel: 01503 262730 or 263757

website: www.cornishdreamcottages.co.uk

The* FHG *GOLF GUIDE* *Where to Play Where to Stay* *2005

Available from most bookshops, the 2005 edition of **THE GOLF GUIDE** covers details of every UK golf course – well over 2800 entries – for holiday or business golf. Hundreds of hotel entries offer convenient accommodation, accompanying details of the courses – the 'pro', par score, length etc.

In association with 'Golf Monthly' and including Holiday Golf in Ireland, France, Portugal, Spain, The USA, South Africa and Thailand .

£9.99 from bookshops or from the publishers (postage charged outside UK) • FHG Publications, Abbey Mill Business Centre, Paisley PA1 1TJ

Cottages for Romantics
Old world charm, log fires, antiques, beautifully furnished with the comforts of home. Private gardens, spectacular views, peace ~ for families, friends and couples to enjoy. Nestling on a south-facing hillside, near coast ~ heated pool, tennis, badminton, lake, shire horses, etc. Enchanting 70 acre estate with bluebell wood, walking and wildlife.
Delicious fare also available
by candlelight 'at home' or in our tiny inn.
O. Slaughter, Trefanny Hill, Duloe,
Near Liskeard, Cornwall, PL14 4QF
Tel: 01503 220 622
e-mail: enq@trefanny.co.uk
website: www.trefanny.co.uk
A Country Lover's Paradise
with an abundance of country walks
from your garden gate and
coastal walks only 4 miles away.
'relax in a little bit of heaven'
THE COTTAGES
AT
Trefanny
Hill
Nr. LOOE
'views from your garden gate'
Discover the magic of Trefanny Hill

St Anthony – Helford River

Enchanting creekside cottages in a timeless and tranquil hamlet. Springtime bluebell woods and hedgerows banked with primroses, reflections of multi-coloured sails off sandy beaches, the solitary blue flash of a Kingfisher in autumn, smoke grey herons and shining white egrets standing patiently by the shoreline all evoke the atmosphere of this truly beautiful corner of Cornwall.

- Stunning coastal and riverside walks
- Great country inns and local food
- Warm and comfortable with cosy log fires
- Our own sailing dinghies and fishing boats
- Moorings and easy launching
- National Trust and private gardens nearby
- Short breaks, open all year including Christmas

St Anthony Holidays, Manaccan, Helston, Cornwall TR12 6JW
Tel: 01326 231 357 • E-mail; infpw@StAnthony.co.uk • www.StAnthony.co.uk

The MALMAR Hotel

Trenance, Mawgan Porth, Cornwall TR8 4DA

tredragonlodge@hotmail.com • www.malmarhotel.com

- Beautifully situated in tranquil location, panoramic sea views. Close to beach, coastal path and lovely valley walks.
- Licensed family hotel, highly commended for our service, friendly atmosphere and home cooking.
- Dogs welcome, may sleep with you, and are allowed on the beach all year.
- TV lounge, board games, cards, library available for guests' use.
- Family, double, single rooms, most en suite, majority ground floor. Colour TVs.
- BB&EM from £232 per week.

SPECIAL BREAKS

Four nights for the price of ***three***

PETS **FREE** **FREE** colour brochure

See us @ malmarhotel.com

James & Pippa McLuskie: Newquay
(01637) 860324

FREE or REDUCED RATE entry to Holiday Visits and Attractions – see our READERS' OFFER VOUCHERS on pages 101-116

When making enquiries or bookings, a stamped addressed envelope is always appreciated

Mawgan Porth Bay,
Near Newquay,
Cornwall TR8 4BN

Tel: St Mawgan 01637 860512
e-mail: adogfriendly@aol.com • web: www.dogfriendlyhotel.co.uk

GIVE YOURSELVES & YOUR DOGS A BREAK

at our family-run White Lodge Hotel overlooking beautiful Mawgan Porth Bay, near Newquay, Cornwall

• Dogs most welcome - FREE OF CHARGE. • Your dogs sleep with you in your bedroom. • Direct access to sandy beach and coastal path. • Dog loving proprietors with 20 years' experience in catering for dog owners on holiday with their dogs. • ALL bedrooms with colour TV, tea/coffee makers, alarm clocks, radios, heaters etc. • Fantastic sea views from most rooms. • Well-stocked residents' lounge bar, dining room & sun patio with outstanding sea views across the bay. • Large free car park within hotel grounds.

• Winter break packages • The White Lodge is now Open all Year

Phone for full colour brochure* • *ALL PRICES INCLUDE VAT AT 17½%

SPECIAL 6 DAYS (5 NIGHTS) CHRISTMAS BREAK ONLY £305 Half Board	***SPECIAL 6 DAYS (5 NIGHTS) NEW YEAR BREAK ONLY £260 Half Board***	***SPECIAL 6 DAYS (5 NIGHTS) BREAKS ONLY £205-£217.50 BB&EM***	***WEEKLY TERMS FROM £287-£304.50 FOR 5-COURSE EVENING DINNER, BED AND 4-COURSE BREAKFAST WITH CHOICE OF MENU***

See also Colour Advertisement on page 15

Dewolf Guest House 100 Henver Road, Newquay TR7 3BL

The amenities of Newquay are close at hand, Porth Beach only a short walk from the Guest House. Double or Family rooms including two Chalets situated in the rear garden, ideal for pets. All rooms non-smoking with en suite facilities, colour TV and tea/coffee making facilities. B&B from £22 per person based on two sharing. Licensed bar. Off-road car parking available. Special breaks available. Suitable for M1 Disabled. Open all year. NATC Approved. Awaiting Diamond Rating.

Tel: 01637 874746 • e-mail: holidays@dewolfguesthouse.com • www.dewolfguesthouse.com

QUARRYFIELD Caravan & Camping Park, Crantock, Near Newquay.

Superbly situated overlooking beautiful Crantock Bay and the River Gannel estuary, park with fully equipped modern caravans for hire, and separate level camping field. Bar, pool, children's play area.

Contact: MRS WINN, TRETHERRAS, NEWQUAY, CORNWALL TR7 2RE
Tel & Fax: 01637 872792

Trethiggey Touring Park

Quintrell Downs, Newquay

Our friendly, family run park is just minutes by car from Newquay's famous surf beaches and 15 miles from the amazing Eden Project. Beautifully landscaped, the park has panoramic countryside views and is ideal for touring caravans, tents and campervans. We also have luxury holiday homes for hire. Facilities include shop, off-licence, free showers, electric hook-ups, laundry, children's play area, TV/games room, fishing and take-away food in summer.

Open from March 1st to January 1st including Christmas and New Year. Short Breaks available. Off season rallies welcome.

For more information phone 01637 877672 or see our website: www.Trethiggey.co.uk • e-mail: enquiries@trethiggey.co.uk

Retorrick Mill, *St Mawgan, Newquay TR8 4BH (01637 860460).*
Retorrick Mill is situated in the beautiful Lanherne Valley, within walking distance of the sea at Mawgan Porth, its sandy beach and eating places. 1 mile from St Mawgan picturesque village, shop, pub and Post Office. Halfway between Newquay and old port of Padstow. Activites include: surfing, golf, riding, fishing and walking, with coastal path only one mile away. The bungalows are bright and well-furnished with own parking. Gardens of 9 acres. Pets welcome. Brochure on request.
Contact: Mr & Mrs Oliver. Cottage and Bungalows ETC ★★ SELF-CATERING

Raintree House Holidays

A range of well equipped houses and bungalows near Trevose Golf Club, sandy beaches, scenic walks.

Mrs Watts, "WHISTLERS", Treyarnon Bay, Padstow PL28 8JR

e-mail: gill@raintreehouse.co.uk Tel: 01841 520228/520130 *web: www.raintreehouse.co.uk*

Shanice ••• Padstow
Rent from £300 per week
Sleeps up to 4 • patio • views
Near Rick Stein's and Camel Trail

"Tia loves it"

01473 327479 or 0797 353 8670 • www.Brookfarm.demon.co.uk

GEORGIAN HOUSE HOTEL **20 CHAPEL STREET, PENZANCE TR18 4AW • Tel/Fax: 01736 365664**
www.theaa.co.uk/hotels • e-mail: georgianhouse@btopenworld.com

Warm and friendly family-run hotel, midway between harbour and shopping centre. Full menu for breakfast and evening meals; special diets catered for. B&B from £25. AA ◆◆◆◆ *Two-bedroom holiday cottage also available all year.*

All rooms with colour TV and hairdryer • Tea/coffee facilities • Full central heating • Most rooms with private en suite facilities • Licensed bar • Private car park • Open all year • Special breaks • Pets very welcome

Cornwall near Perranporth

Greenmeadow Cottages Highly praised luxury cottages, sleep six, superbly clean, comfortable and spacious. Open all year. Short breaks out of season. Pets welcome in two of the cottages. Non-smoking available. Ample off road parking.

For brochure and bookings tel: 01872 540483

See also Colour Advertisement on page 16

CHIMNEYS **Port Gaverne, Port Isaac, Cornwall PL29 3SQ.**
Tel & Fax: 01208 880254

A charming 18th Century Cottage just 10 metres from the beach making it a wonderful venue for pets and their owners. Four bedrooms, two bathrooms, lounge, dining room and kitchen. Good size garden. Close to Eden Project. Brochure available from **Mrs Holmes.**

Step onto the Coastal Path...

Escape the pressures of life. Relax! explore the Cornish Coast from Green Door Cottages in Port Gaverne.

8 comfortable, restored 18th Century cottages set around a sheltered courtyard, plus 2 prestigious apartments with panoramic sea views beside a picturesque cove, directly on the Coastal path, less than half a mile from Port Isaac.
An ideal location for your holiday and short breaks. Well behaved dogs are very welcome.

Call now for a brochure on:
01208 880293

Green Door Cottages
PORT GAVERNE
email: enquiries@greendoorcottages.co.uk
web: www.greendoorcottages.co.uk

See also Colour Advertisement on page 14

See also Colour Advertisement on page 17

See also Colour Advertisement on page 18

TRENCREEK FARM HOLIDAY PARK

Hewaswater, St Austell PL26 7JG • Tel: 01726 882540
website: www.trencreek.co.uk

Visiting the Eden Project in Cornwall? We may be able to help with accommodation! Self-catering and camping facilities available. Heated outdoor swimming pool, tennis court and fishing lakes. Children and pets welcome. Self-catering available from £50 for two nights.

See also Colour Advertisement on page 16

BOSINVER HOLIDAY COTTAGES

Nestling in a hidden valley near the sea, the Eden Project and Lost Gardens of Heligan, our small farm has friendly animals and ponies. Choose from our 16th century thatched farmhouse or cottages privately set in their own gardens surrounded by wildflower meadows. Wander down to the fishing lake or village pub, swim in the pool, play tennis, or relax and listen to the birdsong.
No pets during Summer School holidays. ETC ★★★★ **Brochure: Pat Smith, Bosinver Farm, St Mewan, St Austell PL26 7DT**

Tel: 01726 72128 • E-mail: reception@bosinver.co.uk • Internet: www.bosinver.co.uk

See also Colour Advertisement on page 17

HOLIDAY COTTAGE - *ST BREWARD*

Warm and lovely cottage sleeping four in great comfort and utter peace. Log fires, large garden with stream. Glorious walking. Available all year. Terms from £130 to £375 per week, depending on season. Dogs welcome, £10 per week. St Breward is a picturesque village high on Bodmin Moor and within easy reach of both coasts. Situated four miles from the A30. **Sleeps 4/5.**

For further details please contact:
Mrs Paddy Powell (01208 850186)
website: www.vacation-cornwall.com

SANDBANK HOLIDAYS

St Ives Bay, Hayle, Cornwall TR27 5BL
Website: www.sandbank-holidays.co.uk

High quality Apartments and Bungalows for 2-6 persons. Peaceful garden setting close to miles of sandy beach, acres of grassy dunes and SW Coastal Path. Dogs Welcome. Fully equipped for your self-catering holiday. Heated, Colour TV, Microwave etc. Spotlessly clean.

***All major debit and credit cards accepted * Tel: 01736 752594**

The Links Holiday Flats

Lelant, St Ives, Cornwall TR26 3HY

If it's views you want, this is the place for you!

Magnificent location alongside and overlooking West Cornwall Golf Course, Hayle Estuary and St Ives Bay. Both flats have lovely views. Wonderful spot for walking. We are five minutes from the beach and dogs are allowed there all year round. Two well-equipped flats which are open all year.

Your hosts are Bob and Jacky Pontefract • Phone or fax 01736 753326

The Rosevine Hotel **Porthcurnick Beach, St Mawes, Truro TR2 5EW**

Tel: 01872 580206 • Fax: 01872 580230

Cornwall's new luxury hotel. De luxe bedrooms and suites. Award-winning cuisine. Beautiful sub-tropical gardens facing directly over the safe sandy beach fronting the National Trust coastline. Warm heated indoor pool. Children and pets most welcome.

CORNWALL'S ONLY RAC 3 DINING AWARDS & BLUE RIBBON HOTEL RAC ★★★ AA 3 Red Stars

e-mail: info@rosevine.co.uk • website: www.rosevine.co.uk

See also Colour Advertisement on page 16

DALSWINTON HOUSE

e-mail: dalswinton@bigwig.net
website: www.dalswinton.com

A Victorian stone built Cornish house of character in a glorious rural setting. Standing in ten acres of gardens and meadowland, the house overlooks the Vale of Lanherne and the village of St Mawgan with views to the sea at the dog friendly beach of Mawgan Porth. Our hotel offers a comfortable, friendly atmosphere and great food prepared with fresh local produce. Regret no children under 16. All rooms en suite and non-smoking.

● DOGS FREE OF CHARGE AND ALLOWED EVERYWHERE EXCEPT THE DINING ROOM ● EIGHT ACRES OF PRIVATE MEADOWLAND FOR DOG EXERCISE ● BED AND BREAKFAST FROM £32 PER PERSON PER NIGHT ● SHORT BREAK AND WEEKLY RATES AVAILABLE ● CAR PARKING AND HEATED OUTDOOR POOL ● TEA / COFFEE & COLOUR TV IN ALL ROOMS ● LICENSED BAR & A RESTAURANT SERVING 3 COURSE DINNER ● GARDEN CHALET FOR SELF-CATERING ● EASY ACCESS TO NEWQUAY AIRPORT & THE EDEN PROJECT ●

DALSWINTON HOUSE, ST MAWGAN-IN-PYDAR, CORNWALL TR8 4EZ. TEL: (01637) 860385

See also Colour Advertisement on page 13

Willapark Manor Hotel

Bossiney, Near Tintagel, Cornwall PL34 0BA
Telephone: 01840 770782

One of the most beautifully situated Country House Hotels in England

website: www.willapark.co.uk ETC ★★

See also Colour Advertisement on page 18

BOSSINEY FARM CARAVAN & CAMPING PARK
TINTAGEL, CORNWALL PL34 0AY

Tel: 01840 770481 ETC ★★★★

★ Family-run Park renowned for cleanliness and hospitality ★ 20 Luxury Letting Vans ★ Fully serviced, H&C with shower, room heater ★ All with TV ★ On the coast at Tintagel ★ Ideal for touring ★ Superb value for money

SEND FOR OUR COLOUR BROCHURE TODAY!
www.bossineyfarm.co.uk

TRETHEVY MANOR - TINTAGEL

Mrs Lynda Spring, Trethevy Manor, Trethevy Tintagel, Cornwall PL34 0BG * *Tel/Fax: 01840 770636*

E-mail: manor1151@talk21.com * Website: www.trethevy-manor.co.uk

2 comfortable well equipped self-contained stone built cottages adjoining 12th century Manor House. Exposed beams, interesting history, thoughtfully chosen furnishings. An area of outstanding natural beauty, the dramatic Rocky Valley and St Nectans Glen waterfall are nearby. Lovely beaches, spectacular coastal walks. Wonderful gardens and traditional country inns within easy reach.

King Harry Ferry Cottages

Two comfortable, well-equipped cottages set in an Area of Outstanding Natural Beauty, each with its own charming garden. Individually furnished with co-ordinating furnishings. Full central heating and double glazed. Microwave, colour TV and video, telephone, washing machine, fridge and all bed linen. We also offer use of our boat during your stay. All these included in the price. Pets are welcome. Beautiful woodland walks for you to stroll through. Perfect for fishing and bird watching.

Tel: 01872 861915

High Quality Cottages to Let near Truro

www.kingharry-info.co.uk • E-mail: jean@kingharry.f9.co.uk

See also Colour Advertisement on page 16

TOAD HALL COTTAGES (08700 777345). Over 200 outstanding waterside and rural properties in truly beautiful locations in Devon, Cornwall and Exmoor. Call for our highly acclaimed brochure. Pets welcome.
e-mail: thc@toadhallcottages.com website: www.toadhallcottages.com

POWELLS COTTAGE HOLIDAYS, 51 HIGH STREET, SAUNDERSFOOT, PEMBROKESHIRE SA69 9EJ. 400 carefully selected cottages throughout Cornwall, Devon, Pembrokeshire, Gower and Cotswolds chosen with you and your pet in mind. For colour brochure FREEPHONE 0800 378771 (24 hours).
website: www.powells.co.uk

CLASSY COTTAGES – Spectacular cottages feet from beach. Isolated residence on coast, farm cottages. Open log fires. Dog friendly beaches. Indoor swimming pool. Local pubs serving good food, and allowing dogs. ETC ★★★★ - ★★★★★. Contact FIONA & MARTIN NICOLLE (07000 423000). [pw! Pets £12 per week]
e-mail: nicolle@classycottages.co.uk website: www.classycottages.co.uk

WEST CORNWALL COTTAGE HOLIDAYS, WEST CORNWALL (01736 368575). Coastal and country cottages, town houses and apartments. Pets with well behaved owners welcome in many of our properties. [Pets £10 per week]
website: www.westcornwallcottageholidays.com

CLASSIC COTTAGES (01326 565 555). Featuring 500 hand selected coastal and country holiday homes throughout the West Country.
website: www.classic.co.uk

A fine selection of Self-catering and similar Cottages on both coasts of Cornwall and on Scilly. Pets welcome in many cottages. Free colour brochure from: CORNISH TRADITIONAL COTTAGES, BLISLAND, BODMIN PL30 4HS (01208 821666; Fax: 01208 821766). [Pets £12 per week]
website: www.corncott.com

Bodmin

Quaint county town of Cornwall, standing steeply on the edge of Bodmin Moor. Pretty market town and touring centre. Plymouth 31 miles, Newquay 20, Wadebridge 7.

PENROSE BURDEN, ST BREWARD, BODMIN PL30 4LZ (01208 850277 & 850617; Fax: 01208 850915). Holiday Care Award Winning Cottages featured on TV. Open all year. Outstanding views over wooded valley. Free Salmon and Trout fishing. Daily meal service. Superb walking area. Dogs welcome, wheelchair accessible. [Pets £15 per week]
website: www.penroseburden.co.uk

MRS JOAN HARRISON, WILBURY, SUNNYBANKS LANE, FLETCHERS BRIDGE, BODMIN PL30 4AN (01208 74001). Spacious house, centrally situated. Three double bedrooms. Optional evening meal. The surrounding area is breathtakingly beautiful, especially in springtime. Short walks from the house will take you to some of the county's best beauty spots like Cardinham Woods which is ideal for dog walking. B&B £18, £15 for stays of more than one night. Stannah Stair Lift.

Bodmin Moor

Superb walking area attaining a height of 1375 feet at Brown Willy, the highest point in Cornwall.

DARRYNANE COTTAGES, DARRYNANE, ST BREWARD, BODMIN MOOR PL30 4LZ (Tel & Fax: 01208 850885) Absolutely fabulous detached cottages. Set in fenced private gardens. Unique moorland valley setting. Waterfalls, woods, river. Woodburning stoves, four-poster beds, Eden Project and Camel Trail close by. ETC ★★★ [Pets £5 per short break, £10 per week]
email: enquiries@darrynane.co.uk website: www.darrynane.co.uk

SYMBOLS

- **Indicates that pets are welcome free of charge.**
- £ **Indicates that a charge is made for pets: nightly or weekly.**
- pw! **Shows some special provision for pets; exercise facility, feeding or accommodation arrangement.**
- ☐ **Indicates separate pets accommodation.**

Boscastle

Picturesque village in tiny harbour, with rocky beach, some sand, and fine scenery. Tintagel 4 miles.

BOSCASTLE/CRACKINGTON-HAVEN AREA. Modern bungalow sleeping 2-6, heating; microwave; TV. Near sandy beaches, spectacular coastal path. Beautiful scenery, walking distance local store and Inn. Just off A39 and central to most tourist attractions. Spring and Autumn £90-£200 per week. Pets welcome. MRS PROUT (01840 250289). [🐕]

Bude

Popular seaside resort overlooking a wide bay of golden sand and flanked by spectacular cliffs. Ideal for surfing; sea water swimming pool for safe bathing.

MINESHOP, CRACKINGTON HAVEN, BUDE EX23 0NR. Cornish Character Cottages, sleep 1 to 8, in tranquil location. Footpath leads through fields/woods to beach/pub. Excellent walking, breathtaking scenery. Open all year. Proud to be inspected and featured in The Good Holiday Cottage Guide. For more details phone CHARLIE or JANE (01840 230338). [£11 per pet per week.]
e-mail: tippett@mineshop.freeserve.co.uk website: www.mineshop.co.uk

HEDLEY WOOD CARAVAN & CAMPING PARK, BRIDGERULE, (NR BUDE), HOLSWORTHY EX22 7ED (01288 381404). 16 acre woodland family-run site; children's adventure areas, bar, clubroom, shop, laundry, meals & all amenities. Static caravans for hire, Caravan Storage available. [pw! 🐕]
website: www.hedleywood .co.uk

IVYLEAF BARTON HOLIDAY COTTAGES, NEAR BUDE EX23 9LD. Seven cottages sleeping 2-8 in converted stone barns with spectacular views. Comfortable, well-equipped with all modern conveniences. Laundry. Tennis court. Certain cottages welcome pets. Contact: ROBERT B BARRETT (01288 321237 or 01225 832018; Fax: 01288 321937).
e-mail: ivyleafcottages@aol.com website: www.cornwall-online.co.uk/ivyleaf-barton

Crackington Haven

Small coastal village in North Cornwall set amidst fine cliff scenery. Small sandy beach, Launceston 18 miles, Bude 10, Camelford 10.

HENTERVENE HOLIDAY PARK, CRACKINGTON HAVEN, NEAR BUDE EX23 0LF (01840 230365). Luxury caravans to let. First-class facilities for families and pets. Open all year. Short breaks. Caravan Sales and Tourer Storage. [Pets £15 per week].
e-mail: contact@hentervene.co.uk website: www.hentervene.co.uk

Five 18th century converted barns, beamed ceilings, log fires and secluded rural setting. Ideal touring base. Five miles to coast at Crackington Haven. Sleep 2/6. Pets welcome. Open all year. From £75 short breaks, £140 per week. ETC ★★★. APPLY: LORRAINE HARRISON, TRENANNICK COTTAGES, WARBSTOW, LAUNCESTON PL15 8RP (01566 781443). [pw! Pets £10 per stay]
e-mail: lorraine.trenannick@i12.com website: www.trenannickcottages.co.uk

Crafthole

Village near sea at Portwrinkle. Fine views over Whitsand Bay and River Lynner. Golf course nearby. Torpoint 6 miles.

THE LISCAWN INN, CRAFTHOLE, NEAR TORPOINT PL11 3BD (01503 230863; Fax: 01503 230675). Charming, family-run 14th Century Hotel. Close to Coastal Path in the forgotten corner of Cornwall. En suite accommodation; bar meals available; cask ales a speciality. Open all year. Self-catering suites available. [🐕]
e-mail: enquiries@liscawn.co.uk website: www.liscawn.co.uk

Crantock

Village near the coast 2miles/3 km SW of Newquay across the River Gannel

CRANTOCK BAY HOTEL, WEST PENTIRE, CRANTOCK TR8 5SE (01637 830229; Fax: 01637 831111). Superbly located for a holiday with your dogs; beach 10 minutes' walk. Comfortable bedrooms, quality restaurant, indoor pool, tennis etc. AA ★★★ [Pets £3 per night]
e-mail: stay@crantockbayhotel.co.uk website: www.crantockbayhotel.co.uk

Cusgarne (near Truro)

Located four miles east of Redruth.

CUSGARNE (NEAR TRURO), JOYCE & GEORGE CLENCH, SAFFRON MEADOW, CUSGARNE, TRURO TR4 8RW (01872 863171). A cosy, single storey, clean, detached dwelling within grounds of Saffron Meadow. Own enclosed garden, secluded and surrounded by wooded pastureland, five miles west of Truro. [Pets £10]

Delabole

Village 2 miles west of Camelford.

JOHN AND SUE THEOBALD, TOLCARNE, TREBARWITH ROAD, DELABOLE PL33 9DB. Quiet, comfortable guesthouse in beautiful North Cornwall close to coast path, beaches and surfing. Private bathroom, TV lounge. Kennel and covered run for pets left home during the day. Woodturning courses available. Ample parking. For free brochure call 01840 213558. [pw! 🐕]

Falmouth

Well-known port and resort on Fal estuary, ideal for boating, sailing and fishing; safe bathing from sandy beaches. Of interest is Pendennis Castle (18th century). Newquay 26, Penzance 26, Truro 11.

PETER WATSON, CREEKSIDE HOLIDAY HOUSES, RESTRONGUET, FALMOUTH TR11 5ST (Tel & Fax: 01326 372722). Spacious houses sleep 2/4/6/8. Peaceful, picturesque water's edge hamlet. Boating facilities. Use of boat. Own quay, beach. Secluded gardens. Near Pandora Inn. Friday bookings. Dogs welcome. [£15 per week]

SELF-CATERING BUNGALOW. Sleeps 6. Walking distance of harbour and town. Dogs welcome. Low Season: £200 to £250; High Season: £290 to £400. ETC ★★★. Apply MRS J. A. SIMMONS, 215A PERRY STREET, BILLERICAY, ESSEX CM12 0NZ (01277 654425). [Pets £10 weekly.]

CREEKSIDE COTTAGES offer a fine selection of individual water's edge, village and rural cottages, sleeping from 2-10. All offer peaceful, comfortable and fully equipped accommodation. Just come and relax. For a colour brochure phone 01326 375972. [Pets £20 per week]
website: www.creeksidecottages.co.uk

PENMORVAH MANOR HOTEL & COURTYARD COTTAGES, BUDOCK WATER, NEAR FALMOUTH TR11 5ED (01326 250277; Fax: 01326 250509). Situated in 6 acres of mature gardens and woodland. Ideal for visiting Cornwall's superb gardens.Close to Falmouth and Coastal Paths. Well behaved dogs welcome. AA ★★★ Hotel, ETC ★★★★ Self-catering. [Pets £5 per night.]
e-mail: reception@penmorvah.co.uk website: www.penmorvah.co.uk

Fowey

Historic town, now a busy harbour, Regatta and Carnival Week in August.

OLD FERRY INN, BODINNICK-BY-FOWEY PL23 1LX (01726 870237; Fax: 01726 870116). Family-run Inn, ideal for many varied walks. Excellent à la carte restaurant; bar meals available. Comfortable bedrooms with colour TV and tea/coffee. Rate £60-£85 per night for two people sharing. ETC ◆◆◆◆ [Pets £3 per night per pet]
e-mail: ferryinn@bodinnick.fsnet.co.uk website: www.oldferryinn.com

NEAR FOWEY. Fabulous Listed farmhouse and large, spacious barn in own gardens and grounds. Exceptionally high standard, en suite facilities, tasteful furnishings. Sleep 6. Brochure on request, (01726 814263). [Pets £12 per week].
e-mail: sarahfurniss@aol.com website: www.foweyvacations.com

A useful Index of Towns/Villages and Counties appears on page 426 – please also refer to Contents Page 3.

Hayle

Town with small harbour 3 miles SE of St Ives.

MRS G. GILBERT, THE STUDIO, 17 HIGHER CHURCH STREET, HAYLE TR27 4LR (01736 755038). Self-catering, double-bed apartment, cot and single fold-away bed available. Pretty walled courtyards, lovely beaches and walks. Same inclusive price all year. Please telephone. [🐕]

Helford

Village on inlet on South side of Helford River, 6 miles East of Helston.

SELECTIVE CORNISH RETREATS. GREEN BANK COTTAGE is a pretty detached cottage, set in a peaceful hamlet close to the Helford river. The cottage is well equipped with enclosed garden, access to private woodland. Spa, gym and sauna facility included. (Tel & Fax: 0700 267 6474). [Pets £10 per week]
e-mail: schr@connexions.co.uk **website: www.connexions.co.uk/schr**

Helston

Ancient Stannary town and excellent touring centre, noted for the annual "Furry Dance". Nearby is Loe Pool, separated from the sea by a bar. Truro 17 miles, St Ives 15, Redruth 11, Falmouth & Penzance 12.

BOSCREGE CAMPING & CARAVAN PARK, ASHTON, HELSTON, CORNWALL TR13 9TG. (Tel & Fax: 01736 762231) Award-winning, quiet, rural family park close to beaches and attractions. Colour brochure available. Pets welcome. [🐕]
e-mail: enquires@caravanparkcornwall.com website: www.caravanparkcornwall.com

Lerryn

Village 3 mile south-west of Lostwithiel, at head of creek of River Lerryn.

LERRYN VILLAGE, 4 OLD MILL, LERRYN, LOSTWITHIEL PL22 0QB (01208 872375). Sleeps up to 4 people. Characterful, well appointed accommodation in the beautiful riverside village of Lerryn. Excellent dog walking area and in a central village location. River views. Open all year. No smokers. [pets £10 a week]
e-mail: sue@lerrynvillage.co.uk website: www.lerrynvillage.co.uk/greenview

Liskeard

Pleasant market town and good centre for exploring East Cornwall. Bodmin Moor and the quaint fishing villages of Looe and Polperro are near at hand. Plymouth 19 miles, St Austell 19 miles, Launceston 16, Fowey (via ferry) 15, Bodmin 13, Looe 9.

LINDA & NEIL HOSKEN, HOPSLAND HOLIDAYS, HOPSLAND COMMONMOOR, LISKEARD PL14 6EJ (Tel & Fax: 01579 344480). Hi, I'm Ki, an adorable border collie. Come and stay with your pets at my converted barn cottages. Fully equipped. Own field to exercise in or 150 yards from open moorland. ETC ★★★★ [pw! Pets from £12 per week]
e-mail: hopslandholidays@aol.com website: www.hopslandholidays.co.uk

SUE JEWELL, BOTURNELL FARM COTTAGES, ST PINNOCK, LISKEARD PL14 4QS (01579 320880; Fax: 01579 320375). Cosy character cottages set in 25 acres of fields and woodland between Looe and Bodmin. Linen, electricity included. Well equipped. Dog creche. Pets welcome free. [🐕]
website: www.dogs-holiday.co.uk/

CUTKIVE WOOD HOLIDAY LODGES, ST IVE, LISKEARD PL14 3ND (01579 362216). Six well-equipped cedar-clad lodges on country estate with wonderful views. Great for children, dogs welcome. Ideal for Eden Project, beaches, moors etc. Short breaks. Open all year. [pw! Pets £10 per week]
e-mail: holidays@cutkivewood.co.uk website: www.cutkivewood.co.uk

CELIA HUTCHINSON, CARADON COUNTRY COTTAGES, EAST TAPHOUSE, NEAR LISKEARD PL14 4NH (Tel & Fax: 01579 320355). Luxury cottages in the heart of the Cornish countryside. Ideal centre for exploring Devon and Cornwall, coast and moor and Eden Project. Meadow and paddock (enclosed). Central heating and log burners for cosy off-season breaks. [Pets £10 per week.]
website: www.caradoncottages.co.uk

REDGATE SMITHY, REDGATE, ST CLEER, LISKEARD PL14 6RU (01579 321578). Homely B&B near beautiful Golitha Falls on southern edge of Bodmin Moor. Excellent walking. Friendly dog welcome. Beds and bowls provided. Brochure available. From £25. [🐕]
e-mail: enquiries@redgatesmithy.clara.co.uk website: www.redgatesmithy.co.uk

ROSECRADDOC HOLIDAYS, ROSE CRADDOC LODGE, LISKEARD PL14 5BU (Tel & Fax: 01579 346768). Three comfortable, well-equipped bungalows on purpose built holiday estate. Peaceful open gardens in woodland setting. One bungalow adapted for wheelchair use. Ideal centre for touring. Contact: Mrs N. Arthur. [Pets £12 per week]

MRS V.M. NORTHCOTT, "PENDOWER HOUSE", EAST TAPHOUSE, LISKEARD PL14 4NH (01579 320332). All comforts. Open all year. Main road, Good food. Moderate terms. Ground floor single suite. Central for Cornwall. [🐕]

MR AND MRS HUNSTONE, RIVERMEAD FARM, TWOWATERSFOOT, LISKEARD PL14 6HT (01208 821464). Self-catering Apartments and Farm Cottage convenient for both coasts and moors. Fishing on River Fowey. Pets welcome at a charge.
website: www.rivermeadfarm.co.uk

Lizard

The most southerly point in England, with fine coastal scenery and secluded coves. Sandy beach at Housel Bay. Truro 28 miles, Helston 11.

MULLION HOLIDAY PARK, WESTSTAR HOLIDAYS (0870 444 0080). Award-winning holiday park near Helston in an Area of Outstanding Natural Beauty, close to safe sandy beaches. Dogs welcome! Quote WP. ETC ★★★★ [Pets £35 per week]
website: www.weststarholidays.co.uk/pw

Looe

Twin towns linked by a bridge over the River Looe. Capital of the shark fishing industry; nearby Monkey Sanctuary is well worth a visit.

TREMAINE GREEN COUNTRY COTTAGES, PELYNT, NEAR LOOE PL13 2LT (01503 220333). A beautiful hamlet of 11 award-winning traditional cosy craftsmen's cottages. Clean, comfortable and well equipped. Set in lovely grounds with country/coastal walks and The Eden Project nearby. ETC ★★★ [Pets £16 per week]
e-mail: stay@tremainegreen.co.uk website: www.tremainegreen.co.uk

MRS BARBIE HIGGINS, TREWITH HOLIDAY COTTAGES, TREWITH, DULOE PL14 4PR (01503 262184; mobile: 07968 262184). Four refurbished cottages in peaceful location with panoramic views near Looe. Fully equipped, 1-3 bedrooms, tastefully furnished. Full central heating. Well behaved dogs welcome. [Pets from £12 per week]
e-mail: holiday-cottages@trewith.freeserve.co.uk website: www.trewith.freeserve.co.uk

VALLEYBROOK, PEAKSWATER, LANSALLOS, LOOE PL13 2QE. Small secluded site near Looe and Polperro, just 10 miles from the Eden Project. High quality Scandinavian pine lodges, cottages. Short breaks available. Open all year. Dogs welcome. Contact DENISE, KEITH or BRIAN HOLDER (01503 220493).
website: www.valleybrookholidays.co.uk

NEAR LOOE. In picturesque Cornish fishing village of Polperro, one of the finest on the South Cornish coast, spectacularly situated holiday cottages sleeping from two to eight persons at a charge of £175 to £475 per cottage per week. With terraced gardens and fabulous outlook over harbour encompassing 15 mile sea views. Excellent selection of quality restaurants and olde worlde pubs nearby, and on offer delicious pasties and locally made ice-cream. Private parking, two minutes shops, beach, quay and National Trust cliff walks. Open all year, children and pets most welcome. All cottages are fully furnished and equipped, to include a colour television, microwave, electric oven, refrigerator, duvets and pillows. GRAHAM WRIGHT, GUARDIAN HOUSE, LISKEARD, CORNWALL PL14 6AD (01579 344080). [🐕]

COLDRINNICK COTTAGES, DULOE, NEAR LOOE. Attractively converted barns set in large secluded gardens. Excellent locality for walking and relaxing. Sleeps 2/6 people. Ideal place for families and dogs alike. ETC ★★★★. For a brochure contact BILL AND KAYE CHAPMAN, COLDRINNICK FARM, DULOE, LISKEARD PL14 4QF (01503 220251). [Pets £15 per week, pw!]
website: www.cornishcottage.net

LOOE BAY HOLIDAY PARK, WESTSTAR HOLIDAYS (0870 444 0080). Award-winning holiday park near Looe in an Area of Outstanding Natural Beauty, close to safe sandy beaches. Dogs welcome! Quote WP ETC ★★★★ David Bellamy Conservation Award. [Pets £35 per week].
website: www.weststarholidays.co.uk/pw

MRS ANN BRUMPTON, TALEHAY HOLIDAY COTTAGES, PELYNT, NEAR LOOE PL13 2LT (Tel & Fax: 01503 220252). Cosy, traditional cottages set in four acres of unspoilt countryside offering peace and tranquillity. Breathtaking coastal and country walks. An ideal location for dogs and their owners. Non-smoking. Close to the Eden Project. C.T.B. approved. ETC ★★★★ [Pets £15 per week]
e-mail: paul@talehay.co.uk website: www.talehay.co.uk

TALLAND CARAVAN PARK, TALLAND BAY, LOOE PL13 2JA (01503 272715). Fully equipped two and three bedroom caravans. Direct access to coastal path and beach. Shop, clubroom, laundry, play area and swimming pool. Short Breaks off-season. Pets welcome. [Pets £30 per week, pw!]

Idyllic 18th century country cottages for romantics and animal lovers. Looe three miles. Wonderful walks from your gate. Cottages warm and cosy in winter. Personal attention and colour brochure from: B. WRIGHT, TREWORGEY COTTAGES, DULOE, LISKEARD PL14 4PP (01503 262730). ETC ★★★★★ Quality Award. [Pets £16 per week.]
website: www.cornishdreamcottages.co.uk

O. SLAUGHTER, TREFANNY HILL, DULOE, NEAR LISKEARD PL14 4QF (01503 220622). Nestling on a south-facing hillside, near coast. Delicious food. Heated pool, tennis, badminton, lake, shire horses. Enchanting 70 acre estate with bluebell wood, walking and wildlife.
e-mail: enq@trefanny.co.uk website: www.trefanny.co.uk

Manaccan

Village 7 miles east of Helston.

Enchanting creekside cottages in a timeless and tranquil hamlet. Stunning coastal and riverside walks, country inns, local food, warm and comfortable with cosy log fires. Dinghies, moorings. Short breaks. Open all year. ST ANTHONY HOLIDAYS, MANACCAN, HELSTON TR12 6JW (01326 231 357). [Pets £3 per night, £21 per week].
e-mail: infpw@StAnthony.co.uk website: www.StAnthony.co.uk

Mawgan Porth

Modern village on small sandy bay. Good surfing. Inland stretches the beautiful Vale of Lanherne. Rock formation of Bedruthan Steps is nearby. Newquay 6 miles west.

THE MALMAR HOTEL, TRENANCE, MAWGAN PORTH TR8 4DA (01637 860324). Small Licensed Hotel. Close to beach and coastal path. Two good golf courses nearby. Good English cooking. Rooms with tea making facilities, colour TV, most ground floor/en suite. [🐕]
e-mail: tredragonlodge@hotmail.com website: www.malmarhotel.com

WHITE LODGE HOTEL, MAWGAN PORTH BAY, NEAR NEWQUAY TR8 4BN (01637 860512). Give yourselves and your dogs a quality holiday break at this family-run hotel overlooking beautiful Mawgan Porth Bay. Lounge bar, sun patio, dining room. Car park. 20 years' experience.This hotel is open all year – Winter Break packages. Phone for free brochure. [🐕 pw!]
e-mail: adogfriendly@aol.com website: www.dogfriendlyhotel.co.uk

Mevagissey

Central for touring and walking. Eden project nearby.

MRS M.R. BULLED, MENAGWINS, GORRAN, MEVAGISSEY PL26 6HP (01726 843517). Traditional cottage, sleeps two to five. Linen, towels, electricity supplied. Beach one mile. Large garden. Central for touring/walking. Near Eden Project. Pets welcome. [🐕]

Mousehole

Picturesque fishing village with sand and shingle beach. Penzance 3 miles.

In Mousehole, a quaint and unspoilt fishing village, are three personally supervised and fully equipped self-catering flats, two with full sea views. All have microwave, cooker, fridge, TV, all bedding and towels provided. Open all year from £80 per week. Apply: MR A.G. WRIGHT, 164 PORTLAND ROAD, SELSTON, NOTTINGHAM NG16 6AN (01773 775347) [🐕]
e-mail: alang23@hotmail.com

Mullion

Village 5 miles south of Helston; much of surrounding area owned by National Trust.

RUSS & JAN STANLAND, CAUNCE HEAD, PREDANNACK, MULLION TR12 7HA (01326 240128; Fax: 01326 240011). Quality B&B in our beautiful 350 year-old Cornish stone house in hamlet on the beautiful Lizard Peninsula. Two pretty double four-poster bedrooms with en suite bathrooms. Wonderful dog walking area - footpaths run through our gardens! Children over 12 welcome. [🐕]
e-mail: jan@cauncehead.co.uk **website: www.cauncehead.co.uk**

Mylor

Village situated at the mouth of Mylor Creek, 2 miles East of Penryn.

LITTLE ALBION COTTAGE. Comfortable cottage in 300 year old converted stables, ideally situated for fun-packed holiday. Sleeps 6. Spacious and well-equipped. Large garden. Ample parking. Dog-sitting available. Contact: PATRICK POLGASE (Tel & Fax: 01326 373607).
website: www.cottageholidayscornwall.com

Newquay

Popular family holiday resort surrounded by miles of golden beaches. Semi-tropical gardens, zoo and museum. Ideal for exploring all of Cornwall.

WHITE LODGE HOTEL, MAWGAN PORTH BAY, NEAR NEWQUAY TR8 4BN (01637 860512). Give yourselves and your dogs a quality holiday break at this family-run hotel overlooking beautiful Mawgan Porth Bay. Lounge bar, sun patio, dining room. Car park. 20 years' experience.This hotel is open all year–Winter break packages. Phone for free brochure. [🐕 pw!]
e-mail: adogfriendly@aol.com **website: www.dogfriendlyhotel.co.uk**

MRS DEWOLFREYS, DEWOLF GUEST HOUSE, 100 HENVER ROAD, NEWQUAY TR7 3BL (01637 874746). Double or family rooms, two chalets in rear garden. All rooms non-smoking with en suite facilities, colour TV and tea/coffee making facilities. Ideal for pets. [🐕]
e-mail: holidays@dewolfguesthouse.com website: www.dewolfguesthouse.com

QUARRYFIELD CARAVAN & CAMPING PARK, CRANTOCK, NEWQUAY. Fully equipped modern caravans overlooking beautiful Crantock Bay. Separate camping field. Bar, pool, children's play area. Contact: MRS WINN, TRETHERRAS, NEWQUAY TR7 2RE (Tel & Fax: 01637 872792). [Pets £1.50 per night; £10 per week camping, £15 per week in caravan]

TRETHIGGEY TOURING PARK, QUINTRELL DOWNS, NEWQUAY TR8 4QR (01637 877672). Friendly, family-run park minutes from surfing beaches. Touring caravans, tent and campervans welcome. Luxury holiday homes for hire. Shop, off-licence, free showers, electric hook-ups, laundry, children's play area, TV/games room, fishing and take-away food in summer. ETC ★★★★
e-mail: enquiries@trethiggey.co.uk website: www.Trethiggey.co.uk

RETORRICK MILL, ST MAWGAN, NEWQUAY TR8 4BH (01637 860460). Old cottage and comfortable bungalows, within walking distance of picturesque village of St Mawgan and sandy beach at Mawgan Porth. Set in nine acres of beautiful gardens, halfway between Newquay and the fishing village of Padstow. From £120 to £380 weekly. Pets welcome. ETC ★★

Padstow

Bright little resort with pretty harbour on Camel estuary. Extensive sands. Nearby is Elizabethan Prideaux Place. Newquay 15 miles, Wadebridge 8.

RAINTREE HOUSE HOLIDAYS, WHISTLERS, TREYARNON BAY, PADSTOW PL28 8JR (01841 520228/520130). We have a varied selection of accommodation. Small or large, houses and apartments, some by the sea. All in easy reach of our lovely beaches. Please write or phone for brochure. [🐕]
e-mail: gill@raintreehouse.co.uk website: www.raintreehouse.co.uk

SHANICE, PADSTOW PL28 8DU (01473 327479 OR 07973 538670). Modern home, sleeps 4 (one double, two single). Wonderful views, patio, barbecue. Short walk to Stein's and Camel Trail. Heating, gas wood-burner, TV+DVD. Open all year.
website: www.Brookfarm.demon.co.uk

Penzance

Well-known resort and port for Scilly Isles, with sand and shingle beaches. Truro 27 miles, Helston 13, Land's End 10, St Ives 8.

GLENCREE HOUSE, 2 MENNAYE ROAD, PENZANCE TR18 4NG. Large Victorian Guesthouse just off seafront. Spacious en suite rooms, some with sea views. All with colour TVs and tea/coffee making facilities. Open fires, full central heating. Unrestricted parking. Excellent breakfast choices. Ideal
location for beaches, SW coastal path, Scilly Isles. Open all year. B & B from £18 pppn. Please contact HELEN CAHALANE (01736 362026) [Pets £1 per night]
e-mail: stay@glencreehouse.co.uk website: www.glencreehouse.co.uk

TORWOOD HOUSE HOTEL, ALEXANDRA ROAD, PENZANCE TR18 4LZ. Torwood is a small, licensed, family-run hotel, situated in a beautiful tree-lined avenue 500 metres from the seafront. All rooms en suite, with TV/DVD, tea/coffee makers and radios. Dinner available on request. For further details telephone LYNDA SOWERBY on 01736 360063.
e-mail: Lyndasowerby@aol.com website: www.torwoodhousehotel.co.uk

GEORGIAN HOUSE HOTEL, 20 CHAPEL STREET, PENZANCE TR18 4AW (Tel & Fax: 01736 365664). Friendly, comfortable hotel near ferry, public transport and beaches. Spacious en suite rooms. Parking. Full breakfast and dinner menu; special diets. Open all year. Cottage also available. AA ◆◆◆◆ [🐕]
e-mail: georgianhouse@btopenworld.com website: www.theaa.co.uk/hotels

Perranporth

North coast resort 6 miles south west of Newquay

GREENMEADOW COTTAGES, NEAR PERRANPORTH. Spacious, clean luxury cottages. Sleep six. Open all year. Short breaks out of season. Non-smoking available. Ample off road parking. Pets welcome in two of the cottages. For brochure and bookings tel: 01872 540483.

Polperro

Picturesque and quaint little fishing village and harbour. Of interest is the "House of the Props". Fowey 9 miles, Looe 5..

POLPERRO. In picturesque Cornish fishing village of Polperro, one of the finest on the South Cornish coast, spectacularly situated holiday cottages sleeping from two to eight persons at a charge of £175 to £475 per cottage per week. With terraced gardens and fabulous outlook over harbour encompassing 15 mile sea views. Excellent selection of quality restaurants and olde worlde pubs nearby, and on offer delicious pasties and locally made ice-cream. Private parking, two minutes shops, beach, quay and National Trust cliff walks. Open all year, children and pets most welcome. All cottages are fully furnished and equipped, to include a colour television, microwave, electric oven, refrigerator, duvets and pillows. GRAHAM WRIGHT, GUARDIAN HOUSE, LISKEARD, CORNWALL PL14 6AD (01579 344080). [🐕]

Port Gaverne

Hamlet on east side of Port Isaac, near Camel Estuary.

CHIMNEYS, PORT GAVERNE, PORT ISAAC PL29 3SQ (Tel & Fax: 01208 880254). A charming 18th Century Cottage only 10 metres from beach. Four bedrooms, two bathrooms, lounge, dining room and kitchen. Good size garden. Brochure from Mrs. Holmes. [🐕]

GREEN DOOR COTTAGES. PORT GAVERNE. A delightful collection of 18C Cornish buildings built around a sunny enclosed courtyard, and 2 lovely apartments with stunning sea views. Situated in a picturesque, tranquil cove ideal for children. Dogs allowed on the beach year round. Half a mile from Port Isaac, on the Cornish Coastal Path. Traditional pub directly opposite. ETC ★★★/★★★★
For brochure: (01208 880293) [🐕]
e-mail: enquiries@greendoorcottages.co.uk website: www.greendoorcottages.co.uk

Homes from home around our peaceful courtyard garden 100 yds from sea in bygone fishing hamlet. Each sleeps six and has full CH, fridge-freezer, washer-dryer, dishwasher, microwave, video. £160 (February), £680 (August) weekly. Daily rates off-season. Resident owner. APPLY:- MALCOLM LEE, GULLROCK, PORT GAVERNE, PORT ISAAC PL29 3SQ (01208 880106). [🐕]

Port Isaac

Attractive fishing village with harbour. Much of the attractive coastline is protected by the National Trust. Camelford 9 miles. Wadebridge 9.

LONG CROSS HOTEL & VICTORIAN GARDENS, TRELIGHTS, PORT ISAAC PL29 3TF (01208 880243). Set in magnificent gardens in an Area of Outstanding Natural Beauty. Tavern in the grounds for your enjoyment. Spacious en suite rooms. Pets' corner. Perfect base for touring. Children's adventure play area. Excellent food served all day. Bargain Spring/Autumn Breaks. [Pets £3.00 per night.]
website: www.longcrosshotel.co.uk

Porthleven

Small town with surprisingly big harbour. Grand woodland walks. 2 miles SW of Helston.

GREYSTONES GUEST HOUSE, 40 WEST END, PORTHLEVEN, HELSTON TR13 9JL (Tel & Fax: 01326 565583; Mobile: 07720 588194). Picturesque fishing village ideal for touring. Dogs/children welcome. Overlooking sea, near harbour, beaches, shops, pubs and restaurants. Tea and coffee facilities, colour TV. En suite facilities. From £20 pppn. [🐕]
e-mail: mawbb@tiscali.co.uk

Portreath

Coastal village 4 miles north west of Redruth.

Charming elegantly furnished self catering cottages between Newquay and St Ives. Sleep 2 to 6. Fully equipped including linen. Beautiful beaches. Laundry and games room. Ample parking. Colour brochure – FRIESIAN VALLEY COTTAGES, MAWLA, CORNWALL TR16 5DW (01209 890901) [🐕]

Portscatho

Tiny cliff-top resort on Roseland Peninsula overlooking beach or rocks and sand. Harbour and splendid views. Falmouth 5 miles.

PETER AND LIZ HEYWOOD, TREWINCE MANOR, PORTSCATHO, NEAR TRURO TR2 5ET (01872 580289). Georgian Manor house estate with luxury lodges and manor house apartments. Lounge bar and restaurant. Superb walking and sailing. Dogs welcome. [pw! Pets £24 per week]
e–mail: bookings@trewince.co.uk website: www.trewince.co.uk

PLEASE SEND A STAMPED ADDRESSED ENVELOPE WITH ENQUIRIES

Praa Sands

Magnificent stretch of sands and dunes. Nearby is picturesque Prussia Cove. Penzance 7½ miles, Helston 6..

Well appointed Bungalows. One chalet bungalow sleeps 8 plus in 4 bedrooms. Lovely peaceful countryside with large garden not overlooked. 2 miles inland. One 3 bedroomed sleeps 6 plus. Overlooking sea. Large garden. Both fully equipped. Dogs very welcome. APPLY – MRS J. LAITY, CHYRASE FARM, GOLDSITHNEY, PENZANCE TR20 9JD (01736 763301). [Pets £20 per week]

St Agnes

Patchwork of fields dotted with remains of local mining industry. Watch for grey seals swimming off St. Agnes Head.

CHIVERTON PARK, BLACKWATER, TRURO TR4 8HS (01872 560667). Caravan and touring holidays only a short drive from magnificent beaches. Quiet, spacious; laundry, shop, play area and games room. All amenities. No club, bar or disco. [1 dog £15 pw, extra dog £10]
e-mail: info@chivertonpark.co.uk website: www.chivertonpark.co.uk

THE BEACON COUNTRY HOUSE HOTEL, GOONVREA ROAD, ST AGNES TR5 0NW (01872 552318). Set in quiet and beautiful area, with fabulous views. Luxurious bedrooms, all en suite. Non-smoking throughout. Open all year. A relaxed and rewarding stay guaranteed. ETC/AA ★★ [🐕]
e-mail: info@beaconhotel.co.uk website: www.beaconhotel.co.uk

THE DRIFTWOOD SPARS HOTEL, TREVAUNANCE COVE, ST AGNES TR5 0RT (01872 552428/553323). Take a deep breath of Cornish fresh air at this comfortable Hotel ideally situated for a perfect seaside holiday. Dogs allowed on beach. Miles of footpaths for 'walkies'. Children and pets welcome. [Pets £2 per night]
website: www.driftwoodspars.com

St Austell

Old Cornish town and china clay centre with small port at Charlestown (1½ miles). Excellent touring centre. Newquay 16 miles, Truro 14, Bodmin 12, Fowey 9, Mevagissey 6.

TRENCREEK FARM HOLIDAY PARK, HEWASWATER, ST AUSTELL PL26 7JG (01726 882540). Self-catering and camping with country views and within easy reach of the sea. Tennis court, heated swimming pool and fishing lakes etc.
website: www.trencreek.co.uk

BOSINVER HOLIDAY COTTAGES, ST MEWAN, ST AUSTELL PL26 7DT (01726 72128). Individual cottages and lodges in peaceful garden surroundings. Close to major holiday attractions. Short walk to shop and pub. Phone for brochure. No pets during Summer School holidays. [pw!, Pets £25 per week].
e-mail: reception@bosinver.co.uk website: www.bosinver.co.uk

St Breward

North Cornwall Village 4 miles south of Camelford, edge Bodmin Moor, 12 miles from coast.

Warm and lovely cottage sleeps four/five in great comfort and utter peace. Log fires, large garden with stream, glorious moorland and coastal walking. Available all year. £130 - £375 per week depending on season. Contact MRS PADDY POWELL (01208 850186). [Dogs £10 per week].
website: www.vacation-cornwall.com

Please mention ***PETS WELCOME*** when making enquiries about accommodation featured in these pages.

St Ives

Picturesque resort, popular with artists, with cobbled streets and intriguing little shops. Wide stretches of sand.

SANDBANK HOLIDAYS, ST IVES BAY, HAYLE (01736 752594). High quality Apartments and Bungalows for 2-6 persons. Heated, Colour TV, Microwave etc. Short Breaks and weekly rates. Dogs welcome. [Pets £14 to £21 per week]
website: www.sandbank-holidays.co.uk

BOB AND JACKY PONTEFRACT, THE LINKS HOLIDAY FLATS, LELANT, ST IVES TR26 3HY (Tel & Fax: 01736 753326). Magnificent location overlooking golf course and beach. Wonderful spot for walking. Five minutes from beach where dogs allowed all year. Two well-equipped flats open all year. [🐕]

St Mawes

Friendly little harbour town on north bank of Percuil River.

THE ROSEVINE HOTEL, PORTHCURNICK BEACH, PORTSCATHO, ST MAWES TR2 5EW (01872 580206; Fax: 01872 580230). Cornwall's "AA TOP 200" luxury hotel. De luxe bedrooms and suites. Award-winning cuisine. Beautiful sub-tropical gardens facing directly over the safe sandy beach fronting the National Trust coastline. Warm heated indoor pool. RAC ★★★, AA 3 Red Stars [🐕]
e-mail: info@rosevine.co.uk website: www.rosevine.co.uk

St Mawgan

Delightful village in wooded river valley. Ancient church has fine carvings.

DALSWINTON HOUSE, ST MAWGAN, NEAR NEWQUAY TR8 4EZ (01637 860385). Old Cornish house standing in ten acres of secluded grounds. All rooms en suite, colour TV, tea/coffee facilities. Solar heated outdoor swimming pool. Restaurant and bar. Out-of-season breaks. No children under 16. ETC ◆◆◆◆. [🐕 pw!]
e-mail: dalswinton@bigwig.net website: www.dalswinton.com

St Tudy

Village 5 miles north east of Wadebridge.

Comfortable end of terrace cottage in picturesque and friendly village. Enclosed garden and parking. Ideal location for exploring all Cornwall. Short Breaks and brochure available. Contact: MRS R REEVES, POLSTRAUL, TREWALDER, DELABOLE PL33 9ET (Tel & Fax: 01840 213120). [🐕]
e-mail: aandr.reeves@virgin.net website: www.uk-holiday-cottages.co.uk/maymear

Tintagel

Attractively situated amidst fine cliff scenery; small rocky beach. Famous for associations with King Arthur, whose ruined castle on Tintagel Head is of interest. Bude 19 miles, Camelford 6.

SANDY AND DAVE WILSON, SALUTATIONS, ATLANTIC ROAD, TINTAGEL PL34 0DE (01840 770287). Comfortable, well-equipped, centrally heated cottages sleeping two. Ideal for touring, walking and relaxing. Close to Coastal Path and village amenities. Private parking. Ring for brochure. Pets Free. [🐕]
e-mail: sandyanddave@tinyworld.co.uk website: www.salutationstintagel.co.uk

WILLAPARK MANOR HOTEL, BOSSINEY, TINTAGEL PL34 0BA (01840 770782). Beautiful character house amidst 14 acres and only minutes from the beach. All en suite rooms. Children and pets welcome. Open all year. SAE for brochure. ETC ★★ [🐕]
website: www.willapark.co.uk

BOSSINEY FARM CARAVAN AND CAMPING PARK, TINTAGEL PL34 0AY (01840 770481). Family-run Park. 20 Luxury Letting Vans; fully serviced, H&C with shower, room heater, TV. On the coast at Tintagel. Colour brochure available. BGHP ★★★★ [Pets welcome: 1st pet free, charge for subsequent pets, £10 per week]
website: www.bossineyfarm.co.uk

MRS LYNDA SPRING, TRETHEVY MANOR, TRETHEVY, TINTAGEL PL34 0BG (Tel & Fax: 01840 770636). Two comfortable, well-equipped, Self-contained Cottages adjoining historical 12th Century Manor House. One-and-a-half miles from Tintagel. Sandy beaches, spectacular coastal and country walks. [🐕]
e-mail: manor1151@talk21.com website: www.trethevy-manor.co.uk

Truro

Bustling Cathedral City with something for everyone. Museum and Art Gallery with interesting shop and cafe is well worth a visit.

TOWNHOUSE ROOMS AND BREAKFAST, 20 FALMOUTH ROAD, TRURO TR1 2HX (01872 277374; Fax: 01872 241666). Not a hotel, or a traditional B&B. We aim to give you lovely rooms, real value for money and the flexibility to enjoy your stay. All rooms en suite. 5 minutes' walk from restaurants and shops. Dogs welcome by arrangement. RAC ◆◆◆◆ *WARM WELCOME AWARD.* [🐕]
e-mail: info@trurohotels.com website: www.trurohotels.com

KING HARRY FERRY COTTAGES, FEOCK, TRURO TR3 6QJ (01872 861915). Two comfortable well equipped cottages in own charming gardens. Pets welcome. Beautiful woodland walks. Perfect for fishing and bird watching. [🐕]
e-mail: jean@kingharry.f9.co.uk website: www.kingharry-info.co.uk

Wadebridge

Town on River Camel, 6 miles north-west of Bodmin

Three barn converted luxury cottage-style self catering homes near Wadebridge. Found along a leafy drive, with wonderful views, beside the lazy twisting Camel River with its "Trail" for walking and cycling. CORNWALL TOURISM AWARDS 2002 - Self Catering Establishment of the Year - "Highly Commended". Sleep 2-7 plus cot. Two dogs per cottage welcome. MRS SUE ZAMARIA, COLESENT COTTAGES, ST TUDY, WADEBRIDGE, CORNWALL PL30 4QX (Tel & Fax: 01208 850112). [pw! Pets £15 per week]
e-mail: welcome@colesent.co.uk website: www.colesent.co.uk

ISLES OF SCILLY

St Mary's

Largest of group of granite islands and islets off Cornish Coast. Terminus for air and sea services from mainland. Main income from flower-growing. Seabirds, dolphins and seals abound.

MRS PAMELA MUMFORD, SALLAKEE FARM, ST MARY'S TR21 0NZ (01720 422391). Self-catering farm cottage, available all year round. Sleeps 5. Woodburner. Near beach and coastal paths. Pets welcome. Write or phone for details. ETC ★★★

See also Colour Advertisement on page 00

Alston, Ambleside

See also Colour Advertisement on page 21

Smallwood House Hotel

Compston Road, Ambleside,
Cumbria LA22 9DJ

015394 32330
www.smallwoodhotel.co.uk

where quality and the customer come first **...try us**

See also Colour Advertisement on page 20

IVY HOUSE HOTEL & RESTAURANT

Hawkshead, Near Ambleside, Cumbria LA22 0HS
Telephone: 015394 36204 • Website: www.ivyhousehotel.com

Family-run Listed Georgian hotel, full of great charm and character, 11 en suite bedrooms with colour television and equipped with hot drink trays.

Contact Rob or Julia Treeby for Brochure.

RAC Dining Award

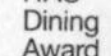

015394 36611

Betty Fold, Hawkshead Hill, Ambleside LA22 0PS

e-mail: holidays@bettyfold.freeserve.co.uk • website: www.bettyfold.co.uk

Situated near Hawkshead and Tarn Hows, large country house in spacious grounds in the heart of Lake District National Park. Betty Fold offers self-catering accommodation in ground floor apartment with private entrance, sleeps 4. One double en suite and one small twin with bathroom and colour TV. Open-plan kitchen/livingroom with electric cooker, fridge microwave. Terms inclusive of heat, light, power, bed linen and towels.

'Rest awhile in style'

Quality B&B. Tranquil settings in the heart of the village. Own grounds. Car park. All ensuite. Kettle, clock/radio, TV, Fridge, CD & Video players. Heated indoor pool, sauna, hot tub, sun lounge and rooftop terrace. Special breaks. Friendly service where pets are welcome. **www.oldvicarageambleside.co.uk**

Contact Ian, Helen or Liana
The Old Vicarage,
Vicarage Road,
Ambleside LA22 9DH
Tel: **015394 33364**

Scalebeck Holiday Cottages Scalebeck, Great Asby, Appleby CA16 6TF

Tel: 01768 351006 ✻ Fax: 01768 353532 ✻ E-mail: mail@scalebeckholidaycottages.com

ETC ★★★★ Prices £105 to £415

Comfortable and well-equipped self-catering accommodation in the tranquil and picturesque Eden Valley, centrally located for the Lakes and Yorkshire Dales National Parks, Northumberland and Scottish Borders.

Witsend One bedroom with 6 ft four-poster double bed. Sleeps 2 +2
Folly Two bedrooms, one double, one single bed and bunks. Sleeps 5
Rum'un Two bedrooms, one double, one twin. Sleeps 4 +1

• Ground floor bedrooms. • Fully appointed bathrooms with power shower. • Living-flame gas fires. •Gas central heating. • Car park. • Fixed stairgate. • Cot and high chair. • Colour TV/Video. Microwave. • Cycle store. • Coin-operated washing machine. • Dryer. • Public telephone. • Games room. Table tennis/pool table. • No smoking. • Pets welcome. • BBQ/Patio area.

A Luxury Break in Cumbria at Superb Value Prices!

When you fancy pampering yourself and your pet with a touch of luxury, enjoy the relaxing comfort and superb value of the award-winning Appleby Manor Country House Hotel. Excellent restaurant, relaxing lounges, indoor leisure club and breathtaking scenery all around.

★★★ 78%

Phone 017 683 51571 or e-mail now for a full-colour brochure and a free interactive CD-ROM

Appleby-in-Westmorland, Cumbria CA16 6JB
E-mail: reception@applebymanor.co.uk
www.applebymanor.co.uk

Best Western
APPLEBY MANOR
COUNTRY HOUSE HOTEL

SKIDDAW VIEW HOLIDAY HOME PARK

Bothel, Near Bassenthwaite CA7 2JG. Tel: 016973 20919
E-mail: office@skiddawview.com Web: www.skiddawview.co.uk

We have quality Lodge, Cottage and Holiday Home accommodation for 2-5 persons. Short breaks available. Peaceful, relaxing surroundings with panoramic views, pets warmly welcome. Please telephone for brochure and prices.

Seven specially designed holiday cottages in converted farm buildings on this 120 acre hill farm. Sleep 2-5. Each cottage is self-contained, centrally heated and double-glazed, with lovely views over an Area of Oustanding Natural Beauty. Ideal for walking, cycling, golf, course fishing, boating. Hadrian's Wall, Ullswater, Gretna Green and Scottish Borders closeby. Well-behaved dogs welcome. Tariff from £170 - £360.

Talkin Head, Near Brampton CA8 1LT Tel: 01697 73435
e-mail: harriet@talkinhead.co.uk • www.talkinhead.co.uk

NEW HOUSE FARM

BUTTERMERE/LORTON VALLEY,
COCKERMOUTH, CUMBRIA CA13 9UU
web: www.newhouse-farm.co.uk
e-mail: hazel@newhouse-farm.co.uk
Tel: 01900 85404 • Fax: 01900 85478

Situated in the quietest and most beautiful part of the Lakes, New House Farm has 15 acres of open fields, ponds, streams and woods which guests and dogs may wander around at leisure and there is easy access to nearby lakes and fells. There are six luxurious en suite bedrooms, all with spectacular views, an elegant dining room and three sitting rooms, all with open fires. Good food. Welcoming hosts.
BED & BREAKFAST FROM £52, DINNER, BED & BREAKFAST FROM £74.

"THE LORTON VALE - A PLACE FOR ALL SEASONS"

Which? Hotel Guide Award Winner • Good Hotel Guide • *AA* ◆◆◆◆◆

See also Colour Advertisement on page 23

ETC ◆◆◆◆ Tel: 01228 577308 ETC ★★★★

NEW PALLYARDS, HETHERSGILL, CARLISLE CA6 6HZ

One modern bungalow, 3/4 bedrooms, sleeps 8. 2 lovely cottages on farm. Bed and Breakfast, Half Board. En suite double/family, twin/single rooms. Disabled welcome. Won the National Award for the Best Breakfast in Britain and have been filmed for BBC TV.

B&B from £25.00, Dinner £13.00 DB&B weekly rate £160.00 - £170.00. Self Catering £120.00 - £672.00.
E-mail: info@newpallyards.freeserve.co.uk Website: www.newpallyards.freeserve.co.uk

GRAHAM ARMS HOTEL

Longtown, Near Carlisle, Cumbria CA6 5SE

A warm welcome awaits at this 180-year-old former Coaching Inn. Situated six miles from the M6 (J44) and Gretna Green, The Graham Arms makes an ideal overnight stop or perfect touring base for the Scottish Borders, English Lakes, Hadrian's Wall and much more. 15 comfortable en suite bedrooms, including four-poster and family rooms with TV, radio etc. Meals and snacks served throughout the day. Friendly 'local's bar' and new 'Sports bar' serving real ale and a fine selection of malt whiskies. Secure courtyard parking for cars, cycles and motorcycles. Pets welcome with well behaved owners!

Visit our website on www.grahamarms.com • Tel & Fax: 01228 791213
Email: office@grahamarms.com • Website: www.grahamarms.com
Bed and full traditional breakfast £30– £36. Special rates for weekend and midweek breaks. RAC ★★

- GRANGE END COTTAGE -

A charming and luxurious 3 bedroomed, 18th century, Georgian cottage. Sleeps 6. Oak beams, inglenook fireplace, 4-poster bed, fully-fitted kitchen, washing machine, tumble drier and dishwasher. Situated only one mile from historic Cartmel village, with 12th century priory, cobbled streets, racecourse and four great pubs. Lake Windermere is only 10 minutes' drive. One of the very best cottages in one of the most peaceful and picturesque valleys in South Lakeland with walks available right from the doorstep.

Tel: 01524 702955 ETC ★★★★ Website: www.holidaycottagescumbria.com

When making enquiries please mention FHG Publications

LOWESWATER COTTAGES

at Scale Hill

Loweswater, Cockermouth,
Cumbria CA13 9UX
Tel: 01900 85232
Fax: 01900 85321

Nestling among the magnificent Loweswater/ Buttermere fells and lakes, luxury cottages available all year. Open fires, central heating, en suite bathrooms, modern kitchens, gardens. Four country inns with good food within 3 miles, one only ½ mile. Crummock Water 10 minutes walk through National Trust woods. Children and pets welcome. Family-run. Colour brochure. Pets £25 per week. Abandon the car, walks are from the doorstep.

e-mail: thompson@scalehillloweswater.co.uk
web: www.loweswaterholidaycottages.co.uk

ETC
★★★★ / ★★★★★

Rose Cottage

Lorton Road, Cockermouth CA13 9DX

Family-run guest house on the outskirts of Cockermouth. Warm, friendly atmosphere. Ample off-road parking. All rooms en suite with colour TV, tea/coffee, central heating and most have double glazing. Pets most welcome in the house (excluding dining room), and there are short walks nearby. Ideal base for visiting both Lakes and coast. ETC ◆◆◆◆

Tel & Fax: 01900 822189 website: www.rosecottageguest.co.uk

See also Colour Advertisement on page 19

The Coppermines & Coniston Lakes Cottages

ETC ★★ - ★★★★★

Unique Lakeland cottages for 2 – 30 of quality and character in stunning mountain scenery. Log fires, exposed beams. Pets welcome!

Tel: 015394 41765
Book online
www.coppermines.co.uk

See also Colour Advertisement on page 19

FREE or REDUCED RATE entry to Holiday Visits and Attractions – see our READERS' OFFER VOUCHERS on pages 101-116

Readers are requested to mention this guidebook when seeking accommodation (and please enclose a stamped addressed envelope).

Cragside

A quiet, comfortable guest house with beautiful views of the surrounding fells yet close to the centre of Keswick. All rooms are en suite,tastefully decorated and centrally heated and have clock radio, colour TV and tea/coffee making facilities.

Children of all ages welcome. Rest assured you will have a comfortable and relaxed stay with us. Bed and Breakfast from £20. £130 per week en suite. Children of all ages welcome. Pets welcome. • 39 Blencathra Street, Keswick CA12 4HX

Tel & Fax: 017687 73344 • e-mail: wayne-alison@cragside39blencathra.fsnet.co.uk • www.SmoothHound.co.uk/hotels/cragside

Lakeland Cottage Holidays

Warm Comfortable Houses and Cottages

in Keswick and Beautiful Borrowdale

Tel: 017687 76065

Wonderful Walks Waiting@lakelandcottages.co.uk

COLEDALE INN

ETC ◆◆◆

Braithwaite, Near Keswick, Cumbria CA12 5TN. Tel: 017687 78272

A friendly, family-run Victorian Inn in a peaceful hillside position above Braithwaite, and ideally situated for touring and walking. All bedrooms are warm and spacious, with en suite shower room and colour television. Children are welcome, as are pets. Home-cooked meals, and real ales. Open all year. **website: www.coledale-inn.co.uk**

Rickerby Grange

AA/ETC ◆◆◆◆

RAC ◆◆◆◆ SPARKLING DIAMOND AWARD

Portinscale, Keswick, Cumbria CA12 5RH

Set within its own garden with private car parking, in the picturesque village of Portinscale near the shores of Lake Derwentwater within walking distance of the market town of Keswick. Ideally situated for exploring all parts of the Lakes. Offering comfort, friendly service, these being the essential qualities provided by the resident proprietor. A well-stocked bar offering draught beers; comfortable lounge and elegant dining room where a four course dinner can be enjoyed with a varied selection of wines. All rooms en suite with tea and coffee making facilities, colour TV, telephone.

DB&B from £49, Winter Rates Available (Special Breaks). Open all Year.

Brochure on request, contact Joe or Audrey on 017687 72344

e-mail: joe@ricor.co.uk • website: www.ricor.co.uk

Woodside Penrith Road, Keswick CA12 4LJ • Tel: 017687 73522

Late 19th century property set in almost an acre of mature grounds, a short walk down bridle path to town. Extensively refurbished, with larger than average rooms all en suites. Large private car park, and for those using cycles, secure storage, hosepipe, repair stand and associated tools for your use. Hearty English breakfast together with cereal, fruit and yoghurt. We will cater for special needs on request. Credit cards accepted. Dogs welcome. Bed and Breakfast from £23.

e-mail: ann@pretswell.freeserve.co.uk website: www.woodside.uk.net

MIDTOWN COTTAGES, High Lorton

Two well equipped cottages, both with central heating, furnished to a high standard, all with dishwashers & freezers. Overlooking the Fells, at the north end of Lorton Vale. Pets welcome. Non-smoking. Short breaks from £160. Contact Mr & Mrs M. Burrell:

Telephone: 01264 710165 • e-mail: info@midtown-cottages.com

website: www.midtown-cottages.com • ETC ★★★★

See also Colour Advertisement on page 20

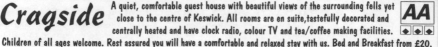

"YOUR PETS & YOUR HOLIDAY"

Combine COMFORT, PEACE AND QUIET, RELAX, FISH, STROLL OR WALK

(SECLUDED COTTAGES with private fishing)

Tranquil, comfortable cottages, set in their own secret valley, overlooking the fishing lakes amidst Lakeland's beautiful Eden Valley countryside, only 30 minutes' drive from Ullswater, North Pennines, Hadrian's Wall and Scottish Borders.

*Well fenced exercise areas for dogs.
* Clean, well maintained and equipped.
* Linen provided. * Beds freshly made for you.
* Exceptional wildlife and walking area.
* Excellent Coarse Fishing for residents only.
* Golf courses nearby. * You & your pets very welcome.
* Kennel available if required. * Open all year – breaks/weeks.

Flexible Terms

Relax and escape to "YOUR" hideaway in the country.

Tel/Fax 01768 898711 24hr Brochure line

e-mail: info@crossfieldcottages.co.uk
website: www.crossfieldcottages.co.uk

Booking & Availability
01768 898711, 6-10 p.m. or SAE to:

CROSSFIELD COTTAGE, KIRKOSWALD,
PENRITH, CUMBRIA CA10 1EU

RING NOW! It's never too early or too late!

ETC ★★★

PETS – NO PROBLEM!

Owned by Vets

Janet and Peter, 1 Friars Ground, Kirkby-in-Furness LA17 7YB

"Sunset Cottage" is a spacious self-catering 17th century two bedroomed character cottage with garden. Original features include inglenook fireplace, oak beams, flagstone floor and oak panelling. Panoramic views over sea/mountains; ideal for walking and birdwatching. Coniston/Windermere 20 minutes. Terms from £135. Open all year.

E-mail: enquiries@southlakes-cottages.com • Web: www.southlakes-cottages.com

A warm welcome awaits you at TOSSBECK, a working farm situated in the unspoilt Lune Valley. The farmhouse is a 17th century Listed building featuring oak panelling and mullioned windows. B&B from £20 with reductions for children. Short break offers. One double en suite and a family/double/twin room with adjoining private facilities, both with TV and drink making facilities. Refreshments served on arrival. An ideal touring base for Lakes and Dales or as a stopover point as situated between M6 junctions. Non-smoking. ETC ◆◆◆

Brochure from: **Pauline Bainbridge, Tossbeck Farm, Middleton, Kirkby Lonsdale LA6 2LZ**

Tel: 015242 76214. • e-mail: postmaster@tossbeck.f9.co.uk • website: www.tossbeck.co.uk

HIGHFOLD COTTAGE • LITTLE LANGDALE

Very comfortable Lakeland cottage, ideally situated for walking and touring. Superb mountain views. Sleeps 5. Personally maintained. Pets welcome. Weekly £210–£375. **MRS C.E. BLAIR, 8 THE GLEBE, CHAPEL STILE, AMBLESIDE LA22 9JT • 015394 37686 • www.highfoldcottage.co.uk**

NEAR HOWE HOTEL & COTTAGES

is the ideal answer for a quiet away from-it-all holiday or a break when travelling North or South. Bar with log fire on colder nights.

3 self-catering cottages sleep up to 4 persons, Saddle Back Barn sleeping up to 7 with 3 bedrooms en suite. B&B £21 to £26 per person. ***ETC ★★★★ SELF-CATERING.***

Mungrisdale, Penrith CA11 0SH • Tel/Fax: Threlkeld (017687) 79678

E-mail: nearhowe@btopenworld.com • Website: www.nearhowe.co.uk

ETC ◆◆◆

NEWBY BRIDGE HOTEL
Overlooking Lake Windermere

RIVERSIDE HOTEL
Overlooking River Kent

DAMSON DENE HOTEL
Tranquil Rural Location

Many rooms feature four-poster beds, some with en suite jacuzzi bath
Seasonal Breaks from £129 per person for three nights including Dinner, Bed and Breakfast.

Newby Bridge Hotel
Newby Bridge
Cumbria
LA12 8NA
Tel: 015395 31222
info@newbybridgehotel.co.uk

Riverside Hotel
Beezon Road
Kendal
Cumbria
LA9 4BZ
Tel: 015397 34861
info@riversidekendal.co.uk

Damson Dene Hotel
Crosthwaite
Cumbria
LA8 8JE
Tel: 015395 68676
info@damsondene.co.uk

Stunning Offers... Stunning Hotels... Stunning Locations....

www.bestlakesbreaks.co.uk

LYVENNET COTTAGES Four different cottages in and around the small farming village of Kings Meaburn in beautiful unspoilt 'Lyvennet Valley'. Ideal touring centre for the Lakes, Dales, Hadrian's Wall, superb area for dog walks. Attractively furnished, fuel, power and linen inclusive. All have colour TV, microwave, fridge, washing machine, central heating, parking and private fishing. Children, pets and horses welcome, cots and highchairs on request. Open all year. Terms from £130 to £440.

Contact: Janet Addison, The Mill, Kings Meaburn, Penrith, Cumbria CA10 3BU
Tel: 01931 714661/714226 • Fax: 01931 714598 • Web: www.lyvennetcottages.co.uk ETC ★★★/★★★★

ETC ★★★

SECLUDED COTTAGES with Private Fishing
Crossfield Cottages, Kirkoswald, Penrith, Cumbria CA10 1EU
24 hour Brochure line: 01768 898711 (manned most Saturdays)

Tranquil quality cottages overlooking lake amid Lakeland's beautiful Eden Valley countryside, only 30 minutes' drive from Ullswater, North Pennines, Hadrian's Wall and Scottish Borders. Residents' coarse fishing on doorstep. Cottages sleep 2—6, well equipped and maintained. **PETS VERY WELCOME.**

e-mail: info@crossfieldcottages.co.uk **website: www.crossfieldcottages.co.uk**

Your Stepping Stone to the Cumbrian Lake District

ETC ★★★★★

Carrock Cottages are three recently renovated stone built cottages set on the fringe of the Lakeland Fells.
A quiet rural location near the lovely villages of Hesket Newmarket with its award winning brewery, Caldbeck and Greystoke.
Explore the beauty of the Lake District National Park or head North to historic Carlisle and on to Hadrian's Wall.
Fell walking & other activities close to hand as well as excellent restaurants.
A warm welcome guaranteed.
Accommodation for 1 to 12 people.
On-site games room, spa facilities.
Home cooked meals service.

Carrock House, Hutton Roof, Penrith, Cumbria CA11 0XY
Tel: Malcolm or Gillian on 01768 484 111 or Fax: 017684 888 50

www.carrockcottages.co.uk • info@carrockcottages.co.uk

See also Colour Advertisement on page 22

PLEASE MENTION THIS GUIDE WHEN YOU WRITE OR PHONE TO ENQUIRE ABOUT ACCOMMODATION.

IF YOU ARE WRITING, A STAMPED, ADDRESSED ENVELOPE IS ALWAYS APPRECIATED.

All pets free of charge at **Tanglewood Caravan Park**

CAUSEWAY HEAD, SILLOTH-ON-SOLWAY, CUMBRIA CA7 4PE

e-mail: tanglewoodcaravanpark@hotmail.com •• website: www. tanglewoodcaravanpark.co.uk

Friendly, quiet tree-sheltered site just a mile inland from beautiful coastline and this charming harbour town. Friendly pub/club with adjacent children's games room. Large modern holiday homes for hire, electric hook-ups available.

"The ideal holiday for you and your pet" **Write or phone for colour brochure TEL: 016973 31253**

See also Colour Advertisement on page 23

Land Ends Cabins, **Watermillock, Near Ullswater CA11 0NB**

Tel: 017684 86438 • Only one mile from Ullswater, our four detached log cabins have a peaceful fellside location in 25-acre grounds with two pretty lakes. Ducks, moorhens, red squirrels and wonderful birdlife. Doggy heaven! Sleep 2-5. **e-mail: infolandends@btinternet.com • www.landends.co.uk**

LONSDALE HOUSE HOTEL

11 Daltongate, Ulverston, Cumbria LA12 7BD

Family-run Hotel situated right in the heart of Ulverston (South Lakes festival town) offers friendly service, great food and comfortable accommodation. Dogs are most welcome, provided they are accompanied by well-behaved owners, and can stay in the rooms. A short walk from the hotel, on the edge of the National Park, overlooking Ulverston, is Sir John Barrow's Monument on Hoad Hill. A popular place for walking with superb views of the Lake District peaks and panoramic view of Morecambe Bay. There are also some good walks along the bay coast a short drive from the hotel. Lonsdale House Hotel is an excellent base to explore the Lake District because we are about 15 minutes from Lake Windermere and about 30 minutes from Windermere village, Coniston and Cartmel. Phone ***01229 582598*** *for a brochure and find out about our special breaks.*

www.lonsdalehousehotel.co.uk

See also Colour Advertisement on page 20

Visit the FHG website

www.holidayguides.com

for details of the wide choice of accommodation featured in the full range of FHG titles

Quality Holiday Homes in England's Beautiful Lake District

Over 200 ETC inspected and graded properties throughout the southern and central Lake District. Lakelovers are sure to have a property to meet your needs.

Free Leisure Club membership with every booking

Tel: 015394 88855 • Fax: 015394 88857

e-mail: bookings@lakelovers.co.uk • www.lakelovers.co.uk ETC ★★★ – ★★★★★

Lakelovers, Belmont House, Lake Road, Bowness-on-Windermere, Cumbria LA23 3BJ

See also Colour Advertisement on page 22

Applethwaite House

ETC ◆◆◆

Situated in a quiet cul-de-sac just minutes from the village centre, shops, public transport and local park. We promise you a warm welcome and clean comfortable accommodation with a relaxed and friendly atmosphere. All rooms en suite with colour TV and complimentary hot drinks. Vegetarians catered for and families very welcome. Pets stay FREE but owners must pay. Prices from £20.00 depending on season. Non-smoking.

1 Upper Oak Street, Windermere, Cumbria LA23 2LB
Telephone: 015394 44689
E-mail: info@applethwaitehouse.co.uk
Website: www.applethwaitehouse.co.uk

Set in the foothills of Wansfell Pike, at the head of the Troutbeck Valley.

THE **Mortal Man** INN

Troutbeck, Windermere LA23 1PL

Tel: 015394 33193

website: www.themortalman.co.uk

We offer a relaxed, friendly, comfortable atmosphere in which to unwind. The Inn boasts twelve en suite rooms, two bars and a restaurant, all with spectacular views of the valley. Ideal for walking, golf and water sport holidays.

Dogs and children always welcome

B&B from £30 pppn.

ETC ★★ • Silver Award for Quality

Kirkwood Guest House

Prince's Road, Windermere LA23 2DD • Tel/Fax: 015394 43907

KIRKWOOD occupies a quiet spot between Windermere and Bowness, offering a warm and friendly atmosphere with an individual personal service. Rooms are large, en suite with TV and tea/coffee making facilities; some have four-poster beds. Your hosts will be pleased to help plan tours or walks with maps provided. Three-night special breaks available. B&B £25 -£32.

e-mail: info@kirkwood51.co.uk **website: www.kirkwood51.co.uk**

When making enquiries or bookings, a stamped addressed envelope is always appreciated

RECOMMENDED COTTAGE HOLIDAYS. 1st choice for dream cottages at very competitive prices in all holiday regions of beautiful Britain. Pets welcome. All properties inspected. For free brochure call: 08700 718 718.
website: www.recommended-cottages.co.uk

Alston

Small market town 16 miles north-east of Penrith.

ROCK HOUSE ESTATE, VALLEY VIEW, NENTHEAD, ALSTON CA9 3NA (01434 382684). Five luxury cottages sleeping 2-14. Ideal for walking/cycling. All linen and fuel included. Four-poster bed, spa bath, sauna, real fire. Short breaks. Open all year. [Pets £20 each].
e-mail: Info@RockHouseEstate.co.uk website: www.RockHouseEstate.co.uk

Ambleside

Popular centre for exploring Lake District at northern end of Lake Windermere. Picturesque Stock Ghyll waterfall nearby, lovely walks. Associations with Wordsworth. Penrith 30 miles, Keswick 17, Windermere 5.

2 LOWFIELD, OLD LAKE ROAD, AMBLESIDE. Ground floor garden flat half a mile from town centre; sleeps 4. Lounge/diningroom, kitchen, bathroom/WC, two bedrooms. Linen supplied. Children and pets welcome. Parking for one car. Bookings Saturday to Saturday. Terms from £130 to £200 per week. Contact: MR P. F. QUARMBY, 3 LOWFIELD, OLD LAKE ROAD, AMBLESIDE LA22 0DH (Tel & Fax: 015394 32326). [🐕]

GREENHOWE CARAVAN PARK, GREAT LANGDALE, AMBLESIDE LA22 9JU (015394 37231; Fax: 015394 37464; Freephone: 0800 0717231). Permanent Caravan Park with Self Contained Holiday Accommodation. An ideal centre for Climbing, Fell Walking, Riding, Swimming, Water Skiing or just a lazy holiday. ETC ★★★★ [Pets £5 per night, £25 per week]
website: www.greenhowe.com

KIRKSTONE FOOT, KIRKSTONE PASS ROAD, AMBLESIDE LA22 9EH (015394 32232; Fax: 015394 32805). Superior cottage and apartment complex, set in peaceful gardens, adjoining the Lakeland fells and village centre. Open all year. ETC ★★★★/★★★★★ [pw! Pets £3.00 per night.]
e-mail: enquiries@kirkstonefoot.co.uk website: www.kirkstonefoot.co.uk

SMALLWOOD HOUSE HOTEL, COMPSTON ROAD, AMBLESIDE LA22 9DJ (015394 32330). Where quality and the customer come first. Try us. ETC ◆◆◆◆ [Pets £2 per night]
website: www.smallwoodhotel.co.uk

IVY HOUSE HOTEL AND RESTAURANT, HAWKSHEAD, NEAR AMBLESIDE LA22 0HS (015394 36204). Family-run listed Georgian hotel. 11 en suite bedrooms with colour TV and equipped with hot drinks trays. No charge for dogs. Children most welcome. Write or telephone Rob or Julia Treeby for brochure. ETC ◆◆◆◆, RAC Dining Award. [🐕]
website: www.ivyhousehotel.com

BETTYFOLD, HAWKSHEAD HILL, AMBLESIDE LA22 0PS (015394 36611). Ground floor apartment sleeping four. Private entrance. Set in peaceful and spacious grounds, ideal for walkers and families with pets. Open all year. [Pets £2 per night.]
e-mail: holidays@bettyfold.freeserve.co.uk website: www.bettyfold.co.uk

THE OLD VICARAGE, VICARAGE ROAD, AMBLESIDE LA22 9DH (015394 33364). 'Rest a while in style'. Quality B&B set in tranquil wooded grounds in the heart of the village. Car park. All rooms en suite. Kettle, clock/radio, TV. Heated indoor pool, sauna, hot tub, sun lounge and rooftop terrace. Special breaks. Friendly service where your pets are welcome. Telephone IAN OR HELEN BURT.
website: www.oldvicarageambleside.co.uk

A useful Index of Towns/Villages and Counties appears on page 426 – please also refer to Contents Page 3.

Appleby-in-Westmorland

Pleasant touring centre on River Eden, between Pennines and Lake District. Castle and Moot Hall of historic interest. Trout fishing, swimming pool, tennis, bowls. Kendal 24 miles, Penrith 13.

KEITH AND DIANE BUDDING, SCALEBECK HOLIDAY COTTAGES, SCALEBECK, GREAT ASBY, APPLEBY CA16 6TF (01768 351006; Fax: 01768 353532). Comfortable and well-equipped self-catering accommodation in the tranquil and picturesque Eden Valley, centrally located for the Lakes and Yorkshire Dales National Parks, Northumberland and Scottish Borders. ETC ★★★★. [pw! £15 per week]
e-mail: mail@scalebeckholidaycottages.com

APPLEBY MANOR COUNTRY HOUSE HOTEL, ROMAN ROAD, APPLEBY-IN-WESTMORLAND CA16 6JB (017683 51571; Fax: 017683 52888). Enjoy the comfort of Cumbria's award-winning Country House Hotel with superb meals, relaxing lounges, indoor leisure club and breathtaking scenery all around. Phone for a full colour brochure and interactive CD-ROM. [pw!, Pets £10 per stay]
e-mail: reception@applebymanor.co.uk website: www.applebymanor.co.uk

Bassenthwaite

Village on Bassenthwaite Lake with traces of Norse and Roman settlements.

SKIDDAW VIEW HOLIDAY HOME PARK, BOTHEL, NEAR BASSENTHWAITE CA7 2JG (016973 20919). Quality lodge, cottage and holiday home accommodation for 2-5 in peaceful, relaxing surroundings. Please telephone for brochure and prices. [pw!]
e-mail: office@skiddawview.com website: www.skiddawview.co.uk

Borrowdale

Scenic valley of River Derwent, splendid walking and climbing country.

MARY MOUNT HOTEL, BORROWDALE, NEAR KESWICK CA12 5UU (017687 77223). Set in 4½ acres of gardens and woodlands on the shores of Derwentwater. 2½ miles from Keswick in picturesque Borrowdale. Superb walking and touring. All rooms en suite with colour TV and tea/coffee making facilities. Licensed. Brochure on request. ETC ★★ [pw!]
e-mail: mawdsley1@aol.com website: www.marymounthotel.co.uk

Brampton

Market town with cobbled streets. Octagonal Moat Hall with exterior staricases and iron stocks.

LONG BYRES HOLIDAY COTTAGES, TALKIN HEAD FARM, TALKIN HEAD, NEAR BRAMPTON CA8 1LT (01697 73435). Seven holiday cottages, sleeping 2 to 5, in an Area of Oustanding Natutal Beauty. Self-contained, centrally heated and double-glazed. Ideal for walking, cycling, golf, coarse fishing and boating.
e-mail: harriet@talkinhead.co.uk website: www.talkinhead.co.uk

Broughton-in-Furness

Village 8 miles NW of Ulverston.

J. JACKSON, THORNTHWAITE FARM, WOODLAND HALL, WOODLAND, BROUGHTON-IN-FURNESS LA20 6DF (Tel & Fax: 01229 716340). Two well-equipped cottages and two caravans in excellent walking area. Wildlife/birdwatchers paradise. Private fishing lake. Ancient woodlands, quiet, relaxing, warm welcome. Established 1968. ETC ★★★ [Pets £15 per week]
e-mail: info@lakedistrictcottages.co.uk website: www.lakedistrictcottages.co.uk

When making enquiries please mention FHG Publications

Buttermere

Between lake of same name and Crummock Water. Magnificent scenery. Of special note is Sour Milk Ghyll waterfall and steep and impressive Honister Pass. Keswick 15 miles, Cockermouth 10.

NEW HOUSE FARM, BUTTERMERE/LORTON VALLEY, COCKERMOUTH CA13 9UU (01900 85404; Fax: 01900 85478). New House Farm has 15 acres of fields, woods, streams and ponds which guests and dogs can wander around. Luxurious en suite accommodation and fine traditional food. Off season breaks. AA ◆◆◆◆◆. [🐕]
e-mail: hazel@newhouse-farm.co.uk website: www.newhouse-farm.co.uk

Carlisle

Important Border city and former Roman station on River Eden. Castle is of historic interest, also Tullie House Museum and Art Gallery. Good sports facilities inc. football and racecourse. Kendal 45 miles, Dumfries 33, Penrith 18.

NEW PALLYARDS, HETHERSGILL, CARLISLE CA6 6HZ (01228 577308). Relax and see beautiful North Cumbria and the Borders. Self-catering accommodation in one Bungalow, 3/4 bedrooms; two lovely Cottages on farm. Also Bed and Breakfast or Half Board – en suite rooms. ETC ◆◆◆◆/★★★★ [Pets from £7 per week]
e-mail: info@newpallyards.freeserve.co.uk website: www.newpallyards.freeserve.co.uk

GRAHAM ARMS HOTEL, ENGLISH STREET, LONGTOWN, CARLISLE CA6 5SE (Tel & Fax: 01228 791213). 14 bedrooms en suite, one with private facilities, including four-poster and family rooms, all with tea/coffee facilities, TV and radio. Secure courtyard locked overnight. Pets welcome with well-behaved owners. RAC ★★. [🐕]
e-mail: office@grahamarms.com website: www.grahamarms.com

Cartmel

Village 4 miles south of Newby Bridge.

RATHER SPECIAL COTTAGES. Winners of ETC's highest award for self-catering and Winners of Cumbria for Excellence 1998 and 1999. Pets and children welcome. Nine cottages sleeping 2-6. Open all year. Please telephone for details. ETC ★★★★. Contact: MR M. AINSCOUGH, LONGLANDS AT CARTMEL, CARTMEL LA11 6HG (015395 36475; Fax: 015395 36172).
e-mail: longlands@cartmel.com website: www.cartmel.com

GRANGE END COTTAGES, CARTMEL (01524 702955). Luxurious 3 bedroomed 18th century Georgian cottage. Sleeps 6. Oak beams, inglenook fireplace, 4-poster bed, fully-fitted kitchen, washing machine, tumble drier and dishwasher. [Pets £12 per week]
website: www.holidaycottagescumbria.com

Cockermouth

Market town and popular touring centre for Lake District and quiet Cumbrian coast. On Rivers Derwent and Cocker. Penrith 30 miles, Carlisle 26, Whitehaven 14, Keswick 12.

LOWESWATER COTTAGES AT SCALE HILL, LOWESWATER, COCKERMOUTH CA13 9UX (01900 85232; Fax: 01900 85321). Nestling among the fells and lakes, luxury cottages available all year. Open fires, central heating, en suite bathrooms, modern kitchens, gardens. Country Inn ½ mile away. Crummock Water 10 minutes' walk through woods. ETC ★★★★/★★★★★. See also advert on p000. [Pets £25 per week].
e-mail: thomson@scalehillloweswater.co.uk website: www.loweswaterholidaycottages.co.uk

ROSE COTTAGE GUEST HOUSE, LORTON ROAD, COCKERMOUTH CA13 9DX (Tel & Fax: 01900 822189). Family-run guest house on the outskirts of Cockermouth. Warm, friendly atmosphere. Parking. All rooms en suite with colour TV, tea/coffee, central heating. Pets welcome. Ideal base for visiting both Lakes and coast. ETC ◆◆◆◆
website: www.rosecottageguest.co.uk

Coniston

Village 8 miles south-west of Ambleside, dominated by Old Man of Coniston (2635ft).

LAKELAND HOUSE, TILBERTHWAITE AVENUE, CONISTON LA21 8ED (015394 41303). Village centre guest house, hearty breakfasts, from £20 per person. Two self-catering cottages also available, sleeping two to six - one with lake views, one with four-poster. Small charge for pets.
e-mail: info@lakelandhouse.co.uk website: www.lakelandhouse.co.uk

THE COPPERMINES AND CONISTON LAKES COTTAGES. (015394 41765). Unique Lakeland cottages for 2 – 30 of quality and character in stunning mountain scenery. Log fires, exposed beams. Pets welcome! ETC ★★ - ★★★★★ Book online. [Pets £20 per week]
website: www.coppermines.co.uk

Crosthwaite

Hamlet 4 miles west of Kendal

DAMSON DENE HOTEL, CROSTHWAITE LA8 8JE (015395 68676). Tranquil location only 10 minutes from Lake Windermere. Best Lakes Breaks from £129 per person for 3 nights. [pets pw!]
e-mail: info@damsondene.co.uk website: www.bestlakesbreaks.co.uk

Duddon Valley

Remote, unspoilt and idyllic corner of the Lake District, a delight for walkers and nature lovers.

MRS C. BRADLEY, TROUTAL FARM, SEATHWAITE, DUDDON VALLEY, NEAR BROUGHTON IN FURNESS LA20 6EF (01229 716235). Farm Bed and Breakfast in an unspoilt area near Wrynose and Hard Knott Passes between Coniston and Eskdale. Two en suite double rooms, one twin, accommodating up to 6. [Horses £10 per week, 1 dog free].
website: www.troutalfarm.co.uk

Eskdale

Lakeless valley, noted for waterfalls and ascended by a light-gauge railway. Tremendous views. Roman fort. Keswick 35 miles, Broughton-in-Furness 10 miles.

MRS J. P . HALL, FISHERGROUND FARM, ESKDALE CA19 1TF (01946 723319). Self-catering to suit everyone. Three pine lodges and a stone cottage – on a delightful traditional farm. Adventure playground. Raft pool and games room. Pets' and children's paradise. Brochures available. ETC ★★★ [pets]
e-mail: holidays@fisherground.co.uk website: www.fisherground.co.uk

THE BURNMOOR INN, BOOT, ESKDALE CA19 1TG (019467 23224; Fax: 019467 23337). Nine en suite bedrooms plus two bed self-catering cottage to let. Dogs welcome to be in the bar with you for lunch and dinner. We do not make a charge for well behaved dogs. Special breaks available all year. Call for a brochure. [pets]
e-mail: enquiries@burnmoor.co.uk website: www.burnmoor.co.uk

HOLLIN HEAD, ESKDALE. With hundreds of walks right from the door, Hollin Head is a comfortable Lakeland cottage sleeping 2-8 people. Coal fire, modern kitchen, walled garden, pets welcome. Contact: RIVENDELL, BASSENTHWAITE, KESWICK, CUMBRIA CA12 4QP (01768 776836; mobile: 07811 211666). [pets]
e-mail: sally@hollinhead.co.uk website: www.hollinhead.co.uk

Gamblesby

Village 8 miles NE of Penrith.

CHURCH COURT COTTAGES, GAMBLESBY, PENRITH CA10 1HR. Four beautiful, well-equipped, sandstone cottages in picturesque village. Excellent traffic-free walks from doorstep. Wonderful views of the hills of the Lake District and North Pennines. Penrith 15 minutes. Contact: MARK COWELL or PATRICIA CLOWES (01768 881682). [pets]
e-mail: markcowell@tiscali.co.uk website: www.gogamblesby.co.uk

Grasmere

Village famous for Wordsworth associations; the poet lived in Dove Cottage (preserved as it was), and is buried in the churchyard. Museum has manuscripts and relics.

GRASMERE HOTEL, BROADGATE, GRASMERE LA22 9TA (015394 35277). A family-run 13 bedroomed Country House Hotel. Quietly situated in the village with ample parking and a licensed lounge. All rooms en suite. Award-winning restaurant overlooking large secluded gardens, river and surrounding hills. Superb five-course dinners and carefully chosen wine list. Special breaks throughout the year. [Pets £5 per stay].
website: www.grasmerehotel.co.uk

LAKE VIEW COUNTRY HOUSE & SELF-CATERING APARTMENTS, GRASMERE LA22 9TD (015394 35384/35167). Luxury B&B or 3 Star Self-Catering accommodation in unrivalled location near to village yet secluded with wonderful views and lakeshore access. All B&B rooms en suite, some with whirlpool baths. Ground floor accommodation available. No smoking. Featured in "Which?" Good B&B Guide.

Hawkshead

Quaint village in Lake District between Coniston Water and Windermere. The 16th century Church and Grammar School, which Wordsworth attended, are of interest. Ambleside 5 miles.

HIDEAWAYS, THE MINSTRELS' GALLERY, THE SQUARE, HAWKSHEAD LA22 0NZ (015394 42435; Fax: 015394 36178). Cosy barns and cottages, log fires, stunning views, great walking from doorstep, free fishing and pets welcome in most. Some 5 star, with whirlpool baths!
e-mail: bookings@lakeland-hideaways.co.uk website: www.lakeland-hideaways.co.uk

SAWREY HOUSE COUNTRY HOTEL & RESTAURANT, NEAR SAWREY, HAWKSHEAD LA22 0LF (015394 36387; Fax: 015394 36010). Quality family-run hotel in three acres of peaceful gardens with magnificent views across Esthwaite Water. Excellent food, warm friendly atmosphere. Lounge, Bar. Pets welcome. Non-Smoking. AA 2 Rosettes for food. AA ◆◆◆◆◆. [Pets £10 per night.]
website: www.sawreyhouse.com

THE KINGS ARMS HOTEL, HAWKSHEAD, AMBLESIDE LA22 0NZ (015394 36372). Join us for a relaxing stay amidst the green hills and dales of Lakeland, and we will be delighted to offer you good food, homely comfort and warm hospitality in historic surroundings. We hope to see you soon! Self-catering cottages also available.
website: www.kingsarmshawkshead.co.uk

Kendal

Market town and popular centre for touring the Lake District. Of historic interest is the Norman castle, birthplace of Catherine Parr. Penrith 25 miles, Lancaster 22, Ambleside 13.

ANNE TAYLOR, RUSSELL FARM, BURTON-IN-KENDAL, CARNFORTH, LANCS. LA6 1NN (01524 781334). Bed, Breakfast and Evening Meal offered. Ideal centre for touring Lakes and Yorkshire Dales. Good food, friendly atmosphere on working dairy farm. Modernised farmhouse. Guests' own lounge. [🐕]
e-mail: miktaylor@farming.co.uk

RIVERSIDE HOTEL, BEEZON ROAD, KENDAL (015397 34861). Lovely riverside location. Best Lakes Breaks from £129 per person for 3 nights. [🐕 pw!]
e-mail: info@riversidekendal.co.uk website: www.bestlakesbreaks.co.uk

MRS HELEN JONES, PRIMROSE COTTAGE, ORTON ROAD, TEBAY CA10 3TL (015396 24791). Adjacent M6 J38 (10 miles north of Kendal). Excellent rural location for North Lakes and Yorkshire Dales. Superb facilities include jacuzzi bath, king and four-poster beds. One acre garden. Self-contained ground floor flat and self-catering bungalow, disabled friendly, also available. Pets welcome, very friendly. National Accessible Scheme Level II. ETC ◆◆◆◆ [🐕]
e-mail: info@primrosecottagecumbria.co.uk website: www.primrosecottagecumbria.co.uk

Keswick

Famous Lake District resort at north end of Derwentwater with Pencil Museum and Cars of the Stars Motor Museum. Carlisle 30 miles, Ambleside 17, Cockermouth 12.

ROYAL OAK HOTEL, BORROWDALE, KESWICK CA12 5XB (017687 77214). Traditional Lakeland hotel with friendly atmosphere. Home cooking, cosy bar, comfortable lounge and some riverside rooms. Winter and Summer discount rates. Brochure and Tariff available. AA ★ Hotel. [🐕]
e-mail: info@royaloakhotel.co.uk website: www.royaloakhotel.co.uk

MR ANDY PETERS, SEYMOUR HOUSE, 36 LAKE ROAD, KESWICK CA12 5DQ (01768 772764; Freephone: 0800 0566401; mobile: 07721 957899). Set in quiet cul-de-sac, short walk to town centre and lake. 10 well appointed rooms, 4 en suite, all with colour TV, tea/coffee, shaver points and central heating. Full English breakfast, vegetarians and special diets catered for. Open Christmas and New Year. [Pets £3 per night.]
e-mail: andy042195@aol.com website: www.seymour-house.com

KESWICK COTTAGES, KENTMERE, HOW LANE, KESWICK CA12 5RS (017687 73895). Cottages and apartments in and around Keswick. Properties are well maintained and clean. From a one bedroom cottage to a four bedroom house. Children and pets welcome. [Pets £10 per week]
e-mail: info@keswickcottages.co.uk website: www.keswickcottages.co.uk

DERWENT WATER MARINA, PORTINSCALE, KESWICK CA12 5RF – Lakeside Studio Apartments. Self catering apartments .Three apartments sleep 2 plus bed settee. one apartment sleeps 4-6. Superb views over the lake and fells. Includes colour TV, heating and bed linen. Non-smoking. (017687 72912) for brochure. [🐕 pw!]
website: www.derwentwatermarina.co.uk

OVERWATER HALL, OVERWATER, NEAR IREBY, KESWICK CA7 1HH (017687 76566). Elegant Country House Hotel in spacious grounds. Dogs very welcome in your room. 4 night mid-week breaks from £280 per person, inclusive of Dinner, Room and Breakfast. Mini breaks also available all year. Award-winning restaurant. See also advertisement on page 159. [pw!, 🐕]
e-mail: welcome@overwaterhall.co.uk website: www.overwaterhall.co.uk

ORCHARD HOUSE, APPLETHWAITE, NEAR KESWICK. Three superb detached family houses two miles from Keswick and Lake Derwentwater. All have large private gardens and fabulous views. Central heating, laundry, freezer, video, etc. One sleeps up to twelve in six bedrooms, the others up to eight in four bedrooms. Pets welcome. Booking and brochure telephone (01946 723319). ETC ★★★ [🐕]
e-mail: holidays@fisherground.co.uk website: www.orchardhouseholidays.co.uk

CRAGSIDE GUEST HOUSE, 39 BLENCATHRA STREET, KESWICK CA12 4HX (Tel & Fax: 017687 73344). Quiet, comfortable guest house close to the centre of Keswick. All rooms en suite, tastefully decorated, centrally heated and have clock radio, colour TV and tea/coffee making facilities. AA ◆◆◆. [🐕]
e-mail: wayne-alison@cragside39blencathra.fsnet.co.uk
website: www.SmoothHound.co.uk/hotels/cragside

Warm, comfortable houses and cottages in Keswick and beautiful Borrowdale, welcoming your dog. Inspected and quality graded. LAKELAND COTTAGE HOLIDAYS, KESWICK CA12 4QX (017687 76065; Fax: 017687 76869). [Pets £15 per week]
e-mail: info@lakelandcottages.co.uk website: www.lakelandcottages.co.uk

COLEDALE INN, BRAITHWAITE, NEAR KESWICK, CUMBRIA CA12 5TN (017687 78272). Friendly, family-run Victorian Inn in peaceful situation. Warm and spacious en suite bedrooms with TV. Children and pets welcome. Open all year. ETC ◆◆◆ [🐕]
website: www.coledale-inn.co.uk

JOE FAGAN, RICKERBY GRANGE, PORTINSCALE, KESWICK CA12 5RH (017687 72344). Delightfully situated in quiet village. Licensed. Imaginative home-cooked food, attractively served. Open all year. ETC/AA ◆◆◆◆ RAC ◆◆◆◆ Sparkling Diamond Award. [Pets £2.50 per night, £15 per week]
e-mail: joe@ricor.co.uk website: www.ricor.co.uk

WOODSIDE, PENRITH ROAD, KESWICK CA12 4LJ (017687 73522). Friendly family-run establishment. All our rooms are en suite. We have ample private parking and large gardens. Non-smoking. Dogs welcome. [charge for pets]
e-mail: ann@pretswell.freeserve.co.uk website: www.woodside.uk.net

MIDTOWN COTTAGES, HIGH LORTON. Two well equipped cottages, both with central heating, furnished to a high standard. All cottages have dishwashers & freezers. Overlooking Fells, at north end of Lorton Vale. Pets welcome. Non- smoking. For details contact MR & MRS BURRELL (01264 710165). ETC ★★★★ [Charge made for pets]
e-mail: info@midtown-cottages.com website: www.midtown-cottages.com

Kirkby-in-Furness

Small coastal village (A595). 10 minutes to Ulverston, Lakes within easy reach. Ideal base for walking and touring.

JANET AND PETER, 1 FRIARS GROUND, KIRKBY-IN-FURNESS LA17 7YB (01229 889601). "Sunset Cottage, self catering 17th century two-bedroom character cottage with garden. Original features. Panoramic views over sea/mountains; Coniston/Windermere 20 minutes. Open all year. [charge for pets]
e-mail: enquiries@southlakes-cottages.com website: www.southlakes-cottages.com

Kirkby Lonsdale

Georgian buildings and quaint cottages. Riverside walks from medieval Devil's Bridge.

MRS PAULINE BAINBRIDGE, TOSSBECK FARM, MIDDLETON, KIRKBY LONSDALE LA6 2LZ (015242 76214). 17th Century Listed farmhouse on a working farm situated in the Lune Valley. B&B from £20. Children and well-behaved pets welcome. Non-smoking. Brochure available. ETC ◆◆◆ [🐕]
e-mail: postmaster@tossbeck.f9.co.uk website: www.tossbeck.co.uk

Kirkby Stephen

5 miles south on B6259 Kirkby Stephen to Hawes road.

COCKLAKE HOUSE, MALLERSTANG CA17 4JT (017683 72080). Charming, High Pennine Country House B&B in unique position above Pendragon Castle in Upper Mallerstang Dale offering good food and exceptional comfort to a small number of guests. Two double rooms with large private bathrooms. Three acres riverside grounds. Dogs welcome.

Kirkoswald

Village in the Cumbrian hills, lying north west of the Lake District. Ideal for touring. Penrith 7 miles.

SECLUDED COTTAGES WITH PRIVATE FISHING, KIRKOSWALD CA10 1EU (24 hour brochure line 01768 898711, manned most Saturdays). Quality cottages, clean, well equipped and maintained. Centrally located for Lakes, Pennines, Hadrian's Wall, Borderland. Enjoy the Good Life in comfort. Pets' paradise. Guests' coarse fishing. Bookings/enquiries 01768 898711. ETC ★★★ [pw! £2.50 per pet per night, £14 per week].
e-mail: info@crossfieldcottages.co.uk website: www.crossfieldcottages.co.uk

SYMBOLS

- 🐕 **Indicates that pets are welcome free of charge.**
- £ **Indicates that a charge is made for pets: nightly or weekly.**
- pw! **Shows some special provision for pets; exercise facility, feeding or accommodation arrangement.**
- ⌂ **Indicates separate pets accommodation.**

Lake District

North-west corner of England between A6/M6 and the Cumbrian Coast. Fells. valleys and 16 lakes, the largest being Lake Windermere.

BOWNESS LAKELAND HOLIDAYS. Traditional Lakeland cottages, well-equipped and furnished to a high standard, set in Bowness-on-Windermere and the surrounding scenic South Lakes. Ideal setting from which to explore the Lake District. Pets welcome in many properties. Brochure available. Winter Short Breaks. Contact: 131 RADCLIFFE NEW ROAD, WHITEFIELD, MANCHESTER M45 7RP (0161 796 3896; Fax: 0161 272 1841).
e-mail: info@bownesslakelandholidays.co.uk website: www.bownesslakelandholidays.co.uk

Langdale

Dramatic valley area to the west of Ambleside, in the very heart of the National Park.

THE BRITANNIA INN, ELTERWATER, AMBLESIDE LA22 9HP (015394 37210; Fax: 015394 37311). The very picture of a traditional inn, the Britannia overlooks the green in the delightful village of Elterwater in the heart of the Lake District. Home cooked meals and real ales are served in cosy bars with oak beams and log fires. ETC ★★ [🐕]
e-mail: info@britinn.co.uk website: www.britinn.co.uk

Little Langdale

Hamlet 2 miles west of Skelwith Bridge. To west is Little Langdale Tarn, a small lake.

HIGHFOLD COTTAGE, LITTLE LANGDALE. Very comfortable Lakeland cottage, ideally situated for walking and touring. Superb mountain views. Sleeps 5. Personally maintained. Pets welcome. Weekly £210–£375. ETC ★★★. MRS C.E. BLAIR, 8 THE GLEBE, CHAPEL STILE, AMBLESIDE LA22 9JT (015394 37686). [🐕]
website: www.highfieldcottage.co.uk

Maryport

Maryport, a delightful harbourside town boasting a Roman Fort, Georgian buildings and Victorian Docks, has many fascinating links with famous men and historical events.

EAST HOUSE GUEST HOUSE, ALLONBY, MARYPORT CA15 6PJ (01900 881264). Well-equipped two and four bedroomed self-catering cottages. Sleep 2 - 10. In centre of village, close to beach. Open all year.

Mungrisdale

Small village ideal for touring. Keswick 8 miles.

NEAR HOWE HOTEL AND COTTAGES, MUNGRISDALE, PENRITH CA11 0SH (Tel & Fax: 017687 79678). Quiet, away from-it-all. Within easy reach of Lakes, walking. Bar, log fire in cold weather. Five bedrooms en suite. B&B from £21 to £26 per person. ETC ◆◆◆/★★★★ *SELF-CATERING*. [Pets – Hotel £2 per day. Cottages £10 per week.]
e-mail: nearhowe@btopenworld.com website: www.nearhowe.co.uk

Newby Bridge

Village at southern end of Lake Windermere, 8 miles from Ulverston

NEWBY BRIDGE HOTEL, NEWBY BRIDGE LA12 8NA (015395 31222). Overlooking the southern shores of Lake Windermere. Best Lakes Breaks from £129 per person for 3 nights. [🐕 pw!]
e-mail: info@newbybridgehotel.co.uk website: www.bestlakesbreaks.co.uk

PLEASE SEND A STAMPED ADDRESSED ENVELOPE WITH ENQUIRIES

Penrith

Market town and centre for touring Lake District. Of interest are 14th century castle, Gloucester Arms (1477) and Tudor House. Excellent sporting facilities. Windermere 27 miles, Keswick 18.

LYVENNET COTTAGES, THE MILL, KINGS MEABURN, PENRITH CA10 3BU (01931 714661/714226; Fax: 01931 714598) Four different cottages in and around the small farming village of Kings Meaburn in beautiful unspoilt 'Lyvennet Valley'. Ideal touring centre for the Lakes and Dales. ETC ★★★/★★★★
website: www.lyvennetcottages.co.uk

SECLUDED COTTAGES WITH PRIVATE FISHING, KIRKOSWALD CA10 1EU (24 hour brochure line 01768 898711, manned most Saturdays). Quality cottages, clean, well equipped and maintained. Centrally located for Lakes, Pennines, Hadrian's Wall, Borderland. Enjoy the Good Life in comfort. Pets' paradise. Guests' coarse fishing. Bookings/enquiries 01768 898711. ETC ★★★ [pw! £2.50 per pet per night, £14 per week].
e-mail: info@crossfieldcottages.co.uk website: www.crossfieldcottages.co.uk

CARROCK COTTAGES. Three recently renovated stone built cottages set on the fringe of the Lakeland Fells. Games room, spa facilities. Home cooked meals service. Ideal for fell walking. Excellent restaurants nearby. A warm welcome guaranteed. ETC ★★★★★ Contact MALCOLM OR GILLIAN (01768 484111; Fax: 01768 488850). [Pets £15 per week].
e-mail: info@carrockcottages.co.uk website: www.carrockcottages.co.uk

Ravenstonedale

Village located between the Lake District and Yorkshire Dales National Park, 4 miles SW of Kirkby Stephen.

MRS D. METCALFE, FELLVIEW, HIGH GREENSIDE, RAVENSTONEDALE, KIRKBY STEPHEN CA17 4LU (015396 23671). At foot of Howgills, 18th century farmhouse. En suite accommodation. Colour TV, tea/coffee facilities, own entrance. Dogs welcome. B&B £21. 3 nights £54.

Silloth-on-Solway

Solway Firth resort with harbour and fine sandy beach. Mountain views. Golf, fishing. Penrith 33 miles, Carlisle 23, Cockermouth 17.

MR AND MRS M.C. BOWMAN, TANGLEWOOD CARAVAN PARK, CAUSEWAY HEAD, SILLOTH CA7 4PE (016973 31253). Friendly country site, excellent toilet and laundry facilities. Tourers welcome or hire a luxury caravan. Telephone or e-mail for a brochure. [🐕]
e-mail: tanglewoodcaravanpark@hotmail.com website: www.tanglewoodcaravanpark.co.uk

Troutbeck

Village north of Lake Windermere, Church has east window by Burne-Jones.

HOLBECK GHYLL LODGE, TROUTBECK. Well-equipped Lakeland stone lodge. Two twin rooms, double room en suite. Dining/livingroom with open fire and sofa bed; dining kitchen; utility room. Ample parking. Available Easter to end October. ETC ★★★★. MRS KAYE, HOLMDENE, STONEY BANK ROAD, HOLMFIRTH HD9 7SL (01484 684605; Fax: 01484 689051). [Pets £10 per week]
e-mail: maggie@holbecklodge.com website: www.holbecklodge.com

Ullswater

Lake stretching for 7 miles with attractive Lakeside walks.

MR & MRS BURNETT, (FELL VIEW HOLIDAYS), FELL VIEW, GLENRIDDING, PENRITH CA11 0PJ (Tel & Fax: 017684 82342; Evenings 01768 867420). Sleep 2-6. Our comfortable well-equipped cottages/apartments/static holiday home have only a field between them and the lake, and have magnificent views of the mountains. Our gardens and grounds are full of birds and flowers which everyone can enjoy. ETC ★★★★ [🐕 pw!]
e-mail: enquiries@fellviewholidays.com website: www.fellviewholidays.com

LAND ENDS CABINS, WATERMILLOCK, NEAR ULLSWATER CA11 0NB (017684 86438). Only one mile from Ullswater, our four detached log cabins have a peaceful fellside location in 25 acre grounds with two pretty lakes. Doggy heaven! Sleep 2-5. [🐕]
e-mail: infolandends@btinternet.com website: www.landends.co.uk

Ulverston

Old town and port with cobbled streets and market square. Laurel and Hardy Museum worth a visit.

LONSDALE HOUSE HOTEL, 11 DALTONGATE, ULVERSTON LA12 7BD (01229 582598). Situated in the heart of Ulverston. Friendly service, great food and comfortable accommodation. Pets welcome. Brochure available. [Pets £2 per night]
website: www.lonsdalehousehotel.co.uk

Whitehaven

A port on the Irish Sea, 7 miles south of Workington. Fine Georgian architecture and historic links with America.

ALVA HOUSE, NEAR MOOR ROW, WHITEHAVEN CA24 3JX (01946 814537; mobile: 07734 948722). Secluded Edwardian family home. On cycling and walking routes. Fell views. Warm welcome. Terms from £18 to £23pppn. Open all year. Non-smoking. Contact: KATHY CUNLIFFE.
e-mail: cunliffek@aol.com website: www.alva-house.com

Windermere

Famous resort on lake of same name, the largest in England. Magnificent scenery. Car ferry from Bowness, one mile distant. Kendal 9 miles.

LOW SPRINGWOOD HOTEL, THORNBARROW ROAD, WINDERMERE LA23 2DF (015394 46383). Millie and Lottie (Boxers) would like to welcome you to their peaceful Hotel in its own secluded gardens. Lovely views of Lakes and Fells. All rooms en suite with colour TV etc. Some four-posters. Brochure available. [🐕 pw!]

WATERMILL INN, INGS, NEAR STAVELEY, KENDAL LA8 9PY (01539 821309; Fax: 01539 822309). Shelly and friends (Dogs) welcome you to the award-winning Inn. 16 real ales. Cosy fires, en suite rooms, excellent bar meals. Doggie water and biscuits served in the bar. Good doorstep dog walking. ETC ◆◆◆. [Pets £2 per night].
e-mail: all@watermillinn.co.uk website: www.watermillinn.co.uk

LANGDALE CHASE HOTEL WINDERMERE LA23 1LW (015394 32201). Magnificent country house hotel on edge of Lake Windermere with panoramic views of lakes and fells. Open log fires, excellent food and friendly service. [🐕]

Hundreds of self-catering holiday homes in a variety of wonderful locations, all well equipped and managed by our caring staff. Pets welcome. Free leisure club membership. For brochure, contact: LAKELOVERS, BELMONT HOUSE, LAKE ROAD, BOWNESS-ON-WINDERMERE LA23 3BJ. (015394 88855; Fax: 015394 88857). ETC ★★★ - ★★★★★ [Pets £15.00 per week.]
e-mail: bookings@lakelovers.co.uk website: www.lakelovers.co.uk

APPLETHWAITE HOUSE, 1 UPPER OAK STREET, WINDERMERE LA23 2LB (015394 44689). A warm welcome, clean, comfortable rooms and a hearty breakfast awaits you in our family-run guest house. Quiet yet convenient location. All rooms have colour TV and complimentary hot drinks. Non-smoking. B&B from £20 per person. Pets stay free. [🐕]
e-mail: info@applethwaitehouse.co.uk website: www.applethwaitehouse.co.uk

THE MORTAL MAN INN, TROUTBECK, WINDERMERE LA23 1PL (015394 33193). Set in beautiful Troutbeck Valley, good food and wine, real ales and a perfect location for walkers of all abilities. B&B from £30 pppn. Dogs go free. ETC ★★, Silver Award for Quality. [🐕]
website: www.themortalman.co.uk

KIRKWOOD GUEST HOUSE, PRINCE'S ROAD, WINDERMERE LA23 2DD. (Tel & Fax: 015394 43907). Situated between Windermere and Bowness. Warm and friendly atmosphere. Large en suite rooms with TV and tea/coffee making facilities. Three-night special breaks. ETC ◆◆◆◆ [🐕]
e-mail: info@kirkwood51.co.uk website:www.kirkwood51.co.uk

Ashbourne

DOG AND PARTRIDGE COUNTRY INN

Swinscoe, Ashbourne DE6 2HS
Tel: 01335 343183

ETC/AA/RAC ★★

Mary and Martin Stelfox welcome you to a family-run 17th century Inn and Motel set in five acres, five miles from Alton Towers and close to Dovedale and Ashbourne. We specialise in family breaks, and special diets and vegetarians are catered for. All rooms have private bathrooms, colour TV, direct-dial telephone, tea-making facilities and baby listening service. Ideal for touring Stoke Potteries, Derbyshire Dales and Staffordshire Moorlands. Open Christmas and New Year. 'Staffs Good Food Winners 2003'.

Restaurant open all day, non-residents welcome.
e-mail: info@dogandpartridge.co.uk website: www.dogandpartridge.co.uk

The Kings at Ivy House

Georgian Grade II Listed Guest House with many original features including log fires, flagstone floors and listed barns. Spectacular views. All rooms en suite with baths. Ideally situated in Peak Park. Superb home-cooked evening meals. Lovely relaxed atmosphere. Non-smoking. Dogs welcome. B&B £38. Dinner £18. Open all year. Winter Breaks available.

Mervyn and Debbie King,
The Kings at Ivy House,
Biggin-by-Hartington, Newhaven,
Buxton, Derbyshire SK17 0DT
Tel: 01298 84709
E-mail: kings.ivyhouse@lineone.net
Web: SmoothHound.co.uk/hotels/kingsivy.html

THE CHARLES COTTON HOTEL

Hartington, Near Buxton SK17 0AL **Tel: 01298 84229 Fax: 01298 84301**
e-mail: info@charlescotton.co.uk
Website: www.charlescotton.co.uk

ETC ★★

The Charles Cotton is a small comfortable hotel in the heart of the Derbyshire Dales, pleasantly situated in the village square of Hartington, with nearby shops catering for all needs. It is renowned throughout the area for its hospitality and good home cooking. Pets and children are welcome; special diets catered for. The Charles Cotton makes the perfect centre to relax and explore the area, whether walking, cycling, brass rubbing, pony trekking or even hang-gliding. Open Christmas and New Year.

A useful Index of Towns/Villages and Counties appears on page 426 – please also refer to Contents Page 3.

PEAK COTTAGES (0114 262 0777). Quality self-catering accommodation in the Derbyshire Dales and Peaks. Whether you are a walker, climber, potholer, antiquarian, historian, naturalist, gardener or sportsman – Derbyshire has it all. Pets Welcome. Telephone for colour brochure.
website: www.peakcottages.com

Ashbourne

Market town on River Henmore, close to its junction with River Dove. Several interesting old buildings. Birmingham 42 miles, Nottingham 29, Derby 13.

HOLLY MEADOW FARM, BRADLEY, ASHBOURNE DE6 1PN (01335 370261). Comfortable en suite Bed and Breakfast on working farm. Close to Peak District and Dovedale. Views, quiet location, birds and wildlife. Ideal walking and touring. ETC ◆◆◆◆ [🐕].
e-mail: babette_lawton@yahoo.com website: www.hollymeadowbandb.freeserve.co.uk

TONY AND LINDA STODDART, CORNPARK COTTAGE, LEEK ROAD, UPPER MAYFIELD, NEAR ASHBOURNE DE6 2HR (Tel & Fax: 01335 345041). Self-catering open-plan barn conversion. Overlooking the hills of Dovedale. Large garden, tennis court, fishable pond, surrounded by fields. Sleeps up to 4 (plus well-behaved pets). Open all year, prices from £160-£290 per week.
e-mail: linda@accommodationcornpark.com website: www.selfcateringcornpark.com

DERBYSHIRE COTTAGES. In the grounds of a 17th century Inn, close to Peak District, Alton Towers and Ashbourne. Each has own patio, fully fitted kitchen, colour TV. Children and pets welcome. Phone MARY (01335 300202) for further details. [pw! 🐕]
website: www.dogandpartridge.co.uk

MRS M.A. RICHARDSON, THROWLEY HALL FARM, ILAM, ASHBOURNE DE6 2BB (01538 308202/ 308243). Self-catering accommodation in farmhouse for up to 12 and cottage for seven people. Also Bed and Breakfast in farmhouse. Central heating, en suite rooms, TV, tea/coffee facilities in rooms. No smoking. Children and pets welcome. Near Alton Towers and stately homes. ETC ★★★/★★★★ *SELF-CATERING*, ETC ◆◆◆◆. [🐕]

MRS M.M. STELFOX, DOG AND PARTRIDGE COUNTRY INN, SWINSCOE, ASHBOURNE DE6 2HS (01335 343183). 17th century Inn offering ideal holiday accommodation. Many leisure activities available. All bedrooms with washbasins, colour TV, telephone and private facilities. ETC/AA/RAC ★★[🐕, pw!]
e-mail: info@dogandpartridge.co.uk website: www.dogandpartridge.co.uk

Biggin

Situated 8 miles north of Ashbourne.

THE KINGS AT IVY HOUSE, BIGGIN-BY-HARTINGTON, NEWHAVEN, BUXTON SK17 0DT (01298 84709). Georgian Grade II Listed Guest House with many original features. Spectacular views. All rooms en suite with baths. B&B £38, Dinner £18. Open all year. Dogs welcome. ETC ◆◆◆◆◆ and Gold Award. [🐕]
e-mail: kings.ivyhouse@lineone.net website: www.SmoothHound.co.uk/hotels/kingsivy.html

Buxton

Well-known spa and centre for the Peak District. Beautiful scenery and good sporting amenities. Leeds 50 miles, Matlock 20, Macclesfield 12.

THE CHARLES COTTON HOTEL, HARTINGTON, NEAR BUXTON SK17 0AL (01298 84229; Fax: 01298 84301). Small hotel. Good home cooking and hospitality. In heart of Derbyshire Dales. Special diets catered for. Ideal for relaxing, walking, cycling, hang-gliding. ETC ★★[🐕]
e-mail: info@charlescotton.co.uk website: www.charlescotton.co.uk

THE DEVONSHIRE ARMS, PEAK FOREST, NEAR BUXTON SK17 8EJ (01298 23875) Situated in a village location in the heart of the Peak District. All rooms en suite with tea/coffee and colour TV. Meals served every day. Excellent walking area. ETC ◆◆◆ [🐕]
website: www.devarms.com

PRIORY LEA HOLIDAY FLATS. Close to Poole's Cavern Country Park. Fully equipped. Sleep 2/6. Cleanliness assured. Terms from £90-£255. Open all year. Short Breaks available. ETC ★★/★★★. MRS GILL TAYLOR, 50 WHITE KNOWLE ROAD, BUXTON SK17 9NH (01298 23737). [pw! Pets £1 per night.]

Peak District National Park

A green and unspoilt area at the southern end of the Pennines, covering 555 square miles.

SHEFFIELD/HATHERSAGE. Sleeps 4. Well-equipped converted barn, fenced garden, in open countryside, ideal for Peak Park and Sheffield. For brochure phone 0114 2301949. ETC ★★★★. [Pets £10 per week].

WHEELDON TREES FARM, EARL STERNDALE, BUXTON SK17 0AA (Tel & Fax: 01298 83219). Sleep 2-6. 18th century bar conversion offers seven cosy self-catering holiday cottages. Laundry, payphone and games room. ETC ★★★★ [ ]

BIGGIN HALL, PEAK PARK (01298 84451). Close Dove Dale. 17th century hall sympathetically restored. Bathrooms en suite, log fires, C/H comfort, warmth and quiet. Fresh home cooking. Beautiful uncrowded footpaths. Brochure on request. ETC ★★
website: www.bigginhall.co.uk

DALES HOLIDAY COTTAGES now offer a range of superb, personally inspected holiday properties, in beautiful rural locations within the Peak District and Derbyshire Dales. Cosy cottages, many welcome pets, and short breaks are available. FREE brochure. DALES HOLIDAY COTTAGES, CARLETON BUSINESS PARK, SKIPTON, NORTH YORKSHIRE BD23 2AA (0870 909 9500).
website: www.dales-holiday-cottages.com

Wirksworth

An ancient Saxon town, once the principle lead mining centre of the Peak District, 4 miles south of Matlock.

HOG COTTAGE, DERBYSHIRE. South-facing stone cottage offering Pure Luxury. Overlooking historic market town of Wirkworth. Welcome pack. Bedding/towels, electricity/gas central heating all included in the price. Contact: ANNA FERN (07714 230117). [Pets £10 per week]
e-mail: hogcottage@bluelagoon.co.uk website: www.bluelagoon.co.uk

See also Colour Advertisement on page 27

See also Colour Advertisement on page 24

See also Colour Advertisement on page 24

Parkers Farm Holiday Park

Come and stay on a real 400-acre farm in South Devon

FARM COTTAGES • CARAVANS • TOURING SITE

All very clean, with 2 fully tiled toilet/shower blocks (no meters). Electric hook-ups. Views across Dartmoor, 12 miles Torquay; central for touring Devon and Cornwall. Terms from £90 Low Season to £480 High Season. Discounts for couples. Small shop, family bar and restaurant takeaway main season. Games room, laundry, pay phone, etc.

How to find us from Exeter: Take A38 to Plymouth. When you see the sign "26 miles Plymouth", take the second left at Alston Cross signposted to Woodland and Denbury

British Farm Tourist Award, AA Four Pennants, 2004 Gold Award for Quality and Service, Silver David Bellamy Conservation Award, Practical Caravan 2004 Top 100 Parks, Rose Award 2005. ETC ★★★★

HIGHER MEAD FARM, ASHBURTON, NEWTON ABBOT, DEVON TQ13 7LJ
Tel: (01364 652598) • Fax: (01364 654004)
e-mail: parkersfarm@btconnect.com • website: www.parkersfarm.co.uk

---

ETC ★★★ - ★★★★

Mrs Angela Bell
Wooder Manor, Widecombe in the Moor,
Near Ashburton TQ13 7TR
Tel & Fax: (01364) 621391

website: www.woodermanor.com
e-mail: angela@woodermanor.com

Cottages and converted coach house on 160-acre working family farm nestled in the picturesque valley of Widecombe, surrounded by unspoilt woodland moors and granite tors. Half-a-mile from village with post office, general stores, two good pubs (dogs welcome) and National Trust Information Centre. Excellent centre for touring Devon with a variety of places to visit and exploring Dartmoor by foot or on horseback. Accommodation is clean and well-equipped with colour TV, central heating, laundry room. Children welcome. Large gardens and courtyard for easy parking. Open all year, so take advantage of off-season reduced rates. Short Breaks available. Two properties suitable for disabled visitors. Colour Brochure.

Blagdon Manor Hotel and Restaurant

Ashwater, North Devon
EX21 5DF

Tel: 01409 211224
Fax: 01409 211634

Restaurant

Enjoy excellent cuisine using locally sourced produce. Dinner available every night for residents. 2 courses - £21, 3 courses - £25.

Accommodation

7 en suite bedrooms. Panoramic views of the Devon countryside and Dartmoor. A beautifully restored Grade II Listed building, enjoys a peaceful location halfway between Dartmoor and Exmoor and only 20 minutes from the North Cornish coast at Bude. 3 Acres of Gardens and 17 acres of fields. Dogs Welcome. Children over the age of 12. Double/twin rooms are £100 per night, based on 2 people sharing, inclusive of full English breakfast. Single occupancy £72. We make a small charge of £5 per night for dogs.

Liz and Steve along with our 2 chocolate Labradors, Nutmeg and Cassia, look forward to welcoming you to Blagdon Manor.

86% **Website: www.blagdon.com • Email: stay@blagdon.com**

See also Colour Advertisement on page 34

"Easily the best choice of cottages in Devon... ...and comfortably the best value."

Contact us now for a free colour guide and unbiased recommendation service to the best value pet friendly cottages around Exmoor and Devon's unspoilt National Trust Coast.

North Devon Holiday Homes

19 Cross Street, Barnstaple EX31 1BD
Tel:(01271) 376322 (24 hrs) Fax:(01271) 346544
E-mail: info@northdevonholidays.co.uk
Website: www.northdevonholidays.co.uk

See also Colour Advertisement on page 29

MRS V.M. CHUGG **VALLEY VIEW** TEL: 01271 343458

Guineaford, Marwood, Near Barnstaple, Devon EX1 4EA

Friendly Bed and Breakfast accommodation in bungalow situated on 300-acre farm. Near Marwood Hill Gardens and Arlington Court. Colour television and video. Children most welcome, free babysitting. Evening Meal available if required. Bedtime drink at no extra charge. Open all year round. Dogs by arrangement.

Terms from £16.

YOUR PET STAYS FREE

Sandy Cove Hotel stands in 20 acres of cliff, coast and garden. The Hotel Restaurant overlooks the sea and cliffs with spectacular views of the bay. You will probably wonder how we can do it for the price when we offer a FIVE-COURSE MEAL including seafood platters with lobster, smoked salmon and steak. Every Saturday a Swedish Smorgasbord and Carvery carved by the Chef, and followed by dancing till late. Live entertainment weekly from Whitsun until September. All bedrooms have colour TV, telephone, tea making and are en suite. The cocktail bar overlooks the bay and you have the use of the hotel's 80º heated indoor pool and recreation centre with sauna, sunbed, gym equipment and whirlpool, ALL FREE OF CHARGE.

Please return this advertisement to qualify for "Pets Stay Free" offer. Bargain Breaks and weekly rates available all year. Includes 5-course Evening Meal and coffee. Children— free accommodation. Please send for free brochure pack. Children under 5 years completely free, including meals.

Indoor pool heated to 80ºF with roll-back sides to enjoy the sun

Sandy Cove Hotel
Combe Martin Bay, Devon, EX34 9SR
Tel: (01271) 882243 & 882888
e-mail: rg14003483@aol.com

ETC ★★★

See also Colour Advertisement on page 31

FREE or REDUCED RATE entry to Holiday Visits and Attractions — see our READERS' OFFER VOUCHERS on pages 101-116

A Georgian country house set in 7 hilltop acres with magnificent views over the Torridge estuary to Lundy Island. Log-fires, king-size beds, garden room bar with library, maps and a warm welcome await our guests.

Breakfasts use home produced and prize-winning locally sourced ingredients. There are ground floor rooms set around the courtyard garden with easy access. All rooms are en suite and have teletext television, well-stocked hospitality tray with tea and coffee making facilities, telephones and hairdryers.

Selected by the AA as "One of Britain's Best in 2004."

Bed & Breakfast from £32. Self-catering from £229 for 4. No Smoking.

website: www.thepinesateastleigh.co.uk
e-mail: pirrie@thepinesateastleigh.co.uk

The Pines at Eastleigh

Hotel & Cottages
Eastleigh, Near Bideford,
North Devon EX39 4PA
Tel: 01271 860561

AA 

Waterside Cottage Bideford, Devon

Waterside Cottage is a pretty cottage right on the tidal River Torridge with glorious unrestricted views over the river and with moorings for a boat. Back garden wall is on the riverside, and from the garden and cottage you can watch boats coming or going, or fish. Enclosed garden with garden furniture.

• Two bedrooms • Private parking • Dogs welcome • On the Coastal Path – ideal for walking.

SAE please for colour brochure with details of this and other seafront cottages to P.W. Barnes, 140 Bay View Road, Bideford EX39 1BJ or telephone 01237 473801 for prices and vacancies, or visit our website www.seabirdcottages.co.uk

MIDSHIPS, Instow, Bideford

Tel: 01271 861146

A comfortable cottage, less than 50 yards from the sandy, estuary beach. 'Midships' sleeps up to five, with gas central heating, colour TV, washing machine, dryer and fridge/freezer and a small walled courtyard with flower tubs at the back. The Tarka trail runs through Instow and there is cycling, sailing and walking, plus boat trips to Lundy Island. The village has good restaurants and pubs for meals out, a small Post Office and village shop. The market towns of Bideford and Barnstaple are within easy reach for cinema and leisure centre etc. Modern cottage, sleeps 5, also available nearby. Contact: **Mrs M. Baxter, Panorama, Millards Hill, Instow, Bideford EX39 4JS.**

Lake House Cottages and B&B

North Devon/Cornwall Border

Lake Villa, Bradworthy, Devon EX22 7SQ

ETC ★★★

Come and stay in one of four cosy, character cottages in peaceful countryside, half-a-mile from Bradworthy village square in this hidden corner of Devon. Perfectly situated to explore the spectacular coastline of North Devon and Cornwall as well as the West Country moors. There are also several gardens within reach (Rosemoor, Eden Project) and other places of interest. The cottages sleep five/six, four, three and two and are well furnished and fitted with everything you will need for a great cottage holiday for you and your pet. There are also two en suite B&B rooms available, with balcony, in our own home. Tennis court and gardens.

Brochure: Peter & Lesley Lewin on 01409 241962 • e-mail: info@lakevilla.co.uk • website: www.lakevilla.co.uk

A HAVEN OF PEACE AND TRANQUILLITY

At Little Comfort Farm, Braunton, North Devon ETC★★★

Five spacious self-catering cottages with secluded gardens on organic family farm. Just minutes from golden sandy beaches where dogs are allowed. Well-stocked coarse fishing lake. Private 1½ km walk. Wood fires for cosy winter breaks. Pets very welcome. Tel: 01271 812 414 Fax: 01271 817 975

E-mail: jackie.milsom@btclick.com **www.littlecomfortfarm.co.uk**

Devoncourt is a development of 24 self-contained flats, occupying one of the finest positions in Torbay, with unsurpassed views. At night the lights of Torbay are like a fairyland to be enjoyed from your very own balcony. EACH FLAT HAS:

Marina views	**Heating**	**Sea Views over Torbay**
Private balcony	**Own front door**	**Separate bathroom and toilet**
Separate bedroom	**Bed-settee in lounge**	**Lounge sea views over Marina**
Kitchenette - all electric	**Private car park**	**Opposite beach**
Colour television	**Overlooks lifeboat**	**Short walk to town centre**
Double glazing	**Open all year**	**Mini Breaks October to April**

DEVONCOURT HOLIDAY FLATS
BERRYHEAD ROAD, BRIXHAM, DEVON TQ5 9AB
Tel: 01803 853748 (or 07050 853748 after office hours)
website: www.devoncourt.net

Woodlands Guest House

Parkham Road, Brixham, South Devon TQ5 9BU.

Overlooking the beautiful Brixham Harbour and Torbay - The English Riviera.

Dogs most welcome – free of charge • Your dogs sleep with you in your bedroom • Near dog-friendly parks and beaches • Bedrooms en suite • All bedrooms with colour TV, tea/coffee making facilities, mini-fridge etc. • Fantastic panoramic views over Brixham, Harbour, Marina, the Sea and Torbay • Ideal holiday base from which to explore Glorious South Devon • Car park within grounds and unrestricted on-road parking outside.

BED & 4-COURSE BREAKFAST WITH CHOICE OF MENU - EN SUITE ROOMS - ONE NIGHT FROM ONLY £24 TO £30 PER PERSON INCLUSIVE - REDUCTIONS FOR LONGER STAYS. PHONE 01803 852040 OR FAX 01803 850011 PAUL OR RITA POPE FOR FREE COLOUR BROCHURE.

e-mail: woodlandsbrixham@btinternet.com • website: www.dogfriendlyguesthouse.co.uk

---

Please mention ***PETS WELCOME*** when making enquiries about accommodation featured in these pages.

SNAPDOWN FARM CARAVANS

Chittlehamholt, Umberleigh, North Devon EX37 9PF (01769) 540708

6 ONLY – 6 berth CARAVANS with all facilities in beautiful, peaceful, unspoilt country setting - down our quiet lane, on the farm, well away from busy roads. Each with outside seats and picnic table. Field and woodland walks, abundant wildlife, help feed and milk the goats. Easy reach sea and moors. Well behaved pets welcome. **£110 to £290 per caravan per week inc. gas and electricity in caravans. Illustrated brochure available. (Discount for couples early/late season.)**

Northcott Barton Farm Cottage ETC ★★★★

Beautifully equipped, spotlessly clean three bedroom cottage with large enclosed garden. A walker's and country lover's ideal: for a couple seeking peace and quiet or a family holiday. Very special rates for low season holidays, couples and short breaks. Near golf, riding, Tarka trail and R.H.S. Rosemoor. Character, comfort, beams, log fire, *"Perfick"*. Pets Welcome, no charge. **For availability please contact Sandra Gay, Northcott Barton, Ashreigney, Chulmleigh, Devon EX18 7PR • Tel/Fax: 01769 520259 • e-mail: sandra@northcottbarton.co.uk • website: www.northcottbarton.co.uk**

See also Colour Advertisement on page 26

Graded ★★★★

MANLEIGH HOLIDAY PARK

COMBE MARTIN EX34 0NS (01271 883353)

Quiet family-run site set in beautiful countryside near village, beaches, rocky coves and Exmoor. Chalets and caravans for hire. Swimming pool, children's play area, laundry. Scenic dog walk. **New for 2005** - bistro serving delicious home-made food.

Colour Brochure: L Whitney

www.manleighholidaypark.co.uk

YEATHERIDGE FARM CARAVAN PARK ETC ★★★★

Geoffrey and Elizabeth Hosegood • East Worlington, Crediton EX17 4TN

***Telephone:* 01884 860330 • *Website:* www.yeatheridge.co.uk**

We are a small central park with panoramic views on a genuine working farm with plenty of animals to see! We also offer peace and space with freedom to roam the farm with its woodland walks, coarse fishing lake, indoor heated swimming pools with 200ft water flume, TV lounge, children's play area, hot and cold showers, wash cubicles - ALL FREE. A welcome for dogs. Other amenities include horse riding from the park, electric hook-up points, campers' dish washing, laundry room, shop with frozen food, fresh dairy products, ice pack service. Summer parking in our storage area to save towing. Ideally situated for touring coast, Exmoor and Dartmoor. Golf and tennis locally. Four caravans for letting.

Write, or phone for FREE colour brochure.

Oburnford Farm **Cullompton, Devon EX15 1LZ**

Mrs Margaret Chumbley Tel & Fax: 01884 32292

e-mail: margaretchumbley@amserve.com

Treat yourself to a "special break" and enjoy our welcoming friendly family atmosphere. Listed Georgian Farmhouse set in large gardens. Pets most welcome. Ideal National Trust, coasts, moors and M5 (J28). *Bed and Breakfast with Evening meals and "Free Wine" £32 per night.*

FOREST GLADE Caravan & Camping Park

A small country estate surrounded by forest in which deer roam.
Situated in an area of outstanding natural beauty.
Large, flat, sheltered camping/touring pitches. Modern facilities building, luxury 2/6 berth full service holiday homes, also self contained flat for 2 persons.
Colour brochure on request.

FREE Indoor Heated Pool

AA DELUXE

FOREST GLADE HOLIDAY PARK (PW), CULLOMPTON, DEVON EX15 2DT

Motor caravans welcome - Facilities for the disabled. Dogs welcome. Tourers please book in advance. ETC ★★★★

Tel: 01404 841381 (Evenings to 8pm) Fax: 01404 841593; E-mail: enquiries@forest-glade.co.uk; Website: www.forest-glade.co.uk

See also Colour Advertisement on page 34

PRINCE HALL *Hotel*

The Country House Hotel in the Heart of Dartmoor

Tel: 01822 890403
Fax: 01822 890676

near Two Bridges
Dartmoor
Devon PL20 6SA

Enter the impressive double-door porch of Prince Hall Hotel and you enter a countryside cocoon of comfort, relaxation and tranquillity complemented by superb cuisine and wines. Well-behaved dogs are assured of a wagging-tail reception from resident black Labrador, Bosun, and are allowed in all public rooms except the restaurant.

The nine en suite bedrooms and public areas are spacious and elegant, furnished in true country house style. Exposed beams, original fireplaces and four-poster beds are some of the many above-average features of this hotel. Views over the moorlands and the West Dart River are magnificent, and even the most laid-back will probably feel the urge to take a short walk; your canine companions will most likely encourage you to go further...

In the AA rosetted restaurant innovative menus focusing on local ingredients are freshly prepared and beautifully presented; an extensive cross-section of New World and classic wines makes up the interesting wine list.

Walking, fishing, riding, golf or shooting – these country sports and activities are all within easy, if not immediate, reach of the hotel. Although situated in the heart of Dartmoor, Prince Hall Hotel is the perfect starting point to partake of the West Country's other many and varied attractions.

e-mail: bosun@princehall.co.uk
website: www.princehall.co.uk

Recommended by Best Loved Hotels,
The Good Hotel Guide,
VisitBritain, Which? Hotel Guide,
The Good Britain Guide and others

WELL-BEHAVED DOGS ARE GENUINELY WELCOMED

See also Colour Advertisement on page 32

Apartments at Dartmouth, Devon

Comfortable holiday apartments with private balconies – superb river and harbour views. Sailing, boating, fishing, coastal walks within easy reach. Available all year round with colour TV, linen and parking. From £105 per week.

SAE or phone for FREE colour brochure

RIVERSIDE COURT, SOUTH EMBANKMENT, DARTMOUTH TQ6 9BH

Tel: 01803 832093 • Fax: 01803 835135 • Website: www.dartsideholidays.com

Watermill Cottages, *Hansel, Dartmouth TQ6 0LN*

Comfortable, well equipped, stone cottages in peaceful riverside setting. Wonderful walks in and around our idyllic valley near dog-friendly Slapton Sands and coastal path. Sleep 3-6. Wood fires. Winter Breaks from £95.

Brochure: 01803 770219 or e-mail: graham@hanselpg.freeserve.co.uk
Pam and Graham Spittle **website: www.watermillcottages.co.uk**

See also Colour Advertisement on page 24

Torcross Apartments Situated directly on the beach in the unspoilt countryside of the South Hams between the blue waters of Start Bay and the Slapton Ley Nature Reserve. Seven miles to Dartmouth. Central heating. Ground floor apartments and lift to all floors. Half-price Breaks. In-house bar, restaurant, private car park. Lovely walks.

Visit our **website: www.torcross.com** **e-mail: enquiries@torcross.com**

Torcross, South Devon TQ7 2TQ. Tel: 01548 580206 Fax: 01548 580996

see also colour advertisement on page 30

Green Tourism Bronze Award

The Old Bakehouse

ETC ★★★/★★★★

Mrs S.R. Ridalls, 7 Broadstone, Dartmouth TQ6 9NR • Tel & Fax: 01803 834585

Character cottages with beams and old stone fireplaces, one with four-poster bed. In conservation area, 2 minutes from historic town centre and river. Blackpool Sands 15 minute drive. Free parking. Open all year.

Autumn/Winter/Spring breaks • website: www.oldbakehousedartmouth.co.uk • e-mail: gparker@pioneer.ps.co.uk

THE ROYAL OAK INN

Dunsford, Near Exeter EX6 7DA

Tel: 01647 252256

Enjoy a friendly welcome in our traditional Country Pub in the picturesque thatched village of Dunsford. Quiet en suite bedrooms are available in the tastefully converted cob barn. Ideal base for touring Dartmoor, Exeter and the coast, and the beautiful Teign Valley. Real Ale and home-made meals are served. Well-behaved children and dogs are welcome.

Please ring Mark or Judy Harrison for further details.

ETC ★★★

The Lord Haldon Country House Hotel

AA ★★★

Dunchideock, Near Exeter, Devon EX6 7YF • Tel: 01392 832483 • Fax: 01392 833765

Extensive gardens amid miles of rolling Devon countryside.

e-mail: enquiries@lordhaldonhotel.co.uk website: www.lordhaldonhotel.co.uk

See also Colour Advertisement on page 30

Comfort for country lovers in Exmoor National Park. All rooms en suite with TV. Meals prepared with local and some organic produce. Stabling £50 per week. Dogs no charge.

B&B £24–£32, DB&B £42–£50 **ETC ◆◆◆◆**

Jaye Jones & Helen Asher, Twitchen Farm, Challacombe, Barnstaple EX31 4TT

Telephone 01598 763568 E-mail: holidays@twitchen.co.uk Website: www.twitchen.co.uk

Stag Hunters Hotel

Brendon, Exmoor EX35 6PS

Family-run village inn with frontage to the East Lyn river, set in four acres of garden and paddock. Accommodation available in 12 en suite bedrooms with central heating, TV and tea/coffee making facilities. Meals are available in the bar and restaurant using fresh local produce; vegetarian dishes served. This cosy hotel features log fires, fine wines and traditional ales. Fishing, shooting and riding available; own stables. Ample car parking. Open all year. Terms on request.

Tel: 01598 741222
Fax: 01598 741352

E-mail: enquiries@staghunters.fsnet.co.uk • website: www.staghunters.com

Somewhere Different, Somewhere Special!
2004 A Rural Retreat of the Year.
The Which? Good Hotel Guide.

- Grade 1 Elizabethan Manor set in 3,500 acres of rolling countryside
- Fabulous food, generous hospitality and 15 individual rooms
- Attractive special mid-week rates • Just off A303/A30
- Explore the pretty thatched Devon village of Gittisham
- Discover miles of Jurassic Coastline – Sidmouth to Lyme Regis

Visitors welcome for Lunch or Dinner.

Combe House Hotel and Restaurant

Gittisham, Honiton, Nr EXETER, Devon, EX14 3AD

Tel: 01404 540 400 • Fax: 01404 46004

e-mail: stay@thishotel.com • www.thishotel.com

COMBE HOUSE
HOTEL & RESTAURANT

THE FOREST INN

Hexworthy, Dartmoor PL20 6SD

A haven for walkers, riders, fishermen, canoeists or anyone just looking for an opportunity to enjoy the natural beauty of Dartmoor. The restaurant specialises in home-cooked foods using local produce wherever possible. As an alternative, there is an extensive range of snacks which can be enjoyed in the more informal setting of the Huccaby Room. With the emphasis on Devon beers and ciders, you have the opportunity to quench your thirst after the efforts of the day with a drink at the bar or relaxing on the chesterfields in the lounge area, complete with log fire for winter evenings.

Tel: 01364 631211 • Fax: 01364 631515 • e-mail: info@theforestinn.co.uk

RAC SELECTED SITE

Hedley Wood Caravan & Camping Park

Bridgerule (Near Bude), Holsworthy, Devon EX22 7ED Tel: 01288 381404 • Fax: 01288 382011 AA

16 acre woodland family-run site with outstanding views, where you can enjoy a totally relaxing holiday with a laid-back atmosphere, sheltered and open camping areas. Just 10 minutes' drive from the beaches, golf courses, riding stables and shops.On site facilities include: Children's Adventure Areas, Bar, Clubroom, Shop, Laundry, Meals and all amenities. Free Hot Showers/Water. Static caravans for hire. Caravan storage available. Nice dogs/pets are very welcome. Daily kennelling facility. Dog walks/nature trail.

Visit our website: www.hedleywood.co.uk or write or phone for comprehensive brochure

See also Colour Advertisement on page 35

THE CREST

AA ◆◆◆ *Guest Accommodation*

A modern chalet-style house nestling in the picturesque Umborne Valley, an Area of Outstanding Natural Beauty. The guest wing affords complete privacy with large modern en suite bedrooms. Large sun lounge. Double glazed. Lying in two-and-a-half acres of garden. PETS WELCOME.

WILMINGTON, NEAR HONITON. EX14 9JU **TELEPHONE: 01404 831 419**
EMAIL: michael.maltby@btconnect.com **MOBILE: 07967 894670**

HOPE BARTON BARNS

Tel: 01548 561393
www.hopebarton.co.uk

Open All Year

Nestling in its own valley close to the sandy cove, Hope Barton Barns is an exclusive group of 17 stone barns in two courtyards and 3 luxury apartments in the converted farmhouse. Heated indoor pool, sauna, gym, lounge bar, tennis court, trout lake and a children's play barn. We have 35 acres of pastures and streams with sheep, goats, pigs, chickens, ducks and rabbits. Superbly furnished and fully equipped, each cottage is unique, and vary from a studio to four bedrooms, sleeping 2 to 10. Farmhouse meals. Ample parking. Golf, sailing and coastal walking nearby. A perfect setting for family summer holidays, walking in Spring/Autumn or just a "get away from it all" break. Free-range children and well behaved dogs welcome. For full colour brochure please contact: ***Mike or Judy Tromans.***

Hope Cove - Near Salcombe - South Devon - TQ7 3HT

WIDMOUTH FARM

ETC ★★★

Watermouth, Near Ilfracombe, Devon EX34 9RX

Comfortable, well equipped cottages in 35 acres of gardens, pasture, woodland and private beach. Wonderful scenery. Ideal for birdwatching, painting, sea fishing & golf. Dogs welcome. Tel: 01271 863743

E-mail:holiday@widmouthfarmcottages.co.uk • www.widmouthfarmcottages.co.uk

See also Colour Advertisement on page 28

Varley House, Chambercombe Park, Ilfracombe EX34 9QW

Tel: 01271 863927; Fax: 01271 879299; E-mail: info@varleyhouse.co.uk; www.varleyhouse.co.uk

Built at the turn of the 20th century for returning officers from the Boer War, Varley generates a feeling of warmth and relaxation, combined with an enviable position overlooking Hillsborough Nature Reserve. Winding paths lead to the Harbour and several secluded coves. Our attractive, spacious, fully en suite, non-smoking bedrooms all have colour TV, central heating, generous beverage tray, hairdryer and clock radio alarm. Superb food, beautiful surroundings and that special friendly atmosphere so essential to a relaxing holiday. Cosy separate bar. Car Park. Children over 5 years of age. Dogs by arrangement. Bed and Breakfast from £26 per person. Weekly from £175 per person. Dinner available. 4 courses £14.95, 2 courses £10.95.

St Brannocks House

Come and see me sometime!

Hi! I'm Sam the Daxi and my friends can come and stay here ***free***. Look forward to seeing you.

Phone or write to Barbara Clarke

Tel/Fax: 01271 863873

ETC/RAC ★★

email: stbrannocks@aol.com

St Brannocks Road, Ilfracombe EX34 8EQ

www.stbrannockshotel.co.uk

See also Colour Advertisement on page 26

Instow Beach Haven Cottage

Two seafront cottages overlooking the sandy beach. Instow is a quiet yachting village with soft yellow sands and a pretty promenade of shops, old houses, pubs and cafés serving drinks and meals. Beach Haven has extensive beach and sea views from the house and garden, sleeps 5/6, own parking, gas fired central heating, colour TV, washing machine. Lawned garden overlooking sea with terrace and garden furniture. Coastal walks and cycle trails, boat to Lundy Island. Dog welcome. Other sea front cottages available.

Ring 01237 473801 for prices and vacancies only or send SAE for brochure to Mrs P.I. BARNES, 140 Bay View Road, Northam, Bideford, Devon EX39 1BJ or see www.seabirdcottages.co.uk

Dittiscombe Holiday Cottages, South Devon

Perfectly situated to explore the delights of South Devon, Dittiscombe valley is a relaxed and peaceful setting for a holiday any time of the year. Our comfortable stone cottages have private gardens and views. We have our own nature trail and wildlife walks, and there are dog-friendly beaches and coast and country activities nearby.

Visit our website for more information, prices and availability:

www.dittiscombe.co.uk or for a brochure ring: **01548 521272**

Dogs welcome • Woodburners • Open all year • Short Breaks

Dittiscombe Holiday Cottages, Slapton,
Near Kingsbridge, South Devon TQ7 2QF

See also Colour Advertisement on page 37

Relax in a setting so peaceful, you can actually hear the silence!

Comfortable and Unpretentious.

Pets welcome with well-behaved owners.

Beachdown

Comfortable fully-equipped detached cedarwood chalets with parking alongside.
Just 150 yards from the beach and the South West Coastal Path.
Beachdown is located within the beautiful South Hams area of South Devon.
Nestled within a private and level secluded site of over two and a half acres.
A stress busting stay is always on the cards.

••••• ***Short Breaks Available*** •••••

Call Nigel/Gareth for a brochure on 01548 810089 or visit our website.

CHALLABOROUGH BAY, KINGSBRIDGE, SOUTH DEVON TQ7 4JB

Tel: 01548 810089

e-mail: enquiries@beachdown.co.uk • website: www.beachdown.co.uk

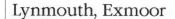

COUNTISBURY LODGE HOTEL

Countisbury Hill, Lynmouth EX35 6NB

AA ♦♦♦♦

www.countisburylodge.co.uk

A former Victorian vicarage with magnificent views over the Lyn Valley and sea.
Extremely quiet and peaceful yet within 5 minutes' walk of the picturesque village of Lynmouth.
Licensed bar. All our bedrooms are centrally heated and en suite.
Private parking. Pets welcome free of charge.

ALSO SELF CATERING COTTAGE AND APARTMENT AVAILABLE

Brochure/Tariff with pleasure from

Pat & Paul Young (01598 752388)

Moorlands Woody Bay, Devon EX31 4RA. Tel: 01598 763224

Two self-contained apartments within a family-run guesthouse sleeping two or three persons. Ground floor: one bedroom, lounge, kitchen and bathroom and has its own entrance and private patio area. First floor: two bedrooms, lounge with screened kitchen and shower room. The house is set in six acres of garden surrounded by Exmoor countryside. Guests are welcome to use all the hotel amenities; bar, dining room and outdoor swimming pool. Dogs welcome with well-behaved owners. Telephone for brochure. www.moorlandshotel.co.uk

See also Colour Advertisement on page 36

Self-contained holiday flat at LYNTON AND LYNMOUTH RAILWAY STATION

Ideal for four in two bedrooms (cot available). Sitting room. Bathroom and separate WC. Kitchen/dining room. Children and pets welcome. £130 to £200 per week.

W. PRYOR, STATION HOUSE, LYNTON, DEVON EX35 6LB • Tel: (01598) 752275 or 752381 • Fax: (01598) 752475

EXMOOR VALLEY

Two delightful genuine modernised XVII Century Cottages by a stream on a 100-acre farm with "ABRS Approved" Riding Stables. Also a Bungalow with fenced garden and panoramic views of Exmoor. All have modernised kitchens, central heating, colour television and video, washing machine, tumble dryers, dishwasher and microwave. Linen available if required. Thoroughly inspected before arrival. Pets welcome at £15 each weekly. Safe for children and pets to play.

Horse riding over Exmoor. Free fishing.

We offer weekend and midweek breaks throughout the year.

www.outovercott.co.uk

Exmoor Sandpiper Inn

Countisbury, Lynmouth, Devon EX35 6NE

01598 741263

e-mail: info@exmoor-sandpiper.co.uk

A romantic Coaching Inn dating in part back to the 13th century. On Exmoor, high above the twin villages of Lynmouth and Lynton, we are surrounded by rolling hills.

We have 16 en suite bedrooms, comfortable sofas in the bar and lounge areas, and five fireplaces, including a 13th century inglenook. Our extensive menus include local game and fish, particularly Lynmouth Lobster; specials are featured daily. Eat a hearty meal or choose from our Lite Bites. Good wines are available by the bottle or the glass.

Stay with us to relax, or to follow one of the seven circular walks through stunning countryside that start from the Inn. Horse riding for experienced riders or complete novices can be arranged. Plenty of parking. Dogs and children, and walkers with muddy boots are very welcome!

There is NO charge for dogs.
Details and brochures on request.

See also Colour Advertisement on page 33

Two self-catering cottages.
(See classified ad under Morchard Bishop)

WEST AISH FARM

Morchard Bishop

Contact:
Caroline & Mark de Souza
for brochure.
Tel: 01363 877427
www.westaishfarm.co.uk

Totally tranquil, with stunning views.
A warm welcome awaits you.

Situated in the pretty village of Mortehoe, The Smugglers offers luxury accommodation from twin rooms to family suites. Treat yourselves and your pets to beautiful coastal walks and golden beaches, before you sample our delicious home cooked meals, real ales and warm, year round hospitality.

The Smugglers, North Morte Road, Mortehoe, N. Devon EX34 7DR Tel/Fax: 01271 870891

Quality en suite accommodation in small, friendly hotel magnificently situated on cliff-side above secluded cove with spectacular sea views. Superb food, well-stocked licensed bar lounge. TV and tea-making facilities in all rooms. Please write or telephone for full details.

LUNDY HOUSE HOTEL

Mortehoe, North Devon EX34 7DZ • Tel: 01271 870372
e-mail: info@lundyhousehotel.co.uk • website: www.lundyhousehotel.co.uk

See also Colour Advertisement on page 34

CROSS HOUSE

Fore Street, Northam,
Bideford EX39 1AN
Tel: 01237 472042
e-mail: cymacassar@eurobell.co.uk

'Come as a guest leave as a friend'. We can offer you three 'Home from Home' cottages, all with 'Olde Worlde' charm and up-to-date amenities. We are ideally situated for touring with Exmoor, Clovelly, Lynton, Lynmouth, Tarka Trail within easy reach. Relax on one of the many beaches, the nearest one mile away. Well-behaved owners welcome!

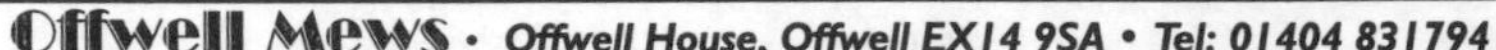

Offwell Mews • ***Offwell House, Offwell EX14 9SA • Tel: 01404 831794***

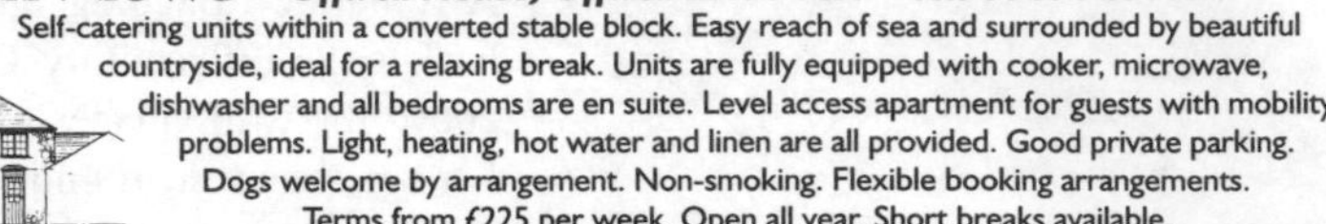

Self-catering units within a converted stable block. Easy reach of sea and surrounded by beautiful countryside, ideal for a relaxing break. Units are fully equipped with cooker, microwave, dishwasher and all bedrooms are en suite. Level access apartment for guests with mobility problems. Light, heating, hot water and linen are all provided. Good private parking. Dogs welcome by arrangement. Non-smoking. Flexible booking arrangements. Terms from £225 per week. Open all year. Short breaks available.

FLUXTON FARM
Ottery St Mary,
Devon EX11 1RJ

Cat lovers' paradise in charming 16th century farmhouse set in lovely Otter Valley. Two acres of beautiful gardens with pond and stream. Five miles from beach at Sidmouth. All rooms en suite, TV and Teasmaids. Central heating. Peace and quiet. Pets welcome free of charge. Plenty of dog walking space. Brochure available. Terms from: B&B £25 per person per night .

Tel: 01404 812818 **AA ◆◆**

AMBER HOUSE HOTEL ***6 Roundham Road, Paignton TQ4 6EZ***
Lisa & Aaron Linger ***Tel: 01803 558372***

❋ Family-run Hotel. ❋ Colour TV, tea/coffee making facilities. ❋ All en suite.
❋ Ground floor rooms. ❋ Non-smoking. ❋ Good food, highly recommended.
❋ Large car park. ❋ Spacious garden and patio. ❋ Park and beach 5 minutes' walk.
❋ Warm welcome to pets and their families. ❋ B&B from £20 per night. ❋ PETS FREE.

See also Colour Advertisement on page 26

SOUTH DEVON • NEAR TORBAY

Luxury 6-berth all electric caravans new in 2000/2002 and other 4,6 and 8 berths to let. All with toilets and showers. All with electricity, colour TV and fridges. Dogs on lead welcome.

Tourist Board graded park ★★★★.

Launderette, shop and payphone. Also separate area for tourers, motor caravans and tents with modern toilet/shower block with family rooms.
Electric hook-ups and hard standings.

J. & E. BALL, Dept PW, Higher Well Farm Holiday Park
Stoke Gabriel, Totnes, S. Devon TQ9 6RN Tel: 01803 782289

See also Colour Advertisement on page 30

Sand Pebbles Hotel

Sand Pebbles stands in its own grounds with twelve en suite rooms overlooking the sea or countryside with colour televisions, radios and beverage trays. Our lovely restaurant has an enviable reputation for serving superb food. We are just 300 yards from the safe, sandy beaches that Hope Cove is renowned for, and the coastal walks which give some of the most spectacular views in the south west. Hope Cove has a timeless quality all of its own and is one of England's most delightful places to retreat for a short break or a long holiday. There's nowhere else quiet like it. Well behaved children and dogs are welcome. Please call Steve or Lorraine for a brochure.

Sand Pebbles Hotel & Restaurant, Hope Cove, Devon TQ7 3HF Tel: 01548 561673
Website: www.sandpebbleshotel.co.uk

See also Colour Display Advertisement on page 37

The Port Light Hotel, Restaurant & Inn

A totally unique location, set amidst acres of National Trust coastal countryside. Luxury en suite rooms, easy access onto the gardens. Close to secluded sandy cove (dogs permitted) 20 minutes' walk. No charge for pets which are most welcome throughout the hotel and can dine with you. *Sean & Hazel Hassall.*

Port Light Hotel, Bolberry Down,
Malborough, Near Salcombe, South Devon TQ7 3DY
Tel: (01548) 561384 or (07970) 859992
• info@portlight.co.uk • www.portlight.co.uk

Doggies' Heaven, Walkers' Paradise, Romantics' Dream

We are Really Totally Pet-Friendly

See also Colour Advertisement on page 28

HOPE BARTON BARNS Tel: 01548 561393. An exclusive group of 17 barns & 3 luxury apartments in converted farmhouse. Indoor pool, sauna, gym, lounge bar, tennis court, lake & children's play barn. 35 acres of pastures & streams with sheep, goats, pigs, chickens, ducks & rabbits. Superbly equipped, the accommodation varies from a studio to 4 bedrooms, sleeping 2 - 10. Ample parking. Golf, sailing & coastal walking. Children & well behaved dogs welcome. For colour brochure contact Mike or Judy Tromans.
Hope Cove, Near Salcombe, South Devon TQ7 3HT www.hopebarton.co.uk Open All Year. ★★★★

SALCOMBE HOUSEBOAT HOLIDAYS

SALCOMBE BOAT & MARINE Co. Ltd.
Strand Court, Whitestrand, Devon TQ8 8ET

Relax on Salcombe's beautiful tranquil estuary. Well equipped Houseboats for self catering. Motor boat & rowing dinghy incl. Children & pets very welcome. For our brochure please telephone: 01548 843730

See also Colour Advertisement on page 37

LEIGH FARM SELF-CATERING HOLIDAYS
WESTON, SIDMOUTH, DEVON EX10 0PH

Cottage & Bungalows 150 yards from National Trust Valley leading to Coastal Path & Beach. Lovely cliff-top walks and level walks around nearby Donkey Sanctuary fields.

Contact: Geoff & Gill Davis • Tel: 01395 516065 • Fax: 01395 579582 • e-mail: leigh.farm@virgin.net website: www.streets-ahead.com/leighfarm ETC ★★★★

ETC ★★★★ ***Boswell Farm Cottages***

17th century farmhouse with seven individual cottages, beautifully converted from period farm buildings, each with its enclosed, delightful garden. Idyllic walks in Area of Outstanding Natural Beauty, two miles from beach and World Heritage coastline.

Mr & Mrs B. P. Dillon, Boswell Farm, Sidford, Sidmouth EX10 0PP • Tel &Fax: 01395 514162
e-mail: dillon@boswell-farm.co.uk • website: www.boswell-farm.co.uk

See also Colour Advertisement on page 25

A most attractive, well-equipped, south-facing cottage with large garden, on the edge of the village of Bishop's Nympton, three miles from South Molton.

Ideal holiday centre, easy reach of Exmoor, the coast, sporting activities and places of interest.

- Three bedrooms: one double, one twin-bedded with washbasin and one single.
- Two bathrooms with toilets.

Court Green, Bishop's Nympton, Near South Molton • Sleeps 5

- Sitting and dining rooms, large kitchen. Central heating, electric wood/coal effect fires, TV.

One mile sea trout/trout fishing on River Mole. Well behaved pets welcome. Terms April to October £220 to £240.

Mrs J. Greenwell,
Tregeiriog,
Near Llangollen
LL20 7HU
Tel: 01691 600672

LANGSTONE MANOR HOLIDAY PARK

Peaceful Holiday Park, offering camping, cottages, static caravans. Ideal location outside Tavistock with direct access onto Dartmoor. Bar & evening meals. Games room. Excellent location. AA★★★ ETC ★★★★

Tel & Fax 01822 613371 jane@langstone-manor.co.uk www.langstone-manor.co.uk

---

TAVISTOCK - EDGE OF DARTMOOR Comfortably furnished studio cottage five miles from the market town of Tavistock. Ideal for two. Private walled garden. Pets welcome. Private parking, free coal for open fire. All linen provided. Wonderful walking, riding, fishing country with excellent local pubs. Terms £195 per week.

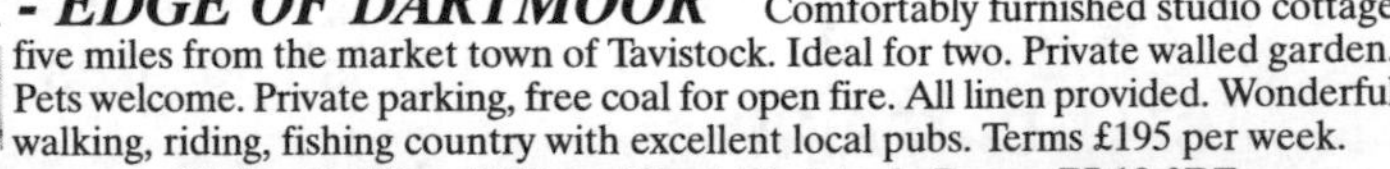

Higher Quither, Milton Abbot, Tavistock, Devon PL19 0PZ
Contact: Mrs P.G.C. Quinton. Tel: 01822 860284.

Cutaway Cottage

Thurlestone, Kingsbridge, Devon TQ7 3NF

Self-catering cottage within fenced garden in the middle of the village, on private road. • 5 minutes to pub & shop.
• 20 minutes to beaches & sea • Ideal for children, dog walkers & bird watchers.

Phone ***Pat*** on 01548 560688

When making enquiries or bookings, a stamped addressed envelope is always appreciated

Red House Hotel & Maxton Lodge Holiday Apartments

Red House Hotel, Rousdown Road, Chelston, Torquay TQ2 6PB
Telephone: 01803 607811; Fax: 01803 605357
E-mail: stay@redhouse-hotel.co.uk Website: www.redhouse-hotel.co.uk

- Serviced or self-catering accommodation available
- Indoor and Outdoor Swimming Pools
- Spa Pool, Sauna, Gym, Indoor Recreation Room
- Beauty Salon and Solarium
- Licensed Bar and Restaurant
- Launderette, parking and garden
- Close to shops, parks and seafront

See also Colour Advertisement on page 36.

Edeswell Farm

Rattery, South Brent TQ10 9LN
Tel: 01364 72177
E-mail: welcome@edeswellfarm.co.uk
Website: www.edeswellfarm.co.uk

Enjoy a peaceful relaxing holiday at this small, friendly family-run park. Set in 23 acres of beautiful countryside near Dartmoor, but within easy reach of the coast, it is an ideal location for families and couples. We have 22 holiday caravan homes and 3 cottages for hire, large indoor heated swimming pool, games room and outdoor play area in the woods; animal and wildlife discovery centre. Coarse and trout fishing next door. Pets welcome.

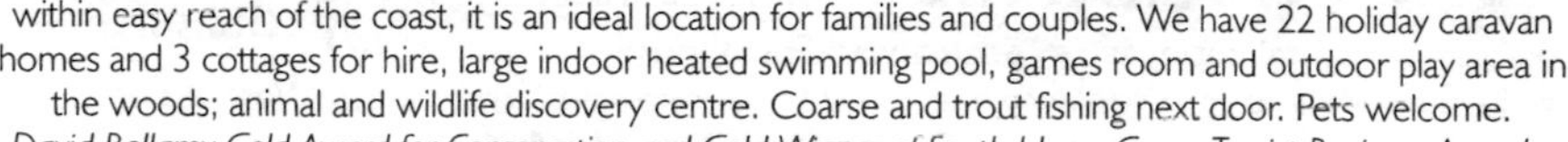

David Bellamy Gold Award for Conservation and Gold Winner of South Hams Green Tourist Business Awards.

"Most people's idea of the ideal Devon Inn"

Staverton, Near Totnes TQ9 6PA
Tel: 01803 762274 • Fax: 01803 762506
website: www.seatroutinn.com

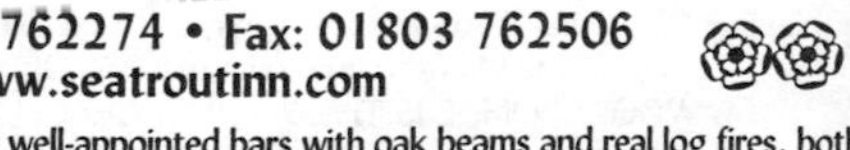

The Inn has two well-appointed bars with oak beams and real log fires, both pleasant places to relax and unwind after a day's walking or touring. 10 bedrooms, delightfully decorated in a comfortable cottage style, have private bathrooms, central heating, direct-dial telephone, tea/coffee making facilities and colour TV. Guests dining in the Hotel may choose from the award-winning restaurant or the relaxing and leisurely atmosphere of the bars or, on warmer summer days, the attractive patio garden. An extensive menu ranges from light snacks to full meals, with vegetarian dishes always available. 'Buster' joins Nick and Nicky in welcoming all pet owners. Bed and Breakfast from £29pppn.

Downe Lodge

Tel & Fax: 01803 812828
info@downelodge.co.uk • www.downelodge.co.uk

Woodland dog walking on doorstep. Cottage available with 1 or 3 bedrooms. Private garden. En suite Bed and Breakfast from £25-£28pppn. Beautiful, quiet position convenient for Dartmoor and the coast.

Broadhempston, Totnes TQ9 6BY **Pets welcome free.**

❖ WEST PUSEHILL FARM COTTAGES ❖ www.wpfcottages.co.uk

Nestling within the Kenwith Valley, our cottages are set along the beautiful North Devon Coast.

◆ 11 cottages, from farm buildings built from traditional local stone in 1854. ◆ 40 ft heated outdoor pool set amongst secluded, sheltered lawns. ◆ Perfectly situated to explore coast and countryside. ◆ Many "award winning" attractions close by. ◆ Pets and children welcome. ◆ Resident proprietors. ◆ Open all year. ◆ Walks, Golf, Riding & Fishing nearby.

West Pusehill Farm, Westward Ho!, North Devon EX39 5AH ◆ Tel: 01237 475638/474622

See also Colour Advertisement on page 36

STATIC VANS, CHALETS & CAMPING

- ★ ***Sauna bath***
- ★ ***Indoor Heated Pool***
- ★ ***Pets welcome***
- ★ ***24-hour shop***

STATION ROAD, WOOLACOMBE, NORTH DEVON
Telephone: Woolacombe (01271) 870159

SUPERB SEA VIEWS

Pebbles Hotel

Family-run Hotel set in National Trust land overlooking the sea and beaches. Glorious coastal walks direct from Hotel. All 6 bedrooms en suite, with TV and tea/coffee making facilities. Write or phone for colour brochure.

COMBESGATE BEACH, WOOLACOMBE
NORTH DEVON EX34 7EA (01271) 870426 • www.pebbleshotel.com

ETC ★

Woolacombe holiday cottages

short breaks • pets special offers

- Quality coastal cottages • Seafront to Farmhouse
- 1 – 5 bedrooms • Woolacombe, Croyde, Georgeham, Willingcott, West Down ...

Tel & Fax: 01271 870846
www.woolacombe-cottages.co.uk • info@woolacombe-cottages.co.uk

See also Colour Advertisement on page 28

Chichester House

The Esplanade, Woolacombe, North Devon EX34 7DJ
HOLIDAY APARTMENTS ON SEA FRONT

Quiet, relaxing, fully furnished apartments. Uninterrupted sea and coastal views. Watch the sun go down into the sea from your own balcony. Open all year. Free parking.

"WOOLACOMBE IS THE 7th BEST BEACH IN THE WORLD" – DAILY MAIL

SAE Resident Proprietor: Mrs Joyce Bagnall **Tel: 01271 870761**

See also Colour Advertisement on page 25

Readers are requested to mention this guidebook when seeking accommodation (and please enclose a stamped addressed envelope).

Sunnymeade Country Hotel

West Down,
Near Woolacombe,
North Devon EX34 8NT

Small, friendly, comfortable country hotel with our own large enclosed garden set in beautiful countryside.

- *A few minutes away from Ilfracombe, Exmoor and Woolacombe's Blue Flag Beach, (where dogs are allowed).*
- *Award-winning home cooked traditional English food, using fresh local produce.*
- *Special diets can be accommodated* • *Vegetarian choice always available*
- *Licensed Bar* • *Deaf accessible* • *10 en suite rooms, 4 on the ground floor.*
- *Open all year including Christmas.*
- *Pets Welcome – dogs are free*
- *Lots of lovely walks accessible right from the door.*

English Tourism Council ◆◆◆ GUEST ACCOMMODATION

Telephone: 01271 863668 • Fax: 01271 866061
website: www.sunnymeade.co.uk

See also Colour Advertisement on page 35

FARM & COTTAGE HOLIDAYS (01237 479698). 500 superb cottages. The widest selection of cottages throughout Devon, Cornwall and Somerset in rural and coastal locations.
website: www.farmcott.co.uk

POWELLS COTTAGE HOLIDAYS, 51 HIGH STREET, SAUNDERSFOOT, PEMBROKESHIRE SA69 9EJ. Many of our top quality holiday properties accept pets. Cottages in Devon, Cornwall, Cotswolds, Pembrokeshire and Heart of England. For colour brochure FREEPHONE 0800 378771 (24 hours). website: www.powells.co.uk

RECOMMENDED COTTAGE HOLIDAYS. 1st choice for dream cottages at very competitive prices in all holiday regions of beautiful Britain. Pets welcome. All properties inspected. For a free brochure call: 08700 718718.
website: www.recommended-cottages.co.uk

HOLIDAY HOMES & COTTAGES S.W, 365A TORQUAY ROAD, PAIGNTON TQ3 2BT (01803 663650; Fax: 01803 664037). Hundreds of Self-Catering Holiday Cottages, Houses, Bungalows, Apartments, Chalets and Caravans in Devon and Cornwall. Please write or phone for free colour brochure.
e-mail: holcotts@aol.com website: www.swcottages.co.uk

TOAD HALL COTTAGES (08700 777345). Over 200 outstanding waterside and rural properties in truly beautiful locations in Devon, Cornwall and Exmoor. Call for our highly acclaimed brochure. Pets welcome.
e-mail: thc@toadhallcottages.com website: www.toadhallcottages.com

MARSDENS COTTAGE HOLIDAYS, DEPT 14, 2 THE SQUARE, BRAUNTON EX33 2JB (01271 813777; Fax: 01271 813664). Experience the charms of a North Devon holiday from the comfort and luxury of a Marsdens holiday cottage. Write or phone today for your free colour brochure. [Pets £15 per week].
e-mail: holidays@marsdens.co.uk website: www.marsdens.co.uk

HELPFUL HOLIDAYS (01647 433535). Wonderful variety of cottages all over the West Country. Ideal for countryside rambles. Many welcome pets.
website: www.helpfulholidays.net

SWEETCOMBE COTTAGE HOLIDAYS, ROSEMARY COTTAGE, WESTON, NEAR SIDMOUTH EX10 0PH (01395 512130; Fax: 01395 515680). Selection of Cottages, Farmhouses and Flats in Sidmouth and East Devon, all personally selected and very well-equipped. Gardens. Pets welcome. Please ask for our colour brochure. [🐕]
e-mail: enquiries@sweetcombe-ch.co.uk website: www.sweetcombe-ch.co.uk

COAST & COUNTRY COTTAGES, CHURCH STREET, SALCOMBE TQ8 8DH (01548 843773). 350 self-catering properties in and around Salcombe and throughout beautiful South Devon, the ideal destination for a holiday or short break with your dog all year round. [Pets £15 per week].
website: www.coastandcountry.co.uk

CLASSIC COTTAGES (01326 565 555). Featuring 500 hand selected coastal and country holiday homes throughout the West Country.
website: www.classic.co.uk

Ashburton

Delightful little town on southern fringe of Dartmoor. Centrally placed for touring and the Torbay resorts. Plymouth 24 miles, Exeter 20, Kingsbridge 20, Tavistock 20, Teignmouth 14, Torquay 14, Totnes 8, Newton Abbot 7.

PARKERS FARM HOLIDAY PARK, HIGHER MEAD FARM, ASHBURTON, NEWTON ABBOT TQ13 7LJ (01364 652598; Fax: 01364 654004). Farm Cottages and Caravans to let, also level touring site with two toilet/shower blocks and electric hook-ups. Central for touring; 12 miles Torquay. ETC ★★★★, AA Four Pennants. [pw! Pets £16 per week]
e-mail: parkersfarm@btconnect.com website: www.parkersfarm.co.uk

MRS A. BELL, WOODER MANOR, WIDECOMBE IN THE MOOR, NEAR ASHBURTON TQ13 7TR (Tel & Fax: 01364 621391). Cottages nestled in picturesque valley. Surrounded by unspoilt woodland and moors. Clean and well equipped, colour TV, central heating, laundry room. Two properties suitable for disabled visitors. Colour brochure available. ETC ★★★ to ★★★★ [pw! £15 per week for first dog]
e-mail: angela@woodermanor.com website: www.woodermanor.com

Ashwater

Village 6 miles south-east of Holsworthy.

BLAGDON MANOR HOTEL AND RESTAURANT, ASHWATER, NORTH DEVON EX21 5DF (01409 211224 Fax: 01409 211634) Beautifully restored Grade II Listed building in peaceful location 20 minutes from Bude. 7 en suite bedrooms, three-acre gardens. No children under 12 years. AA ★★ 86% [pw! Dogs £5 per night]
email: stay@blagdon.com website: www.blagdon.com

Axminster

Small friendly market town, full of old world charm, set in the beautiful Axe Valley. Excellent centre for touring Devon, Somerset and Dorset. 5 miles from coast.

Tranquil location. Wonderful scenery. Close to World Heritage Coast. Eight acres including six hole golf course. Luxuriously appointed rooms. Evening meals by arrangement. AA/ETC ★★★★★. Self-catering cottages also available. LEA HILL, MEMBURY, NEAR AXMINSTER EX13 7AQ (01404 881881; Fax: 01404 881890). [🐕]
e-mail: reception@leahill.co.uk website: www.leahill.co.uk

Barnstaple

The largest town in Devon, once an important centre for the wool trade, now a lively shopping centre with thrice weekly market, modern leisure centre, etc.

NORTH DEVON HOLIDAY HOMES, 19 CROSS STREET, BARNSTAPLE EX31 1BD (01271 376322; Fax: 01271 346544). Free colour guide to the best value pet friendly cottages around Exmoor and Devon's National Trust Coast. [Pets £10 per week.]
e-mail: info@northdevonholidays.co.uk website: www.northdevonholidays.co.uk

MRS V.M. CHUGG, VALLEY VIEW, MARWOOD, BARNSTAPLE EX31 4EA (01271 343458). Bungalow on 300 acre farm. Bed and Breakfast accommodation. Near Marwood Hill Gardens and Arlington Court. Children most welcome, free baby-sitting. Dogs by arrangement. Terms from £16. [pw!]

Berrynarbor

This peaceful village overlooking the beautiful Sterridge valley has a 17th century pub and even older church, and is half-a-mile from the coast road between Combe Martin and Ilfracombe.

SANDY COVE HOTEL, BERRYNARBOR EX34 9SR (01271 882243 or 882888). Hotel set amidst acres of gardens and woods. Heated swimming pool. Children and pets welcome. A la carte restaurant. All rooms en suite with colour TV, tea-making. Free colour brochure on application. ETC ★★★ [🐕 one dog]
e-mail: rg14003483@aol.com

Bideford

Neat port village overlooking the beautiful Sterridge Valley has a 17th century pub and even older church, and is half-a-mile from the coast road between Combe Martin and Ilfracombe.

THE PINES AT EASTLEIGH, NEAR BIDEFORD EX39 4PA (01271 860561). Luxury cottages also B&B. Log-fires, king-size beds, garden room bar with library, maps and a warm welcome await our guests. Children welcome. B&B from £32; Cottages from £229 for 4 persons. No smoking. AA ◆◆◆◆ [pw! 🐕]
e-mail: pirrie@thepinesateastleigh.co.uk website: www.thepinesateastleigh.co.uk

WATERSIDE COTTAGE, BIDEFORD. Pretty cottage right on riverside with moorings for boat. Two bedrooms. Enclosed garden. Private parking. Dogs welcome. For details of this and other seafront cottages contact P.W. BARNES, 140 BAY VIEW ROAD, BIDEFORD EX39 1BJ (01237 473801).
website: www.seabirdcottages.co.uk

MIDSHIPS, INSTOW, BIDFORD (01271 861146). Comfortable cottage, less than 50 yards from beach. Sleeps up to five, with gas central heating, colour TV, washing machine, dryer, fridge/freezer. Bideford and Barnstaple nearby. Modern cottage, sleeps five, also available. MRS M. BAXTER, PANORAMA, MILLARDS HILL, INSTOW, BIDEFORD EX39 4JS. [🐕]

Bigbury-on-Sea

A scattered village overlooking superb coastal scenery and wide expanses of sand.

MR SCARTERFIELD, HENLEY HOTEL, FOLLY HILL, BIGBURY-ON-SEA TQ7 4AR (01548 810240). Edwardian cottage-style hotel, spectacular sea views. Overlooking beach, dog walking. En suite rooms with telephone, tea making, TV etc. Home cooking. No smoking establishment. Licensed. ETC ★★ HOTEL and SILVER AWARD. AA ★★ 72%, GOOD HOTEL GUIDE, CESAR AWARD WINNER 2003, "WHICH?" GUIDE, COASTAL CORKER 2003. [Pets £4.00 per night.]

MRS J. TUCKER, MOUNT FOLLY FARM, BIGBURY-ON-SEA, KINGSBRIDGE TQ7 4AR (01548 810267). Cliff top position, with outstanding views of Bigbury Bay. Spacious, self catering wing of farmhouse, attractively furnished. Farm adjoins golf course and River Avon. Lovely coastal walks, ideal centre for South Hams and Dartmoor. No smoking. Always a warm welcome, pets too! [Pets £15 per week]
website: www.bigburyholidays.co.uk

Bradworthy

Village to the north of Holsworthy. Well placed for North Devon and North Cornish coasts.

PETER & LESLEY LEWIN, LAKE HOUSE COTTAGES AND B&B (01409 241962). Four well equipped cottages sleeping two to five/six. Quiet rural position; one acre gardens and tennis court. Half-a-mile from village shops and pub. Spectacular coast eight miles. Also two lovely en suite B&B rooms, all facilities, from £21. ETC ★★★ [🐕]
e-mail: info@lakevilla.co.uk website: www.lakevilla.co.uk

Braunton

5 miles north west of Barnstaple. To the south west are Braunton Burrows nature reserve, a lunar landscape of sand dunes noted for rare plants, and the 3 mile stretch of Saunton Sands.

LITTLE COMFORT FARM, BRAUNTON, NORTH DEVON EX33 2NJ (01271 812 414; Fax: 01271 817 975). Five spacious self-catering cottages sleeping 2-10 on organic family farm, just minutes from golden sandy beaches where dogs are allowed. Well-stocked coarse fishing lake. Private 1½km farm trail. Wood fires for cosy winter breaks. PETS VERY WELCOME [pw! Pets £18 per week].
e-mail: jackie.milsom@btclick.com website: www.littlecomfortfarm.co.uk

Brixham

Lively resort and fishing port, with quaint houses and narrow winding streets. Ample opportunities for fishing and boat trips.

DEVONCOURT HOLIDAY FLATS, BERRYHEAD ROAD, BRIXHAM TQ5 9AB (01803 853748 or 07050 853748 after office hours). 24 self-contained flats with private balcony, colour television, heating, private car park, all-electric kitchenette, separate bathroom and toilet. Open all year. [Pets £10 per week.]
e-mail: devoncourt@devoncoast.com website: www.devoncoast.info

WOODLANDS GUEST HOUSE. Dogs most welcome free of charge, they sleep with you in your bedroom. Dog-friendly parks and beaches nearby. Rooms en suite with TV, tea/coffee facilities, mini-fridge etc. Overlooking the beautiful Brixham Harbour and Torbay - The English Riviera. Prices range from £24 to £30 pppn. Phone PAUL OR RITA POPE (01803 852040; Fax: 01803 850011) for a brochure. [🐕]
e-mail: woodlandsbrixham@btinternet.com website: www.dogfriendlyguesthouse.co.uk

BRIXHAM HOLIDAY PARK, FISHCOMBE COVE, BRIXHAM TQ5 8RB (01803 853324). Situated on coastal path. Choice of one and two-bedroomed chalets. Indoor heated pool, free club membership, comfortable bar offering meals and takeaway service, launderette. 150 yards from beach with lovely walks through woods beyond. ETC ★★★★. [Pets £30 per week]
e-mail: enquiries@brixhamholpk.fsnet.co.uk website: www.brixhamholidaypark.co.uk

Bude

Popular seaside resort overlooking a wide bay of golden sand and flanked by spectacular cliffs. Ideal for surfing; sea water swimming pool for safe bathing.

HEDLEY WOOD CARAVAN & CAMPING PARK, BRIDGERULE, (NR BUDE), HOLSWORTHY EX22 7ED (01288 381404). 16 acre woodland family-run site; children's adventure areas, bar, clubroom, shop, laundry, meals & all amenities. Static caravans for hire, Caravan Storage available. [pw! 🐕]
website: www.hedleywood .co.uk

Chittlehamholt

Standing in beautiful countryside in the Taw Valley and just off the B3227. Barnstaple 9 miles, South Molton 5.

SNAPDOWN FARM CARAVANS, CHITTLEHAMHOLT, UMBERLEIGH, NORTH DEVON EX37 9PF (01769 540708). 6 only – 6 berth caravans with flush toilets, showers, colour TV, fridges, cookers and fires. Laundry room. Picnic tables. Unspoilt countryside. Field and woodland walks. Terms £110 to £290 per caravan per week inc. gas and electricity in caravans. [Pets £1.50 per night, £8.75 per week.]

Chulmleigh

Mid-Devon village set in lovely countryside, just off A377 Exeter to Barnstaple road. Exeter 23 miles, Tiverton 19, Barnstaple 18.

SANDRA GAY, NORTHCOTT BARTON FARM COTTAGE, NORTHCOTT BARTON, ASHREIGNEY, CHULMLEIGH EX18 7PR (Tel & Fax: 01769 520259). Three bedroom character cottage, large enclosed garden, log fire. Special rates low season, couples and short breaks. Near golf, riding, Tarka Trail and RHS Rosemoor. ETC ★★★★ [🐕]
e-mail: sandra@northcottbarton.co.uk website: www.northcottbarton.co.uk

Combe Martin

Coastal village with harbour set in sandy bay. Good cliff and rock scenery. Of interest is the Church and "Pack of Cards" Inn. Barnstaple 14 miles, Lynton 12, Ilfracombe 6..

WATERMOUTH COVE COTTAGES, WATERMOUTH, NEAR COMBE MARTIN EX34 9SJ (0870 241 3168). Beautiful cottages, most with four-poster and log fire, set in grounds of Watermouth Castle, 200 yards from harbour/coastal path. Pets welcome all year. ETC ★★★ [Pets £20 per week]
e-mail: stay@coastalvalleyhideaways.co.uk website: www.coastalvalleyhideaways.co.uk

MS L. WHITNEY, MANLEIGH HOLIDAY PARK, RECTORY ROAD, COMBE MARTIN EX34 0NS (01271 883353). Quiet family-run site in beautiful countryside near village. Chalets and caravans for hire. Swimming pool, children's play area, laundry. Graded ★★★★. [Pets £3 per night, £18 per week. pw!]
e-mail: info@manleighpark.co.uk website: www.manleighpark.co.uk

Crediton

Ancient small town formerly the seat of the bishops of the South West.

GEOFFREY AND ELIZABETH HOSEGOOD, YEATHERIDGE FARM CARAVAN PARK, EAST WORLINGTON, CREDITON EX17 4TN (01884 860330). Woodland walks, coarse fishing lake, indoor heated swimming pools with 200ft water flume, TV lounge, children's play area. ALL FREE. A welcome for dogs. Modern facilities. Write, or phone for FREE colour brochure. [pw! Pets £1-£2. ⌂]
website: www.yeatheridge.co.uk

Cullompton

Small market town off the main A38 Taunton - Exeter road. Good touring centre. Noted for apple orchards which supply the local cider industry. Taunton 19 miles, Exeter 13, Honiton 11, Tiverton 9.

FOREST GLADE HOLIDAY PARK (PW), KENTISBEARE, CULLOMPTON EX15 2DT (01404 841381; Fax: 01404 841593). Country estate with deluxe 2/4/6 berth caravans. All superbly equipped. Many amenities on site. Mother and Baby Room. Campers and tourers welcome. SAE for colour brochure. ETC ★★★★, AA Four Pennants De Luxe, David Bellamy Gold Award. [Pets 50p/£1 per night, pw!]
e-mail: enquiries@forest-glade.co.uk website: www.forest-glade.co.uk

MRS M. CHUMBLEY, OBURNFORD FARM, CULLOMPTON EX15 1LZ (Tel & Fax: 01884 32292). Listed Georgian Farmhouse set in large gardens. Ideal National Trust, coasts, moors and M5 (J28). Bed, Breakfast and Evening meal and "Free Wine" £32 per night. Pets most welcome. [🐕]
e-mail: margaretchumbley@amserve.com

Dartmoor

365 square miles of National Park with spectacular unspoiled scenery, fringed by picturesque villages.

DEVONSHIRE INN, STICKLEPATH, OKEHAMPTON EX20 2NW (01837 840626). A real country pub! Out the back door past the water wheels, cross the river by ford or footbridge and up through the woods onto the north edge of Dartmoor proper. Dogs and horses always welcome, fed and watered. 1994 Winner National Beta Petfood Golden Bowl Competition for most dog-friendly pub!

THE EDGEMOOR COUNTRY HOUSE HOTEL, HAYTOR ROAD, LOWERDOWN CROSS, BOVEY TRACEY TQ13 9LE (01626 832466; Fax: 01626 834760). Country House Hotel in peaceful wooded setting adjacent Dartmoor National Park. Many lovely walks close by. All rooms en suite. Dogs welcome. See our website for further details. AA ★★★, Rosettes for Excellent Food [pw! 🐕]
e-mail: edgemoor@btinternet.com website: www.edgemoor.co.uk

MRS J. COLTON, PEEK HILL FARM, DOUSLAND, YELVERTON PL20 6PD (01822 854808). Good breakfast and comfy beds; TV, kettle in rooms. Views from Dartmoor to Bodmin. Picnics can be provided. Good walking. Pleasant stay guaranteed. Open all year except Christmas. [🐕]
website: www.peekhill.freeserve.co.uk

CHERRYBROOK HOTEL, TWO BRIDGES, YELVERTON PL20 6SP (01822 880260). Set in the heart of Dartmoor National Park. Seven comfortably furnished en suite bedrooms. Good quality home-cooked food with menu choice. Ideal for touring. Warmest welcome. ETC/AA ◆◆◆◆ [🐕]
e-mail: info@cherrybrook-hotel.co.uk website: www.cherrybrook-hotel.co.uk

DARTMOOR COUNTRY HOLIDAYS, MAGPIE LEISURE PARK, DEPT PW, BEDFORD BRIDGE, HORRABRIDGE, YELVERTON PL20 7RY (01822 852651). Purpose-built pine lodges in peaceful woodland setting. Sleep 2-7. Furnished to very high standard (microwave, dishwasher etc). Easy walk to village and shops. Launderette. Dogs permitted. [Pets £18 per week]
website: www.dartmoorcountryholidays.co.uk

PRINCE HALL HOTEL, NEAR TWO BRIDGES, DARTMOOR PL20 6SA (01822 890403; Fax: 01822 890676). Small, friendly, relaxed country house hotel with glorious views onto open moorland. Walks in all directions. Nine en suite bedrooms. Log fires. Gourmet cooking. Excellent wine list. Fishing, riding, golf nearby. Three-Day Break from £90 per pppn. AA/VisitBritain ★★ AA Rosette for food. [🐕]
e-mail: bosun@princehall.co.uk website: www.princehall.co.uk

Dartmouth

Historic port and resort on the estuary of the River Dart, with sandy coves and pleasure boat trips up the river. Car ferry to Kingswear.

DARTSIDE HOLIDAYS, RIVERSIDE COURT, SOUTH EMBANKMENT, DARTMOUTH TQ6 9BH (01803 832093; Fax: 01803 835135). Comfortable holiday apartments with private balconies and superb river and harbour views. Available all year with colour TV, linen and parking. From £105 per week. Free Colour Brochure on request. [Pets £20 per week.]
website: www.dartsideholidays.com

PAM & GRAHAM SPITTLE, WATERMILL COTTAGES, HANSEL, DARTMOUTH TQ6 0LN (01803 770219). Comfortable, well equipped, old stone cottages in peaceful riverside setting. Wonderful walks in and around our idyllic valley near Slapton Sands and coastal paths. Sleep 3-6. Open all year. Telephone for brochure. [Pets £15 per week]
e-mail: graham@hanselpg.freeserve.co.uk website: www.watermillcottages.co.uk

TORCROSS APARTMENTS, SLAPTON SANDS, TORCROSS VILLAGE, NEAR KINGSBRIDGE, SOUTH DEVON TQ7 2TQ (01548 580206; Fax: 01548 580996). Fully equipped self-catering apartments with lovely lake and sea views. Resident owners and spotlessly clean. Half-price Breaks. Private car park. [Pets £15 to £40 per week]
e-mail: enquiries@torcross.com website: www.torcross.com

MRS S.R. RIDALLS, THE OLD BAKEHOUSE, 7 BROADSTONE, DARTMOUTH TQ6 9NR (Tel & Fax: 01803 834585). Five cottages (one with four-poster bed). Sleep 2–6. Near river, shops, restaurants. Blackpool Sands 15 minutes' drive. TV, linen free. Open all year. Free parking. Green Tourism Bronze Award. ETC ★★★/★★★★ [🐕]
e-mail: gparker@pioneer.ps.co.uk website: www.oldbakehousedartmouth.co.uk

Dunsford

Attractive village in upper Teign valley with Dartmoor to the west. Plymouth 35 miles, Okehampton 16, Newton Abbot 13, Crediton 9, Exeter 8.

ROYAL OAK INN, DUNSFORD, NEAR EXETER EX6 7DA (01647 252256). Welcome to our Victorian country inn with real ales and home-made food. All en suite rooms are in a 300-year-old converted barn. Well behaved children and dogs welcome. [🐕]

Exeter

Chief city of the South-West with a cathedral and university. Ample shopping, sports and leisure facilities.

MRS SALLY GLANVILL, RYDON FARM, WOODBURY, EXETER EX5 1LB (Tel & Fax: 01395 232341). 16th Century Devon Longhouse on working dairy farm. Bedrooms with private or en suite bathrooms, hairdryers, tea/coffee facilities. Romantic 4-poster. Open all year. ETC/AA ◆◆◆◆. From £28 to £38. [🐕]

THE LORD HALDON COUNTRY HOUSE HOTEL, DUNCHIDEOCK, NEAR EXETER EX6 7YF (01392 832483, Fax: 01392 833765). Extensive gardens amid miles of rolling Devon countryside. ETC ★★★, AA ★★★ and 2 Rosettes. [Pets £5 per night.]
e-mail: enquiries@lordhaldonhotel.co.uk website: www.lordhaldonhotel.co.uk

Exmoor

265 square miles of unspoiled heather moorland with deep wooded valleys and rivers, ideal for a walking, pony trekking or fishing holiday

JAYE JONES AND HELEN ASHER, TWITCHEN FARM, CHALLACOMBE, BARNSTAPLE EX31 4TT (01598 763568). Comfort for country lovers in Exmoor National Park. All rooms en suite with TV. Meals prepared with local and some organic produce. Stabling £50 per week. Dogs no charge. B&B £24–£32, DB&B £42–£50. ETC ◆◆◆◆ [🐕, ⌂]
e-mail: holidays@twitchen.co.uk website: www.twitchen.co.uk

THE STAG HUNTERS HOTEL, BRENDON, EXMOOR EX35 1PS (01598 741222; Fax: 01598 741352). Family-run village inn set in four acres of garden and paddock. 12 en suite rooms with CH, TV and tea/coffee. Open all year. Shooting, fishing and riding. [🐕]
e-mail: enquiries@staghunters.fsnet.co.uk website: www.staghunters.com

Gittisham

Village 2 miles south-west of Honiton.

COMBE HOUSE HOTEL AND RESTAURANT, GITTISHAM, HONITON, NEAR EXETER EX14 3AD (01404 540400; Fax: 01404 46004). Romantic Elizabethan Manor set in 3,500 acres of stunning countryside. Fabulous food, generous hospitality, 15 rooms. Near the sea. Pets welcome. AA Top 200 Hotels UK, Johansens, 2004 Rural Retreat of the Year, The Which? Good Hotel Guide.[🐕]
e-mail: stay@thishotel.com website: www.thishotel.com

Hexworthy

Hamlet on Dartmoor 7 miles west of Ashburton.

THE FOREST INN HEXWORTHY, DARTMOOR PL20 6SD (01364 631211; Fax: 01364 631515). A haven for walkers, riders, fishermen, canoeists or anyone just looking for an opportunity to enjoy the natural beauty of Dartmoor. Restaurant using local produce wherever possible; extensive range of snacks; Devon beers and ciders.[🐕]
e-mail: info@theforestinn.co.uk

Holsworthy

Town 9 miles east of Bude.

TAMARSTONE FARM, PANCRASWEEK, HOLSWORTHY EX22 7JT (01288 381734). Peacefully situated by river-bordered meadows and woodlands on the Devon/Cornwall border. Three bedroom cottage sleeping seven, and basically equipped static caravan sleeping two adults and two children. [pw! Pets £15 per week]
e-mail: pets@tamarstone.co.uk website: www.tamarstone.co.uk

TINNEY WATERS, PYWORTHY. Self-catering. Three beautiful lakes - carp, tench, bream. No day tickets, no close season. Ideal for birdwatching. Contact: J. MASON (01409 271362).
e-mail: jeffmason@freenetname.com website: www.tinneywaters.co.uk

Honiton

Busy South Devon town now happily by-passed. Noted for lace and pottery. Excellent touring centre. Newton Abbot 31 miles, Exmouth 18, Taunton 18, Exeter 17, Budleigh Salterton 16, Lyme Regis 15, Chard 13, Sidmouth 10.

MRS S. KIDWELL, THE CREST, WILMINGTON, NEAR HONITON EX14 9JU (01404 831 419; Mobile: 07967 894670). A modern chalet-style house nestling in the picturesque Umborne Valley. The guest wing affords complete privacy with large modern en suite bedrooms. Large sun lounge. Double glazed. Lying in two-and-a-half acres of garden. Pets Welcome. AA ◆◆◆ [🐕]
E-mail: michael.maltby@btconnect.com

Hope Cove

Attractive fishing village, flat sandy beach and safe bathing. Fine views towards Rame Head; cliffs. Kingsbridge 6 miles.

HOPE BARTON BARNS, HOPE COVE, NEAR SALCOMBE TQ7 3HT (01548 561393). 17 stone barns in two courtyards and three luxury apartments in farmhouse. Farmhouse meals. Free range children and well behaved dogs welcome. For full colour brochure please contact: Mike or Judy Tromans. [pw! 🐕]
website: www.hopebarton.co.uk

Ilfracombe

This popular seaside resort clusters round a busy harbour. The surrounding area is ideal for coastal walks.

WIDMOUTH FARM, NEAR ILFRACOMBE EX34 9RX (01271 863743). Comfortable, well equipped cottages in 35 acres of gardens, pasture, woodland and private beach. Wonderful scenery. Ideal for birdwatching, painting, sea fishing & golf. Dogs welcome. ETC ★★★. [pw! Pets £15 per week].
e-mail: holiday@widmouthfarmcottages.co.uk website: www.widmouthfarmcottages.co.uk

VARLEY HOUSE, CHAMBERCOMBE PARK, ILFRACOMBE EX34 9QW (01271 863927; Fax: 01271 879299). Relax with your dog, fabulous walks nearby. Fully en suite non-smoking rooms with lots of thoughtful extras. Superb food, beautiful surroundings. Bar. Car Park. Children welcome over five years. ETC ◆◆◆◆ AA ◆◆◆◆ Selected Award. [🐕] WE WANT YOU TO WANT TO RETURN.
e-mail: info@varleyhouse.co.uk website: www.varleyhouse.co.uk

ST BRANNOCKS HOUSE, ST BRANNOCKS ROAD, ILFRACOMBE EX34 8EQ (01271 863873). Good food and excellent accommodation guaranteed at this friendly Hotel. All rooms TV, tea making; en suite. Licensed bar. Parking. Children and pets welcome. RAC/ETC ★★ [🐕]
e-mail: stbrannocks@aol.com website: www.stbrannockshotel.co.uk

A useful Index of Towns/Villages and Counties appears on page 426 – please also refer to Contents Page 3.

Instow

On estuaries of Taw and Torridge, very popular with boating enthusiasts. Barnstaple 6 miles, Bideford 3.

BEACH COTTAGE, INSTOW. Two seafront cottages with extensive beach and sea views. Sleep 5/6. Enclosed garden, own parking. Central heating, colour TV, coastal walks. Dog welcome. For colour brochure send SAE to Mrs P. I. BARNES, 140 BAY VIEW ROAD, NORTHAM, BIDEFORD EX39 1BJ (01237 473801). [Dog £10 per week]
website: www.seabirdcottages.co.uk

Kingsbridge

Pleasant town at head of picturesque Kingsbridge estuary. Centre for South Hams district with its lush scenery and quiet coves.

DITTISCOMBE HOLIDAY COTTAGES. Traditional stone cottages in tranquil valley, close to beaches, South West Coast Path and Slapton. Woodburners. Children's play area. Dogs welcome. Open all year. Low season Short Breaks. ETC ★★★★, Green Tourism Silver Award. RUTH & JON SAUNDERS, DITTISCOMBE, SLAPTON, NEAR KINGSBRIDGE, SOUTH DEVON TQ7 2QF (01548 521272)
e-mail: info@dittiscombe.co.uk website: www.dittiscombe.co.uk

BEACHDOWN, CHALLABOROUGH BAY, KINGSBRIDGE TQ7 4JB. Comfortable, fully-equipped chalets on private, level and secluded site in beautiful South Hams. 150 yards from beach and South West Coastal Path. Contact: NIGEL or GARETH (01548 810089). [pw! Pets £15.00 per week].
e-mail: enquiries@beachdown.co.uk website: www.beachdown.co.uk

MRS B. KELLY, BLACKWELL PARK, LODDISWELL, KINGSBRIDGE TQ7 4EA (01548 821230). 17th century Farmhouse, five miles from Kingsbridge. Ideal centre for Dartmoor, Plymouth, Torbay, Dartmouth and many beaches. Some bedrooms en suite. Bed and Breakfast. Evening meal optional. Dogsitting. Pets welcome free of charge. [pw! 🐕]

MOUNTS FARM TOURING PARK, THE MOUNTS, NEAR EAST ALLINGTON, KINGSBRIDGE TQ9 7QJ (01548 521591). Family-run site in the heart of South Devon. We welcome tents, touring caravans and motor caravans. Children and pets welcome. Many safe, sandy beaches nearby.

King's Nympton

3 miles north of Chulmleigh. Winner of CPRE Award for Devon Village of the year 1999.

COLLACOTT FARM, KING'S NYMPTON, UMBERLEIGH, NORTH DEVON EX37 9TP (01769 572491). Eight Country Cottages sleeping from 2 to 12 in rural area; lovely views, private patios and gardens. Well furnished and equipped. Heated pool, tennis court, BHS approved riding school. Laundry room. Open all year. [pw!, Pets £3 per night, £20 per week]
e-mail: info@collacott.co.uk website: www.collacott.co.uk

Lynmouth/Exmoor

Small resort with Harbour at foot of cliff below Lynton, on Lynmouth Bay.

BATH HOTEL, TORS HOTEL, LYNMOUTH, EXMOOR, NORTH DEVON EX35 6EL (01598 752238). Great views of harbour. Quality rooms and service. Ideal for moors. Pets welcome. Prices from £31.00 pppn. Off-season discounts available. AA ★★ [🐕]
website: www.torslynmouth.co.uk

SYMBOLS

- **🐕 Indicates that pets are welcome free of charge.**
- **£ Indicates that a charge is made for pets: nightly or weekly.**
- **pw! Shows some special provision for pets; exercise facility, feeding or accommodation arrangement.**
- **⌂ Indicates separate pets accommodation.**

Lynton/Lynmouth

Picturesque twin villages joined by a unique cliff railway (vertical height 500 ft). Lynmouth has a quaint harbour and Lynton enjoys superb views over the rugged coastline.

COUNTISBURY LODGE HOTEL, COUNTISBURY HILL, LYNMOUTH EX35 6NB (01598 752388). Former Victorian vicarage, peacefully secluded yet only 5 minutes to Lynmouth village. En suite rooms, central heating. Ideal for birdwatching and moors. Parking. Short Breaks. Also available S/C cottage and apartment. AA ◆◆◆◆ [🐕]
website: www.countisburylodge.co.uk

MOORLANDS. Where countryside and comfort combine. Two self-contained apartments within a family-run guesthouse, within the Exmoor National Park. Hotel amenities available for guests' use. Contact: MR I. CORDEROY, MOORLANDS, WOODY BAY, PARRACOMBE, NEAR LYNTON, DEVON EX31 4RA (01598 763224). [🐕]
website: www.moorlandshotel.co.uk

MRS W. PRYOR, STATION HOUSE, LYNTON EX35 6LB (01598 752275/752381; Fax: 01598 752475). Holiday Flat situated in the former narrow gauge railway station closed in 1935, overlooking the West Lyn Valley. Centrally placed for Doone Valley and Exmoor. Parking available. £130 - £200 per week. [🐕]

R.S. BINGHAM, NEW MILL FARM, BARBROOK, LYNTON EX35 6JR (01598 753341). Exmoor Valley. Two delightful genuine modernised XVII century cottages by stream on 100-acre farm with A.B.R.S. Approved riding stables. Free fishing. ETC ★★★★. SAE for brochure. [pw! Pets £15 per week.]
website: www..outoverccott.co.uk

EXMOOR SANDPIPER INN, COUNTISBURY, LYNMOUTH EX35 6AG (01598 741263). Romantic coaching inn on Exmoor. 16 en suite bedrooms, extensive menus with daily specials, good wines. Horse riding, walking. No charge for dogs. [🐕]
e-mail: info@exmoor-sandpiper.co.uk

Morchard Bishop

An old traditional Devon village almost equal distance from both moors and both coasts.

CAROLINE & MARK DE SOUZA, WEST AISH FARM, MORCHARD BISHOP, NEAR CREDITON EX17 6RX (01363 877427). Two Self-Catering Cottages set in a former cobbled farmyard on a southerly slope with stunning views to Dartmoor. One cottage sleeps 5. Bungalow sleeps 4. £225 – £400. Short Breaks (3 nights) from £100. Non-smokers preferred. If you have forgotten what peace and quiet is like, come and stay with us! [🐕 pw!]
website: www.westaishfarm.co.uk

Mortehoe

Adjoining Woolacombe with cliffs and wide sands. Interesting rock scenery beyond Morte Point. Barnstaple 15 miles.

LUNDY HOUSE HOTEL, MORTEHOE, NORTH DEVON EX34 7DZ (01271 870372). Quality en suite accommodation in small, friendly hotel. Superb food, licensed bar lounge, restaurant. TV & tea-making facilities in all rooms. Write or phone for full details. [🐕]
e-mail: info@lundyhousehotel.co.uk website: www.lundyhousehotel.co.uk

THE SMUGGLERS, NORTH MORTE ROAD, MORTEHOE EX34 7DR (Tel & Fax: 01271 870891). In the pretty village of Mortehoe. The Smugglers offers luxury accommodation from twin rooms to family suites. En suite rooms, Satellite TV, Full English Breakfast, Licensed Bar, Beer Garden, Home-cooked Meals. Well trained pets welcome.

Northam

Town 2 miles north of Bideford.

MRS CYMA CASSAR, CROSS HOUSE, FORE STREET, NORTHAM, BIDEFORD EX39 1AN (01237 472042). Three cottages, all with 'Olde Worlde' charm and up-to-date amenities. Exmoor, Clovelly, Lynton, Lynmouth, Tarka Trail within easy reach. Many beaches, the nearest one mile away. [🐕]
e-mail: cymacassar@eurobell.co.uk

Okehampton

Market town on edge of Dartmoor.

MRS PAM JEFFERY, NORTHLAKE, EXETER ROAD, OKEHAMPTON EX20 1QH (01837 53100). A warm welcome awaits at this friendly bed and breakfast with views across Dartmoor. Superbly sited for walking, cycling, riding and touring. Day kennelling available. [🐕] [pw!]
e-mail: pamjeffery@northlakedevon.co.uk website: www.northlakedevon.co.uk

BOB & SUE ANNEAR, BEER FARM, OKEHAMPTON EX20 1SG (01837 840265; Fax: 01837 840245). Barn conversions, now four comfortable cottages. Each sleep 4-6. TV/video, microwave, dishwasher, CH. Games room. Children welcome. Horses by arrangement. Excellent mid-Devon base for walking/touring. ETC ★★★★ *SELF-CATERING*. [Dogs £15 per week]
e-mail: beerfarm.oke@which.net website: www.beerfarm.co.uk

Offwell

Award winning small village in Area of Outstanding Natural Beauty. Honiton 3 miles, World Heritage Jurassic Coast 5.

OFFWELL MEWS, OFFWELL, NEAR HONITON EX14 9SA (01404 831794). Fully equipped self-catering units within a converted stable block. En suite bedrooms. Private parking. Dogs welcome by arrangement. Non-smoking. Flexible booking. Short breaks available. Open all year.

Ottery St Mary

Pleasant little town in East Devon, within easy reach of the sea. Many interesting little buildings including 11th century parish church. Birthplace of poet Coleridge.

MRS A. FORTH, FLUXTON FARM, OTTERY ST MARY EX11 1RJ (01404 812818). Charming 16th Century farmhouse with large garden. Good food. Peace and quiet. Cat lovers' paradise. AA ◆◆ [🐕 pw!]

Paignton

Popular family resort on Torbay with long, safe sandy beaches and small harbour. Exeter 25 miles, Newton Abbott 9, Torquay 3.

LISA & AARON LINGER, AMBER HOUSE HOTEL, 6 ROUNDHAM ROAD, PAIGNTON TQ4 6EZ (01803 558372). Family-run licensed hotel. All en suite; ground floor rooms. Good food. Highly recommended. Non-smoking. A warm welcome assured to pets and their families. [🐕]

J. AND E. BALL, DEPARTMENT P.W., HIGHER WELL FARM HOLIDAY PARK, STOKE GABRIEL, TOTNES TQ9 6RN (01803 782289). Within 4 miles Torbay beaches and 1 mile of River Dart. Central for touring. Dogs on leads. Tourist Board Graded Park ★★★★. [pw! Pets £2 per night, £14 per week in statics, free in tents and tourers]

Plymouth

Historic port and resort, impressively rebuilt after severe war damage. Large naval docks at Devonport. Beach of pebble and sand.

CHURCHWOOD VALLEY, WEMBURY BAY, NEAR PLYMOUTH PL9 0DZ (01752 862382). Relax in one of our comfortable log cabins, set in a peaceful wooded valley near the beach. Enjoy wonderful walks in woods and along the coast. Abundance of birds and wildlife. Up to two pets per cabin. [Pets £5 per week]
e-mail: churchwoodvalley@btinternet.com website: www.churchwoodvalley.com

CRANBOURNE HOTEL, 278/282 CITADEL ROAD, THE HOE, PLYMOUTH PL1 2PZ (01752 263858/661400/224646; Fax: 01752 263858). Convenient for Ferry Terminal and City Centre. All bedrooms with colour TV and tea/coffee. Licensed bar. Keys provided for access at all times. Under personal supervision. Pets by arrangement. ◆◆◆◆ [🐕]
e-mail: cran.hotel@virgin.net website: www.cranbournehotel.co.uk

Salcombe

Fishing and sailing centre in sheltered position. Fine beaches and coastal walks nearby.

HAZEL AND SEAN HASSALL, BOLBERRY FARM COTTAGES, BOLBERRY, NEAR SALCOMBE, DEVON TQ7 3DY (01548 561384). Luxury Barn conversion cottages. Private gardens. Close to coastal path and pet friendly beaches. Dog wash. Short Breaks out of season. The Pets Holiday Specialist. ETC ★★★★★ [🐕]
e-mail: info@bolberryfarmcottages.co.uk website: www.bolberryfarmcottages.co.uk

SAND PEBBLES HOTEL, HOPE COVE, NEAR KINGSBRIDGE TQ7 3HF (01548 561673). In own grounds overlooking sea and countryside. Tastefully furnished en suite rooms, TV, beverage facilities. Excellent restaurant. Golf, tennis, riding, within easy reach. [Pets £3 per night].
website: www.sandpebbleshotel.co.uk

THE PORT LIGHT, BOLBERRY DOWN, MALBOROUGH, NEAR SALCOMBE TQ7 3DY (01548 561384 or 07970 859992). A totally unique location set amidst acres of National Trust coastline. Luxury en suite rooms. Superb home-cooked fare, specialising in local seafood. Licensed bar. Pets welcome throughout the hotel. Short Breaks throughout the year. Special Breed Weeks. [🐕]
e-mail: info@portlight.co.uk website: www.portlight.co.uk

THE SALCOMBE BOAT MARINE COMPANY LTD, WHITESTRAND, SALCOMBE TQ8 8ET (Tel & Fax: 01548 843730, Mobile:07976 962239). A holiday with a difference. Unwind with a houseboat holiday on Salcombe's tranquil estuary. Write or phone for brochure. [Pets £20 weekly.]

HOPE BARTON BARNS, HOPE COVE, NEAR SALCOMBE TQ7 3HT (01548 561393). 17 stone barns in two courtyards and three luxury apartments in farmhouse. Farmhouse meals. Free range children and well behaved dogs welcome. For full colour brochure please contact: Mike or Judy Tromans. ★★★★ [pw! 🐕]
website: www.hopebarton.co.uk

Seaton

Bright East Devon resort near Axe estuary. Shingle beach and chalk cliffs; good bathing, many lovely walks in vicinity. Exeter 23 miles, Sidmouth 11.

AXEVALE CARAVAN PARK, COLYFORD ROAD, SEATON EX12 2DF (0800 06888816). A quiet, family-run park with 68 modern and luxury caravans for hire. Laundry facilities, park shop. All caravans have a shower, toilet, fridge and TV. Relaxing atmosphere. ETC ★★★
website: www.axevale.co.uk

MILKBERE HOLIDAYS, 3 FORE STREET, SEATON EX12 2LE (01297 22925 – brochure/01297 20729 – bookings). Attractive self-catering Cottages, Bungalows, Apartments. Coast and Country on Devon/Dorset border. Free colour brochure. Pets welcome. [Pets £20 per week].
e-mail: info@milkberehols.com website: www.milkberehols.com

Shaldon

Delightful little resort facing Teignmouth across the Teign estuary. Sheltered by the lofty prominence of Shaldon Ness, beach side activities are largely concerned with boats and sailing; beaches are mainly of sand. Mini golf course. The attractions of Teignmouth are reached by a long road bridge or passenger ferry.

GLENSIDE HOUSE, RINGMORE ROAD, SHALDON TQ14 0EP (01626 872448). Charming, waterside cottage hotel. Level river walks to beach. En suite available. Garden, car park. B&B from £23.00. Telephone for brochure. ETC/AA ◆◆◆. [Pets £3.50 daily, £15 weekly.]
e-mail: glensidehouse@amserve.com website: www.tuckedup.com/glensidehouse.html

Sidmouth

Sheltered resort, winner of many awards for its floral displays. Good sands at Jacob's Ladder beach.

OTTERFALLS AND OTTERS RISE, NEW ROAD, UPOTTERY EX14 9QD (FREECALL 0808 145 2700; Fax: 01404 861706). 23 luxurious fully equipped self-catering cottages and lodges set in 130 acres. Fishing lakes, heated indoor pool. Wonderful walking, including special pet "off-lead" walkways. [pw! Pets £25 per week]
e-mail: hols@otterfalls.co.uk website: www.otterfalls.co.uk

LEIGH FARM SELF-CATERING HOLIDAYS, WESTON, SIDMOUTH EX10 0PH. Cottage & Bungalows 150 yards from National Trust Valley leading to Coastal Path and beach. Lovely cliff top walks and level walks around nearby Donkey Sanctuary fields. ETC ★★★★ Contact: Geoff & Gill Davis (01395 516065; Fax: 01395 579582). [pw! Pets £17 per week]
e-mail: leigh.farm@virgin.net website: www.streets-ahead.com/leighfarm

BOSWELL FARM COTTAGES, SIDFORD, SIDMOUTH EX10 0PP (Tel & Fax: 01395 514162) 17th century farmhouse with seven individual cottages, beautifully converted from period farm buildings, each with its enclosed, delightful garden. Facilities available - art studio, tennis court and trout pond. Idyllic walks in Area of Outstanding Natural Beauty, two miles from beach and World Heritage coastline. ETC ★★★★ [pw! Pets £19 per week.]
e-mail: dillon@boswell-farm.co.uk website: www.boswell-farm.co.uk

South Molton

On the southern edge of Exmoor, 12 miles east of Barnstaple, this busy market town is noted for its antiques and elegant Georgian buildings.

COURT GREEN, BISHOP'S NYMPTON, NEAR SOUTH MOLTON. A most attractive, well-equipped, south-facing cottage with large garden, three miles from South Molton. Fishing available. Well-behaved pets welcome. Contact: MRS J. GREENWELL, TREGEIRIOG, NEAR LLANGOLLEN LL20 7HU (01691 600672). [ ]

Tavistock

Birthplace of Sir Francis Drake and site of a fine ruined Benedictine Abbey. On edge of Dartmoor, 13 miles north of Plymouth

LANGSTONE MANOR HOLIDAY PARK (Tel & Fax 01822 613371). Peaceful Holiday Park, offering camping, cottages, static caravans. Ideal location outside Tavistock with direct access onto Dartmoor. Bar and evening meals. Games room. Excellent location. ETC ★★★★, AA ★★★
e-mail: jane@langstone-manor.co.uk website: www.langstone-manor.co.uk

MRS P.G.C. QUINTON, HIGHER QUITHER, MILTON ABBOT, TAVISTOCK PL19 0PZ (01822 860284). Modern self-contained barn conversion. Own private garden. Terms from £195 inc. linen, coal and logs. Electricity metered. [pw!]

Thurlestone

Village resort above the cliffs to the north of Bolt Tail, 4 miles west of Kingsbridge.

CUTAWAY COTTAGE, THURLESTONE, KINGSBRIDGE TQ7 3NF. Self-catering cottage within a fenced garden in the middle of the village. Private road, 5 minutes to pub & shop, 20 minutes to beaches & sea, Ideal for children, dog walkers & bird watchers. Phone PAT on 01548 560688 [ ]

Torquay

Popular resort on the English Riviera with a wide range of attractions and entertainments. Yachting and watersports centre with 10 superb beaches and coves.

RED HOUSE HOTEL AND MAXTON LODGE HOLIDAY APARTMENTS, ROUSDOWN ROAD, CHELSTON, TORQUAY TQ2 6PB (01803 607811; Fax: 01803 605357). Choose either the friendly service and facilities of a hotel or the privacy and freedom of self-catering apartments. The best of both worlds! AA/ETC ★★ Hotel & ★★★ Self-catering. [in flats; £3 per night in hotel]
e-mail: stay@redhouse-hotel.co.uk website: www.redhouse-hotel.co.uk

Torrington

Pleasant market town on River Torridge. Good centre for moors and sea. Exeter 36 miles, Okehampton 20, Barnstaple 12, Bideford 7.

SALLY MILSOM, STOWFORD LODGE, LANGTREE, NEAR TORRINGTON EX38 8NU (01805 601540). Sleep 4/6. Away from the crowds. Four delightful cottages with heated indoor pool, and two secluded period farm cottages. Peaceful countryside, convenient North Devon coast and moors. Magnificent views and walks. Phone for brochure. ETC ★★★. [Pets £10 per week, pw!]
e-mail: stowford@dial.pipex.com website: www.stowford.dial.pipex.com

Totnes

Town at tidal estuary of River Dart, 7 miles west of Torquay

EDESWELL FARM, RATTERY, SOUTH BRENT TQ10 9LN (01364 72177). Friendly family-run park. 22 holiday caravan homes and 3 cottages for hire, large indoor heated swimming pool, games room and outdoor play area. Wildlife Discovery Centre. **ETC ★★★** *DAVID BELLAMY GOLD AWARD* [Pets £15 per week]
e-mail: welcome@edeswellfarm.co.uk Website: www.edeswellfarm.co.uk

SEA TROUT INN, STAVERTON, NEAR TOTNES TQ9 6PA (01803 762274; Fax: 01803 762506). Hidden away in the tranquil Dart Valley but conveniently placed for Dartmoor, Torbay and the South Devon coast. Delightful cottage- style bedrooms, two traditional English bars and elegant restaurant. ETC ★★
website: www.seatroutinn.com

MRS ANNE TORR, DOWNE LODGE, BROADHEMPSTON, TOTNES TQ9 6BY (Tel & Fax: 01803 812828) Woodland dog walking on doorstep. Cottage available with one or three bedrooms. Private garden. En suite B&B available. Beautiful, quiet position convenient for Dartmoor and the coast. [🐕]
e-mail: info@downelodge.co.uk website: www.downelodge.co.uk

Westward Ho!

An excellent resort with 3 miles of golden sands, amusements, pubs, clubs and restaurants. 2 miles north west of Bideford.

WEST PUSEHILL FARM COTTAGES, WEST PUSEHILL FARM, WESTWARD HO!, NORTH DEVON EX39 5AH (01237 475638/474622). Nestling within the Kenwith Valley, 11 cottages with heated outdoor pool. Perfectly situated to explore coast and countryside. Many attractions close by. Pets and children welcome. Open all year. [Pets £20 per week].
website: www.wpfcottages.co.uk

Woolacombe

Favourite resort with long, wide stretches of sand. Barnstaple 15 miles, Ilfracombe 6.

MRS VIVIEN LAWRENCE, COVE COTTAGE, SHARP ROCK, MORTEHOE, WOOLACOMBE EX34 7EA (01271 870403). First floor flat overlooking Barricane beach where dogs permitted, (10 minute walk) Sea views, garden. Colour TV/video. Fridge/freezer, washer/dryer. Microwave. C.H. included early/late season. Open all year. Sleeps 5 + cot. Resident proprietor. ETC ★★ [pw! pets £1 per day, £7 per week].
e-mail: vivien@lawrence6232.fsnet.co.uk

SEABREEZE, 5 THE CRESCENT, MORTEHOE, WOOLACOMBE EX34 7DX (Tel & Fax: 01271 870161). Sleeps 4-5. Split level cottage-style apartment. Stunning sea views over Mortehoe and Woolacombe. Very roomy. Beach five minutes' walk. Flagstone flooring. Parking available. B&B accommodation also available.
e-mail: reservations@seabreezebandb.co.uk website: www.seabreezebandb.co.uk

EUROPA PARK, STATION ROAD, WOOLACOMBE (01271 870159). Static vans, chalets, camping. Full facilities. Pets welcome. Indoor heated swimming pool, sauna, 24-hour shop. Pets welcome. AA *THREE PENNANTS.*
e-mail: europaparkwoolacombe@yahoo.co.uk website: www.europapark.co.uk

PEBBLES HOTEL, COMBESGATE BEACH, WOOLACOMBE EX34 7EA (01271 870426). Family-run Hotel overlooking sea and beaches. All rooms en suite, with colour TV, tea/coffee making etc. Special Short Break packages. Write or phone for colour brochure. ETC ★ [🐕]
website: www.pebbleshotel.com

WOOLACOMBE HOLIDAY COTTAGES (Tel & Fax: 01271 870846). Quality coastal cottages. Seafront to Farmhouse, 1– 5 bedrooms. Woolacombe, Croyde, Georgeham, Willingcott, West Down. Short breaks, pets, special offers.
e-mail: info@woolacombe-cottages.co.uk website: www.woolacombe-cottages.co.uk

SUNNYMEADE COUNTRY HOTEL, WEST DOWN, NEAR WOOLACOMBE EX34 8NT (01271 863668; 01271 866061). Small country hotel set in beautiful countryside. A few minutes away from Ilfracombe, Exmoor and Woolacombe's Blue Flag Beach. 10 en suite rooms, 4 on the ground floor. Deaf accessible. Pets welcome-dogs are free. ETC ◆◆◆ [🐕, pw!]
website: www.sunnymeade.co.uk

MRS JOYCE BAGNALL, CHICHESTER HOUSE, THE ESPLANADE, WOOLACOMBE EX34 7DJ (01271 870761). Holiday apartments on sea front. Fully furnished, sea and coastal views. Watch the sun go down from your balcony. Open all year. SAE Resident Proprietor. [Pets £8 per week, pw!]

Tamarisk Farm **West Bexington, Dorchester DT2 9DF**

On slope overlooking Chesil beach, three large (one for wheelchair disabled Cat 1, M3) and two small COTTAGES (ETC 3/4 Stars), and two secluded CHALETS (not ETC graded), each standing in own fenced garden. Sleep 4/6. On organic farm with arable, sheep, cattle, horses, market garden (organic vegetables, meat and wholemeal flour available) and conservation. Good centre for touring, sightseeing, glorious walks by the sea and inland. Lovely place for dogs. Very quiet. Sea views. Terms from £175-£690.

e-mail: holidays@tamariskfarm.com • www.tamariskfarm.co.uk • Mrs Josephine Pearse • Tel: 01308 897784

Alum Dene Hotel

2 Burnaby Road, Alum Chine, Bournemouth BH4 8JF Tel: 01202 764011

Renowned for good old fashioned hospitality and friendly service. Come and be spoilt at our licensed hotel. All rooms en suite, colour TV. Some have sea views. 200 metres sea. Parking. Christmas House party. No charge for pets.

THE VINE HOTEL

22 Southern Road, Southbourne
Bournemouth BH6 3SR
Telephone: 01202 428309

A small, family, award-winning Hotel only 3 minutes' walk from dog friendly beach and shops. All rooms en suite; tea/coffee making facilities and colour TV. Residential licence with attractive bar. Full central heating. Forecourt parking. Open all year.

Pets Welcome – Free of Charge. FHG Diploma STB ◆◆◆

- A SHORT WALK TO GOLDEN SANDY BEACHES •
- MOST WITH PRIVATE BATHROOMS •
- CLEANLINESS AND COMFORT ASSURED •
- LAUNDRY ROOM • FREE PRIVATE PARKING •
- DOGS WELCOME • COLOUR TV IN ALL UNITS •
- NO VAT CHARGED •

CONTACT: M. DE KMENT, 4 CECIL ROAD, BOURNEMOUTH BH5 1DU (07788 952394)

From a honeymoon couple...to a "tribe" of two dozen

Self catering in Bournemouth and surrounding areas allows you...

TIME TO CHOOSE - the location, the places, your meals & your own holiday timetable.

FREEDOM - to really enjoy... our golden sands, warm, clean seas and glorious attractions in Bournemouth & surrounding areas.

TO HOLIDAY IN STYLE - with the choice of 200 self-catering flats, houses, bungalows & cottages from budget to executive quality.

We have been family-run for over 45 years. Many of our properties offer sea views and a selection allow pets. Call today for our FREE BROCHURE or use our website for our online brochure, availability and bookings.

01202 428 717 / 417 757
www.bournecoast.co.uk

BOURNEMOUTH HOLIDAY APARTMENTS

Modern well-equipped flats. Ideally situated close to sea and shops. Sleeps one to ten persons. Car parking space for each apartment. Discounts for bookings of over one week. Children and pets welcome. Brochure available from:

Mike & Lyn Lambert, Aaron, 16 Florence Road, Bournemouth BH5 1HF
Tel: 01202 304925 or 01425 474007 • e-mail: mikelyn_lambert@btinternet.com

Guests enjoying the lounge

THE *REALLY* DOG-FRIENDLY PLACE
WHITE TOPPS

Small, friendly and catering only for guests with dogs. In a nice quiet position close to lovely walks on the beach (dogs allowed) and Hengistbury Head. Plus the New Forest isn't far away. There's no charge for pets, of course and the proprietor, Marjorie Titchen, just loves dogs.

• DOG(S) ESSENTIAL–ANY SIZE, ANY NUMBER, ANYWHERE • GROUND FLOOR ROOM FOR ELDERLY DOGS • RESIDENTIAL LICENCE • ADULTS ONLY (14yrs +) • GENEROUS HOME COOKING • VEGETARIANS WELCOME• NOT SUITABLE FOR DISABLED • PARKING

WHITE TOPPS, 45 CHURCH ROAD, SOUTHBOURNE, BOURNEMOUTH, DORSET BH6 4BB
TEL: 01202 428868 • e-mail: Thedogplace1@aol.com • www.whitetopps.co.uk

IF YOU DON'T LOVE DOGS YOU WON'T LIKE WHITE TOPPS

See also Colour Advertisement on page 40

Langtry Manor
The Country House Hotel in Bournemouth

Built by Edward VII as a Lovenest for Lillie Langtry. A rare gem of a hotel where the building, food, service and history blend to form something quite exceptional. Four posters, Jacuzzi's, complimentary leisure club and award-winning restaurant. Midweek and weekend breaks. As featured on BBC Holiday Show. Pets welcome by arrangement.

"Best Hotel in Bournemouth" - The Guardian

Derby Road, East Cliff, Bournemouth BH1 3QB
Tel: (01202) 553887 www.langtrymanor.com

See also Colour Advertisement on page 40

FROGMORE FARM
CHIDEOCK, BRIDPORT
DT6 6HT

Enjoy Bed and Breakfast on a 90-acre grazing farm set in beautiful West Dorset, overlooking Lyme Bay. En suite shower rooms available. Cosy TV lounge with wood fire; guests' dining room, tea making facilities. Children and dogs welcome. OR CHOOSE our lovely self catering Cottage, sleeps 5. Fully equipped, bed linen supplied; lounge with woodburner and colour TV. Car essential. Open all year. Brochure and terms free on request.

Apply MRS S. NORMAN Tel: 01308 456159

✦ EYPE HOUSE CARAVAN & CAMPING PARK ✦

Small, quiet family-run park lying on the Heritage Coastal Path, 200 yards from the beach.

Static vans for hire from £160 to £400, tent pitches (all terraced with sea views) £8.50 to £14.50 for four people. Sorry, no tourers. **Children and dogs welcome.**

Eype, Bridport DT6 6AL Telephone: 01308 424903

When making enquiries please mention FHG Publications

DOG DAYS IN DORSET • Bring and bury your bones, wonderful tail-wagging walks to smugglers' beaches, hidden valleys and woodland ways. Private peaceful park. Chalet bungalows (1 or 2 bedrooms), sleep 2-6. Pets free (of course), house-trained owners welcome!

For brochure please telephone Margaret/Rachael 01308 421521

e-mail: mail@golden-acre.com • www.golden-acre.com

Golden Acre, Eype, Near Bridport DT6 6AL • Part of Dorset's World Heritage Coastline.

Lancombes House ~ Holiday Cottages

ETC ★★★

Four superbly converted cottages, each with its own sitting-out area, barbecue and garden furniture. Some have fenced gardens. Spacious open plan living areas, most with wood burning stoves. Deep in the heart of Hardy country, this is a delightful area to explore whether on foot or horseback. There are many things to do and pets and children are very welcome. Prices start at £120 for mini-breaks; open all the year round.

Mr Karl Mansfield, Lancombes House, West Milton, Bridport DT6 3TN
Tel: 01308 485375 website: www.lancombeshouse.co.uk

Dolphins River Park

Small, very peaceful park set in beautiful landscaped grounds of mature trees, shrubs and lawns on the banks of the River Char.

Luxury fully self-contained 4 and 6 berth Caravans for hire and sale.

(Facilities include laundry room, local tourist information)

Direct access to footpaths and fields.

One mile from the beach. ***WELL CARED FOR PETS WELCOME.***

Colour Brochure available from:

Dolphins, Berne Lane, Charmouth, Dorset DT6 6RD

FREEPHONE: 0800 0746375

British Graded Holiday Parks

British Holiday Home Parks Association

MANOR FARM HOLIDAY CENTRE

Charmouth, Bridport, Dorset DT6 6QL (01297) 560226

Two and three bedroomed houses, Luxury caravans. All units for four to six people. Children and pets welcome. Swimming pool and children's pool. Licensed bar with family room. Shop. Launderette. Children's play area. Ten minutes' walk to safe sand and shingle beach. Many fine walks locally. Golf, riding, tennis, fishing and boating all nearby.

SAE TO MR. F. LOOSMORE FOR COLOUR BROCHURE

The Queen's Armes Hotel

The Street, Charmouth, Dorset DT6 6QF Telephone 01297 560339

Phillip and Carole Mapstone

Former coaching inn built around 1500, oak beams and panelling. Log fires; 11 unique bedrooms, 10 en suite, the other has its own bathroom. Guest lounge, licensed bar and dining room. Vegetarians and Vegans catered for.

An abundance of National Trust land, footpaths and Heritage coastline. Dogs welcome.

ETC 4 Diamond Award **Smoking permitted in guest conservatory only.**

NEW FOREST

Country Holiday Chalet on small, quiet, secluded woodland park.Sleeps four. Fenced private garden. Dogs welcome. Car parking. £150 to £350 per week. Write enclosing SAE or telephone:

Mrs L.M Bowling, Owlpen Caravans Ltd, Owlpen, 148 Burley Road, Bransgore, Near Christchurch, Dorset BH23 8DB Tel: 01425 672875 Mobile: 07860 547391

THE STABLES

Hyde Crook, Frampton DT2 9NW • 01300 320075

The Stables is a comfortable country house developed around a 1935 cottage overlooking the valley of Frampton. Set in a small area of woodland off the A37, in the heart of Thomas Hardy country, we enjoy uninterrupted views of open countryside. There is unrestricted off-road parking and 20 acres of ground with wild life, ducks, sheep and horses. All guest accommodation is contained in a separate wing of the house and comprises a comfortable sitting room/TV lounge on the ground floor, with private staircase to a twin en suite bedroom, double bedroom, single bedroom and bathroom on the first floor. The twin beds can be converted to a king-size for stays of two nights or more. All rooms are double glazed with central heating, and a log fire is lit in the sitting room in the cooler seasons. Terms from £22pppn. The Stables specialises in pet friendly facilities for dogs and horses.

e-mail: cobalangley@aol.com • website: www.framptondorset.com

ETC ◆◆◆◆ CHURCHVIEW GUEST HOUSE

Winterbourne Abbas, Dorchester, Dorset DT2 9LS Tel/Fax: 01305 889296

Our 17th century Guest House, noted for hospitality, delicious breakfasts and evening meals, makes an ideal base for touring beautiful West Dorset. Our character bedrooms are comfortable and well-appointed. Meals, served in our beautiful dining room, feature local produce, with relaxation provided by two attractive lounges and licensed bar. Hosts, Jane and Michael Deller, are pleased to give every assistance, with local information to ensure a memorable stay. Short breaks available. Non-smoking.

Terms: Bed and Breakfast: £28 – £38; Dinner, Bed and Breakfast: £42 – £54.

E-mail: stay@churchview.co.uk • Website: www.churchview.co.uk

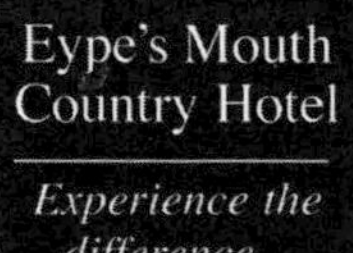

Set in the small Dorset village of Eype, **Eype's Mouth Country Hotel**, is a family run 18 bedroom hotel nestling between the downlands and clifftops at the end of a winding narrow lane. With superb sea views and only a few minutes walk to the beach, the hotel occupies a unique position on the Heritage Coastline. This stunning location provides the opportunity to walk along the Coastal Path with much to explore and observe in this area of unspoilt beauty. Owners, Kevin and Glenis, are dedicated to providing a warm welcome, good food and the comfort and hospitality to the best possible standard. Creating a relaxed, friendly atmosphere is paramount, so you can be assured of a pleasant and enjoyable stay.

Eype's Mouth Country Hotel, Eype, Bridport, Dorset DT6 6AL

Telephone: 01308 423300 **Email:** info@eypesmouthhotel.co.uk **Web:** eypesmouthhotel.co.uk

WESTOVER FARM COTTAGES

In an area of outstanding beauty, Wootton Fitzpaine epitomizes picturesque West Dorset. Within walking distance of sea. 4 beautiful cottages sleep 6/7 with large secluded gardens. Car parking. Logs, Linen available, 3 bedrooms. £180-£650. Pets welcome.

Wootton Fitzpaine, Near Lyme Regis, Dorset DT6 6NE

Brochure: Jon & Debby Snook 01297 560451

e-mail: wfcottages@aol.com ***website: www.lymeregis.com/westover-farm-cottages/*** ***ETC★★★/★★★★***

Mrs J Tedbury, Little Paddocks, Yawl Hill Lane, Lyme Regis DT7 3RW Tel: 01297 443085

A six-berth caravan on Devon/Dorset border in a well kept paddock overlooking Lyme Bay and surrounding countryside. Situated on a smallholding with animals, for perfect peace and quiet. Fully equipped except linen. Electric light, fridge, TV. Calor gas cooker and fire. Dogs welcome.Terms from £110. Also fully equipped chalet for two. Terms from £90. SAE please.

Little Hewish Barn A 150 year old brick and flint barn, converted to provide comfortable accommodation of a very high standard, including oil-fired central heating. There are two double bedrooms (one converts to twin), both with en suite bath/shower facilities. Spacious open-plan living/dining area features a wood-burning stove, fully-equipped kitchen, dishwasher, washer/dryer, TV/video, stereo etc. Children and well-behaved pets are very welcome. Fully-enclosed patio garden and ample on-site parking. Prices are all inclusive – no hidden extras. 'Per person per night' pricing outside of peak periods. **ETC ★★★★★ Little Hewish Barn, Milton Abbas, Blandford Forum, Dorset DT11 0DP • Tel: 01258 881235 • Fax: 01258 881393. e-mail: terry@littlehewish.co.uk**

See also Colour Advertisement on page 40

Country Inn set in the heart of lovely Piddle Valley. Within easy reach of all Dorset's attractions. All rooms en suite with colour TV, tea and coffee, telephone; swimming pool (May-September). Riverside garden, restaurant where Half Board guests choose from à la carte menu at no extra cost.

Bed and Breakfast: £30.00 per person per night.

Dinner, Bed and Breakfast: £45 per person per night.

10% discount for seven nights.

Low Season Breaks: two nights Dinner, Bed and Breakfast £90 per person. **Third night Dinner, Bed and Breakfast – FREE (OCT - APR) excluding Bank Holiday weekends.**

ETC ◆◆◆◆ AA

Telephone: 01300 348358; Fax: 01300 348153

SEND FOR BROCHURE

See also Colour Advertisement on page 41

An **award winning Holiday Park** near Poole, set in a beautiful woodland setting and close to safe sandy beaches. Dogs most welcome!

Quote: WP

0870 444 0080

book online: www.weststarholidays.co.uk/pw

THREE HORSESHOES

Powerstock, Dorset DT6 3TF

01308 485328

www.threehorseshoesinn.com

Dogs and families welcome

'The shoes' is a Victorian inn tucked away in a peaceful part of West Dorset. The surrounding countryside is excellent for walking and is filled with plenty of interest, from Iron Age forts and Roman roads to formal gardens and museums. Dogs are welcome in the three spacious double en suite guest rooms. Two have superb views looking out over the valley, with their own entrance, and the third is ideal as a family room. A single room with sink is also available. The Inn boasts a great reputation for excellent cuisine. Fresh local produce is used wherever possible, even the herbs are picked daily from the on-site herb garden. Light lunches are available daily with an à la carte menu for the evening. Combine this with an expansive fine wine list, log fires in the winter and sunsets over the valley from the terraced garden in the summer and you have an enjoyable evening awaiting you.

Self-Catering Barn Cottages

White Horse Farm

ETC ★★★★

Comfortable, well-equipped barn conversions, set in 2 acres of paddock, duck-pond and gardens in beautiful Hardy countryside. Surrounded by all rural pursuits and within easy reach of several tourist attractions. 100 yards from inn serving good food and local ales. We have all-year-round appeal and are friendly, helpful hosts.

Middlemarsh, Sherborne, Dorset DT9 5QN • 01963 210222

Visit our website: www.whitehorsefarm.co.uk e-mail: enquiries@whitehorsefarm.co.uk

When making enquiries or bookings, a stamped addressed envelope is always appreciated

See also Colour Advertisement on page 38

Lulworth Cove - Cromwell House Hotel, BH20 5RJ Tel: 01929 400253/400332; Fax: 01929 400566

Catriona and Alistair Miller welcome guests to their comfortable family-run hotel, set in secluded gardens with spectacular sea views. Situated 200 yards from Lulworth Cove, with direct access to the Dorset Coastal Footpath. A heated swimming pool is available for guests' use from May to October. Accommodation is in 17 en suite bedrooms, with TV, direct-dial telephone, and tea/coffee making facilities; most have spectacular sea views. Restaurant, bar wine list. Two nights dinner, bed and breakfast (fully en suite) from £90. Off peak mid week breaks available. Open all year except Christmas. **ETC/AA/RAC ★★**

See also Colour Advertisement on page 38

Dormer Cottage

Woodlands at Hyde, Near Wareham BH20 7NT

Proprietor: Mrs M.J.M Constantinides

Tel: 01929 471239

In the midst of 'Hardy Country', a secluded cottage, sleeping 5, converted from a former barn and forming part of the ex Dower House of Hyde Estate. All linen provided. Golf, pony-trekking, riding nearby. Pets and children most welcome. SAE please for terms and further particulars.

Ideal for a quiet holiday far from the madding crowd.

Gorselands Caravan Park, West Bexington-on-Sea, Dorset DT2 9DJ

Attractive secluded park set in coastal valley overlooking Chesil Beach, part of Dorset's World Heritage Jurassic Coastline. Tourist Board graded. Glorious sea views. Country and seaside walks. An ideal base for discovering Dorset's charming villages and Heritage coastline. The beach is a mile either by car or through the meadows, and the fishing is excellent. Pets are most welcome.

Tel: 01308 897232 • Fax: 01308 897239

See also Colour Advertisement on page 41

Abbotsbury

Village of thatched cottages; Benedictine monks created the famous Abbotsbury Swannery.

MRS JOSEPHINE PEARSE, TAMARISK FARM, WEST BEXINGTON, DORCHESTER DT2 9DF (01308 897784). Self Catering properties sleep 4/6. Overlooking Chesil Beach: three large (one for wheelchair disabled Cat 1, M3) and two small Cottages (ETC 3/4 Stars), and two secluded Chalets (not ETC graded). Part of organic farm with arable, sheep, cattle, horses and market garden with vegetables, meat and wholemeal flour available. Good centre for touring, sightseeing, walking. Glorious sea views, very quiet. Lovely place for dogs. Terms from £175 to £690. [🐕]
e-mail: holidays@tamariskfarm.com website: www.tamariskfarm.co.uk

Bournemouth

One of Britain's premier holiday resorts with miles of golden sand, excellent shopping and leisure facilities. Lively entertainments include Festival of Lights at the beginning of September.

Self-contained two bedroom apartments in quiet avenue, one minute from clean, sandy beaches and five minutes from shops. Sleeps 2-6. Includes linen. Fully equipped kitchen, cooker, fridge, microwave, colour TV, toilet and shower. Central heating. Electric meter. Parking. Terms from £200. Contact: MRS HAMMOND, STOURCLIFFE COURT, 56 STOURCLIFFE AVENUE, SOUTHBOURNE, BOURNEMOUTH BH6 3PX (01202 420698). [Pets £5 weekly]

ALUM DENE HOTEL, 2 BURNABY ROAD, ALUM CHINE, BOURNEMOUTH BH4 8JF (01202 764011) Renowned for good old fashioned hospitality and friendly service. Come and be spoilt at our licensed hotel. All rooms en suite, colour TV. Some have sea views. 200 metres sea. Parking. Christmas House party. No charge for pets. [🐕]

ANNE & RICHARD REYNOLDS, THE VINE HOTEL, 22 SOUTHERN ROAD, SOUTHBOURNE, BOURNEMOUTH BH6 3SR (01202 428309). Small, family, Hotel only 3 minutes' walk from dog friendly beach and shops. All rooms en suite. Residential licence. FHG Diploma, STB ◆◆◆ [🐕]

HOLIDAY FLATS AND FLATLETS a short walk to golden, sandy beaches. Most with private bathrooms. Cleanliness and comfort assured. Dogs welcome. Contact: M DE KMENT, 4 CECIL ROAD, BOURNEMOUTH BH5 1DU (07788 952394). [Pets £20 per week]

BOURNECOAST. (01202 428717/01202 417757). Self-catering allows you the time to choose the location, the places, your meals and timetable; the freedom to enjoy our golden sands, clean seas and glorious attractions; to holiday in style in a choice of 200 self-catering properties. Call for our FREE brochure or visit our website. Est 1960, K.W. Simmons MBE.
website: www.bournecoast.co.uk

MIKE AND LYN LAMBERT, AARON, 16 FLORENCE ROAD, BOURNEMOUTH BH5 1HF (01202 304925/01425 474007 Fax: 01425 475151). Modern Holiday Apartments sleeping one to ten persons, close to sea and shops. Fully fitted kitchens and individual gas boilers. Clean, well-equipped flats. Car park. Write or phone for colour brochure and terms. [Pets £25 per week]
e-mail: mikelyn_lambert@btinternet.com

BILL AND MARJORIE TITCHEN, WHITE TOPPS HOTEL, 45 CHURCH ROAD, SOUTHBOURNE, BOURNEMOUTH BH6 4BB (01202 428868). Situated in quiet position close to lovely walks and beach. Dogs essential. Free parking. Residential licence. [🐕 pw!]
e-mail: Thedogplace1@aol.com website: www.whitetopps.co.uk

LANGTRY MANOR, DERBY ROAD, EAST CLIFF, BOURNEMOUTH BH1 3QB (01202 553887). A rare gem of a hotel where the building, food, service and history blend to form something quite exceptional. Midweek and weekend breaks. Pets welcome by arrangement.
website: www.langtrymanor.com

Bridport

Market town of Saxon origin noted for rope and net making. Harbour at West Bay has sheer cliffs rising from the beach.

MRS S. NORMAN, FROGMORE FARM, CHIDEOCK, BRIDPORT DT6 6HT (01308 456159). The choice is yours - Bed and Breakfast in charming farmhouse, OR self-catering Cottage equipped for five, pets welcome. Brochure and terms free on request. [1st dog free, 2nd dog £3.00 per night, £15 per week]

EYPE HOUSE CARAVAN & CAMPING PARK, EYPE, BRIDPORT DT6 6AL (01308 424903) Small, quiet family-run park lying on the Heritage Coastal Path, 200 yards from the beach. Static vans for hire from £160 to £400, tent pitches (all terraced with sea views) £8.50 to £14.50 for four people. Sorry, no tourers. Children and dogs welcome.

GOLDEN ACRE, EYPE, NEAR BRIDPORT DT6 6AL (01308 421521). Private peaceful park. Chalet bungalows (1 or 2 bedrooms), sleep 2-6. Wonderful walks, part of World Heritage Coastline. Pets free (of course), house-trained owners welcome! [🐕]

MR KARL MANSFIELD, LANCOMBES HOUSE, WEST MILTON, BRIDPORT DT6 3TN (01308 485375). Pretty cottages in converted barns. Panoramic views to sea four miles away. Set in 10 acres, some have fenced gardens. Many walks from our land. ETC ★★★ [🐕]
website: www.lancombeshouse.co.uk

Charmouth

Small resort on Lyme Bay, 3 miles Lyme Regis. Sandy beach backed by undulating cliffs where many fossils are found. Good walks.

DOLPHINS RIVER PARK, BERNE LANE, CHARMOUTH DT6 6RD (FREEPHONE 0800 0746375). Luxury 4 and 6 berth caravans on small, peaceful park. Coin-op laundry. One mile from beach. Colour brochure available. BGHP ★★★★ [Pets £2.50 per night, £12.50 per week]

MR F. LOOSMORE, MANOR FARM HOLIDAY CENTRE, CHARMOUTH, BRIDPORT DT6 6QL (01297 560226). All units for four to six people. Ten minutes' level walk to beach, many fine local walks. Swimming pools, licensed bar with family room, shop, launderette. Sporting facilities nearby. Children and pets welcome. SAE for colour brochure. [Pets from £20 per week]

THE QUEEN'S ARMES HOTEL, THE STREET, CHARMOUTH DT6 6QF (01297 560339). Former coaching inn c.1500. Log fires; 11 unique bedrooms, 10 en suite, one with own bathroom. Lounge, bar and dining room. Vegetarians and vegans catered for. ETC ◆◆◆◆ [🐕]

Christchurch

Residential town near coast. Yachting based on Christchurch harbour and Christchurch Bay.

COUNTRY HOLIDAY CHALET on small, quiet, secluded woodland park. Sleeps four. Fenced private garden. Dogs welcome. Car parking. £150 to £350 per week. BH & HPA Member. Write enclosing SAE or telephone: MRS L.M. BOWLING, OWLPEN CARAVANS LTD, OWLPEN, 148 BURLEY ROAD, BRANSGORE, NEAR CHRISTCHURCH, DORSET BH23 8DB (01425 672875; mobile 07860 547391). [🐕 pw!]

Dorchester

Busy market town steeped in history. Roman remains include Amphitheatre and villa.

GRACE COTTAGE. Charming cottage with enclosed garden. Lounge/dining room, study/bedroom, two bedrooms, well-equipped kitchen, two bathrooms. Pub nearby. Non-smokers only. Good touring centre. ETC ◆◆◆◆. Apply: MRS WILLIS, LAMPERTS COTTAGE, SYDLING ST NICHOLAS DT2 9NU (01300 341659; Fax: 01300 341699). [🐕]
e-mail: nickywillis@tesco.net

CHURCHVIEW GUEST HOUSE, WINTERBOURNE ABBAS, DORCHESTER DT2 9LS (Tel & Fax: 01305 889296). Beautiful 17th Century Licensed Guest House set in the heart of West Dorset, character bedrooms, delightful period dining room, two lounges and bar. Non-smoking. B&B £28–£38 pp. B&BEM £42–£54. Short breaks available. ETC ◆◆◆◆. [🐕]
e-mail: stay@churchview.co.uk website: www.churchview.co.uk

MRS JACOBINA LANGLEY, THE STABLES B&B, HYDE CROOK (OFF A37), FRAMPTON DT2 9NW (01300 320075; Fax: 01300 321718). Comfortable country house in 20 acres with uninterrupted country views. Guest accommodation in separate wing, fully double-glazed, with central heating. All pets most welcome. [pw! £1.50 per night]
e-mail: cobalangley@aol.com website: www.framptondorset.com

Eype

Village near coast 2km south-west of Bridport.

EYPE'S MOUTH COUNTRY HOTEL, EYPE, BRIDPORT DT6 6AL (01308 423300). Experience the tranquillity of Dorset. Situated in a secret spot, down a leafy lane, just a five minute walk from the sea. Restaurant with views over Lyme Bay. [Pets £5.00 per night]
e-mail: info@eypesmouthhotel.co.uk website: www.eypesmouthhotel.co.uk

Lyme Regis

Picturesque little resort with harbour, once the haunt of smugglers. Shingle beach with sand at low tide. Fishing, sailing and water ski-ing in Lyme Bay. Taunton 28 miles, Dorchester 24, Seaton 8.

JON AND DEBBY SNOOK, WESTOVER FARM COTTAGES, WOOTTON FITZPAINE, NEAR LYME REGIS DT6 6NE (01297 560451). Within walking distance of the sea. Four beautiful cottages, sleep 6/7, with large secluded gardens. Car parking. Logs, linen available. 3 bedrooms. Well behaved pets welcome. ETC ★★★/★★★★ [Pets £15/£10 per week.]
e-mail: wfcottages@aol.com website: www.lymeregis.com/westover-farm-cottages/

MRS J TEDBURY, LITTLE PADDOCKS, YAWL HILL LANE, LYME REGIS DT7 3RW (01297 443085). A six-berth caravan on Devon/Dorset border overlooking Lyme Bay and surrounding countryside. Situated on a smallholding with animals. Fully equipped. Also fully equipped chalet for two. [🐕]

SYMBOLS

- 🐕 **Indicates that pets are welcome free of charge.**
- £ **Indicates that a charge is made for pets: nightly or weekly.**
- pw! **Shows some special provision for pets; exercise facility, feeding or accommodation arrangement.**
- ⌂ **Indicates separate pets accommodation.**

Milton Abbas

Village 6 miles south-west of Blandford Forum, 1 kilometre north-west of 14/15C Milton Abbey and Milton Abbey boys school.

LITTLE HEWISH BARN, MILTON ABBAS, BLANDFORD FORUM DT11 0DP (01258 881235; Fax: 01258 881393). Converted 150 year old brick and flint barn offering comfortable, very high standard accommodation. Two en suite double bedrooms. Children and well-behaved pets very welcome. ETC ★★★★★ [🐕]
e-mail: terry@littlehewish.co.uk

Piddletrenthide

Village 6 miles north of Dorchester.

THE POACHERS INN, PIDDLETRENTHIDE DT2 7QX (01300 348358; Fax: 01300 348153). On B3143 in lovely Piddle Valley, this delightful Inn offers en suite rooms with colour TV, tea/coffee making, phone. Swimming pool. Restaurant or Bar meals available. Garden – good dog walks! B&B £30.00. ETC/AA ◆◆◆◆. [Pets £2 per night, £10 per week]

Poole

Flourishing port and market town. Three museums with interesting collections and lively displays.

SANDFORD HOLIDAY PARK, WESTSTAR HOLIDAYS (0870 444 0080). Award-winning holiday park near Poole in a beautiful woodland setting and close to safe sandy beaches. Dogs welcome! Quote WP. ETC ★★★★ [Pets £35 per week, pw!]
website: www.weststarholidays.co.uk/pw

Powerstock

Village 4 miles north-east of Bridport.

MRS M. PREECE, THREE HORSESHOES INN, POWERSTOCK DT6 3TF (01308 485328). Victorian Inn tucked away in a peaceful part of West Dorset. Dogs welcome in three spacious en suite double rooms. Excellent cuisine. Log fires. [🐕]
e-mail: info@threehorseshoesinn.com website: www.threehorseshoesinn.com

Sherborne

Town with abbey and two castles, one of which was built by Sir Walter Raleigh with lakes and gardens by Capability Brown.

WHITE HORSE FARM, MIDDLEMARSH, SHERBORNE DT9 5QN. The Willows sleeps 4-6; Toad Hall sleeps 4; Badger's sleeps 2; Ratty's sleeps 2/4; Moley's sleeps 2. Character self-catering holiday cottages in rural location. Well-equipped and comfortable. TV, video, free films. 2 acres of paddock, garden and duck pond. Inn 100 yards. ETC ★★★★. DAVID, HAZEL, MARY AND GERRY WILDING (01963 210222) [🐕]
e-mail: enquiries@whitehorsefarm.co.uk website: www.whitehorsefarm.co.uk

Studland Bay

Unspoilt seaside village at south western end of Poole Bay, 3 miles north of Swanage.

THE KNOLL HOUSE, STUDLAND BH19 3AW (01929 450450; Fax: 01929 450423). Country house hotel within National Trust reserve. Golden beach. 100 acre grounds. Family suites of connecting rooms, six lounges. Tennis, golf, swimming, games rooms, health spa. Daily half-board terms from £92. See our Full Page Advertisement under Studland Bay. [pw! £4 nightly, includes food]
e-mail: info@knollhouse.co.uk website: www.knollhouse.co.uk

THE MANOR HOUSE HOTEL, STUDLAND BAY BH19 3AU (Tel & Fax: 01929 450288). National Trust hotel set in 20 acres on cliffs overlooking Studland Bay. Superb food and accommodation. Log fires and four-posters.Tennis, horse-riding, golf and walking.
website: www.themanorhousehotel.com

Swanage

Traditional family holiday resort set in a sheltered bay ideal for water sports. Good base for a walking holiday.

DORSET COTTAGE HOLIDAYS. Self-catering cottages, town houses, bungalows and apartments. All within 10 miles of Heritage Coastline and sandy beaches. Excellent walking in idyllic countryside. Short breaks from £80, weekly from £135 (per cottage). Open all year. Free brochure tel: 01929 553443. [🐕]
e-mail: enq@dhcottages.co.uk website: www.dhcottages.co.uk

LIMES HOTEL, 48 PARK ROAD, SWANAGE BH19 2AE (01929 422664; Fax: 0870 0548794). Small friendly Hotel. En suite rooms, TV, tea/coffee making facilities. Licensed bar. Children and pets welcome. Credit cards accepted. Telephone or SAE for brochure. ETC◆◆◆◆ [🐕]
e-mail: info@limeshotel.demon.co.uk website: www.limeshotel.demon.co.uk

MRS M. STOCKLEY, SWANAGE BAY VIEW HOLIDAY PARK, 17 MOOR ROAD, SWANAGE BH19 1RG (01929 424154). 4/5/6-berth Caravans. Pets welcome. Easter to October. Colour TV. Shop. Parking space. Rose Award Park [🐕]

Wareham

Picturesque riverside town almost surrounded by earthworks, considered pre-Roman. Nature reserves of great beauty nearby. Weymouth 19 miles, Bournemouth 14, Swanage 10, Poole 6.

MRS L. S. BARNES, LUCKFORD WOOD HOUSE, EAST STOKE, WAREHAM BH20 6AW (01929 463098; Fax: 01929 405715). Peaceful surroundings, delightful scenery. B&B luxurious farmhouse. Breakfast served in conservatory or dining room. Camping facilities include showers, toilets. Caravan and boat storage available. Near Lulworth Cove, Studland, Tank Museum and Monkey World. Open all year. From £28. [Pets £5 per night, £30 per week]
e-mail: info@luckfordleisure.co.uk website: www.luckfordleisure.co.uk

CATRIONA AND ALISTAIR MILLER, CROMWELL HOUSE HOTEL, LULWORTH COVE BH20 5RJ (01929 400253/400332; Fax: 01929 400566). Comfortable family-run hotel, set in secluded gardens with spectacular sea views. Heated swimming pool, 17 en suite bedrooms. Restaurant, bar wine list. ETC/AA/RAC ★★. [🐕]

DORMER COTTAGE, WOODLANDS AT HYDE, NEAR WAREHAM BH20 7NT (01929 471239). In the midst of Hardy Country, secluded cottage. All linen provided. Golf, pony trekking, riding nearby. Children and pets welcome. Beds ready made. [🐕]

West Bexington

Seaside village with pebble beach. Chesil beach stretches eastwards. Nearby is Abbotsbury with its Benedictine Abbey and famous Swannery. Dorchester 13 miles, Weymouth 13, Bridport 6.

GORSELANDS CARAVAN PARK, DEPT PW, WEST BEXINGTON-ON-SEA DT2 9DJ (01308 897232; Fax: 01308 897239). Holiday Park. Fully serviced and equipped 4/6 berth caravans. Shop and launderette on site. Glorious sea views. Good country and seaside walks. One mile to beach. Holiday apartments with sea views and private garden. Pets most welcome. Colour brochure on request. ETC ★★★★ [🐕]

Low Lands Farm, **Low Lands, Cockfield, Bishop Auckland, County Durham DL13 5AW.**
Tel: 01388 718251 • Mobile: 07745 067754 • e-mail: info@farmholidaysuk.com
website: www.farmholidaysuk.com • Two award-winning, beautifully renovated self-catering cottages on a working family farm. Each cottage sleeps up to four people, plus cot. Beams, log fires, gas BBQ, own gardens and parking. Pets and children most welcome; childminding and equipment available. Terms from £150 to £340, incl. linen, towels, electricity and heating. Call Alison or Keith Tallentire for a brochure.

ETC Cat. 3 Disabled Access

See also Colour Advertisement on page 42

Bee Cottage Farmhouse

Charming farmhouse with stunning views. You will be most welcome. Ideal for Newcastle, Durham, Beamish etc. Bed and Breakfast;dinner available, licensed. Great for pets.

MELITA & DAVID TURNER, BEE COTTAGE FARMHOUSE, CASTLESIDE, CONSETT DH8 9HW (01207 508224)

e-mail: welcome@beecottagefarmhouse.freeserve.co.uk • web:www.beecottage.co.uk

Large enclosed garden with patio, BBQ and garden furniture
PETS WELCOME

Superb detached holiday cottage on working farm, ideal for walking/touring in Weardale, the Yorkshire Dales and the Lake District.
Village with pub and shop ½ mile.
•• open-plan lounge/kitchen/diner ••
•• one double and one twin bed bedrooms ••
•• bathroom with bath and shower ••
•• suitable for partially disabled ••

Low Mulberry Holiday Cottage
Details from Mrs Pauline Bowles, Marley Moor Farm, Ingleton, Darlington, Durham DL2 3HZ • 01833 660332

See also Colour Advertisement on page 42

Ivesley Equestrian Centre,
Ivesley, Waterhouses, Durham DH7 9HB. TEL: 0191 373 4324; FAX: 0191 373 4757
e-mail: ivesley@msn.com • website: www.ridingholidays-ivesley.co.uk
Beautifully furnished comfortable country house set in 220 acres in Durham, but very quiet and rural. Excellent dog exercising facilities. En suite bedrooms. Excellent food. Licensed. Fully equipped Equestrian Centre adjacent.

Mrs P. A. Booth

Bishop Auckland

Town on right bank of River Wear, 9 miles south-west of Durham. Castle, of varying dates, residence of the Bishop of Durham.

ALISON & KEITH TALLENTIRE, LOW LANDS FARM, LOW LANDS, COCKFIELD, BISHOP AUCKLAND DL13 5AW (01388 718251; mobile: 07745 067754). Two self-catering cottages on a working livestock farm. Each sleeps up to 4, plus cot. Prices from £150-£340. Call for a brochure. Pets and children most welcome. ETC ★★★★ ETC CATEGORY 3 DISABLED ACCESSIBILITY (one cottage). [Pets £10 per week]
e-mail: info@farmholidaysuk.com website: www.farmholidaysuk.com

Castleside

A suburb 2 miles south-west of Consett.

MELITA & DAVID TURNER, BEE COTTAGE FARMOUSE, CASTLESIDE, CONSETT DH8 9HW (01207 508224). Charming farmhouse with stunning views. You will be most welcome. Ideal for Newcastle, Durham, Beamish etc. Bed and Breakfast; dinner available, licensed. Great for pets. ETC ◆◆◆◆ [pw! 🐕]
e-mail: welcome@beecottagefarmhouse.freeserve.co.uk website: www.beecottage.co.uk

Ingleton

Village 3 miles east of Staindrop.

LOW MULBERRY HOLIDAY COTTAGE. Superb detached holiday cottage on working farm, ideal for walking/touring. One double, one twin room; large enclosed garden. Pets welcome. Details from: MRS PAULINE BOWLES, MARLEY MOOR FARM, INGLETON, DARLINGTON, DURHAM DL2 3HZ (01833 660332).

Teesdale

Admin district of the County of Durham. Ideal area for all outdoor activities.

FROG HALL COTTAGE (Tel & Fax: 01833 622215). Traditional cottage, magnificent views. Rare flora and fauna near Nature Reserve on award-winning environmental farm. Sheep and cows peer over your garden wall. Guided walks arranged.[🐕]
e-mail: kath@herdship.freeserve.co.uk website: www.herdship.co.uk

Waterhouses

6 miles west of Durham.

MRS P. A. BOOTH, IVESLEY EQUESTRIAN CENTRE, IVESLEY, WATERHOUSES, DURHAM DH7 9HB (0191 373 4324; Fax: 0191 373 4757). Beautifully furnished comfortable country house set in 220 acres in Durham but very quiet and rural. Excellent dog exercising facilities. En suite bedrooms. Excellent food. Licensed. Fully equipped Equestrian Centre adjacent. [Pets £2 per night].
e-mail: ivesley@msn.com website: www.ridingholidays-ivesley.co.uk

Mersea Island

Winding lanes cross open countryside, joined to mainland by Strood Causeway.

COOPERS BEACH HOLIDAY PARK, EAST MERSEA, MERSEA ISLAND, NEAR COLCHESTER CO5 8TN. Charming seafront holiday park joined to mainland by causeway. Modern, well-equipped caravans. Ideal for water sports – outdoor heated pool, beach access; tennis, multi-sports court, countryside walks. Call 0870 442 9288 for brochure. ETC ★★★★
website: www.gbholidayparks.co.uk

St Lawrence Bay

On the south side of the River Blackmore estuary, 6 miles north of Burnham-on-Crouch.

WATERSIDE HOLIDAY PARK, MAIN ROAD, ST LAWRENCE BAY, NEAR SOUTHMINSTER CM0 7LY. Attractive park with fine estuary views. Modern quality range of hire caravans. Indoor pool; country club; nature reserves; sheltered beach and interesting walks nearby. Tourers and tents welcome. Call 0870 442 9298 for brochure. ETC ★★★★
website: www.gbholidayparks.co.uk

Weeley (Near Clacton-on-Sea)

Village 6 miles north east of Clacton-on-Sea.

WEELEY BRIDGE HOLIDAY PARK, WEELEY, NEAR CLACTON-ON-SEA CO16 9DH. Small beautifully maintained park in the heart of Essex countryside. Quality modern caravans. Fishing lake, outdoor heated pool, adventure play area, multisports court, country walks; licensed bar. Short drive to coast. Call 0870 442 9295 for brochure. ETC ★★★
website: www.gbholidayparks.co.uk

Terms quoted in this publication may be subject to increase if rises in costs necessitate

---

THE KINGSBRIDGE INN & CHESTER HOUSE HOTEL

VICTORIA STREET, BOURTON-ON-THE-WATER, GLOUCESTERSHIRE GL54 2BU

TELEPHONE 01451 820286 • FAX 01451 820471
E-MAIL: kingsbridgeinn.bourtononthewater@eldridge-pope.co.uk
WEBSITE: www.roomattheinn.info

Bourton-on-the-Water The Venice of the Cotswolds. A haven of peace and comfort tucked away in a quiet backwater of this famous village.

Tel: 01451 830007

ROSE'S COTTAGE **Broadwell, Cotswolds** ETC ★★★★

Delightful country cottage in Broadwell, tastefully decorated and furnished. It is heated by storage radiators and electric log effect burner. On the ground floor is a well-equipped kitchen with hob, oven, microwave, washer-drier and fridge. Lounge has TV, comfortable furniture. Bedroom and a large bathroom upstairs. Small patio. Next door to owners' house. Close to family pub. Good walking area. Welcome provisions, linen and towels provided.

*** Tariff: low £220, mid £270 and high £320. ***

CHARLTON KINGS HOTEL

London Road, Charlton Kings, Cheltenham GL52 6UU
Tel: 01242 231061 • Fax: 01242 241900
e-mail: enquiries@charltonkingshotel.co.uk
website: www.charltonkingshotel.co.uk

Privately owned, with high standards throughout. All rooms beautifully refurbished. All rooms have en suite facilities, most have views of the Cotswold hills and ample car parking is available. Ideally located for Cheltenham and the Cotswolds. Only two miles from the town centre, three miles from the racecourse. The choice is yours, whether you want the ideal base for visiting the numerous picturesque towns and places of interest, or prefer the wide choice of shops and theatres or relax in the magnificent gardens in Cheltenham. ETC/AA/RAC ★★★

RESIDENTIAL AND TABLE LICENCE • 14 BEDROOMS, ALL WITH PRIVATE BATHROOMS
NON-SMOKING ACCOMMODATION AVAILABLE • CHILDREN AND PETS WELCOME.

This charming 13th Century farmhouse hotel, in its own extensive grounds (14 acres), is ideal for dog walking. The Hotel is situated in the village of Clearwell in the Forest of Dean and close to the Wye Valley. Twenty-two en suite bedrooms including Four-Posters and Cottage Suite. The award-winning restaurant serves a selection of traditional food and a comprehensive wine list. B&B from £75 per room.

Tudor Farmhouse Hotel & Restaurant, Clearwell, Near Coleford GL16 8JS WTB ★★★
Tel: 01594 833046 Fax: 01594 837093 E-mail: info@tudorfarmhousehotel.co.uk AA ★★

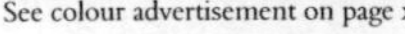

See colour advertisement on page xx

HARTWELL FARM COTTAGES **Near Bibury, Cotswolds ETC ★★★★**

Two traditionally built cottages with far reaching views, on the southern edge of the Cotswolds. Both are fully equipped to a high standard, with heating and woodburning stoves; large private enclosed gardens. Stabling for horses; tennis court. Ideal for touring and horse riding. Glorious walks, excellent pubs. Children and well-behaved dogs welcome. Sleep 3-4/4-5.

Contact: **Caroline Mann: Tel: 01285 740210**
Email: cottages@hartwells89.freeserve.co.uk • www.selfcateringcotswolds.com

A useful Index of Towns/Villages and Counties appears on page 426 – please also refer to Contents Page 3.

ETC ★★

The Bull Hotel

The Market Place, Fairford, Gloucestershire GL7 4AA

Tel: 01285 712535/712217 • Fax: 01285 713782

e-mail: info@thebullhotelfairford.co.uk

website: www.thebullhotelfairford.co.uk

AA ★★

15th century family-run coaching inn. Ideal for touring Cotswolds. A la carte restaurant situated in original stables. Ideal for conferences and weddings. 1½ miles private fishing on River Coln. The hotel has a choice of 22 fully equipped bedrooms with sloping roofs and oak beams. Four-poster beds available. There are good golf courses, squash and tennis courts, sailing facilities and fishing within easy reach of the hotel. Situated in the South Cotswolds. **Tariff: £49.50 - £89.50**

OLD BREWERY HOUSE,
BREWERY YARD, REDBROOK ON WYE,
MONMOUTHSHIRE NP25 4LU
01600 713819.
e-mail: enquiries@oldbreweryhouse.com
website: www.oldbreweryhouse.com

Welcoming en suite accommodation with courtyard garden and private parking. Scenic riverside and off-road walks. Two village pubs serve meals. B&B £55 per room per night. Dogs free. WTB ★★★

B&B £50–£80 per couple.

Pets £7.50 per stay.

GUNN MILL HOUSE **Forest of Dean, Gloucestershire GL17 OEA**

The Lucas family invite you, and your owners, to stay in their Georgian home and 5 acre grounds right in the forest – walks galore! Antiques, a roaring log fire, old-fashioned luxury, with all en suite rooms and suites. First-class home cooked dinners. Licensed. Non-smoking.

Telephone & Fax: 01594 827577

E-mail: info@gunnmillhouse.co.uk Website: www.gunnmillhouse.co.uk

---

The Speech House

Coleford, Forest of Dean GL16 7EL
Tel: 01594 822607 • Fax: 01594 823658

A friendly Hotel set in the heart of the Forest of Dean, perfect for walking dogs. Almost completely enveloped by trees, the Speech House is the perfect place to get away from it all. The hotel has 37 bedrooms, all of which are en suite, plus a Spa and Gym. The hotel has several four-poster beds and was built by King Charles II as a Hunting Lodge. Courtyard ground floor rooms are available. Pets are welcome. **AA/RAC ★★★**

E-mail: relax@thespeechhouse.co.uk • Website: www.thespeechhouse.co.uk

---

the old farm

Barrel Lane, Longhope GL17 0LR

Treat yourself to a stay in our charming 16th century farmhouse with its wealth of old oak beams, fireplaces and character. Relax with afternoon tea, including home-made cakes, in front of the fire or in the sunny south-facing garden. All bedrooms en suite, including four-poster. Sumptuous breakfasts made from local produce and our own free range eggs. Ideal for visiting the Royal Forest of Dean, Cheltenham, Gloucester and the Cotswolds. Good pubs and restaurants, the closest just three minutes' walk. Pets welcome. *Also, three luxury self-catering cottages.*

Tel: 01452 830252 • e-mail: FHG@the-old-farm.co.uk • website: www.the-old-farm.co.uk

---

The Laurels at Inchbrook

Lesley Williams-Allen, The Laurels at Inchbrook
Nailsworth GL5 5HA • Tel & Fax: 01453 834021
e-mail: laurels@inchbrook.fsnet.co.uk

A comfortable, rambling house, cottage and garden set beside the Inch Brook and adjoining fields. Our en suite double, twin and family rooms, are in both the main house and the cottage annexe. There is wheelchair access from the car park and a ground floor room suitable for disabled guests. Breakfast is taken in the dining room on the ground floor of the main house, or in the garden, weather permitting. We offer a wood-panelled study for quiet reading, and a games room/fitness suite with a pool table. There is plenty of space to sit in the garden, where watching wildlife can also give much pleasure - we feed badgers at night by the stream, observe a bat colony, the stream is an otter route, and many birds come to visit us. Pets are most welcome, and there are splendid walks and a country park close by. We are licensed. Nearby Nailsworth is a centre for excellence when it comes to eating out. Ideally placed for exploring the West Country, Bath and Forest of Dean as well as the Cotswolds, our house is perfect for groups and family gatherings. Brochure on request. Self-catering facilities available at certain times of the year. B & B from £22.50 pp. Rooms 2 double, 2 twin, 2 family, 1 disabled, all en suite No smoking, Children and Pets welcome. Never closed.

SWAN HOUSE COUNTRY GUEST HOUSE

Tel: 01594 516504
Fax: 01594 516177

Philip and Elaine extend a warm welcome to our family guesthouse in the village of Newnham near the Forest of Dean. Our 17th century house has six bedrooms, all individually decorated and en suite, with many comforts including electric blankets. There is a choice of evening meals; most dietary needs can be catered for. We have a carefully tended garden which we are happy to share with you. Pets are welcome.

High Street, Newnham-on-Severn, Glouсs GL14 1BY AA ◆◆◆◆

e-mail: enquiries@swanhousenewnham.co.uk • website: www.swanhousenewnham.co.uk

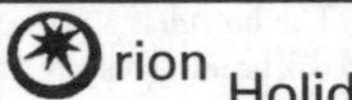

The Cotswold Water Park is a peaceful and attractive location for a tranquil countryside break. Many properties are ETC ★★★★ standard, accept pets and sleep up to 8. **Mill Village** - a luxurious rural retreat. Heated outdoor pool, sauna, tennis, fishing, children's play area etc. **Isis Lakes** - relax and unwind on your own private sun deck; wide range of activities, including fishing, tennis, children's play area, football net, golf practice net. **Spring Lake** – water-ski club, plus a lakeside bar, gymnasium and children's play area.

Orion Holidays • 01285 861839 • Fax: 01285 869188
e-mail: bookings@orionholidays.com • www.orionholidays.com

See also Colour Advertisement on page 42

Established over 30 years AA/RAC ◆◆◆

Large Country House with attractive garden, overlooking fields. Four minutes to town centre. One four-poster bedroom; double, twin or family rooms, all en suite. Tea/coffee making facilities, colour TV in all rooms. TV lounge. Central heating. Children and pets welcome. Car park. Bed and Full English Breakfast from £20.00 to £25.00 pppn. Open all year except Christmas.

THE LIMES **Evesham Road, Stow-on-the-Wold, GL54 1EN**
Tel: 01451 830034/831056 • e-mail: thelimes@zoom.co.uk

Dear Rover, *Well, we've just got back from our holidays – absolute bliss and what a lovely place the Downfield is – we got a really warm welcome from the owners. Great walks in the Cotswolds, comfy rooms, a bar, delicious food and the Joneses I brought with me were really pleased as well. I made lots of new friends – there were even some cats to chase! Why don't you come with me next year and bring your owners with you – Just call Nigel or Maura on the dog and bone on* **01453 764496** ***Lots of licks, Toby*** **ETC/AA**

The Downfield Hotel, 134 Cainscross Road, Stroud, Gloucestershire GL5 4HN ◆◆◆

See also Colour Advertisement on page 42

POWELLS COTTAGE HOLIDAYS, 51 HIGH STREET, SAUNDERSFOOT, PEMBROKESHIRE SA69 9EJ. Many of our top quality holiday properties accept pets. Cottages in Devon, Cornwall, Cotswolds, Pembrokeshire and Heart of England. For colour brochure FREEPHONE 0800 378771 (24 hours). website: www.powells.co.uk

Bourton-on-the-Water

Delightfully situated on the River Windrush which is crossed by miniature stone bridges. Stow-on-the-Wold 4 miles.

KINGSBRIDGE INN AND CHESTER HOUSE HOTEL, VICTORIA STREET, BOURTON-ON-THE-WATER GL54 2BU (01451 820286). All rooms en suite, all with central heating, colour TV, phone, tea/coffee making facilities. Wheelchair friendly. Ideal for touring Cotswolds. [🐕]
e-mail: kingsbridgeinn.bourtononthewater@eldridge-pope.co.uk
website: www.roomattheinn.info

SYMBOLS

- 🐕 **Indicates that pets are welcome free of charge.**
- £ **Indicates that a charge is made for pets: nightly or weekly.**
- pw! **Shows some special provision for pets; exercise facility, feeding or accommodation arrangement.**
- ⌂ **Indicates separate pets accommodation.**

Broadwell

Village near the border of Oxfordshire, 1 mile north of Stow-on-the-Wold.

ROSE'S COTTAGE, BROADWELL, COTSWOLDS (01451 830007). Delightful country cottage, tastefully decorated and furnished. Well-equipped kitchen, lounge with TV, comfortable furniture, bedroom, and a large bathroom. Marvellous walking area. **ETC ★★★★** [🐕]

Cheltenham

Anglo-Saxon market town transformed into elegant Regency resort with the discovery of medicinal springs. 8 miles east of Gloucester.

CHARLTON KINGS HOTEL, LONDON ROAD, CHELTENHAM GL52 6UU (01242 231061; Fax: 01242 241900). Ideal venue for Cheltenham and the Cotswolds. Double en suite room from £47.50 per person for 1 night, £42.50 per person for 3 nights or £38.00 for 5 nights including full English breakfast. All rooms beautifully refurbished, most have views of the Cotswold Hills. We offer a standard of service only a small hotel can provide. [Pets £3 per night]. ETC/AA/RAC ★★★
e-mail: enquiries@charltonkingshotel.co.uk website: www.charltonkingshotel.co.uk

Clearwell (Forest of Dean)

Village 2 miles south of Coleford in the ancient Forest of Dean.

TUDOR FARMHOUSE HOTEL & RESTAURANT, CLEARWELL, NEAR COLEFORD GL16 8JS (Freephone 0800 7835935; Tel: 01594 833046; Fax: 01594 837093). Charming 13th Century farmhouse hotel in extensive grounds, ideal for dog walking. 22 en suite bedrooms including Four Posters and Cottage Suite. Award-winning restaurant. WTB ★★★, AA ★★ and Rosette. [🐕]
e-mail: info@tudorfarmhousehotel.co.uk website: www.tudorfarmhousehotel.co.uk

Cotswolds

An area well known for gentle hillsides and sleepy villages.

CAROLINE MANN, HARTWELL FARM COTTAGES, NEAR BIBURY, COTSWOLDS (01285 740210). Two comfortable, fully equipped cottages with country views. Ideally located for touring. Stabling available. Glorious walks, excellent pubs. Children and well-behaved dogs welcome. ETC ★★★/★★★★
e-mail: cottages@hartwells89.freeserve.co.uk website: www.selfcateringcotswolds.com

Fairford

Small town 8 miles east of Cirencester.

THE BULL HOTEL, MARKET PLACE, FAIRFORD GL7 4AA (01285 712535/712217; Fax: 01285 713782). Ideal for holding conferences and wedding receptions. Restaurant offers à la carte menu and fine wines. The hotel has a choice of 22 fully equipped bedrooms with sloping roofs and oak beams. Four-poster beds available. ETC/AA ★★ [Pets £5 per night, £20 per week]
e-mail: info@thebullhotelfairford.co.uk website: www.thebullhotelfairford.co.uk

FREE or REDUCED RATE entry to Holiday Visits and Attractions – see our READERS' OFFER VOUCHERS on pages 101-116

Forest of Dean

Formerly a royal hunting ground, this scenic area lies between the rivers Severn and Wye.

DRYSLADE FARM, ENGLISH BICKNOR, COLEFORD (Tel & Fax: 01594 860259). Daphne and Phil warmly welcome you and your dogs for B&B at their 18th century farmhouse on family working farm. Situated in Royal Forest of Dean and close to Symonds Yat with ample walking. Excellent breakfast. Terms from £25 - £30. ETC ◆◆◆◆, MOBILITY LEVEL 1.
website: www.drysladefarm.co.uk

OLD BREWERY HOUSE, BREWERY YARD, REDBROOK ON WYE, MONMOUTHSHIRE NP25 4LU (01600 713819). Welcoming en suite accommodation with courtyard garden and private parking. Scenic riverside and off-road walks. Two village pubs serve meals. B&B £55 per room per night. Dogs free. WTB ★★★ [🐕]
e-mail: enquiries@oldbreweryhouse.com website: www.oldbreweryhouse.com

GUNN MILL HOUSE COUNTRY GUEST HOUSE, LOWER SPOUT LANE, MITCHELDEAN GL17 0EA (Tel & Fax: 01594 827577). Eight individually designed rooms including four-poster and suites with direct access to 5-acre garden and Forest of Dean. All en suite, TV. Fine dining. Licensed. ETC ◆◆◆◆ Silver Award. [pw! Pets £7.50 per stay]. SEE DISPLAY ADVERT.
e-mail: info@gunnmillhouse.co.uk website: www.gunnmillhouse.co.uk

THE SPEECH HOUSE, COLEFORD, FOREST OF DEAN GL16 7EL (01594 822607; Fax: 01594 823658). A friendly Hotel set in the heart of the Forest of Dean. The perfect place to get away from it all. 32 en suite bedrooms. Lavish restaurant. Aqua spa and beauty suite. AA/RAC ★★★ [Pets £10 per stay]
e-mail: relax@thespeechhouse.co.uk website: www.thespeechhouse.co.uk

Longhope

Village 9 miles west of Gloucester.

MRS LUCY RODGER, THE OLD FARM, BARREL LANE, LONGHOPE GL17 0LR (01452 830252). Charming 16th century farmhouse, all bedrooms en suite, including four-poster. Ideal for visiting the Royal Forest of Dean, Cheltenham, Gloucester and the Cotswolds. Pets welcome. [🐕]
e-mail: FHG@the-old-farm.co.uk website: www.the-old-farm.co.uk

Nailsworth

Hilly town 4 miles south of Stroud

LESLEY WILLIAMS-ALLEN, THE LAURELS, INCHBROOK, NAILSWORTH GL5 5HA (Tel & Fax: 01453 834021). A lovely rambling licensed house and cottage, where dogs and their owners are encouraged to relax and enjoy. Ideally situated for touring all parts of the Cotswolds and West Country. Brochure. B&B from £22.50. Credit cards accepted. [🐕]
e-mail: laurels@inchbrook.fsnet.co.uk

Newnham-on-Severn

Town on right bank on River Severn, 10 miles south-west of Gloucester.

PHILIP AND ELAINE SHELDRAKE, SWAN HOUSE COUNTRY GUEST HOUSE, HIGH STREET, NEWNHAM-ON-SEVERN GL14 1BY (01594 516504). Family guest house near Forest of Dean. Six individually decorated bedrooms, all en suite, with many comforts. Choice of evening meal. Garden. Pets welcome. Stabling available in village. AA ◆◆◆◆ [Pets £5 per stay]
e-mail: enquiries@swanhousenewnham.co.uk website: www.swanhousenewnham.co.uk

PLEASE SEND A STAMPED ADDRESSED ENVELOPE WITH ENQUIRIES

Painswick

Beautiful little Cotswold town with characteristic stone-built houses.

MISS E. COLLETT, HAMBUTTS MYND, EDGE ROAD, PAINSWICK GL6 6UP (01452 812352; Fax: 01452 813862). Bed and Breakfast in an old Converted Corn Mill. Very quiet with superb views. Three minutes to the centre of the village. Central heating. One double room, one twin, one single, all with TV. From £30 to £55 per night per room. ALL ROOMS EN SUITE. RAC/TBC ◆◆◆. [🐕]
e-mail: ewarland@aol.com

South Cerney

Village 4 miles south east of Cirencester. Airfield to the north.

ORION HOLIDAYS (01285 861839; Fax: 01285 869188). The Cotswold Water Park is a peaceful and attractive location for a tranquil countryside break. Many properties are ETC ★★★★ standard, accept pets and sleep up to 8.
e-mail: bookings@orionholidays.com website: www.orionholidays.com

Stow-on-the-Wold

Charming Cotswold hill-top market town with several old inns and interesting buildings. Birmingham 45 miles, Gloucester 26, Stratford-upon-Avon 21, Cheltenham 18, Chipping Norton 9.

THE LIMES, EVESHAM ROAD, STOW-ON-THE-WOLD GL54 1EN (01451 830034/831056). Large Country House. Attractive garden, overlooking fields, 4 minutes town centre. Television lounge. Central heating. Car park. Bed and Breakfast from £20 to £25.00 pppn. Twin, double or family rooms, all en suite. Children and pets welcome. AA/RAC ◆◆◆, Tourist Board Listed. [🐕]
e-mail: thelimes@zoom.co.uk

Stroud

Cotswold town on River Frome below picturesque Stroudwater Hills, formerly renowned for cloth making. Bristol 32 miles, Bath 29, Chippenham 25, Cheltenham 14, Gloucester 9.

MRS A. RHOTON, HYDE CREST, CIRENCESTER ROAD, MINCHINHAMPTON GL6 8PE (01453 731631). Beautiful country house with enclosed acre garden. All rooms on ground floor opening on to patios and lawns. 500 acres of commons, plus country walks nearby. AA ◆◆◆◆ [🐕]
e-mail: stay@hydecrest.co.uk website: http://www.hydecrest.co.uk

DOWNFIELD HOTEL, CAINSCROSS ROAD, STROUD GL5 4HN (01453 764496). Easy to find – just 5 miles from M5 – and easy to park. Ideal location for exploring Cotswolds. Comfortable lounges, home-cooked evening meal, cosy bar – all at sensible prices. Dogs and children most welcome. ETC/AA ◆◆◆. [🐕]
e-mail: info@downfieldhotel.co.uk website: www.downfieldhotel.co.uk

PLEASE NOTE

All the information in this book is given in good faith in the belief that it is correct. However, the publishers cannot guarantee the facts given in these pages, neither are they responsible for changes in policy, ownership or terms that may take place after the date of going to press. Readers should always satisfy themselves that the facilities they require are available and that the terms, if quoted, still apply.

The Woodlands Lodge Hotel

Bartley Road, Woodlands, New Forest, Hampshire SO40 7GN
Reservations: (023) 80 292257 • Fax: (023) 80 293090
e-mail: reception@woodlands-lodge.co.uk • www.woodlands-lodge.co.uk

The Woodlands Lodge Hotel is a luxuriously restored Georgian Country House, set within the beautiful New Forest, yet only 15 minutes from Southampton. Our attractive gardens have direct access to the forest and are ideal for romantic walks. Golf, fishing and horse riding are available nearby and the hotel is perfectly situated for touring the area. Come and unwind from the stress of everyday life and enjoy pure luxury without ostentation.

All bedrooms enjoy full en suite facilities of whirlpool bath and separate shower and have king sized beds and a full range of amenities. The quality four-course menu is changed seasonally to make use of local produce and is complemented by an interesting wine list. The service is friendly, efficient and informal.

Woodlands Lodge – where a warm welcome awaits you.

See also Colour Advertisement on page 43

Ellerslie Touring Caravan & Camping Park

Only six miles from Continental ferry port

Small partly wooded site on southern slopes of Portsdown Hill. Next door to riding stables, also health and fitness club and 600 yards from 27 hole golf course.

Within easy reach of excellent boating facilities, also many sites of historic interest. Nicely appointed toilet facilities. Chemical emptying. Food preparation and wash room. Raised barbecues allowed. Free showers. Car and Caravan plus two persons, from £8.50 per night.

Southern Tourist Board Graded, AA & RAC Listed

Downend Road, Fareham, Hampshire PO16 8TS

Telephone & Fax: 01329 822248

AA ♦♦♦♦ Guest Accommodation

Harts Lodge

242 Everton Road, Everton, Lymington, Hampshire SO41 OHE

Bungalow (non-smoking), set in three acres. Large garden with small lake. Quiet location. Three miles west of Lymington. Friendly welcome. Double, twin and family en suite rooms, each with tea/coffee making facilities and colour TV. Delicious four-course English breakfast. The sea and forest are five minutes away by car. Horse riding, golf and fishing are nearby. The village pub, ½ mile serves excellent meals. Pets welcome. Bed and Breakfast from £25 per person.

Tel: 01590 645902

"DOLPHINS" is a very caring and homely Victorian cottage in a quiet location, Central Lymington, offering warm hospitality and highest standards of accommodation. Spacious comfortable ground floor accommodation comprising single, double, twin or family room with en suite bathroom. Delicious breakfast provided. Small garden and own access leading to beautiful park to exercise pets within 2 minutes' walk. Colour TV. Very close to beautiful New Forest and Sea Walks. Just 5 minutes from railway/bus/coach stations and ferry. Leisure club facilities, beach chalet & mountain bikes. B&B from £23-£29 pppn; Children half price. Pets FREE. **ETC ♦♦♦♦ Welcome Host.**

Contact: Jane & Mike Finch, "Dolphins", 6 Emsworth Road, Lymington SO41 9BL Tel & Fax: 01590 676108
Mobile 07958 727536 • E-mail: dolphins@easynet.co.uk • Website: www.dolphinsnewforestbandb.co.uk

Efford Cottage

Everton, Lymington, Hampshire SO41 0JD
Tel: 01590 642315 • Fax: 01590 641030
e-mail: effordcottage@aol.com • web: www.effordcottage.co.uk

Guests receive a warm and friendly welcome to our home, which is a spacious Georgian cottage. All rooms are en suite with many extra luxury facilities. We offer a four-course multi-choice breakfast with homemade bread and preserves. Patricia is a qualified chef and uses our home-grown produce. An excellent centre for exploring both the New Forest and the South Coast with sports facilities, fishing, bird watching and horse riding in the near vicinity. Private parking. Dogs welcome. Sorry no children.

Bed and Breakfast from £25–£35 pppn. *Mrs Patricia J. Ellis.*

RAC Sparkling Diamond & Warm Welcome Accolades
STB Winner of " England For Excellence 2000"
RAC/AA/STB ♦♦♦♦♦ Gold Award. STB member with Welcome Host. FHG Diploma 1997/1999/2000
AA Nominated Landlady of Year 1998 & nominated Best British Breakfast Award 1999 & 2001.

AA ★★

ORMONDE HOUSE HOTEL

NEW FOREST TOURISM

SOUTHAMPTON ROAD, LYNDHURST, HAMPSHIRE SO43 7BT

TEL: (023) 8028 2806 • FAX: (023) 8028 2004

E-mail: info@ormondehouse.co.uk • Website: www.ormondehouse.co.uk

A relaxed blend of professionalism and warm hospitality awaits you at our elegant family-run Two Star Hotel, situated opposite the open forest, ideal for easy walking. 19 pretty en suite rooms and four luxury self-contained suites all, with CTV, phone and beverage making. 'Superior' and 'Superior Plus' rooms have sofas, with some 'Superior Plus' rooms and all 'Suites' featuring whirlpool baths and super king-sized zip and link beds. In addition all four suites offer full kitchens with washing/drying machines and dishwashers. Dine with us - our Chefs have an excellent reputation amongst regular guests for freshly prepared dishes, daily changing specials and wickedly tempting puddings. Close to Exbury Gardens and Beaulieu Motor Museum. Special 3 and 4 night breaks available throughout the year.

B&B from £30 pppn; DB&B from £45 pppn.

★★★ CROWN HOTEL • NEW FOREST ★★★

Tired of the same old walks? Enjoy forest, heath and the beach whilst staying at The Crown Hotel. 38 en suite rooms, all individual and recently refurbished. Our Chef of 30 years at The Crown, Stephen Greenhalgh, delights us with his imaginative menus using local produce wherever possible either in the informal bar or the Restaurant overlooking our water featured garden. Dogs are welcome to bring their well behaved owners!

High Street, LYNDHURST, Hampshire SO43 7NF

Tel: 023 8028 2922 • Fax: 023 8028 2751 E-mail: reception@crownhotel-lyndhurst.co.uk • Web: www.crownhotel-lyndhurst.co.uk

See also Colour Advertisement on page 43

ST. URSULA ◆◆◆◆

30 Hobart Road, New Milton, Hants. BH25 6EG

Between sea and New Forest, comfortable family home. Excellent facilities & warm welcome for well behaved pets and owners. Ground floor suite suitable for disabled guests plus single and twin rooms.

Mrs Judith Pearce **B&B from £25** **Tel: 01425 613515**

BEECHEN HOUSE **Clayhill, Lyndhurst, Hampshire SO43 7DN**

Private Victorian home. English breakfast. Secure off-road parking. Comfortable walking distance into New Forest. Non-Smoking. Dogs welcome.

WELCOME HOST

Tel: 023 8028 2006 • website: www.newforest.demon.co.uk/beechen.htm

Ashurst

Three miles north-east of Lyndhurst.

WOODLANDS LODGE HOTEL, BARTLEY ROAD, ASHURST, WOODLANDS SO40 7GN ((023) 80 292257; Fax: (023) 80 293090). Luxury Hotel offering peace and tranquillity. 16 bedrooms, all en suite with whirlpool bath, TV, hairdryer, telephone etc. AA Award winning Restaurant. Direct access to Forest. ETC/AA★★★ [🐕]
e-mail: reception@woodlands-lodge.co.uk website: www.woodlands-lodge.co.uk

Fareham

Old market town, 6 miles north-west of Portsmouth across the harbour.

ELLERSLIE TOURING CARAVAN & CAMPING PARK, DOWNEND ROAD, FAREHAM PO16 8TS (Tel & Fax: 01329 822248). Small partly wooded site. Close to stables, health club, golf course, boating facilities, sites of historic interest; ferry port. Food preparation and wash room. Raised barbecues allowed.

Lymington

Residential town and yachting centre 15 miles east of Bournemouth.

HONEYSUCKLE HOUSE, 24 CLINTON ROAD, LYMINGTON SO41 9EA (Tel & Fax: 01590 676635). Ground floor double room, en suite, non-smoking. Woodland walk, park, quay and marinas nearby. B&B from £25 pppn. [🐕]
e-mail: skyblue@beeb.net

MRS R SQUE, HARTS LODGE, 242 EVERTON ROAD, LYMINGTON SO41 0HE (01590 645902). Bungalow (non-smoking), set in three acres. Accommodation comprising double, twin and family en suite rooms, each with tea/coffee making facilities and colour TV. Horse riding, golf and fishing are nearby. Pets welcome. AA ◆◆◆◆. [Pets £2 per night, £10 per week].

MRS J. FINCH, "DOLPHINS", 6 EMSWORTH ROAD, LYMINGTON SO41 9BL (Tel & Fax: 01590 676108; Mobile: 07958 727536). Spacious ground floor, single, twin, double and family en suite rooms all with colour TV and tea/coffee making facilities. Leisure club facilities, beach chalet and mountain bikes. Very close to New Forest and sea walks. Park two minutes' walk. Please write or telephone for brochure. ETC ◆◆◆◆ Welcome Host. [🐕]
e-mail: dolphins@easynet.co.uk website: www.dolphinsnewforestbandb.co.uk

MRS P. J. ELLIS, EFFORD COTTAGE, EVERTON, LYMINGTON SO41 0JD (Tel & Fax: 01590 642315; Fax: 01590 641030). Friendly, award-winning Georgian cottage standing in grounds of one acre. Excellent centre for New Forest and South Coast. All rooms en suite with luxury facilities. B&B from £25 - £35pppn. No children. RAC/AA/STB ◆◆◆◆◆. [Pets £2 per night.]
e–mail: effordcottage@aol.com website: www.effordcottage.co.uk

Lyndhurst

Good base for enjoying the fascinating New Forest as well as the Hampshire coastal resorts. Bournemouth 20 miles, Southampton 9.

ORMONDE HOUSE HOTEL, SOUTHAMPTON ROAD, LYNDHURST SO43 7BT (023 8028 2806, Fax: 023 8028 2004). Opposite open forest, easy drive to Exbury Gardens and Beaulieu. Elegant, family-run Two Star Hotel with pretty en suite rooms with CTV, phone and beverage making. Superior plus rooms and ground floor suites with whirlpool baths and kingsize beds. Bar, lounge and delicious dinners available. AA ★★. [Pets £3.50 per night, max. 2 per room]
e-mail: info@ormondehouse.co.uk website: www.ormondehouse.co.uk

THE CROWN HOTEL, LYNDHURST, NEW FOREST S043 7NF (023 8028 2922; Fax: 023 8028 2751). A mellow, Listed building in the centre of the village, an ideal base for exploring the delights of the New Forest with your canine friend(s). Free parking, quiet garden, three star luxury and animal loving staff. [Pets £5.00 per night].
e-mail: reception@crownhotel-lyndhurst.co.uk website: www.crownhotel-lyndhurst.co.uk

New Forest

Area of heath and woodland of nearly 150 square miles, formerly Royal hunting grounds.

THE WATERSPLASH HOTEL, THE RISE, BROCKENHURST SO42 7ZP. Prestigious New Forest family-run country house hotel set in large garden. Noted for fine personal service, accommodation and traditional English cuisine at its best. All rooms en suite. Luxury 4-poster with double spa bath. Swimming pool. RAC, AA ★★. Colour brochure available (01590 622344).[🐕]
e-mail: bookings@watersplash.co.uk website: www.watersplash.co.uk

MRS THELMA ROWE, 9 CRUSE CLOSE, SWAY SO41 6AY (Tel & Fax: 01590 683092). Ground floor and first floor suites. Both en suite with sitting room, tea making facilities, fridge, TV and video. Quiet, very comfortable, friendly accommodation. Prices from £24 pp. ETC ◆◆◆◆ [Pets £2 per night for more than one, first dog free]
e-mail: ronrowe@talk21.com website: www.tivertonnewforest.co.uk

MRS E.E. MATTHEWS, THE ACORNS, OGDENS, NEAR FORDINGBRIDGE SP6 2PY (01425 655552). Luxury two bedroomed residential-type caravan. Sleeps 4/6. Maintained to high standard, kitchen, bathroom, sitting/diningroom, own garden. Lovely setting in heart of New Forest. Non-smoking, ample parking. Children over five years. Well-behaved dogs welcome (max. 2). Terms £170 - £299, Easter to mid-October. [Pets £10 per week].
e-mail: acornshols@btopenworld.com website: www.acornshols.btinternet.co.uk

GORSE COTTAGE, BALMER LAWN ROAD, BROCKENHURST. Cottage/bungalow on open forest road close to the village in the New Forest. Beautifully decorated and appointed, sleeps 4 in 2 bedrooms. Conservatory, luxury bathroom, log fire, televisions/video, secluded sunny garden. Pets Welcome. Contact: MR J. GILBERT (0870 3210020) or website for details. ETC ★★★★ [Pets £15 per week]
e-mail: info@gorsecottage.co.uk website: www.gorsecottage.co.uk

WOODSIDE BUNGALOW, NEW FOREST. Small, friendly B&B. Three annexed en suite rooms, courtyard garden. Close to forest tracks, walking, cycling. Dogs welcome. Ideal Autumn/Winter breaks. Tel: 02380 813688.
e-mail: josuco@lineone.net

MRS J. PEARCE, ST. URSULA, 30 HOBART ROAD, NEW MILTON BH25 6EG (01425 613515). Excellent facilities and warm welcome for well behaved pets and owners! Ground floor suite suitable for disabled guests, plus single and twin rooms. Bed & Breakfast from £25. ◆◆◆◆ [🐕]

BEECHEN HOUSE, CLAYHILL, LYNDHURST SO43 7DN (023 8028 2006). Private Victorian home. English breakfast. Secure off-road parking. Comfortable walking distance into New Forest. Non-Smoking. Dogs welcome.
website: www.newforest.demon.co.uk/beechen.htm

Portsmouth

Historic port and naval base, with Nelson's flagship HMS Victory in harbour.

Quality 2-star accommodation with a superb sea front location. Good walking! All rooms en suite, etc. Passenger lift, licensed bar/restaurant, car park. Contact: MARK & JENNY BRUNNING, THE SEACREST HOTEL, 12 SOUTH PARADE, SOUTHSEA, PORTSMOUTH PO5 2JB (02392 733192; Fax: 02392 832523). AA ★★ 72%.
e-mail: seacrest@boltblue.com website: www.seacresthotel.co.uk

Ringwood

Busy market town, centre for trout fishing, trekking and rambling. Bournemouth 13 miles.

MRS ADAMS, THE HIGH CORNER INN, LINWOOD, RINGWOOD, HANTS BH24 3QY (01425 473973, Fax: 01425 483052). Two en suite bedrooms deep in the heart of The New Forest. Real ales, home-cooked food, Sunday carvery and log fires. Pets welcome.

HEREFORDSHIRE

Docklow, Hereford, Ludlow

See also Colour Advertisement on page 49

See also Colour Advertisement on page 44

See also Colour Advertisement on page 43

Docklow

Village 4 miles east of Leominster.

NICHOLSON FARM HOLIDAYS, DOCKLOW, LEOMINSTER HR6 0SL (01568 760346) Self-catering properties on a working dairy farm. Beautiful views, ideal for walking, carp fishing available on the farm, swimming and tennis 10 mins. Dogs are welcome but must not remain in during the owner's absence. Non-smoking. [🐕]

Great Malvern

Fashionable spa town in last century with echoes of that period.

KATE AND DENIS KAVANAGH, WHITEWELLS FARM COTTAGES, RIDGEWAY CROSS, NEAR MALVERN WR13 5JR (01886 880607; Fax: 01886 880360). Charming converted Cottages, sleep 2–6. Fully equipped with colour TV, microwave, barbecue, fridge, iron, etc. Linen, towels also supplied. One cottage suitable for the disabled with full wheelchair access. Short breaks, long lets, large groups. ETC ★★★★ [pw! Pets £10 per week.] Also see Display Advert..
e-mail: info@whitewellsfarm.co.uk website: www.whitewellsfarm.co.uk

Hereford

Well-known touring centre on River Wye. Good sport and entertainment facilities including steeplechasing. Cheltenham 37 miles, Gloucester 28, Ross-on-Wye 15.

CHURCH FARM, CODDINGTON, LEDBURY HR8 lJJ (01531 640271). Black and white 16th-century Farmhouse on a working farm close to the Malvern Hills — ideal for touring and walking. Two double and one twin bedrooms. Excellent home cooking. Warm welcome assured. Open all year. [🐕]
website: www.dexta.co.uk

Pembridge

Tiny medieval village surrounded by meadows and orchards.

MRS N. OWENS, THE GROVE, PEMBRIDGE, LEOMINSTER HR6 9HP (01544 388268). The farm is mixed arable and stock and there are lovely little woodland and riverside walks on the farm itself. Pets welcome under strict control. Friendly farm atmosphere. Sleeps 4. Terms from £175 per week. ETC ★★★. [Pets £5 per week, pw!]
e-mail: nancy@grovedesign.co.uk

Ross-on-Wye

An attractive town standing on a hill rising from the left bank on the Wye. Cardiff 47 miles, Gloucester 17.

THE KING'S HEAD HOTEL, 8 HIGH STREET, ROSS-ON-WYE HR9 5HL (FREEPHONE: 0800 801098). Small coaching inn dating back to the 14th century with all bedrooms offering en suite bathrooms and a full range of modern amenities. Comprehensive menu offers home-cooked food which is served in a warm and friendly atmosphere. Bargain breaks all year round. [🐕]
website: www.kingshead.co.uk

THE ARCHES GUEST HOUSE, WALFORD ROAD, ROSS-ON-WYE HR9 5PT (01989 563348). All rooms en suite with colour TV and beverage making facilities. Centrally heated. Bed and Breakfast. Family room available. Pets welcome. AA/ETC ◆◆◆ [🐕]
e-mail: thearches@which.net

LEA HOUSE, LEA, ROSS-ON-WYE, HR9 7JZ (Tel & Fax: 01989 750652). Double/family en suite; twin/double en suite; twin private bath - all individually styled with TV and beverage tray. Secluded garden. Dogs very welcome. AA ◆◆◆◆ [Dogs £5 per stay]. See Display Advert.
e-mail: enquiries@leahousebandb.com website: www.leahousebandb.com

YE HOSTELRIE, GOODRICH, ROSS-ON-WYE HR9 6HX (01600 890241). Enjoy comfort and good food at this fully centrally heated 17th Century Inn. We have a reputation for quality food at a reasonable price. ETC/AA ★★ [🐕]
e-mail: info@ye-hostelrie.co.uk website: www.ye-hostelrie.co.uk

THE INN ON THE WYE, KERNE BRIDGE, GOODRICH, NEAR ROSS-ON-WYE HR9 5QS (01600 890872; Fax: 01600 890594). Beautifully restored 18th century coaching inn, near Goodrich Castle on the banks of the River Wye. All bedrooms en suite. Peaceful country walks, ideal base for touring. RAC ◆◆◆, AA (Awaiting Grading).
e-mail: theinnonthewye@kernebridge.freeserve.co.uk website: www.theinnonthewye.co.uk

ISLAND COTTAGE HOLIDAYS

ETC ★★★ to ★★★★★

Charming individual cottages in lovely rural surroundings and close to the sea. Over 55 cottages situated throughout the Isle of Wight. Beautiful views, attractive gardens, delightful country walks.

All equipped to a high standard and graded for quality by the Tourist Board.

For a brochure please **Tel: (01929) 480080 • Fax: (01929) 481070**

e-mail: enq@islandcottageholidays.com • website: www.islandcottageholidays.com

Open all year (Sleep 1 - 12) £135 – £1195 per week. Short breaks available in low season (3 nights) £120 – £395

Bonchurch, Cowes, Freshwater

ASHCLIFF HOLIDAY APARTMENT

Bonchurch, Isle of Wight PO38 1NT

Idyllic and secluded position in the picturesque seaside village of Bonchurch. Self-contained apartment within Victorian house, set in large south-facing gardens with sea views and sheltered by a thickly wooded cliff. Large, private car park. ETC ★★★. Dogs very welcome. ***For free brochure Tel: (01983) 853919***

ACTUALLY ON THE BEACH

"The Waterfall", Shore Road, Bonchurch, Ventnor, I.O.W. PO38 1RN

Ground-floor self-contained flat. Sleeps 3 adults. Fully equipped. Parking. Sun verandah and Garden.

Brochure from **Mrs A. Evans e-mail: benbrook.charioteer@virgin.net Tel: 01983 852246**

Small, quiet, family-run country park in rural surroundings close to Cowes. All caravans have full cooker, microwave, fridge and colour TV. Shop and laundry room on site. We welcome your pets. Short breaks can be arranged subject to availability.

Phone 01983 292859 or Fax: 01983 295389 for brochure • Proprietors: Frank and Barbara Marsh
website: www.sunnycottcaravanpark.co.uk • e-mail: sunny.cott@btinternet.com

A peaceful and beautiful 19th century rectory set in two-and-a-half acres of lovely gardens, just two minutes' drive from Freshwater Bay. Good area for walking, golfing, sailing, paragliding and bird watching. Close to National Trust areas. Double and family rooms, all en suite. TV lounge, log fires. Children and pets welcome.

B&B pppn: £24 low season, £26 mid season, £29 high season. Children ½ price.

Mr and Mrs B. Moscoff, Seahorses, Victoria Road, Freshwater PO40 9PP

Tel/Fax: 01983 752574 • e-mail: seahorsesiow@lineone.net • website: www.seahorsesisleofwight.com

HILLGROVE PARK

Field Lane, St Helens, Ryde PO33 1UT

ROSE AWARD CARAVAN HOLIDAY PARK

A small, secluded, family-run holiday caravan park. Only minutes from safe sandy beaches, beautiful countryside and places of interest. Try our centrally heated units for that early or late season break.

Heated swimming pool, large play areas for both older and younger children, games room. Car ferries arranged on any route.

For details ring (01983) 872802 ***or visit our website www.hillgrove.co.uk***

Harrow Lodge Hotel

Family-run Hotel, all rooms en suite with Colour TV, Tea making facilities and have use of adjacent Indoor Leisure Centre. Licensed bar, varied menu. Open April to October. Bed & Breakfast from £26 per person. Dinner, Bed & Breakfast from £34 per person.

Brochure/Details: **Alan & Lyn Aylott.**
Eastcliff Promenade, Shanklin, Isle of Wight PO37 8BD
Tel: 01983 862800 Fax: 01983 868889
website: www.harrowlodge.co.uk

ETC ★★

The *Country Garden Hotel*
Church Hill, Totland Bay, Isle of Wight PO39 0ET
ETC/RAC ◆◆◆◆

Surrounded by lovely walks and hikes. Garden and sea view rooms available. B&B from £43pp/day; DB&B from £57pp/day. Brochure on request. **Phone/Fax: 01983 754521**
e-mail: countrygardeniow@aol.com
www.thecountrygardenhotel.co.uk

See also Colour Advertisement on page 45

Sentry Mead Hotel

MADEIRA ROAD, TOTLAND BAY, ISLE OF WIGHT PO39 0BJ
Tel: 01983 753212 • Fax: 01983 754710
e-mail: pets@sentry-mead.co.uk • website: www.sentry-mead.co.uk

Sentry Mead is a tranquil retreat set in its own spacious gardens where well-behaved dogs are welcome throughout the hotel (except in the dining room) and to sleep in guests' bedrooms; our own Labrador and Retriever always make our canine visitors feel at home as soon as they arrive. Personal care and attention to detail make this a very special 3 star hotel for both pets and people for either a short break or a longer stay.

AA ★★★ RAC ★★★ RAC AWARD FOR SERVICE, HOSPITALITY & COMFORT

See also Colour Advertisement on page 44

Readers are requested to mention this guidebook when seeking accommodation (and please enclose a stamped addressed envelope).

ISLAND COTTAGE HOLIDAYS. Charming individual cottages in lovely rural surroundings and close to the sea. Over 55 cottages situated throughout the Isle of Wight. Beautiful views, attractive gardens, delightful country walks. All equipped to a high standard and graded for quality by the Tourist Board. For a brochure please telephone 01929 480080; Fax: 01929 481070. ETC ★★★ to ★★★★★.
e-mail: enq@islandcottageholidays.com website: www.islandcottageholidays.com

Bonchurch

One mile north-east of Ventnor.

MRS J. LINES, ASHCLIFF HOLIDAY APARTMENT, BONCHURCH PO38 1NT (01983 853919). Self-contained apartment within Victorian house. Large south-facing gardens. Sea views. Large private car park. Pets welcome to use garden. ETC ★★★ [🐕]

A. EVANS, "THE WATERFALL", SHORE ROAD, BONCHURCH, VENTNOR PO38 1RN (01983 852246). Spacious, self-contained Flat. Sleeps 3 adults. Colour TV. Sun verandah and garden. The beach, the sea and the downs. [🐕]
e-mail: benbrook.charioteer@virgin.net

Cowes

Yachting centre with yearly regatta since 1814. Newport 4 miles.

SUNNYCOTT CARAVAN PARK, COWES PO31 8NN (01983 292859; Fax: 01983 295389). Small, quiet, family-run park close to Cowes. All caravans have full cooker, microwave, fridge and colour TV. Shop and laundry room on site. We welcome pets. Short breaks arranged. ETC ★★★★ [Pets £5 per week]
e-mail: sunny.cott@btinternet.com website: www.sunnycottcaravanpark.co.uk

Freshwater

Two kilometres south of Totland. South-west of Farringford, formerly the home of Tennyson.

MR AND MRS B. MOSCOFF, SEAHORSES, VICTORIA ROAD, FRESHWATER PO40 9PP (Tel/Fax: 01983 752574). Peaceful 19th century rectory set in two-and-a-half acres of lovely gardens. Good area for walking, golfing, sailing, paragliding and bird watching. Double and family rooms, all en suite. TV lounge, log fires. B&B pppn: £24 low season, £26 mid season, £29 high season. Children (½ price). [🐕]
e-mail: seahorsesiow@lineone.net website: www.seahorsesisleofwight.com

Ryde

Popular resort and yachting centre, fine sands, pier. Shanklin 9 miles, Newport 7, Sandown 6.

HILLGROVE PARK, FIELD LANE, ST HELENS, NEAR RYDE PO33 1UT (01983 872802). Family-run Caravan Park. Select site 10 minutes sea, 3 minutes bus stop. Many local walks, heated swimming pool. Phone for brochure. Pets welcome (only one per unit). ETC ★★★★ Holiday Park. [Pets £2.00 per night, £15.00 per week]
website: www.hillgrove.co.uk

Shanklin

Safe sandy beaches and traditional entertainments make this a family favourite. Cliff lift connects the beach and the cliff top.

ALAN AND LYN AYLOTT, HARROW LODGE HOTEL, EASTCLIFF PROMENADE, SHANKLIN PO37 8BD (01983 862800; Fax: 01983 868889). Family-run Hotel, all rooms en suite with colour TV. Licensed bar, varied menu. Open April to October. ETC ★★ [Pets £3 per night, £10 per week]
website: www.harrowlodge.co.uk

Totland Bay

Small resort 3 miles south-west of Yarmouth Bay.

TREVOR & JUDY BARNES, LITTLEDENE LODGE GUEST HOUSE, GRANVILLE ROAD, TOTLAND BAY PO39 0AX (Tel & Fax: 01983 752411) Close to beach and scenic downland walking. Friendly and cosy with good fresh food. Small garden for use by all. Pets welcome; no charge. [🐕]
e-mail: littledenehotel@aol.com

COUNTRY GARDEN HOTEL, CHURCH HILL, TOTLAND BAY PO39 OET (Tel & Fax: 01983 754521). All en suite, garden and seaview rooms available; TV, phone, duvets, feather/down pillows, fridge, hairdryer etc. Special winter, spring, autumn rates. ETC/RAC ◆◆◆◆[pw!] Pets £3 per day]
e-mail: countrygardeniow@aol.com website: www.thecountrygardenhotel.co.uk

SENTRY MEAD HOTEL, MADEIRA ROAD, TOTLAND BAY PO39 0BJ (01983 753212; Fax: 01983 754710). Get away from it all at this friendly and comfortable haven, just two minutes from a sandy beach and cliff walks. Bedrooms have en suite bath or shower, colour TV and radio, telephone, hairdryer, beverage tray. Delicious table d'hôte dinners; lunchtime bar menu. AA/RAC ★★★ [Pets £3 per night, £20 per week]
e-mail: pets@sentry-mead.co.uk website: www.sentry-mead.co.uk

Ventnor

Well-known resort with good sands, downs, popular as a winter holiday resort. Nearby is St Boniface Down, the highest point on the island. Ryde 13 miles, Newport 12, Sandown 7, Shanklin 4.

CASTLEHAVEN CARAVAN SITE, BOX PW, NITON, NEAR VENTNOR, ISLE OF WIGHT PO38 2ND (01983 855556/730461). Island's most southerly six-berth, two-bedroomed caravans, all overlooking the Channel. Small, friendly site. Unspoilt seashore/countryside setting. On the shore. Kiosk serving breakfasts/evening meals by arrangement.
e-mail: caravans@castlehaven.co.uk website: www.castlehaven.co.uk

Yarmouth

Coastal resort situated 9 miles west of Newport. Castle built by Henry VIII for coastal defence.

THE ORCHARDS HOLIDAY CARAVAN & CAMPING PARK, NEWBRIDGE, YARMOUTH, ISLE OF WIGHT PO41 0TS (Dial-a-brochure 01983 531331; Fax: 01983 531666). Luxury holiday caravans, some with central heating. Excellent facilities including indoor pool with licensed cafe. Dog exercise areas. Coarse fishing; ideal walking, cycling and golf. Open late February to New Year.
e-mail: info@orchards-holiday-park.co.uk website: www.orchards-holiday-park.co.uk

"TUCKAWAY" – Holiday Chalet in private, secluded position. Sleeps four. Swimming pool. Gardens. Dogs welcome. APPLY: R. BAYLDON, FURZEBRAKE, CRANMORE AVENUE, YARMOUTH PO41 OXR (01983 760082). [🐕]

THE CROFT HOTEL Canterbury Road, Ashford TN25 4DU
Tel: 01233 622140 • Fax: 01233 635271
e-mail: crofthotel@btconnect.com • website: www.crofthotel.com

Set in two acres of well-maintained gardens, the Croft Hotel is conveniently located on the A28 between Ashford and Canterbury. The M20, Ashford International Station, the gateway to Europe, are only minutes away, Junction 9 the closest. The Croft is family-owned and operated, and warmly welcomes children in our large family rooms. The large gardens are at your disposal and we will be happy to recommend activities in the local area. Cots and baby accessories are readily available for infants. 2002/2003 AA Red Diamond Award (Exceptional Standards).

HANSON HOTEL (Lic.) 41 Belvedere Road, Broadstairs CT10 1PF Tel: (01843) 868936

A small friendly Georgian hotel with relaxed atmosphere, centrally situated for beach, shops and transport. B/B only or renowned for excellent food, we offer a 5-course Evening Dinner with choice of menu prepared by Chef/Proprietor ★ Attractive Bar ★ Most en suite.

Children and pets welcome.

OPEN ALL YEAR *S.A.E. or telephone for brochure to Trevor and Jean Webb* SPRING AND WINTER BREAKS

St Margaret's Holiday Park ETC ★★★★

Reach Road, St Margaret's at Cliffe, Nr Dover, Kent CT15 6AE

Exclusive park perched high on the White Cliffs and close to the bustling port of Dover. Modern well-equipped caravans. Superb facilities - indoor pool, gym, spa, sauna, solarium, outdoor play area, Bistro bar and restaurant. Stunning walks around the scenic coastline.

www.gbholidayparks.co.uk Call **0870 442 9286** for brochure

Warden Springs Holiday Park ETC ★★★★

Eastchurch, Isle of Sheppey, Kent ME12 4HF

On Kent's sunshine island, this park overlooks the sea and is surrounded by picturesque countryside and woodland. Range of modern, well equipped caravans. Outdoor heated pool, take away, bar and outdoor play area. Nearby sandy beaches. Delightful coastal walks. Tourers and tents welcome.

www.gbholidayparks.co.uk Call **0870 442 9281** for brochure

Romney Sands Holiday Park ETC ★★★★

The Parade, Greatstone-on-Sea, New Romney, Kent TN28 8RN

Opposite one of the finest sandy beaches in Kent. Great range of caravans and chalets. Indoor pool complex, diner, crazy golf, kid's club, outdoor play area, bowling green, tennis, bar and entertainment venues. Explore the countryside on local walks.

www.gbholidayparks.co.uk Call **0870 422 9285** for brochure

FREE or REDUCED RATE entry to Holiday Visits and Attractions — see our READERS' OFFER VOUCHERS on pages 101-116

PLEASE SEND A STAMPED ADDRESSED ENVELOPE WITH ENQUIRIES

Ashford

Market town on Great Stour River, 13 miles south-west of Canterbury.

Luxury pine lodges, superior self-catering accommodation overlooking two lakes in beautiful Kent countryside. Rough shooting and coarse fishing on our farms. Weeks or short breaks. Contact: ASHBY FARMS LTD, PLACE FARM, KENARDINGTON, ASHFORD TN26 2LZ (01233 733332; Fax: 01233 733326). [Pets £10 per week]
e-mail: info@ashbyfarms.com website: www.ashbyfarms.com

MR R. D. ASPINALL, THE CROFT HOTEL, CANTERBURY ROAD, ASHFORD TN25 4DU (01233 622140; Fax: 01233 635271). The Croft is family owned and operated, and warmly welcomes children in our large family rooms. Minutes from M20 and Ashford International Station. ETC/AA/RAC ◆◆◆◆, AA Red Diamonds Award (2002/3). [Pets £5 per night]
e-mail: crofthotel@btconnect.com website: www.crofthotel.com

Broadstairs

Quiet resort, once a favourite of Charles Dickens. Good sands and promenade.

HANSON HOTEL, 41 BELVEDERE ROAD, BROADSTAIRS CT10 1PF (01843 868936). Small, friendly licensed Georgian Hotel. Home comforts; children and pets welcome. Attractive bar. SAE. [pw! Pets £1 per night, £5 per week]

Dover

Busy passenger port whose white cliffs are the enduring symbol of island Britain.

ST MARGARET'S HOLIDAY PARK, REACH ROAD, ST MARGARET'S AT CLIFFE, NEAR DOVER, CT15 6AE. Exclusive park perched on the White Cliffs. Modern, well-equipped caravans. Superb facilities – indoor pool, gymnasium, spa pool, bar and restaurant. Stunning walks, scenic coastline. Call 0870 442 9286 for brochure. ETC ★★★★
website: www.gbholidayparks.co.uk

Isle of Sheppey

Island off the north coast of Kent, separated from the mainland by the Swale and River Medway.

WARDEN SPRINGS HOLIDAY PARK, EASTCHURCH, ISLE OF SHEPPEY ME12 4HF. On Kent's sunshine island, overlooking the sea, surrounded by picturesque countryside. Modern, well-equipped caravans. Outdoor heated pool, takeaway, bar. Sandy beaches, scenic coastal walks. Tourers and tents welcome. Call 0870 442 9281 for brochure. ETC★★★★
website: www.gbholidayparks.co.uk

New Romney

Town 9 miles south west of Hythe and 2km inland from Littlestone-on-Sea on St Mary's Bay.

ROMNEY SANDS HOLIDAY PARK, THE PARADE, GREATSTONE-ON-SEA, NEW ROMNEY TN28 8RN. Opposite one of Kent's finest sandy beaches. Great range of caravans and chalets. Indoor pool complex, kids' club, sports facilities, entertainment venues. Country walks. Call 0870 442 9285 for brochure. ETC ★★★★
website: www.gbholidayparks.co.uk

St Margaret's Bay

4 miles north-east of Dover

DEREK AND JACQUI MITCHELL, REACH COURT FARM COTTAGES, REACH COURT FARM, ST MARGARET'S BAY, DOVER CT15 6AQ (01304 852159; Tel & Fax: 01304 853902). Situated in the heart of the Mitchell family farm, surrounded by open countryside, these five luxury self-contained cottages are very special. The cottages are set around the old farmyard, which has been attractively set to lawns and shrubs, with open views of the rural valley both front and back. ETC ★★★★
e-mail: jacmitch2002@yahoo.co.uk

7-8 Finchley Road,
Gynn Square,
BLACKPOOL FY1 2LP
www.the-brayton-hotel.com
e-mail: info@the-brayton-hotel.com

- Quiet and pleasantly located licensed hotel.
- Overlooking Gynn gardens and the promenade.
- Short drive or tram ride to all the attractions.
- Excellent 'Home cooked' meals served daily.
- Easy parking. Open all year.

Phone: 01253 351645

Grisedale Farm ETC ◆◆◆◆

- Comfortable farmhouse B&B. 1 Double, 1 Twin, 1 Single.
- Leighton Moss RSPB 300 yards in Area of Outstanding Natural Beauty. • Convenient for Lakes and Dales. M6 10 mins, Exit 35. • Pets welcome. • C.L Site available.

**Mrs A. M. Robinson,
Grisedale Farm,
Leighton,
Carnforth.
Lancashire LA5 9ST
Tel: 01524 734360**

COCKERHAM SANDS COUNTRY PARK

Cockerham, Lancaster LA2 0BB Tel: 01524 751387

A family park situated on an inlet to the Irish Sea. Access to 15 miles of the new Lancashire Coastal Walk. Less than an hour to the Lake District, Morecambe or Blackpool. There is a heated swimming pool (June to September), shop, amusement arcade, launderette and the wonderful Cockerham Country Club with live entertainment at weekends. Modern four and six-berth fully equipped caravans for hire plus touring pitches with electric hook-up. Controlled dogs welcome. Write or telephone for brochure.

Tel: 01253 790324

BELL FARM

Beryl and Peter welcome you to their 18th century farmhouse in the quiet village of Pilling. The area has many footpaths and is ideal for cycling. Easy access to Blackpool, Lancaster, the Forest of Bowland and the Lake District. One family room, one double and one twin. All en suite. Tea and coffee making facilities. Lounge and dining room. All centrally heated. Full English breakfast.

Children and pets welcome.
Open all year except Christmas and New Year.
Bed and Breakfast from £25

Peter Richardson, Bell Farm, Bradshaw Lane, Scronkey, Pilling, Preston PR3 6SN

**SIX ARCHES CARAVAN PARK
SCORTON, GARSTANG
NEAR PRESTON,
LANCS PR3 1AL
TEL: 01524 791683**

Situated on the banks of the River Wyre. Modern caravans and self-catering holiday flats for hire, tourers welcome. Ideally situated for local visitor attractions, Blackpool, Lake District and Trough of Bowland within easy reach. Facilities include outdoor heated pool, club with live entertainment, children's playground and river fishing. Controlled dogs welcome. Telephone for brochure.

Readers are requested to mention this guidebook when seeking accommodation (and please enclose a stamped addressed envelope).

Blackburn

Industrial town on River Darwen and on Leeds and Liverpool Canal.

THE BROWN LEAVES COUNTRY HOTEL, LONGSIGHT ROAD, COPSTER GREEN, NEAR BLACKBURN BB1 9EU (01254 249523; Fax: 01254 245240). Situated on the A59 halfway between Preston and Clitheroe, five miles from Junction 31 on M6 in beautiful Ribble Valley. All rooms ground floor, en suite facilities, TV, tea-making and hairdryer. Guests' lounge and bar lounge. Car parking. Pets by arrangement. All credit cards welcome.
website: www.brownleavescountryhotel.co.uk

Blackpool

Famous resort with fine sands and many attractions and vast variety of entertainments. Blackpool Tower (500ft). Three piers. Manchester 47 miles, Lancaster 26, Preston 17, Fleetwood 8.

MRS C. MOORE, COTSWOLD, 2A HADDON ROAD, NORBRECK, BLACKPOOL FY2 9AH (01253 352227). Quality flats fully equipped. Cross road to beach and trams. Phone or SAE for brochure. [🐕]

THE BRAYTON, 7-8 FINCHLEY ROAD, GYNN SQUARE, BLACKPOOL FY1 2LP (01253 351645). Quiet licensed hotel overlooking Gynn gardens and the promenade. Excellent home-cooked meals served daily. Easy parking. Open all year. ETC ◆◆◆ [🐕]
e-mail: information@the-brayton-hotel.com website: www.the-brayton-hotel.com

Carnforth

Town and railway junction 6 miles north of Lancaster.

MRS A. M. ROBINSON, GRISEDALE FARM, LEIGHTON, CARNFORTH LA5 9ST (01524 734360. Comfortable farmhouse B&B. Leighton Moss RSPB 300 yards in A.O.N.B. Convenient for Lakes and Dales. Close to M6. Pets welcome; dogs free, charge for horses. ETC ◆◆◆◆ [🐕]
website: www.grisedalefarm.co.uk

SYMBOLS

- 🐕 **Indicates that pets are welcome free of charge.**
- £ **Indicates that a charge is made for pets: nightly or weekly.**
- pw! **Shows some special provision for pets; exercise facility, feeding or accommodation arrangement.**
- ⌂ **Indicates separate pets accommodation.**

Cockerham

Village 6 miles south of Lancaster.

COCKERHAM SANDS COUNTRY PARK, COCKERHAM, LANCASTER LA2 0BB (01524 751387). Family park with access to Lancashire Coastal Walk. Heated outdoor swimming pool, shop, launderette, Cockerham Country Club. Modern 4 and 6-berth fully equipped caravans for hire. Touring pitches. [Pets £20 per week]

Mellor

Village 3 miles north-west of Blackburn

ROSE COTTAGE, LONGSIGHT ROAD, CLAYTON-LE-DALE BB1 9EX (01254 813223; Fax: 01254 813831). Picturesque cottage on A59, five miles from M6, M65. Well-appointed rooms with private facilities. Weekend breaks, excellent stop for travellers to Scotland. Credit Cards accepted. [ ]
e-mail: bbrose.cott@talk21.co.uk website: www.SmoothHound.co.uk/hotels/rosecott.html

Pilling

Village 3 miles north east of Pressall.

BERYL AND PETER RICHARDSON, BELL FARM, BRADSHAW LANE, SCRONKEY, PILLING, PRESTON PR3 6SN (01253 790324).18th century farmhouse with one family room, one double and one twin. All en suite, and centrally heated. Full English breakfast is served. Open all year except Christmas and New Year. [h]

Preston

Large town on River Ribble, 27 miles from Manchester.

SIX ARCHES CARAVAN PARK, SCORTON, GARSTANG, NEAR PRESTON PR3 1AL (01524 791683). Modern 4 and 6-berth caravans, touring pitches; large two-bedroom flats to sleep 6. Blackpool 14 miles, Lake District 30 miles. Licensed club with entertainment. Controlled dogs welcome. [Pets £20 per week]

Southport

Elegant seaside resort with Victorian feel. Amusement park, zoo and Birkdale championship golf course.

THE GARDEN COURT, 22 BANK SQUARE, SOUTHPORT PR9 0DG (Tel & Fax: 01704 530219). Victorian town house overlooking Central Promenade, Theatre, Marine Lake and Floral Hall Conference Centre. All attractions within easy walking distance. En suite bedrooms, some four-poster. Friendly, comfortable accommodation from £20 B&B pppn. [ ]

CRIMOND HOTEL & RESTAURANT, KNOWSLEY ROAD, SOUTHPORT PR9 0HN (01704 536456; Fax: 01704 548643). Situated close to the town centre, this hotel can cater for all your needs with the luxury of an indoor swimming pool. Open all year. Table d'hôte service. Full central heating. [Pets £1 per night].
website: www.crimondhotel.com

Market Harborough

Town on River Welland 14 miles south-east of Leicester.

BROOK MEADOW HOLIDAYS. Three self-catering chalets, farmhouse Bed and Breakfast, Carp fishing, camping and caravan site with electric hookups. Phone for brochure. ETC ★★★ to ★★★★. MRS MARY HART, WELFORD ROAD, SIBBERTOFT, MARKET HARBOROUGH LE16 9UJ (01858 880886). [🐕 camping, £5 per night B&B, £10 Self-catering]
e-mail: brookmeadow@farmline.com website: www.brookmeadow.co.uk

Melton Mowbray

Old market town, centre of hunting country. Large cattle market. Church and Ann of Cleves' House are of interest. Kettering 29 miles, Market Harborough 22, Nottingham 18, Leicester 15.

SYSONBY KNOLL HOTEL, ASFORDBY ROAD, MELTON MOWBRAY LE13 OHP (01664 563563; Fax: 01664 410364.). Family-run 3 star hotel on edge of town, plenty of room for exercise on site and longer walks available. Special weekend breaks, pets genuinely welcome. See website for details. ETC/AA ★★★ [🐕]
website: www.sysonby.co.uk

Barton-Upon-Humber

Town on the south bank of the River Humber, 6 miles south-west of Hull.

WEST WOLD FARMHOUSE, DEEPDALE, BARTON-UPON-HUMBER DN18 6ED (Tel & Fax: 01652 633293). Friendly, family-run farmhouse in Deepdale. Easy access to bridleways and Viking Way. Ideal for walking, riding and birdwatching on the Humber Estuary. Close to historic Barton, with excellent eating places. Pets welcome, stabling and grazing for horses.

Horncastle

Market town once famous for annual horse fairs. 13th century Church is noted for brasses and Civil War relics.

LITTLE LONDON COTTAGES, TETFORD, HORNCASTLE. Three very well-equipped properties standing in own gardens on our small estate. Lovely walks. Short breaks and special offers. ETC ★★★★/★★★★★. Contact: MRS S.D. SUTCLIFFE, THE MANSION HOUSE, LITTLE LONDON, TETFORD, HORNCASTLE LN9 6QL (01507 533697; mobile: 07767 321213). [🐕]
e-mail: debbie@sutcliffell.freeserve.co.uk website: www.littlelondoncottages.co.uk

Langton-by-Wragby

Village located south-east of Wragby.

MISS JESSIE SKELLERN, LEA HOLME, LANGTON-BY-WRAGBY, LINCOLN LN8 5PZ (01673 858339). Ground floor accommodation in chalet-type house. Central for Wolds, coast, fens, historic Lincoln. Market towns, Louth, Horncastle, Boston, Spilsby, Alford, Woodhall Spa. Two double bedrooms. Washbasin, TV; bathroom, toilet adjoining; lounge with colour TV, separate dining room. Drinks provided. Children welcome reduced rates. Car almost essential, parking. Numerous eating places nearby. B&B from £20 per person (double/single let). Open all year. Tourist Board Listed [🐕]

Terms quoted in this publication may be subject to increase if rises in costs necessitate

---

Mablethorpe

Coastal resort 11 miles from Louth.

MRS GRAVES, GRANGE FARM, MALTBY-LE-MARSH, ALFORD LN13 0JP (01507 450267). Farmhouse B&B and country cottages set in ten idyllic acres of Lincolnshire countryside. Peaceful base for leisure and sightseeing. Private fishing lake. Many farm animals. Brochure available. Pets welcome. [🐕]
website: www.grange-farmhouse.co.uk

Saltfleet

Small, sleepy village overlooked by derelict windmill. Narrow harbour with moorings for small vessels.

SUNNYDALE HOLIDAY PARK, SEA LANE, SALTFLEET LN11 7RP. Friendly coastal park. Well-equipped caravans for hire. Indoor pool, play areas, shop, bar and beer garden. Market towns, sea resorts and theme parks nearby.Tourers and tents welcome. Call 0870 442 9293 for brochure. ETC★★★
website: www.gbholidayparks.co.uk

LONDON

London

London

Legislative capital and major port. Theatres, shops, museums, places of historic interest. Airports at Heathrow and Gatwick.

ST ATHANS HOTEL, 20 TAVISTOCK PLACE, RUSSELL SQUARE, LONDON WC1H 9RE (Tel: 020-7837 9140; Fax: 020-7833 8352). Family Bed and Breakfast near British Museum, shops, parks and theatres. Russell Square two blocks away, Euston and King's Cross stations ten minutes. LTB LISTED. [🐕]
e-mail: stathans@ukonline.co.uk

FREE or REDUCED RATE entry to Holiday Visits and Attractions — see our READERS' OFFER VOUCHERS on pages 101-116

Norfolk's leading holiday cottage letting agency.

We have the best choice with around 300 cottages now available

For Brochure

Tel: 01603 871872.

Carlton House, Market Place, Reepham, Norfolk, NR10 4JJ.
Visit our website to check availability and details of all our properties.
www.norfolkcottages.co.uk/pw

Bacton-on-Sea

CASTAWAYS HOLIDAY PARK

BH & HPA approved

Set in the quiet, peaceful village of Bacton, with direct access to fine sandy beach, and ideal for beach fishing and discovering Norfolk and The Broads. Modern Caravans, Pine Lodges and Flats with all amenities. Licensed Club. Entertainment. Amusement Arcade. Children's Play Area.

PETS WELCOME

Enquiries and Bookings to:

Castaways Holiday Park, Paston Road, Bacton-on-Sea, Norfolk NR12 0JB • Tel: (01692) 650436 and 650418
website: www.castawaysholidaypark.co.uk

Red House
Chalet & Caravan Park

Small, family-run coastal site with direct access to sandy beach. Caravans, flats and centrally heated chalets. All accommodation has self-contained facilities including colour television. Some accommodation available with sea view. On site licensed bar. Shop and laundry room. Ideal location for touring the Broads or sightseeing North Norfolk. DOGS VERY WELCOME. Open from March to January.

Red House Chalet and Caravan Park,
Paston Road, Bacton-on-Sea, Norfolk NR12 0JB (01692 650815).

Peacock House Old farmhouse. Lovely countryside with good walks. 3½ miles from Dereham, close for Norwich, NT houses, Sandringham, beaches. All rooms en suite, tea/coffee facilities. TV in all rooms. Own lounge, no smoking. Very warm welcome. B&B from £25pp. Open all year. Children and dogs welcome. **ETC ◆◆◆◆ Gold Award.**

Mrs Jenny Bell, Peacock Lane, Old Beetley, Dereham, Norfolk NR20 4DG
Tel: 01362 860371 • e-mail: PeackH@aol.com • web: www.SmoothHound.co.uk/hotels/peacockh.html

Augustus and Sweep, affectionately known as "the boys"

Set in the UK's most beautiful village of Burnham Market, this stylish, fabulous hotel offers a friendly atmosphere with attentive service. Individually designed bedrooms, air conditioned dining rooms, a traditional bar with log fire which attracts many of the locals and is the sort of place where nice dogs like to meet, a sunny patio and garden in which to relax with dogs, and a conservatory. Beach and woodland walks - 1 mile away.

Amazing value mid-week Dinner, Bed and Breakfast Breaks

Johansens 'Inn of the Year' • Egon Ronay 'Inn of the Year' • Catey Award Winner • Good Hotel Guide Cesar Awards 'Inn of the Year' • Voted by The Times as their 2nd Favourite Hotel in England • AA 2 Rosette Restaurant • The Sunday Times 'Golden Pillow Award'

Tel: 01328 738777 • Fax: 01328 730103 • e-mail: reception@hostearms.co.uk • web: www.hostearms.co.uk

The Hoste Arms, 17th Century Inn, The Green, Burnham Market, Norfolk PE31 8HD

See also colour advertisement on page 46

SEE ALSO INSIDE FRONT COVER

CROMER — SELF CATERING COTTAGES

A terrace of four charming almshouses recently modernised and redecorated throughout. Providing **2 & 3 bedroom accommodation for 4/6 persons.**

Central heating is included in the letting fee during the low season, together with duvets, bed linen and towels. **Short breaks available.**

Each cottage has its own enclosed garden, ideal for children and **pets always welcome!** Ample car parking in cottage grounds.

Enjoy a walk with your dog on the miles of open uncrowded beaches in North Norfolk. Cromer has a Cinema and Pier with first-rate live shows.

Also included is membership of Forest Park with its beautiful woodland walks, clubhouse and swimming pool open during the high season.

Detailed brochure and tariff (prices from £195 to £390 p.w.)

Broadgates Cottages, Northrepps,
Forest Park Caravan Site Ltd, Northrepps Road,
Cromer, Norfolk NR27 0JR
Tel: 01263 513290 • Fax: 01263 511992

FOREST PARK
Outstanding Natural Beauty

e-mail: info@broadgates.co.uk • website: www.broadgates.co.uk

KING'S CHALET PARK

Enquiries to: Stenson Guest House, 32 Overstrand Road, Cromer, Norfolk NR27 0AJ

Families Welcome & Pets Free of Charge

Well-equipped Chalets sleeping 2 to 6; shower/ bathroom, microwave, TV. Tourist Board and NNH/GHA Approved. One Twin, one Double bedroom, bed sofa in lounge. Well-equipped kitchenette. Quiet site adjacent to woods, Golf Club and beach. Local shops nearby or pleasant 10 minutes' walk into town.

Telephone: 01263 511308

Chalet 49 ~ Kings Chalet Park, Cromer.

Mrs M. Walker, 39 Pauls Lane, Overstrand, Cromer, Norfolk NR27 0PF Tel: 01263 579269

Luxury, well equipped chalet situated on quiet landscaped site, adjacent to sandy beaches, woods, cliff-top walks and golf courses. Ten minutes' walk to town. Local shops nearby. Two bedrooms, bathroom, fitted kitchen, microwave, colour TV, etc. Sleeps four. Cleaned and maintained by owner. Pets welcome. Open March to October.

Kings Chalet Park, Cromer, Norfolk • *Sleep 2-4* • *Open March to October*

Comfortable, well-equipped chalets situated on beautiful, landscaped, quiet site. Ideally placed for walks to adjacent woods, cliffs and sandy beaches. 10 minutes' walk to town. Golf course and local shops nearby. Plenty of local places of interest to visit. One twin, one double room, bathroom, colour TV, microwave, well-equipped kitchenette. Children welcome. **DETAILS FROM: MRS I. SCOLTOCK, SHANGRI-LA, LITTLE CAMBRIDGE, DUTON HILL, DUNMOW, ESSEX CM6 3QU • TEL: 01371 870482**

See also Colour Advertisement on page 48

THE CLIFTONVILLE HOTEL

"Cromer's Premier Clifftop Hotel"

AA ★★★ Grade II Listed

CROMER - NORFOLK

30 EN SUITE BEDROOMS ALL WITH SEA VIEWS - EXECUTIVE SUITES.
All Day Coffee Shop - A la carte Restaurant
Bolton's Bistro Specialising in Fresh Fish dishes, Cromer Crabs, Local Lobsters, Exotic and Local Fish, Steak and Meat Dishes, Pasta and Vegetarian Special 3 and 4 night breaks

01263 512543 e-mail: reservations@cliftonvillehotel.co.uk www.cliftonvillehotel.co.uk

Scarning Dale

Dale Road, Scarning, East Dereham NR19 2QN
Tel: 01362 687269

A warm welcome awaits you. 16th Century house in 25 acres of landscaped gardens, paddocks and woodland. Excellent home cooking (à la carte and table d'hôte). Indoor heated swimming pool and full size snooker table. Good access Norfolk and Suffolk. Self-catering cottages also available. Dogs welcome in self-catering cottages. Grazing and Stables available.

Tariff: Single £50 – £60; Double £90 – £100.

BARTLES LODGE

Stay in the peaceful, tranquil heart of Norfolk's most beautiful countryside. All rooms tastefully decorated in country style, with full en suite facilities, TVs, tea/coffee making facilities, etc. Overlooking 12 acres of landscaped meadows with its own private fishing lakes. Bed and Breakfast from £24.

Recommended by "Which?" Good Bed & Breakfast Guide.

Bartles Lodge, Church Street, Elsing, Dereham NR20 3EA Tel: 01362 637177

Holly Farm Cottages, High Common, Cranworth, Norfolk IP25 7SX

Two comfortable, single-storey cottages each sleeping 1-4. Fully equipped, including TV/video, dishwasher, washing machine, central heating. Enclosed garden. Ample car parking. Uninterrupted views of beautiful countryside, peaceful lanes for walking/cycling. Local golf and fishing. Convenient for Norwich, North Norfolk Coast and Broads.

Tel: 01362 821468 **e-mail: jennie.mclaren@btopenworld.com**

Experience the great joy of Norfolk We offer your pets 8 acres of lawns, paddock and woodland, with Norfolk's vast beaches within a few minutes' drive. Superbly equipped cottages, leisure centre with indoor pool; animal farm, children's play area, enchanted wood, grass tennis court, croquet lawn.

Vere Lodge, South Raynham, Fakenham NR21 7HE • 01328 838261

www.idylliccottages.co.uk ***For those who demand the very best***

See also Colour Advertisement on page 48

Located on a working farm, a courtyard of 2/3 bedroomed SELF CATERING CHALETS & 2 COTTAGES. All fully equipped, and all with central heating which is included in the letting fee. Situated 20 miles from the coast and 15 miles from Norwich and the Broads. 365 acres of mature woodland adjoining owners' farm – ideal for walking. Private fishing on owner's lake. Pets welcome at charge of £10.

ETC ★★/★★★

MOOR FARM STABLE COTTAGES, FOXLEY, NORFOLK NR20 4QN

Tel or Fax: 01362 688523 • e-mail: moorfarm@aol.com

A useful Index of Towns/Villages and Counties appears on page 426 – please also refer to Contents Page 3.

A warm welcome for you and your pets. Inexpensive, 'live-as-you-please' self-catering holidays in beautiful Norfolk. Chalets, Bungalows, and Cottages near Great Yarmouth & Norfolk Broads.

Debit/Credit cards accepted

SUPERB VALUE FOR 2005 SEASON

Colour Brochure Tel: 01493 732176 7 days a week Find us on the internet: www.carefree-holidays.co.uk

See also Colour Advertisement on page 46

✧ Sunwright Holiday Chalets ✧

Sundowner Holiday Park, Newport, Hemsby, near Great Yarmouth. Fully furnished and equipped self catering chalets, sleep up to 6. Two bedrooms, kitchen with all your cooking needs, lounge with TV, bathroom with shower over bath. Close to beach, Norfolk Broads and many attractions. Pets most welcome!

Contact Mrs Michelle Browne, 50 Mariners Compass, Gorleston, Great Yarmouth, Norfolk NR31 6TS
Tel: 01493 304282, e-mail: sunwrightholiday@aol.com OR visit our website www.sunwrightholidays.co.uk

MARINE BAR with accommodation. Pets are very welcome at a small charge of £1 per night. We do not have en suite rooms but every room has its own basin. Bar meals available all day. Colour television in all bedrooms. Most rooms have a view. £22.50 per person per night, including breakfast. Town centre location. Open all year.

The Marine Bar
HUNSTANTON

10 St Edmunds Terrace, Hunstanton, Norfolk PE36 5EH Tel: 01485 533310

- NORFOLK HOLIDAY HOMES -

VISIT THE BEAUTIFUL AREA OF WEST NORFOLK IN ONE OF OUR LOVELY SELF-CATERING COASTAL OR COUNTRY HOLIDAY HOMES.
OVER 60 TO CHOOSE FROM! SLEEPING 2 TO 10 PEOPLE.
All English Tourism Council Graded.
★★/★★★★ Pets welcome at a rate of £15 per week. ★★/★★★★
WEEKENDS/SHORT BREAKS AVAILABLE out of season.

FREE BROCHURE
Tel: 01485 534267 24 HRS
Fax: 01485 535230
shohol@birdsnorfolkholidayhomes.co.uk
www.norfolkholidayhomes-birds.co.uk

HOLMDENE FARM,

BEESTON, KING'S LYNN PE32 2NJ.

17th century farmhouse situated in central Norfolk within easy reach of the coast and Broads. Sporting activities available locally, village pub nearby. One double room, one twin and two singles. Pets welcome. Bed and Breakfast from £20 per person; Evening Meal from £15. Weekly terms available and child reductions. Two self-catering cottages. Sleeping 4/8. Terms on request.

MRS G. DAVIDSON • Tel: 01328 701284

e-mail: holmdenefarm@farmersweekly.net
website: www.northnorfolk.co.uk/holmdenefarm

Pott Row

Detached 2 bedroom bungalow sleeps 4. In quiet rural Norfolk village close to Sandringham and beaches. Facilities include colour TV, video, microwave, fridge/freezer, washing machine, off road parking, dog run. All dogs welcome FREE. Open all year. Please telephone for brochure.

Mrs. J.E. Ford, 129 Leziate Drove, Pott Row, King's Lynn PE32 1DE Tel: 01553 630356

Please mention ***PETS WELCOME*** when making enquiries about accommodation featured in these pages.

LAVENDER LODGE

Luxury ★★★★ seaside bungalow. Sleeps 6. Fully-equipped. Sky television. 10 minutes' walk to Old Hunstanton's dog friendly beaches. Fenced yard. Near Lighthouse.

FAIRYWOOD COTTAGE

Isolated one bedroom (twin) ★★★ farm cottage. Access to woodland walks. Fully equipped. Dogs welcome. Reasonable rates. Late enquiries welcome.

Mrs Eileen Howling,
Chalk Farm, Narborough,
King's Lynn PE32 1HY
Tel: 01760 337808
Fax: 01760 338771
Mobile: 07958 723420
www.lavenderlodge-norfolk.co.uk

A warm welcome to all pets and their owners at "Whincliff" by the sea. Family/en suite, twin or single room available. Tea/coffee facilities, TV in all rooms, private parking, sea views, unspoilt beach and coastal walks to enjoy.

WHINCLIFF Bed & Breakfast

Mrs Christine Thrower

CROMER ROAD, MUNDESLEY NR11 8DU • TEL: 01263 721554
http://whincliff.freeuk.com • e-mail: whincliff@freeuk.com

KILN CLIFFS CARAVAN PARK

KILN CLIFFS
MUNDESLEY

Peaceful family-run site with NO clubhouse situated around an historic brick kiln. Luxury six-berth caravans for hire, standing on ten acres of grassy cliff top. Magnificent view out over the sea; private path leads down to extensive stretches of unspoilt sandy beach. All caravans fully equipped (except linen) and price includes all gas and electricity. Caravans always available for sale or for hire. Within easy reach are the Broads, Norwich, the Shire Horse Centre, local markets, nature reserves, bird sanctuaries; nearby golf, riding and fishing. Facilities on site include general store and launderette. Responsible pet owners welcome.

Substantial discounts for off-peak bookings – phone for details.

Call for brochure. Mr R. Easton, Kiln Cliffs Caravan Park, Cromer Road, Mundesley, Norfolk NR11 8DF. Tel: 01263 720449

ETC ◆◆◆

Dolphin Lodge

Friendly-run bungalow accommodation. B&B in village setting just two-and-a-half miles from beaches. Many rural walks. Easy reach of all Norfolk attractions including Norfolk Broads. All rooms en suite, tea/coffee facilities, TVs, hairdryers etc.

Mrs G. Faulkner, Dolphin Lodge, 3 Knapton Road, Trunch, North Walsham, Norfolk NR28 0QE Tel: 01263 720961

ST CRISPINS **OLD HUNSTANTON, NORFOLK**

Tel: 01485 534036 • E-mail: st.crispins@btinternet.com

Quietly tucked away in Old Hunstanton village, near a sandy beach and golf course, but within a few hundred yards of three pubs/restaurants. This ground floor annexe sleeps 2 or 3 adults, and is beautifully decorated to a high standard. Short notice bargain breaks usually available early and late season. **PETS WELCOME**

PLEASE MENTION THIS GUIDE WHEN YOU WRITE OR PHONE TO ENQUIRE ABOUT ACCOMMODATION.

IF YOU ARE WRITING, A STAMPED, ADDRESSED ENVELOPE IS ALWAYS APPRECIATED.

The Lifeboat Inn

16th Century Smugglers' Ale House

Ship Lane, Thornham, Norfolk PE36 6LT

Tel: 01485 512236 • Fax: 01485 512323

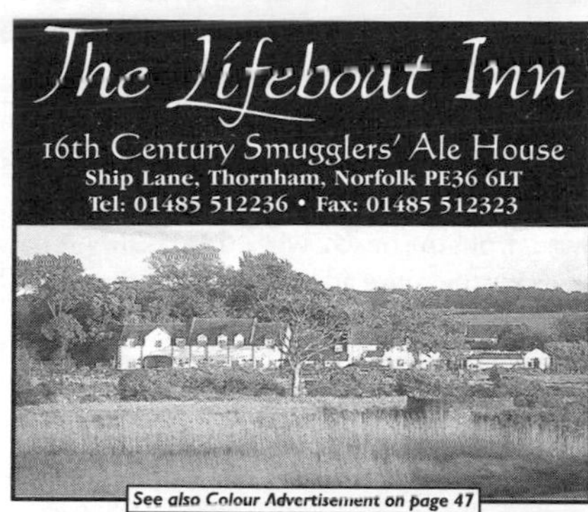

See also Colour Advertisement on page 47

A welcome site for the weary traveller for centuries - roaring open fires on a frosty night, real ales and a hearty meal awaiting. Dogs are welcome in all our bars. Guests arriving at reception are greeted by our grand old fireplace in the lounge. The restaurant (AA rosette) opens every evening offering a varied selection of dishes to suit all tastes. Bird watchers, walkers and nature lovers are spoilt for choice. A walk from our front door will take you to Thornham beach in no time at all and onto the Holme nature reserve. There are numerous and varied walks along miles of open beaches. Truly a walker's paradise - especially if you're a dog. We hope you will come and visit us. For our brochure and tariff which includes details of breaks please ring or visit our website:

www.lifeboatinn.co.uk

See also Colour Advertisement on page 6

Green Farm Hotel and Restaurant

Thorpe Market, North Walsham, North Norfolk NR11 8TH

Tel: 01263 833602 ❖ Fax: 01263 833163

e-mail: grfarmh@aol.com ❖ website: www.greenfarmhotel.co.uk

This charming 16th Century flint-faced Farmhouse Inn offers 14 antique style bedrooms, all en suite, including four-posters, and the food enjoys an enviable reputation for quality, presentation and service. Green Farm is the ideal base to discover and dip into the hidden delights of Norfolk.

Please telephone for details of our special breaks available all year.

INNS of TRADITION

★★★★ Poppyland Holiday Cottages & Touring Park Welcomes Dogs

Poppyland is situated on The Green in the middle of the picturesque village of Thorpe Market, in North Norfolk, just 4 miles south of the well known fishing port of Cromer and approximately 16 miles north of the ancient city of Norwich. The location is ideal for guests who want to just relax with their friend away from the daily pressures on a quiet holiday, or use the cottage as a base to visit local places of interest. The two holiday cottages have their own private entrances and gardens. The touring park is situated in an acre of landscaped garden surrounded by trees. There is a public house /hotel opposite which serves excellent food.

Tel: 01263 833219 for brochure. e-mail: PoppylandHoliday@aol.com or visit our website: poppyland.com

HOLIDAY IN OUR ENGLISH COUNTRY GARDEN

2 acres in rural Norfolk. Ten spacious family-run bungalows & seven-bedroom farmhouse. Games room, heated pool, children's play area, fishing, boating, riding & golf nearby. Near River Staithe with access to Broads. Car parking. Licensed bar. For details & colour brochure contact:

F.G. Delf, Thurne Cottage, The Staithe, Thurne, Norfolk NR29 3BU

Tel: 01692 670242 or 01493 844568 • www.norfolkbroads.co.uk/hederahouse

Bolding Way Holiday Cottages at Weybourne, North Norfolk

2 of our 4 cottages allow pets, both have fully fenced gardens, as well as access to the shared communal gardens with croquet, badminton as well as hens, ducks & geese. Excellent walking. Free membership of the local leisure centre. Holistic therapies. B&B. The sea is just a 10 minute walk. An excellent centre to explore the area, with wonderful views, places to see and visit. Fantastic food!

www.boldingway.co.uk Phone: 01263 588 666 The Stables, Weybourne, Holt NR25 7SW

PLEASE NOTE

All the information in this book is given in good faith in the belief that it is correct. However, the publishers cannot guarantee the facts given in these pages, neither are they responsible for changes in policy, ownership or terms that may take place after the date of going to press. Readers should always satisfy themselves that the facilities they require are available and that the terms, if quoted, still apply.

When making enquiries please mention FHG Publications

NORFOLK COUNTRY COTTAGES. Norfolk's leading holiday cottage letting agency. For brochure tel: 01603 871872. CARLTON HOUSE, MARKET PLACE, REEPHAM, NORFOLK NR10 4JJ.
website: www.norfolkcottages.co.uk/pw

Bacton-on-Sea

Village on coast. 5 miles from North Walsham.

CASTAWAYS HOLIDAY PARK, PASTON ROAD, BACTON-ON-SEA NR12 0JB (01692 650436 and 650418). In peaceful village with direct access to sandy beach. Modern caravans, Pine Lodges and Flats, with all amenities. Licensed club, entertainment, children's play area. Ideal for discovering Norfolk. [Pets £17 per week/£3 p.n./£10 per short break]
website: www.castawaysholidaypark.co.uk

RED HOUSE CHALET AND CARAVAN PARK, PASTON ROAD, BACTON-ON-SEA NR12 0JB (01692 650815). Small family-run site, ideal for touring Broads. Chalets, caravans and flats all with showers, fridges and colour TV. Some with sea views. Licensed. Open March–January. [Pets £10 weekly.]

Beetley

Village 4 miles/6 km north of East Dereham, which is notable for old buildings, including the parish church.

MRS JENNY BELL, PEACOCK HOUSE, PEACOCK LANE, OLD BEETLEY, DEREHAM NR20 4DG (01362 860371). Old farmhouse in lovely countryside. All rooms en suite, tea / coffee facilities. TVs in all rooms. Own lounge, B&B from £25pp. Open all year. Non-smoking. Children and dogs welcome. ETC ◆◆◆◆ Gold Award. [pw! 🐕]
e-mail: PeackH@aol.com website: www.SmoothHound.co.uk/hotels/peacockh.html

Burnham Market

Village 5 miles west of Wells-next-the-Sea.

THE HOSTE ARMS, THE GREEN, BURNHAM MARKET PE31 8HD (01328 738777; Fax: 01328 730103) Fabulous hotel with friendly atmosphere and attentive service. High degree of comfort offered. British brasserie style food served. Traditional bar. AA 2 Rosettes for food.
e-mail: reception@hostearms.co.uk website: www.hostearms.co.uk

Caister-on-Sea

Historic site with Roman ruins and 15th century Caister Castle with 100 foot tower.

Superior brick-built, tiled roof cottages. Adjacent golf course. Lovely walks on dunes and coast. 2-4 night breaks early/late season, Christmas and New Year. Terms from £69 to £345. SAND DUNE COTTAGES, TAN LANE, CAISTER-ON-SEA, GREAT YARMOUTH NR30 5DT (01493 720352; mobile: 07785 561363).
e-mail: sand.dune.cottages@amserve.net
website: www.eastcoastlive.co.uk/sites/sandddunecottages.php

Go BLUE RIBAND for quality inexpensive self-catering holidays where your dog is welcome – choice of locations all in the borough of Great Yarmouth. Detached 3 bedroom bungalows, seafront bungalows, detached Sea-Dell chalets and modern sea front caravans. Free colour brochure: DON WITHERIDGE, BLUE RIBAND HOUSE, PARKLANDS, HEMSBY, GREAT YARMOUTH NR29 4HA (01493 730445). [pw! Pets free at some times, £6 per week at others].
website: www.BlueRibandHolidays.co.uk

ELM BEACH CARAVAN PARK, MANOR ROAD, CAISTER-ON-SEA NR30 5HG (Freephone: 08000 199 360). Small, quiet park offering 6-berth, fully equipped caravans, most with sea views. Entertainment supplied free of charge by neighbouring parks. Pets very welcome. [Pets £20 per week]
e-mail: enquiries@elmbeachcaravanpark.com website: www.elmbeachcaravanpark.com

California

Coastal resort 5 miles North of Great Yarmouth.

CALIFORNIA CHALETS. Fully-appointed holiday chalets, three miles from Great Yarmouth. FREE entry to the club and indoor swimming pool and pets are very welcome. Please ring or write to 15 KINGSTONE AVENUE, CAISTER-ON-SEA, GREAT YARMOUTH NR30 5ET (01493 377175) for details and brochure.
website: www.californiachalets.co.uk

Coltishall

Village to the north east of Norwich.

THE NORFOLK MEAD HOTEL, COLTISHALL, NORWICH NR12 7DN (01603 737531). Renowned restaurant offering superb cuisine and a comprehensive wine list. Well mannered dogs welcome. Johansens recommended. [Pets £6 per night]
e-mail: info@norfolkmead.co.uk website: www.norfolkmead.co.uk

Cromer

Attractive resort built round old fishing village. Norwich 21 miles.

All-electric two and three bedroom Holiday Cottages accommodating four to six persons in beautiful surroundings. Sandy beaches, sports facilities, Cinema and Pier (live shows). Parking. Children and pets welcome. ETC ★★-★★★ Brochure: BROADGATES COTTAGES, NORTHREPPS, FOREST PARK CARAVAN SITE LTD, NORTHREPPS ROAD, CROMER, NORFOLK NR27 0JR (01263 513290; Fax: 01263 511992) [Pets £12 weekly].
e-mail: info@broadgates.co.uk website: www.broadgates.co.uk

KINGS CHALET PARK, CROMER NR27 0AJ (01263 511308) . Well-equipped chalets sleeping 2 to 6; shower/bathroom, microwave and TV. 1 Twin, 1 Double bedroom, bed sofa in lounge, well-equipped kitchenette. Quiet site adjacent to woods, golf club and beaches. Local shops nearby. Pleasant 10 minutes' walk to town. Tourist Board and NNH/GHA Approved. Families welcome. [🐕]

CHALET 49 ~ KINGS CHALET PARK,CROMER. Luxury, well equipped chalet , adjacent to beaches, woods, cliff-top walks and golf courses. Local shops. Two bedrooms, bathroom, fitted kitchen, microwave, colour TV, etc. Sleeps four to five. Cleaned and maintained by owner. Pets welcome. Open March to October. MRS M. WALKER, 39 PAULS LANE, OVERSTRAND, CROMER, NORFOLK NR27 0PF (01263 579269) [Pets £10 per week]

KINGS CHALET PARK, CROMER. Comfortable well-equipped chalets on quiet site; ideally placed for woodland and beach walks. 10 minutes' walk to town, shops nearby. Details from MRS I. SCOLTOCK, SHANGRI-LA, LITTLE CAMBRIDGE, DUTON HILL, DUNMOW, ESSEX (01371 870482). [one Pet free]

CLIFTONVILLE HOTEL, SEAFRONT, CROMER NR27 9AS (01263 512543; Fax: 01263 515700). Ideally situated on the Norfolk coast. Beautifully restored Edwardian Hotel. 30 en suite bedrooms all with sea view. Executive suites. Seafood Bistro, à la carte Restaurant. [pw! pets £4 per night]
e-mail: reservations@cliftonvillehotel.co.uk website: www.cliftonvillehotel.co.uk

Dereham

Situated 16 miles west of Norwich. St Nicholas Church has 16th century bell tower.

SCARNING DALE, SCARNING, EAST DEREHAM NR19 2QN (01362 687269). Self-catering cottages (not commercialised) in grounds of owner's house. On-site indoor heated swimming pool and full-size snooker table. B&B for six also available in house (sorry no pets in house). Grazing and Stables available.

BARTLES LODGE, CHURCH STREET, ELSING, DEREHAM NR20 3EA (01362 637177). Stay in the peaceful, tranquil heart of Norfolk's most beautiful countryside. All rooms en suite, TVs, tea/coffee making facilities, etc. Recommended by "Which?" Good Bed & Breakfast Guide. [pw! Pets £2 per night, £7 per week]

East Dereham

Site of 7th Century nunnery. Archaeological Museum at Bishop Banner's Cottages, with distinctive fruit and flower plaster work.

HOLLY FARM COTTAGES, HIGH COMMON, CRANWORTH IP25 7SX (01362 821468). 2 single-storey cottages each sleeping 1-4. TV/video, dishwasher, washing machine, central heating. Enclosed garden. Ample car parking. Peaceful lanes for walking/cycling. Local golf and fishing. Use of field for pony/horse. [🐕]
e-mail: jennie.mclaren@btopenworld.com

Fakenham

Agricultural centre on River Wensum 23 miles north-west of Norwich.

VERE LODGE, SOUTH RAYNHAM, NEAR FAKENHAM NR21 7HE (01328 838261; Fax: 01328 838300). 14 superbly equipped cottages with leisure centre and heated indoor pool. 8 acres of lawns, paddock and woodland, with Norfolk's vast beaches nearby. [pw! Pets £23 per week + VAT]
e-mail: major@verelodge.co.uk website: www.idylliccottages.co.uk

Foxley

Village 6 miles east of East Dereham.

Self Catering Chalets (2/3 bedrooms) on working farm. All fully equipped, with central heating. 20 miles from coast, 15 from Broads. Mature woodland nearby. Ideal for walking. ETC ★★/★★★. MOOR FARM STABLE COTTAGES, FOXLEY NR20 4QN (Tel & Fax: 01362 688523). [Pets £10 per week]
e-mail: moorfarm@aol.com

Great Yarmouth

Traditional lively seaside resort with a wide range of amusements, including the Marina Centre and Sealife Centre.

CAREFREE HOLIDAYS, CHAPEL BRIERS, YARMOUTH ROAD, HEMSBY, GREAT YARMOUTH NR29 4NJ (01493 732176). A wide selection of superior chalets for live-as-you-please holidays near Great Yarmouth and Norfolk Broads. All amenities on site. Parking. Children and pets welcome. [Pets £10 per week, £5 on short breaks, 2nd pet free.]

MRS MICHELLE BROWNE, SUNWRIGHT HOLIDAYS,50 MARINERS COMPASS, GORLESTON, GREAT YARMOUTH NR31 6TS (01493 304282) Sundowner Holiday Park, near Great Yarmouth. Fully furnished and equipped self catering chalets, sleep up to 6. Close to beach, Norfolk Broads and many attractions. [Pets £15 per week].
e-mail: sunwrightholiday@aol.com website: www.sunwrightholidays.co.uk

Hunstanton

Neat little resort which faces west across The Wash, Norwich 47 miles, Cromer 38.

MRS P. HOLMES, QUEENSBURY HOUSE, 18 GLEBE AVENUE, HUNSTANTON PE36 6BS (01485 534320). Attractive Victorian family house close to the town centre. Ideal base to explore the beautiful coast and countryside of North West Norfolk. Warm friendly welcome and excellent fresh food provided. Cots and high chairs available and pets welcome.

MRS E. PRICE, MARINE BAR, HUNSTANTON PE36 5EH (01485 533310). Overlooking sea and green. Pets welcome. Colour TV in all bedrooms. Open all year except Christmas period. [Pets £1 per night].

BIRDS NORFOLK HOLIDAY HOMES, 62 WESTGATE, HUNSTANTON, NORFOLK PE36 5EL (01485 534267; Fax: 01485 535230). Visit the beautiful area of West Norfolk in one of our lovely self-catering coastal or country holiday homes. Pets welcome. Weekend/Short Breaks available out of season. ETC ★★/★★★★ [Pets £15 per week].
e-mail: shohol@birdsnorfolkholidayhomes.co.uk
website: www.norfolkholidayhomes-birds.co.uk

King's Lynn

Ancient market town and port on the Wash with many beautiful medieval and Georgian buildings.

MRS G. DAVIDSON, HOLMDENE FARM, BEESTON, KING'S LYNN PE32 2NJ (01328 701284). 17th century farmhouse situated in central Norfolk within easy reach of the coast and Broads. Sporting activities available locally, village pub nearby. One double room, one twin and one single. Pets welcome. Bed and Breakfast from £20 per person; Evening Meal from £15. Weekly terms available and child reductions. Two self-catering cottages. Sleeping 4/8. Terms on request. ETC ★★★ [🐕]
e-mail: holmdenefarm@farmersweekly.net website: www.northnorfolk.co.uk/holmdenefarm

MRS J. E. FORD, LEZIATE DROVE, POTT ROW, KING'S LYNN PE32 1DE (01553 630356). Detached bungalow sleeps 4. In quiet village close to Sandringham and beaches. Facilities include colour TV, video, microwave, fridge/freezer, washing machine, off road parking, dog run. [🐕]

King's Lynn/Hunstanton

Bustling port and market town, 14 miles from the coastal resort of Hunstanton with sandy beaches.

MRS EILEEN HOWLING, CHALK FARM, NARBOROUGH, KING'S LYNN PE32 1HY (01760 337808; Fax: 01760 338771; mobile: 07958 723420). Lavender Lodge, a luxury seaside bungalow, near Old Hunstanton. Sleeps 6. Fairywood Cottage, isolated one bedroom farm cottage. Both fully equipped. Dogs welcome. **ETC** ★★★/★★★★ [🐕]
website: www.lavenderlodge-norfolk.co.uk

Mundesley-on-Sea

Small resort backed by low cliffs. Good sands and bathing. Norwich 20 miles, Cromer 7.

47 SEAWARD CREST, MUNDESLEY. West-facing brick built chalet on private site with lawns, flowers and parking. Large lounge/dining room, kitchenette, two bedrooms, bathroom. Beach and shops nearby. Weekly terms from £90. Pets most welcome. SAE please: MRS DOAR, 4 DENBURY ROAD, RAVENSHEAD, NOTTS, NG15 9FQ (01623 798032).

MRS CHRISTINE THROWER, WHINCLIFF BED & BREAKFAST, CROMER ROAD, MUNDESLEY NR11 8DU (01263 721554). Clifftop house, sea views and sandy beaches. Rooms with colour TV and tea-making. Families and pets welcome. Open all year round. [🐕]
e-mail: whincliff@freeuk.com website: http://whincliff.freeuk.com

KILN CLIFFS CARAVAN PARK, CROMER ROAD, MUNDESLEY NR11 8DF (01263 720449). Peaceful family-run site situated around an historic brick kiln. Six-berth caravans for hire, standing on ten acres of grassy cliff top. All caravans fully equipped (except linen) and price includes all gas and electricity. [Pets £5 per week].

Neatishead

Ideal for touring East Anglia. Close to Norwich. Aylsham 14 miles, Norwich 10, Wroxham 3.

ALAN AND SUE WRIGLEY, REGENCY GUEST HOUSE, THE STREET, NEATISHEAD, NORFOLK BROADS NR12 8AD (Tel & Fax: 01692 630233). 18th century three-bedroomed guest house renowned for generous English breakfasts. Ideal East Anglian touring base. Accent on personal service. B&B from £22. ETC/AA ◆◆◆◆ Dogs welcome. [Pets £4 per night.]
e-mail: regencywrigley@btopenworld.com website: www.norfolkbroads.com/regency

FREE or REDUCED RATE entry to Holiday Visits and Attractions – see our READERS' OFFER VOUCHERS on pages 101-116

North Walsham

Market town 14 miles north of Norwich, traditional centre of the Norfolk reed thatching industry.

MR P. O'HARA, GEOFFREY THE DYER'S HOUSE, CHURCH PLAIN, WORSTEAD, NORTH WALSHAM NR28 9AL (01692 536562). 17th century Listed weaver's house in centre of conservation village. Close to Broads, Coast, Norwich. Good walking and touring. All rooms en suite. Wholesome, well-cooked food. Dogs welcome. [🐕]
e-mail: valohara@hotmail.com

MRS. G. FAULKNER, DOLPHIN LODGE, 3 KNAPTON ROAD,TRUNCH, NORTH WALSHAM NR28 0QE (01263 720961). Friendly-run bungalow accommodation. B&B in village setting two-and-a-half miles from beaches. Many rural walks. Easy reach of all Norfolk attractions including Norfolk Broads. All rooms en suite, tea/coffee facilities, TVs, hairdryers etc. ETC ◆◆◆

Old Hunstanton

Coastal resort on the Wash 14 miles north east of King's Lynn.

ST CRISPINS, OLD HUNSTANTON (01485 534036). Ground floor annexe sleeping 2 to 3 adults, near sandy beach and golf course. Beautifully decorated. Bargain breaks early/late season. Pets welcome. [One or two dogs £15 per week]
e-mail: st.crispins@btinternet.com

Thornham

Village 4 miles east of Hunstanton. Site of Roman signal station.

THE LIFEBOAT INN, SHIP LANE, THORNHAM PE36 6LT (01485 512236; Fax: 01485 512323). A welcome sight for the weary traveller for centuries. Dogs welcome. Restaurant (one AA rosette). Bird watching and walking along miles of open beaches. Please ring for brochure and tariff. [🐕]
e-mail: reception@lifeboatinn.co.uk website: www.lifeboatinn.co.uk

Thorpe Market

Village 4 miles south of Cromer.

GREEN FARM HOTEL AND RESTAURANT, THORPE MARKET, NORTH WALSHAM, NORTH NORFOLK NR11 8TH (01263 833602; Fax: 01263 833163). 16th Century flint-faced farmhouse inn. 14 antique style en suite bedrooms. Telephone for details of our special breaks available all year. [Pets £5 per night]
e-mail: grfarmh@aol.com website: www.greenfarmhotel.co.uk

POPPYLAND HOLIDAY COTTAGES & TOURING PARK, THE GREEN, THORPE MARKET (01263 833219). Ideal for guests who want to relax. Two holiday cottages with private entrances and gardens. Touring park in landscaped gardens surrounded by trees. Excellent food nearby.
e-mail: PoppylandHoliday@aol.com website: www.poppyland.com

Thurne

Idyllic Broadland village. Great Yarmouth 10 miles.

HEDERA HOUSE AND PLANTATION BUNGALOWS, THURNE NR29 3BU (01692 670242 or 01493 844568). Adjacent river, seven bedroomed farmhouse, 10 competitively priced bungalows in peaceful gardens. Outdoor heated pool. Enjoy boating, fishing, walking, touring, nearby golf, horseriding, sandy beaches and popular resorts.
website: www.norfolkbroads.co.uk/hederahouse

When making enquiries or bookings, a stamped addressed envelope is always appreciated

Weybourne

Village 4 miles north-east of Holt.

BOLDING WAY HOLIDAY COTTAGES, THE STABLES, WEYBOURNE, HOLT NR25 7SW (01263 588666).Two cottages, each with its own garden (two other cottages available but no pets). 10 minute walk to sea. Free membership of local indoor leisure centre. Open all year. [🐕]
e-mail: holidays@boldingway.co.uk website: www.boldingway.co.uk

Winterton-on-Sea

Good sands and bathing. Great Yarmouth 8 miles.

WINTERTON VALLEY HOLIDAYS. A selection of modern superior fully appointed holiday chalets in a choice of locations near Great Yarmouth. Enjoy panoramic views from WINTERTON, a quiet and picturesque 35-acre estate, while CALIFORNIA has all the usual amenities, with free entry to the pool and clubhouse. Pets are very welcome at both sites. For colour brochure; 15 KINGSTON AVENUE, CAISTER-ON-SEA NR30 5ET (01493 377175).
website: www.wintertonvalleyholidays.co.uk

Wroxham

Village 7 miles north east of Norwich.

WROXHAM PARK LODGE, 142 NORWICH ROAD, WROXHAM NR12 8SA (01603 782991). Elegant Victorian House near north Norfolk coast, Great Yarmouth and Norwich. Open all year. All rooms en suite, tea/coffee making facilities, colour TV. Pets by arrangement. Ring for brochure. ETC ◆◆◆◆ [🐕]

THE BROADS HOTEL, STATION ROAD, WROXHAM, NORWICH NR12 8UR (01603 782869; Fax: 01603 784066). Comfortable hotel owned and run by dog-loving family. Ideally situated for boating, fishing and exploring the beautiful Norfolk countryside and coastline. All rooms fully en suite. [🐕]
website: www.broadshotel.com

• • *Some Useful Guidance for Guests and Hosts* • •

Every year literally thousands of holidays, short breaks and overnight stops are arranged through our guides, the vast majority without any problems at all. In a handful of cases, however, difficulties do arise about bookings, which often could have been prevented from the outset.
It is important to remember that when accommodation has been booked, both parties – guests and hosts – have entered into a form of contract. We hope that the following points will provide helpful guidance.

GUESTS:

- When enquiring about accommodation, be as precise as possible. Give exact dates, numbers in your party and the ages of any children.
- State the number and type of rooms wanted and also what catering you require – bed and breakfast, full board etc. Make sure that the position about evening meals is clear – and about pets, reductions for children or any other special points.
- Read our reviews carefully to ensure that the proprietors you are going to contact can supply what you want. Ask for a letter confirming all arrangements, if possible.
- If you have to cancel, do so as soon as possible. Proprietors do have the right to retain deposits and under certain circumstances to charge for cancelled holidays if adequate notice is not given and they cannot re-let the accommodation.

HOSTS:

- Give details about your facilities and about any special conditions. Explain your deposit system clearly and arrangements for cancellations, charges etc. and whether or not your terms include VAT.
- If for any reason you are unable to fulfil an agreed booking without adequate notice, you may be under an obligation to arrange suitable alternative accommodation or to make some form of compensation.

While every effort is made to ensure accuracy, we regret that FHG Publications cannot accept responsibility for errors, omissions or misrepresentations in our entries or any consequences thereof. Prices in particular should be checked because we go to press early. We will follow up complaints but cannot act as arbiters or agents for either party.

Mount Pleasant Farm

Alnmouth, Alnwick NE66 3BY

Mount Pleasant farm is situated on a hill overlooking seaside village of Alnmouth. Ideal base for beaches, castles, the Farnes, the Cheviots & Holy Island. Farmhouse annexe open-plan sleeps 2. Chalet two bedrooms sleeps 4. Caravan is 6 berth. Pets welcome.

Telephone 01665 830 215 for more details.

Prices on application.

Waren House Hotel **Waren Mill, Bamburgh, Northumberland NE70 7EE**

Tel: 01668 214581 e-mail: enquiries@warenhousehotel.co.uk
web: www.warenhousehotel.co.uk AA ★★★ RAC ★★★ ETC ★★★

Why not let your best friend join you and your partner at our luxurious Country House Hotel. Excellent accommodation, superb food and extensive moderately priced wine list. Rural setting in six acres of grounds on edge of Budle Bay 2 miles from Bamburgh Castle. No children under 14 please.

The Mizen Head Hotel

AA ★★

En suite bedrooms, a residents' conservatory lounge and non-smoking restaurant. Public bar offers good food and real ales with an open log fire in winter. A la carte restaurant uses local produce. Family rooms are available with cots if required. Car park. Children and pets welcome. Local attractions include Bamburgh Castle and Holy Isle. For golfers discounts can be arranged.
website: www.mizenheadhotel.co.uk • e-mail: leadbitterk@vodaphone.net

Bamburgh, Northumberland NE69 7BS
Tel: 01668 214254
Fax: 01668 214104

See also Colour Advertisement on page 48

Etive Cottage, Warenford, Near Belford

Etive is a well-equipped two bedroomed stone cottage with double glazing and central heating. Situated on the outskirts of the hamlet of Warenford with open views to the Bamburgh coast. Fenced garden and secure courtyard parking. Pet and owners welcome pack on arrival - give your pets the holiday they deserve.

For brochure contact Jan Thompson Tel/Fax: 01668 213233

BLUEBELL FARM West Street, Belford, Northumberland NE70 7QE

Sleep 2/6 plus cot. Traditional stone cottages converted from original farm buildings. An ideal base for Heritage Coast, beaches, Holy Island (Lindisfarne), Farne Islands, Kyloe/Cheviot Hills, Scottish Borders. Excellent pubs/food within walking distance. Berwick/Alnwick each 14 miles. Five self-contained cottages providing accommodation in double/ twin/children's bedrooms with linen/duvets/towels; kitchen with gas cookers/microwaves/fridge-freezers, Colour TVs. Garden/patio with barbecue, children's play area. Short Breaks/weekends. Rates £200 to £280 and £332 to £450.

Please contact Phyl Carruthers for details: Tel: 01668 213362; Mobile: 0770 3335430. E-mail: phyl.carruthers@virgin.net

Cresswell Towers Holiday Park ETC ★★★★

Cresswell, Nr Morpeth, Northumberland NE16 5JT

Highly attractive park in natural woodland setting. Modern well equipped caravans. Outdoor heated pool, sun terrace, children's play area, multi sports court, cafe, shop and clubhouse. Spectacular beaches, interesting walks, golf and sea fishing local to the park.

www.gbholidayparks.co.uk

Scotchcoulthard • **Haltwhistle, Northumberland NE49 9NH**
01434 344470 • Fax: 01434 344020 • *Props: A.D. & S.M. Saunders*
e-mail: info@scotchcoulthard.co.uk • www.scotchcoulthard.co.uk

Situated in 178 acres within Northumberland National Park, fully equipped self-catering cottages (sleep 2/7). All bedrooms en suite; open fires. Fridge/freezer, colour TV, microwave; all except one have dishwasher and washing machine. Linen, towels, all fuel incl. Heated indoor pool, games room. Children and dogs welcome. **ETC ★★★★**

Sandy Bay Holiday Park ETC ★★★

North Seaton, Ashington, Northumberland NE63 9YD

Charming coastal park with own beach. Stunning clifftop views and riverside walks. Modern, well equipped caravans. Indoor heated pool, outdoor play area, kid's club, cycle paths, multi sports court, choice of bars and entertainment.

www.gbholidayparks.co.uk Call 0870 442 9310 for brochure

BIRLING VALE, WARKWORTH.

Attractive stone built detached house in secluded garden. Fully equipped, two double bedrooms, one twin, cot. Free central heating. Close to sandy beaches, trout and salmon rivers and many places of interest. Well-trained dogs welcome. Weekly rates from £130 (low season) – £460 (high season).

SAE to Mrs J. Brewis, Woodhouse Farm, Shilbottle, Near Alnwick NE66 2HR Tel: 01665 575222

See also Colour Advertisement on page 49

Warkworth House Hotel

Bridge Street, Warkworth
Northumberland NE65 OXB

ETC ★★★

Set at the heart of the small village of Warkworth with its riverside walks, ideal for walking the dog while enjoying the view. Take a walk on the miles of open uncrowded beaches where your pet can roam free out of danger. Enjoy the many beauties that Northumberland can offer to complete a relaxing short break or holiday. Our kitchen will prepare your evening meal, a treat not to be missed. After which you can relax with coffee in the lounge (pets welcome). Please phone for bookings and brochures.

Tel: 01665 711276 Fax: 01665 713323
E-mail: welcome@warkworthhousehotel.co.uk
Website: www.warkworthhousehotel.co.uk

Readers are requested to mention this guidebook when seeking accommodation (and please enclose a stamped addressed envelope).

DALES HOLIDAY COTTAGES offer a selection of around 50 superb, personally inspected holiday properties, in beautiful rural and coastal locations, including Hadrian's Wall country and the Borders. Cosy cottages to country houses, many welcome pets, and short breaks are available. FREE brochure. DALES HOLIDAY COTTAGES, CARLETON BUSINESS PARK, SKIPTON, NORTH YORKSHIRE BD23 2AA (0870 909 9500).
website: www.dales-holiday-cottages.com

Alnmouth

Seaside village situated at the mouth of the River Aln.

MRS A. STANTON, MOUNT PLEASANT FARM, ALNMOUTH, ALNWICK NE66 3BY (01665 830215). Situated at top of hill on outskirts of seaside village; convenient for castles and Holy Island. Self-contained annexe sleeps 2 adults; open-plan; shower room. Chalet and 6-berth caravan also available. [Pets £5 per week]

Bamburgh

Village on North Sea coast with magnificent castle. Grace Darling buried in churchyard

MR P. LAVERACK, WAREN HOUSE HOTEL, WAREN MILL, BAMBURGH NE70 7EE (01668 214581). Luxurious Country House Hotel. Excellent accommodation, superb food, moderately priced wine list. Rural setting. No children under 14 please. ETC/RAC/AA ★★★. [🐕]
e-mail: enquiries@warenhousehotel.co.uk website: www.warenhousehotel.co.uk

THE MIZEN HEAD HOTEL, BAMBURGH NE69 7BS (01668 214254; Fax: 01668 214104). A warm welcome awaits owners and pets alike at the Mizen Head. Close to the beautiful Northumbrian coastline and just a short drive from many lovely walks in the Ingram Valley. The hotel boasts log fires, good food and real ales. AA ★★
e-mail: leadbitterk@vodaphone.net website: www.mizenheadhotel.co.uk

Belford

Village 14 miles south-east of Berwick-upon-Tweed.

ETIVE COTTAGE, WARENFORD, NEAR BELFORD NE70 7HZ. Well-equipped two-bedroomed cottage with double glazing, central heating. Open views to coast. Fenced garden; secure parking. Welcome pack. Brochure: JAN THOMPSON (Tel & Fax: 01668 213233). [🐕]

BLUEBELL FARM, WEST STREET, BELFORD NE70 7QE (01668 213362; mobile: 0770 333 5430) Sleep 2/6 plus cot. Traditional self-contained stone cottages converted from original farm buildings. Ideal base for Heritage Coast, Holy Island (Lindisfarne), Farne Islands and Scottish Borders. Rates £200 to £280 and £332 to £450. Please contact Phyl Carruthers for details. [Pets £20 per week]
e-mail: phyl.carruthers@virgin.net

Corbridge

Small town on north bank of River Tyne, 3 miles west of Hexham. Nearby are remains of Roman military town of Corstopitum.

MR & MRS MATTHEWS, THE HAYES GUEST HOUSE, NEWCASTLE ROAD, CORBRIDGE NE45 5LP (01434 632010). Stone-built stables in grounds of large country house converted into two self-catering cottages, each accommodating 4/5. ETC ★★★ [Pets £10 per week]
e-mail: mjct@mmatthews.fsbusiness.co.uk website: www.hayes-corbridge.co.uk

Cresswell

Coastal village 4 miles north of Ashington. Beach protected from North Sea by outlying reef.

CRESSWELL TOWERS HOLIDAY PARK, CRESSWELL, NEAR MORPETH NE61 5JT. Highly attractive park in a natural woodland setting. Well-equipped caravans for hire. Outdoor heated pool, multi-sports court, café, shop and clubhouse. Spectacular beaches, golfing and sea fishing. Call 0870 442 9311 for brochure. ETC★★★★
website: www.gbholidayparks.co.uk

Haltwhistle

Small market town about one mile south of Hadrian's Wall.

KATH AND BRAD DOWLE, SAUGHY RIGG FARM, TWICE BREWED, HALTWHISTLE NE49 9PT (01434 344120). Close to the best parts of Hadrian's Wall. A warm welcome and good food. All rooms en suite. Parking. TV. Central heating. Children and pets welcome. Open all year. Prices from £20 pppn. ETC ◆◆◆◆
e-mail: kathandbrad@aol.com website: www.saughyrigg.co.uk

A.D. & S.M. SAUNDERS, SCOTCHCOULTHARD, HALTWHISTLE NE49 9NH (01434 344470; Fax: 01434 344020). Situated in 178 acres within Northumberland National Park, fully equipped self-catering cottages (sleep 2/7). Linen, towels, all fuel incl. Heated indoor pool, games room. Children and dogs welcome. ETC ★★★★ [🐕]
e-mail: info@scotchcoulthard.co.uk website: www.scotchcoulthard.co.uk

Newbiggin-on-Sea

Fishing town and resort on the North Sea coast, 2 miles east of Ashington.

SANDY BAY HOLIDAY PARK, NORTH SEATON, ASHINGTON NE63 9YD. Charming coastal park with own beach. Modern, well-equipped caravans for hire. Indoor heated pool, outdoor activities, choice of bars, take away and entertainment. Call 0870 442 9310 for brochure. ETC★★★
website: www.gbholidayparks.co.uk

Warkworth

Village on River Coquet near North Sea coast north-west of Amble with several interesting historic remains.

BIRLING VALE is an attractive stone built detached house in secluded garden. Fully equipped, two double bedrooms, one twin, cot. Free central heating. Close to sandy beaches, trout and salmon rivers and many places of interest. Well-trained dogs welcome. Weekly rates from £130 Low Season, £250 Mid Season, £460 High Season. SAE to MRS J. BREWIS, WOODHOUSE FARM, SHILBOTTLE, NEAR ALNWICK NE66 2HR (01665 575222). [🐕]

WARKWORTH HOUSE HOTEL, BRIDGE STREET, WARKWORTH NE65 OXB (01665 711276; Fax: 01665 713323). Set in heart of small village, ideal for dog walking. Miles of open uncrowded beaches. Delicious evening meals. Phone for brochure. [🐕]
e-mail: welcome@warkworthhousehotel.co.uk website: www.warkworthhousehotel.co.uk

NOTTINGHAMSHIRE

Burton Joyce

Residential area 4 miles north-east of Nottingham.

MRS V. BAKER, WILLOW HOUSE, 12 WILLOW WONG, BURTON JOYCE, NOTTINGHAM NG14 5FD (0115 931 2070). Large Victorian house in quiet village location, two minutes walk River Trent, four miles city. Attractive accommodation in bright, clean rooms with tea/coffee making facilities, TV. Private parking. From £21 pppn. Reduced rates for children. Good local eating. Please phone first for directions. [🐕]

SYMBOLS

🐕 **Indicates that pets are welcome free of charge.**
£ **Indicates that a charge is made for pets: nightly or weekly.**
pw! **Shows some special provision for pets; exercise facility, feeding or accommodation arrangement.**
⌂ **Indicates separate pets accommodation.**

People-friendly Cottages for Pets! Lovely locations with superb walks in some of England's most picturesque countryside. From Windsor to the Welsh Borders, with lots to choose from in the Cotswolds and Shakespeare's Country. Small, friendly company with personal knowledge of the area - why not tell US what you are looking for and we'll do our best to find the right place for you to call 'home'! **Tel: 01993 831495 • Fax: 01993 831095**
enquiries@cottageinthecountry.co.uk • www.cottageinthecountry.co.uk

See also Colour Advertisement on page 00

Banbury, Burford, South Stoke

The Bell

Shenington,
Banbury,
Oxon OX15 6NQ

Telephone: 01295 670274
E-mail: the_bellshenington@hotmail.com
Web: www.banburytown.co.uk/thebell

The Bell is an early 18th century inn situated in the picturesque village of Shenington, within easy reach of the Cotswolds and Stratford. Well known for our delicious homemade food and warm welcome. Central heating, tea/coffee, pets welcome, TV.

The Inn for all Seasons

AA ★★★, *AA* **Rosette**

Dog owners themselves, Matthew and Heather Sharp extend a warm welcome to others who wish to bring their pets to visit the Cotswolds and stay in a genuinely dog-friendly Inn with dedicated ground floor rooms with direct access to gardens, exercise area and country walks.

The Inn for all Seasons is a family owned and run ★★★ Hotel based on a traditional 16th century English Coaching Inn. Character en-suite bedrooms, inglenooks, log fires and a genuinely friendly inn atmosphere provide the perfect setting to enjoy a rosetted menu prepared by chef/proprietor Matthew and his English led kitchen team. An ideal base for touring, walking, garden visiting. B&B from £46.50 pppn. Dinner B&B from £57.00 pppn.

The Barringtons,
Nr. Burford, Oxfordshire
OX18 4TN
Tel: 01451 844324
email: sharp@innforallseasons.com
www.innforallseasons.com

The picturesque 17th Century Perch and Pike Inn is situated conveniently on the Ridgeway walk between Wallingford and Goring upon Thames and has for many years been a haven for dogs and humans alike.
The four wonderful bedrooms all have en suite bathrooms and for the dogs there is a spacious garden with enough trees for everyone!
The pub has two of its own wonderfully friendly dogs, "Monty", a five year-old Jack Russell and "Rommel", a six month-old black Lab, who will welcome their guests in the usual way.

THE PERCH & PIKE

The Street, South Stoke
Oxfordshire RG8 0JS
www.perchandpike.com
Tel: 01491 872415

See also Colour Advertisement on page 49

COTTAGE IN THE COUNTRY COTTAGE HOLIDAYS (01993 831495; Fax: 01993 831095). Lovely locations with superb walks in some of England's most picturesque countryside. We'll do our best to find the right place for you to call 'home'!
e-mail: enquiries@cottageinthecountry.co.uk website: www.cottageinthecountry.co.uk

Banbury

Town on River Cherwell, 22 miles north of Oxford.

THE BELL, SHENINGTON, BANBURY OX15 6NQ (01295 670274). The Bell is an early 18th century inn situated in the picturesque village of Shenington, within easy reach of the Cotswolds and Stratford. Well-known for our delicious homemade food and warm welcome. [🐕]
e-mail: the_bellshenington@hotmail.com Website: www.banburytown.co.uk/thebell

Burford

Small Cotswold Town on River Windrush, 7 miles west of Witney.

THE INN FOR ALL SEASONS, THE BARRINGTONS, NEAR BURFORD OX18 4TN (01451 844324). Family-run and owned Hotel based on traditional 16th century English Coaching Inn. Ideal base for touring, walking and garden visiting. From £57 pppn DB&B. [🐕]
e-mail: sharp@innforallseasons.com website: www.innforallseasons.com

South Stoke

Village 2 miles north of Goring.

THE PERCH AND PIKE, THE STREET, SOUTH STOKE, NEAR GORING RG8 0JS (01491 872415). Picturesque 17th Century inn situated on the Ridgeway walk between Wallingford and Goring upon Thames. Four en suite bedrooms. Spacious garden for dogs. [🐕]

Tackley

Village 3 miles north-east of Woodstock.

JUNE AND GEORGE COLLIER, 55 NETHERCOTE ROAD, TACKLEY, KIDLINGTON, OXFORD OX5 3AT (01869 331255; mobile: 07790 338225; Fax: 01869 331670). Bed and Breakfast in Tackley. An ideal base for touring, walking and riding. Central for Oxford, The Cotswolds, Stratford-on-Avon, Blenheim Palace. Woodstock four miles. There is a regular train and bus service with local Hostelries serving excellent food. ETC ◆◆◆ [🐕]
e-mail: colliers.bnb@virgin.net

Thame

Town on River Thame 9 miles south west of Aylesbury. Airport at Haddenham.

MS. JULIA TANNER, LITTLE ACRE, TETSWORTH, NEAR THAME OX9 7AT (01844 281423; mobile: 07798 625252). A small country house retreat offering every comfort, set in several private acres. Most rooms en suite. Twin en suite £24pppn, king/double en suite £25pppn, family room (3 sharing) £70 per night. Prices include a full English breakfast. A perfect place to relax - your dog will love it. Three minutes Junction 6 M40. Also self-catering accommodation. AA ◆◆◆◆ [Dogs £1.50 per night, pw! h– Bring dog basket with you.]

Woodstock

Old town 8 miles north-west of Oxford. Home to Oxford City and County Museum.

GORSELANDS HALL, BODDINGTON LANE, NORTH LEIGH, WITNEY, OXFORD OX29 6PU (01993 882292; Fax: 01993 883629). Stone country house with oak beams and flagstone floors. Large secluded garden, with grass tennis court. All rooms are en suite, with colour television. ETC/RAC ◆◆◆◆. [pw! 🐕]
e-mail: hamilton@gorselandshall.com website: www.gorselandshall.com

When making enquiries or bookings, a stamped addressed envelope is always appreciated

GOOD HOTEL GUIDE
Country Hotel of the Year 2003

ETC
★★★
(Silver Award)

★★★ 77%

Food Award

Pen-y-Dyffryn Country Hotel

RHYDYCROESAU, NEAR OSWESTRY, SHROPSHIRE SY10 7JD

This silver stone former Georgian Rectory, set almost a thousand feet up in the Shropshire/Welsh hills, is in a dream situation for both pets and their owners. Informal atmosphere, no traffic, just buzzards, badgers and beautiful country walks, yet Shrewsbury, Chester, Powis Castle & Lake Vyrnwy are all close by. The well-stocked bar and licensed restaurant are always welcoming at the end of another hard day's relaxing. All bedrooms en suite etc; four have private patios, ideal for pets; several have spa baths. Short breaks available from £75 pppd, Dinner, B&B. Pets free.

TEL: 01691 653700

E-MAIL: stay@peny.co.uk WEBSITE: www.peny.co.uk

RYTON FARM HOLIDAY COTTAGES

Ryton, Dorrington, Shrewsbury SY5 7LY Tel: 01743 718449

Choose from a traditional country cottage sleeping six or a recently converted barn for either 2 or 4 persons. Some suitable for visitors with mobility difficulties. Ample parking, well-equipped kitchens, colour TV, fitted carpets. Pets especially welcome. Coarse fishing available. Quietly situated 6 miles south of Shrewsbury overlooking Shropshire Hills, convenient for Ironbridge, Ludlow and Shrewsbury.

Open all year **Weekly bookings or Short Breaks** **www.rytonfarm.co.uk**

UPPER HOUSE FARM COTTAGE

Visit Britain
★★★★

Minsterley, Near Shrewsbury, Shropshire SY5 0AA • ***Tel/Fax: 01743 792831***

Lovingly restored 17th century timbered country cottage in quiet village, sleeps 4, with cast iron double bed and period furniture. Well-equipped, comfortable and clean. Pets especially welcome. Private garden and ample off-road parking. Pubs and shops within walking distance. The perfect touring base for Shropshire's many attractions, with beautiful scenic walks nearby.

Open all year. ***E-mail: k.stanhope1@virgin.net*** ***Please call or e-mail for a brochure***

SELF CATERING COTTAGES

From £160 - £600 per week **ETC ★★★**

Sleeps 2 - 8 people, some ground floor bedrooms
3 beautifully converted barn cottages equipped and furnished to a high standard. Wheelchair friendly. Enclosed patio gardens.

BED & BREAKFAST

From £25 per person

Enjoy large country breakfast and a warm welcome.
Four poster, en suite and single rooms.
Central for Ironbridge, Shrewsbury, Welsh Border, Ludlow.

Church Farm, Rowton, Near Wellington, Telford, Shropshire TF6 6QY • Tel: 01952 770381
e-mail: churchfarm49@beeb.net • website: www.virtual-shropshire.co.uk/churchfarm

FREE or REDUCED RATE entry to Holiday Visits and Attractions — see our READERS' OFFER VOUCHERS on pages 101-116

Bishop's Castle

Small town in the hills on the Welsh Border, 8 miles from Craven Arms.

BROADWAY HOUSE, CHURCHSTOKE, POWYS, SY15 6DU (01588 620770). 17th century Lodge and 18th century Coach House in the grounds of a Regency gentleman's residence on Wales/England border. Picturesque views. Linen and fuel included. Open all year. Sleep five and two. **WTB** ★★★★★ Self Catering. [🐕]
e-mail: enqs@bordercottages.co.uk website: www.bordercottages.co.uk

Church Stretton

Delightful little town in lee of Shropshire Hills. Walking and riding country. Facilities for tennis, bowls, gliding and golf. Knighton 22 miles, Brignorth 19, Ludlow 15, Shrewsbury 12.

F. & M. ALLISON, TRAVELLERS REST INN, UPPER AFFCOT, NEAR CHURCH STRETTON SY6 6RL (01694 781275; Fax: 01694 781555). Fully licensed inn on the main A49. Good base for touring. Ample parking space. Children and dogs welcome. SAE or phone for further details. ETC ◆◆◆ [pw! 🐕]
e-mail: reception@travellersrestinn.co.uk website: www.travellersrestinn.co.uk

MYND HOUSE HOTEL, LUDLOW ROAD, LITTLE STRETTON, CHURCH STRETTON SY6 6RB (01694 722212). Comfortable small family-run hotel and restaurant in quiet village. Fully en suite. Walks from the doorstep. Convenient for Ludlow, Shrewsbury, Ironbridge etc. Short Breaks available. Dogs free. AA ★★ [🐕]
e-mail: info@myndhouse.co.uk website: www.myndhouse.co.uk

MRS C.F. BRANDON-LODGE, NORTH HILL FARM, CARDINGTON, CHURCH STRETTON SY6 7LL (01694 771532). Rooms with a view! B&B in beautiful Shropshire hills. TV in rooms, tea etc. Ideal walking country. From £23 per person. [pw! Pets £1.50 per night, ⌂]
e-mail: cbrandon@btinternet.com website: www.virtual-shropshire.co.uk/northhill/

Ludlow

Lovely and historic town on Rivers Teme and Corve with numerous old half-timbered houses and inns. Impressive Norman castle; river and woodland walks. Golf, tennis, bowls, steeplechase course. Worcester 29 miles, Shrewsbury 27, Hereford 24, Bridgnorth 19, Church Stretton 16.

SALLY AND TIM LOFT, GOOSEFOOT BARN, PINSTONES, DIDDLEBURY, CRAVEN ARMS, SHROPSHIRE SY7 9LB (01584 861326). Converted in 2000 from stone and timbered barns, the three cottages are individually decorated to the highest standards. Each cottage has en suite facilities and private garden or seating area. Situated in a secluded valley. Ideally located for exploring south Shropshire. ETC ★★★★ [🐕]
e-mail: sally@goosefoot.freeserve.co.uk website: www.goosefootbarn.co.uk

CLIVE & CYNTHIA PRIOR, MOCKTREE BARNS, LEINTWARDINE, LUDLOW SY7 0LY (01547 540441). Self-catering cottages around sunny courtyard. Sleep 2-6. Comfortable, well-equipped. Friendly owners nearby. Dogs and children welcome. Non-Smoking. Lovely country walks from door. Ludlow, seven miles. Brochure. ETC ★★★ [🐕] See also colour advertisement page 49.
e-mail: mocktreebarns@care4free.net website: www.mocktreeholidays.co.uk

HENWICK HOUSE, GRAVEL HILL, LUDLOW SY8 1QU (01584 873338). Warm, comfortable Georgian coach house, good traditional English Breakfast. Easy walking distance from town centre and local inns. Lots of nice local walks. TV, tea/coffee making facilities. One double/ one twin en suite, one twin, one single with shared bathroom. B&B from £25 pppn. ETC ◆◆◆

THE MOOR HALL, NEAR LUDLOW SY8 3EG (01584 823209; Fax: 08707 443725). Built in 1789, a splendid example of the Georgian Palladian style. Breathtaking views, 5 acre garden. B&B from £25 pppn. AA ◆◆◆◆ [🐕]
e-mail: info@moorhall.co.uk website: www.moorhall.co.uk

Oswestry

Borderland market town. Many old castles and fortifications including 13th century Chirk Castle, Whittington Castle, Oswestry's huge Iron Age hill fort, Offa's Dyke. Shrewsbury 16, Vyrnwy 18.

PEN-Y-DYFFRYN COUNTRY HOUSE HOTEL, NEAR RHYDYCROESAU, OSWESTRY SY10 7JD (01691 653700). Picturesque Georgian Rectory quietly set in Shropshire/ Welsh Hills. 12 en suite bedrooms, four with private patios. 5-acre grounds. No passing traffic. Johansens recommended. Dinner, Bed and Breakfast from £75.00 per person per day. AA/ETC ★★★. [🐕 pw!]
e-mail: stay@peny.co.uk website: www.peny.co.uk

Shrewsbury

Fine Tudor Town with many beautiful black and white timber buildings, Abbey and Castle. Riverside walks, Quarry Park and Dingle flower garden. 39 miles north-west of Birmingham.

RYTON FARM HOLIDAY COTTAGES, RYTON, DORRINGTON, SHREWSBURY SY5 7LY (01743 718449). Traditional country cottage sleeping 6 or converted barn for 2 or 4 persons. Well-equipped kitchens, colour TV, fitted carpets. Pets especially welcome. [Pets £30 per week].
website: www.rytonfarm.co.uk

UPPER HOUSE FARM COTTAGE, MINSTERLEY, NEAR SHREWSBURY SY5 0AA (Tel & Fax: 01743 792831). Lovingly restored 17th century timbered country cottage. Well-equipped, comfortable and clean. Pets welcome. Private garden and ample off-road parking. Pubs and shops within walking distance. Open all year. [Pets £30 per week]
e-mail: k.stanhope1@virgin.net

Telford

New town (1963). Ten miles east of Shrewsbury. Includes the south bank of the River Severn above and below Ironbridge, site of world's first iron bridge (1777).

CHURCH FARM, ROWTON, NEAR WELLINGTON TF6 6QY (01952 770381).B&B and self-catering in quiet village central for Shrewsbury, Ludlow, Ironbridge and Welsh Borders. En suite rooms, country breakfasts. Barn conversion. sleeps 2 - 8. [Pets £5 per week S/C, B&B no charge]
e-mail: churchfarm49@beeb.net website: www.virtual-shropshire.co.uk/churchfarm

www.classic.co.uk

classic cottages

Featuring 500 hand selected coastal and country holiday homes throughout the West Country

01326 565 555

Allerford, Bath, Brean, Castle Cary

Exmoor • • The Pack Horse

Allerford, Near Porlock, Somerset TA24 8HW
Tel/Fax: 01643 862475
www.thepackhorse.net • e-mail: holidays@thepackhorse.net

Our self-catering apartments and cottage are situated in this unique location within a picturesque National Trust village which has local amenities. The Pack Horse sits alongside the shallow River Aller, overlooking the famous bridge. Enjoy immediate access from our doorstep to the beautiful surrounding countryside, pretty villages, spectacular coast, and Exmoor.

Terms from £220 to £465 per week

OPEN ALL YEAR • PRIVATE PARKING • SHORT BREAKS

Very warm welcome assured

TOGHILL HOUSE FARM Cottages and B&B Accommodation

Luxury barn conversions on working farm just north of Bath. Each cottage is equipped to a very high standard with bed linen provided. You are welcome to roam amongst our many animals and enjoy the outstanding country views. We also provide Bed and Breakfast accommodation in our warm and cosy 17th century farmhouse where all rooms are en suite with TV and tea making facilities. Pets £2 per night, £8 per week.

Brochure - Tel: 01225 891261 • Fax: 01225 892128 • website: www.toghillhousefarm.co.uk
David and Jackie Bishop, Toghill House Farm, Freezing Hill, Wick , Near Bath BS30 5RT

WESTWARD RISE HOLIDAY PARK

Brean, Near Burnham-on-Sea, Somerset TA8 2RD Tel & Fax: 01278 751310

Highly Recommended Luxury 2/6 berth Chalet-Bungalows on a small quiet family-owned Park adjoining sandy beach. ◆ 2 Double Bedrooms ◆ Shower ◆ Toilet ◆ Colour TV ◆ Fridge ◆ Cooker ◆ Duvets and Linen ◆ Open all year ◆ Centrally Heated during winter months ◆ Laundry on Park ◆ Caravan Sales Available ◆ Shops ◆ Clubs ◆ Amusements & Restaurants Nearby ◆ Dogs Welcome

Call now for a FREE BROCHURE. website: www.breansands.freeserve.co.uk

Beachside Holiday Park

Coast Road, Brean Sands, Somerset TA8 2QZ
Tel: 01278 751346 • Fax: 01278 751683

• Chalets and Caravan holiday homes on quiet park. Direct access to beach (pets £20 per week) •
• Full facilities • Colour television • Golf courses nearby • Bars and restaurants nearby •

FREE BROCHURE • FREEPHONE 08000 190322 • www.beachsideholidaypark.co.uk

THE HORSE POND INN AND MOTEL

Tel:
01963 350318
Fax:
01963 351762

Castle Cary is an attractive twelfth century town with easy access to Bath & West Showground, Glastonbury, Yeovil and the Dorset coast. Good walking area. The Horse Pond Inn offers a warm welcome and fresh home cooked meals. Fully en suite rooms, 3 double, 2 family, from £35 to £65. Pets FREE.

The Triangle, Castle Cary BA4 7BD

Spring Cottages

Three single bedroomed cottages with twin or double beds in a converted barn. Each sleeps 2/3 persons using extra folding bed as necessary. Linen, colour TV and basic heating included. Ample car parking. The Gorge/Caves are within walking distance. An acre of paddock to exercise your dog.

£210 – £305 per week. Short breaks out of season.

ETC ★★★★ SELF-CATERING Non-Smoking No Children

Mrs Jennifer Buckland, Spring Cottage, Venns Gate, Cheddar BS27 3LW.

Tel/Fax: 01934 742493 • E-mail: buckland@springcottages.co.uk

Web: www.springcottages.co.uk

BROADWAY HOUSE

Holiday Touring Caravan & Camping Park
Cheddar, Somerset BS27 3DB

•Holiday caravans for hire •Premier touring and camping pitches •Heated swimming pool •Adventure playground •Corner shop •English Pub and Family Room Launderette •Amusements • Bike hire • Activity programme • Nature trails • Skateboard park •BMX track •

Tel: 01934 742610 • Fax: 01934 744950 • e-mail: enquiries@broadwayhouse.uk.com
website: www.broadwayhouse.uk.com

ETC★★★★

CHEDDAR - SUNGATE HOLIDAY APARTMENTS

Church Street, Cheddar, Somerset BS27 3RA

Delightful apartments in Cheddar village, each fully equipped. Sleep two/four. Laundry facilities. Private parking. Family, disabled and pet friendly.

For full details contact Mrs M. Fieldhouse.

Tel: 01934 842273/742264 • Fax: 01934 844994 • www.sungateholidayapartments.co.uk

---

THE YARN MARKET HOTEL

High Street, Dunster TA24 6SF
***Tel:* 01643 821425**
***Fax:* 01643 821475**
e-mail: yarnmarket.hotel@virgin.net
web: www.yarnmarkethotel.co.uk

In the centre of quaint English village, an ideal location for walking and exploring Exmoor, the surrounding coastline and the many local attractions. Comfortable, family-run hotel which provides a friendly, relaxed atmosphere, home cooking, en suite rooms with colour TV, tea making facilities and a residents' lounge. Packed lunches and drying facilities available. Non-smoking. Well behaved dogs welcome.

Party bookings and mid-week breaks a speciality

Pets Welcome *B&B From £35* *ETC ★★★ Hotel*

Riscombe Farm Holiday Cottages – Exmoor National Park

Four charming self-catering stone cottages converted from barns surrounding an attractive courtyard with stables. Very comfortable, with log fires and equipped to a high standard, sleeping 2-7. Peaceful, relaxing location beside the River Exe in the centre of Exmoor National Park. Excellent walking and riding country in the valleys, across the moors or along the spectacular coast.

One and a half miles from Exford Village.

Dogs and horses welcome. Stabling provided.

Leone & Brian Martin,
Riscombe Farm, Exford,
Somerset TA24 7NH
Tel & Fax: 01643 831480
www.riscombe.co.uk *(with vacancy info.)*

Open all year. ETC ★★★★

HUNTERS MOON

ETC ◆◆◆

Exford, Near Minehead, Somerset TA24 7PP

Cosy bungalow smallholding in the heart of Exmoor

★★ Glorious views ★★ Good food ★★ Friendly atmosphere ★★ Open all year ★★

Pets welcome free Optional Evening Meal

Bryan and Jane Jackson Tel: 01643 831695

e-mail: huntersmoon@bushinternet.com • website: www.exmooraccommodation.co.uk

Readers are requested to mention this guidebook when seeking accommodation (and please enclose a stamped addressed envelope).

EXMOOR

UPTON, NEAR WIVELISCOMBE, TAUNTON, SOMERSET TA4 2JH
Tel: 01398 371258 • Fax: 01398 371123
e-mail: ghughes@irisi.u-net.com • website: www.exmoor-cottages.com

West Withy Farm offers you and your dog a haven of peace and tranquillity in the beautiful, undiscovered Brendon Hills on the edge of Exmoor. The glorious countryside of Exmoor, the Brendons and the Quantocks provides a walker's paradise. Two local stone barns have been skilfully converted to provide well-equipped, detached character cottages with full central heating and stoves, sleeping 2- 6.

- **Private south-facing, enclosed, dog-proof gardens**
- **Excellent fly fishing at Wimbleball and Clatworthy Reservoirs**
- **Residents carp lake**
- **Panoramic views**
- **Fully inclusive prices**
- **Short breaks available**
- **Colour TVs • Bed linen and towels provided**

EXMOOR

WESTERMILL FARM

Westermill is wonderful for dogs and owners.
• Four waymarked walks over 500 acre farm • Small paddock where dogs can run free • Stabling and fields for horses.

COTTAGES • In grass paddocks, by stream with views across the river valley. Up to 4 star ETC with woodburners. Ideal for children. Disabled facilities Category 2.

Separate **CAMPSITE** by the river.

EDWARDS FAMILY, Westermill Farm,
Exford, Minehead, Somerset TA24 7NJ
Tel: 01643 831238
Fax: 01643 831216
e-mail: holidays@westermill-exmoor.co.uk
website: www.exmoorfarmholidays.co.uk

The Crown Hotel

Exford, Exmoor National Park, Somerset TA24 7PP

Situated in the middle of Exford, one of the prettiest villages on the Moor and known as the Capital of Exmoor, The Crown is very much the centre of village life. After a day out in the open, where better to return than the Comfort of The Crown Hotel, with its log fires, comfortable lounges, en suite bedrooms, ancient bar and elegant restaurant where Head Chef Robert Skuse serves some of the most wonderfully exciting food on Exmoor. Dogs are welcome in guests' rooms or can be accommodated in our stable block. Why not bring your horse and enjoy a day's hunting with one of the local hunts. (There is a small charge for horses).

AA ★★★ **Tel: 01643 831554/5 • Fax: 01643 831665**

RESTAURANT AWARD

WOODCOMBE LODGES

ETC ★★★★

Four self-catering lodges in a tranquil rural setting on the edge of Exmoor National Park, standing in a beautiful 2½ acre garden with wonderful views towards the wooded slopes of Exmoor. Minehead's seafront, harbour, shops etc. 1½ miles. Close to Dunster, Selworthy, Porlock and many local beauty spots.

Bratton, Near Minehead TA24 8SQ (Tel & Fax: 01643 702789).
e-mail: nicola@woodcombelodge.co.uk **website: www.woodcombelodge.co.uk**

EXMOOR

Secluded country house accommodation and self-contained cottages

~ www.cutthorne.co.uk ~

Set in the heart of Exmoor, perfect dog-walking country, we welcome you and your dog. Cutthorne is a beautifully hidden away country house and is an ideal base for exploring the coast and countryside.

*Spacious and comfortable accommodation
*Log fires *En suite bathrooms
*Four-poster bedroom
*Candlelit dinners *No smoking
*Excellent choice of breakfasts
*Traditional and Vegetarian cooking
*Bed and Breakfast from £32
*Licensed
◆◆◆◆

Two superbly appointed barn conversions overlooking ornamental pond and cobbled yard. Self-catering or with meals in the house. **ETC★★★★**

Ann and Philip Durbin, Cutthorne, Luckwell Bridge,
Wheddon Cross TA24 7EW Telephone and Fax: 01643 831255

MINEHEAD – 16th CENTURY THATCHED COTTAGES

ROSE-ASH – Sleeps 2 ✦ Prettily furnished ✦ All electric.
WILLOW – Inglenook ✦ Oak panelling ✦ Electricity, Gas, CH ✦ Sleeps 6.
LITTLE THATCH – Sleeps 5 ✦ Inglenook ✦ Cosy location ✦ Electricity. Gas, CH.
SAE please to: Mr T. STONE, Troytes Farmstead, Tivington, Somerset TA24 8SU
Private car park – Enclosed gardens – Pets Welcome **Tel: 01643 704531**

KING'S ARMS INN & RESTAURANT

ETC ◆◆◆◆

Bishopton, Montacute, Somerset TAl5 6UU

Blessed with impressive hotel amenities, this 16th century inn has a number of beautifully decorated guest rooms, including a half-tester room and one with a four-poster bed, and all have a private bathroom, colour television, radio and tea and coffee-making facilities. Splendid selection of bar and restaurant meals. Children and pets welcome.

Tel: 01935 822513 Fax: 01935 826549 E-mail: kingsarms@realemail.co.uk Website: www.greeneking-inns.co.uk

Please mention ***PETS WELCOME*** when making enquiries about accommodation featured in these pages.

THE SHIP INN Porlock TA24 8QD (01643 862507)

The thatched 13th century Ship Inn is within walking distance of sea and moor. There is a genuine old bar with stone floors and roaring log fires in winter. There are 10 bedrooms, mainly en suite. Local produce used. Real food, real ales and great accommodation. Gardens to enjoy. Ship's log details special events.

e-mail: mail@shipinnporlock.co.uk • website: www.shipinnporlock.co.uk

---

The Castle Hotel Porlock, Somerset TA24 8PY

Tel: 01643 862504• E-mail: castlehotel@btconnect.com

The Castle Hotel is a small, fully licensed family-run Hotel in the centre of the lovely Exmoor village of Porlock. There are 13 en suite bedrooms, all fully heated, with colour TV and tea/coffee making facilities. The Hotel offers everything from bar snacks to three-course meals which may be taken in the bar or restaurant. All well-behaved children and pets most welcome, ***Pool, darts & skittles.***

see also colour advertisement on page 52

The Old Cider House

Guesthouse and Holiday Cottage Accommodation

Set in picturesque and historic village of Nether Stowey, in the Quantock Hills, this is the ideal spot for a few days' B&B or a week's self-catering.
Guesthouse - 4 diamonds, all en suite, licensed dining, non-smoking.
Cottage - 2 bedrooms, fully-equipped kitchen, CD, DVD, video, non-smoking.

01278 732228

25 Castle Street, Nether Stowey, Somerset TA5 1LN
e-mail: info@theoldciderhouse.co.uk web: www.theoldciderhouse.co.uk

Dabinett Cottage

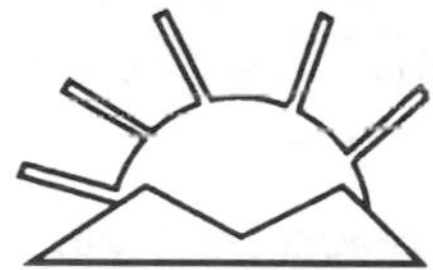

SUNNY BANK HOLIDAY CARAVANS

DONIFORD, WATCHET, SOMERSET TA23 0UD

SMALL PICTURESQUE FAMILY-RUN PARK
OVERLOOKING THE SEA NEAR MINEHEAD/ EXMOOR
CLOSE TO THE STEAM RAILWAY

Top quality caravans • Colour TV • Shower/Bath

• Heated Swimming Pool • Shop • Launderette • Good country walks • Access to Beach

Graded Exceptional by Tourist Board

Also caravans for sale.

Please telephone Peter & Anne Harrison on 01984 632237 for a brochure or visit our website: www.sunnybankcp.co.uk

Croft Holiday Cottages • The Croft, Anchor Street, Watchet. TA23 0BY

Contact: Mrs K. Musgrave • Tel: 01984 631121 • Fax: 01984 631134 • ETC ★★★★

Courtyard of six cottages/bungalows situated in a quiet backwater of the small harbour town of Watchet. Parking, central heating. TV, washing machine, fridge/freezer, microwave. Use of heated indoor pool. Sleeps 2-8 persons £130-£580 per property per week. • **E-mail: croftcottages@talk21.com • www.cottagessomerset.com**

INFIELD HOUSE 36 Portway, Wells, Somerset BA5 2BN

Victorian townhouse a few minutes from city centre and Cathedral. Wonderful walks on Mendip Hills. Bountiful breakfasts. Dinners by arrangement.
No smoking. Parking. Well behaved dogs over 1 year old. AA ◆◆◆◆

Tel: 01749 670989 • Web: www.infieldhouse.co.uk • UK Local Rate tel: 0845 1304645

CLASSIC COTTAGES (01326 565 555). Featuring 500 hand selected coastal and country holiday homes throughout the West Country.
website: www.classic.co.uk

POWELLS COTTAGE HOLIDAYS, 51 HIGH STREET, SAUNDERSFOOT, PEMBROKESHIRE SA69 9EJ. Many of our top quality holiday properties accept pets. Cottages in Devon, Cornwall, Cotswolds, Pembrokeshire and Heart of England. For colour brochure FREEPHONE 0800 378771 (24 hours). website: www.powells.co.uk

Allerford

Village 2 miles east of Porlock.

THE PACK HORSE, ALLERFORD, NEAR PORLOCK TA24 8HW (Tel/Fax: 01643 862475). Self-catering apartments and cottage within picturesque National Trust village. Immediate access to the beautiful surrounding countryside. Stabling available. Open all year. ETC ★★★ [Pets £10 per week]
e-mail: holidays@thepackhorse.net website: www.thepackhorse.net

Bath

The best-preserved Georgian city in Britain, Bath has been famous since Roman times for its mineral springs. It is a noted centre for music and the arts, with a wide range of leisure facilities.

DAVID & JACKIE BISHOP, TOGHILL HOUSE FARM, FREEZING HILL, WICK, NEAR BATH BS30 5RT (01225 891261; Fax: 01225 892128). Luxury barn conversions on working farm 3 miles north of Bath. Each equipped to very high standard, bed linen provided. Also en suite B&B accommodation in 17th century farmhouse. [pw! Pets £2 per night, £8 per week]
website: www.toghillhousefarm.co.uk

Brean

Coastal village with extensive sands. To north is the promontory of Brean Down. Weston-Super-Mare 9 miles.

WESTWARD RISE HOLIDAY PARK, SOUTH ROAD, BREAN, NEAR BURNHAM ON-SEA TA8 2RD (01278 751310). Highly Recommended Luxury 2/6 berth Chalet bungalows. 2 double bedrooms, shower, toilet, TV, fridge, cooker, duvets and linen. Open all year. Call for free brochure. [Pets £10 per week.]
website: www.breansands.freeserve.co.uk

BEACHSIDE HOLIDAY PARK, COAST ROAD, BREAN SANDS TA8 2QZ (FREEPHONE 08000 190322; Tel: 01278 751346; Fax: 01278 751683). Chalets and Caravan holiday homes on quiet park. Direct access to beach (dogs allowed). Full facilities. Colour TV. Golf courses nearby. Bars and restaurants nearby. Free brochure. [Pets £3 per night, £20 per week]
website: www.beachsideholidaypark.co.uk

Castle Cary

Small town 3 miles south-west of Bruton.

MRS INGA FILLSELL, THE HORSE POND INN AND MOTEL, THE TRIANGLE, CASTLE CARY BA7 7BD (01963 350318; Fax: 01963 351762). A warm welcome and fresh home cooked meals. Three double, two family, fully en suite rooms. Easy access to Bath, Glastonbury, Yeovil and Dorset coast. [🐕]

Cheddar

Picturesque little town in the Mendips, famous for its Gorge and unique caves. Cheese-making is a speciality. Good touring centre. Bath 24 miles, Burnham-on-sea 13, Weston-Super-Mare 11.

MRS JENNIFER BUCKLAND, SPRING COTTAGES, VENNS GATE, CHEDDAR BS27 3LW (Tel & Fax: 01934 742493). Three single bedroomed cottages sleeping 2/3 persons. The Gorge/Caves are within walking distance. An acre of paddock to exercise your dog. Non-smoking. No children. Short breaks. ETC ★★★★. [Dogs £3 per night, £20 per week].
e-mail: buckland@springcottages.co.uk website: www.springcottages.co.uk

BROADWAY HOUSE HOLIDAY TOURING CARAVAN & CAMPING PARK, CHEDDAR BS27 3DB (01934 742610; Fax: 01934 744950). Holiday caravans for hire; premier touring and camping pitches. Heated pool, adventure playground, pub, shop, launderette. Superb range of activities - skateboard park, BMX track. ETC ★★★★
e-mail: enquiries@broadwayhouse.uk.com website: www.broadwayhouse.uk.com

SUNGATE HOLIDAY APARTMENTS, CHURCH STREET, CHEDDAR, SOMERSET BS27 3RA. Ideally situated for walking, cycling and touring the Mendips and the West Country. Competitively priced for short or longer holidays. For full details contact Mrs M. FIELDHOUSE (01934 842273/742264; Fax: 01934 844994) ETC ★★★ [Quote for Pets].
website: www.sungateholidayapartments.co.uk

Dunster

Pretty village with interesting features, including Yarn Market, imposing 14th century Castle. Priory Church and old houses and cottages. Minehead 3 miles.

THE YARN MARKET HOTEL, HIGH STREET, DUNSTER TA24 6SF (01643 821425; Fax: 01643 821475). An ideal location for walking and exploring Exmoor. Family-run hotel with a friendly, relaxed atmosphere, home cooking, en suite rooms with colour TV and tea making facilities. Non-smoking. Mid-week breaks a speciality – Pets Welcome. ETC ★★★ Hotel [pw! 🐕]
e-mail: yarnmarket.hotel@virgin.net website: www.yarnmarkethotel.co.uk

When making enquiries please mention FHG Publications

Exford

Fine touring centre for Exmoor and North Devon, on River Exe. Dulverton 10 miles.

LEONE & BRIAN MARTIN, RISCOMBE FARM HOLIDAY COTTAGES, EXFORD, EXMOOR NATIONAL PARK TA24 7NH (Tel & Fax: 01643 831480). Four self-catering stone cottages in the centre of Exmoor National Park. Excellent walking and riding country. Dogs and horses welcome. Stabling provided. Open all year. ETC ★★★★ [Pets £2 per night, £12 per week.]
website: www.riscombe.co.uk (with up-to-date vacancy info.)

BRYAN & JANE JACKSON, HUNTERS MOON, EXFORD, NEAR MINEHEAD TA24 7PP (01643 831695). Cosy bungalow smallholding in the heart of Exmoor. Good food (optional Evening Meal), glorious views, friendly atmosphere. Pets welcome free. Open all year. ETC ◆◆◆ [pw! 🐕].
e-mail: huntersmoon@bushinternet.com website: www.exmooraccommodation.co.uk

Exmoor

265 square miles of unspoiled heather moorland with deep wooded valleys and rivers, ideal for a walking, pony trekking or fishing holiday.

EDGCOTT HOUSE, EXFORD, NEAR MINEHEAD TA24 7QG. (01643 831495). Spacious, comfortable, old country house in the heart of Exmoor. Good food, private bathrooms. Wonderful walking. Pets welcome. [pw! 🐕]

LYNDALE COTTAGE, ROADWATER, EXMOOR NATIONAL PARK TA23 0QY (01984 641426). 18th century stone cottage, combining character with comfort. Located in pretty village, near inn and shop. Sleeps 4 + 2. Open fire and woodburner. Beamed ceilings throughout. Parking and garden 50 yards from door. Excellent walking, inland and coastal. £200 - £400 per week. Please phone, e-mail or check our website for details. [🐕]
e-mail: jojo@lyndale200.fslife.co.uk website: www.uk-holiday-cottages.co.uk/lyndale

DUNKERY BEACON HOTEL, WOOTTON COURTENAY TA24 8RH (01643 841241). Country House Hotel with superb views. Fully en suite rooms, colour TV. Lots of lovely "walkies". Spring/Summer/Autumn Breaks. Write or phone Kenneth or Daphne Midwood for details.[🐕] .
e-mail: Dunkery.Beacon@virgin.net website: www.dunkerybeaconhotel.co.uk

JANE STYLES, WINTERSHEAD FARM, SIMONSBATH TA24 7LF (01643 831222). Five tastefully furnished and well-equipped cottages situated in the midst of beautiful Exmoor. Pets welcome, stabling and grazing, DIY livery. Colour brochure on request. ETC ★★★★ [Dogs and horses £12 per week.]
website: www.wintershead.co.uk

THE EXMOOR WHITE HORSE INN, EXFORD TA24 7PY (01643 831229; Fax: 01643 831246). A warm welcome awaits at this charming 16th Century Inn. Unique in character, giving you a true flavour of Exmoor. 28 ensuite bedrooms, with colour TV, teamaking, radio and hairdryers. Fully licensed Restaurant with varied menu using local produce. ETC ★★★ [Pets £7.50 per night].
e-mail: user@exmoorwhitehorse.demon.co.uk website: www.exmoor-hospitality-inns.co.uk

SIMONSBATH HOUSE HOTEL, SIMONSBATH, EXMOOR TA24 7SH. (01643 831259; Fax: 01643 831557). A peaceful and relaxing location. All rooms en suite; comfortable lounge with log fire. Three-acre gardens, ample parking. AA ★★ 74% [pw! 🐕 ⌂]
website: www.simonsbathhouse.co.uk

WESTERCLOSE HOUSE, WITHYPOOL, EXMOOR NATIONAL PARK TA24 7QR (01643 831302). Moorland cosy cottages including two bungalows in grounds of old hunting lodge overlooking Barle Valley. Dogs and horses welcome. Shop and pub 300 metres. [pw! Dogs £8 per week]
website: www.westerclose.co.uk

WEST WITHY FARM, UPTON, NEAR WIVELISCOMBE, TAUNTON TA4 2JH (01398 371258; Fax: 01398 371123). Two cottages sleeping 2-6. Fully inclusive prices. Walker's paradise in the Brendons and Quantocks. Excellent fly-fishing. Enclosed, dog-proof gardens. Short breaks available. ETC ★★★★ [Pets £11 per week]
e-mail: ghughes@irisi.u-net.com website: www.exmoor.cottages.com

MRS P. EDWARDS, WESTERMILL FARM, EXFORD, MINEHEAD TA24 7NJ (01643 831238; Fax: 01643 831216). Cottages in grass paddocks (Disabled Category 2), with woodburners. Separate campsite by river. Way marked walks. Wonderful for dogs and owners. ETC up to ★★★★ [pw! Pets £1 per night (camp), £10 per week in cottages].
e-mail: holidays@westermill-exmoor.co.uk website: www.exmoorfarmholidays.co.uk

THE CROWN HOTEL, EXFORD TA24 7PP (01643 831554/5; Fax: 01643 831665). Situated in rural England. All bedrooms with bath, colour television, hairdryer. Excellent cuisine and fine wines. Bargain Breaks. Superb dog holiday country. Horses stable £20.00 per night. AA ★★★ and Two Rosettes. [🐕]

WOODCOMBE LODGES, BRATTON, NEAR MINEHEAD TA24 8SQ (Tel & Fax: 01643 702789). Four self-catering lodges in a tranquil rural setting on the edge of Exmoor National Park, standing in a beautiful 2½ acre garden with wonderful views. [Pets £5 per week]
e-mail: nicola@woodcombelodge.co.uk website: www.woodcombelodge.co.uk

CUTTHORNE, LUCKWELL BRIDGE, WHEDDON CROSS TA24 7EW (01643 831255). Enjoy a touch of sheer luxury at our 14th century country house in glorious Exmoor. En suite facilities, log fires, candlelit dinners. ETC ◆◆◆◆. ETC ★★★★ Self Catering available [🐕 in B&B; Pets £15 per week S/C]
website: www.cutthorne.co.uk

Minehead

Neat and stylish resort on Bristol Channel. Sandy bathing beach, attractive gardens, golf course and good facilities for tennis, bowls and horse riding. Within easy reach of the beauties of Exmoor.

MINEHEAD 16TH CENTURY THATCHED COTTAGES. Rose Ash - Sleeps 2, prettily furnished, all electric. Willow - Inglenook, oak panelling, electricity, gas, CH, Sleeps 6. Little Thatch - Sleeps 5, Inglenook, Cosy location, Electricity. Gas, CH. Private car park. Enclosed gardens. Pets welcome. SAE: MR T. STONE, TROYTES FARMSTEAD, TIVINGTON, MINEHEAD TA24 8SU (01643 704531). [🐕]

Montacute

Estate village built of hamstone, 4 miles west of Yeovil.

KING'S ARMS INN & RESTAURANT, BISHOPTON, MONTACUTE, SOMERSET TAL5 6UU (01935 822513; FAX: 01935 826549). 16th century inn with impressive hotel facilities. Fifteen bedrooms, all with private bathroom; Splendid selection of bar and restaurant meals. Children and pets welcome. ETC ◆◆◆◆. [Pets £5 per night]
e-mail: kingsarms@realemail.co.uk website: www.greeneking-inns.co.uk

Porlock

Most attractive village beneath the tree-clad slopes of Exmoor. Picturesque cottages, old Ship Inn and interesting church. Good bathing from pebble beach at delightful Porlock Weir (2 miles).

JACKIE & ALAN COTTRELL, THE SHIP INN, HIGH STREET, PORLOCK TA24 8QD (01643 862507). Thatched 13th century inn within walking distance of sea and moor. There are 10 bedrooms, mainly en suite. Local produce used, international country cooking. Real ales. Resident dog Monty. Sam the black labrador is a regular eater and recent 'best man', Max the Staffy likes beer, and Snoopy and Cleo are getting used to us all. [🐕]
e-mail: mail@shipinnporlock.co.uk website: www.shipinnporlock.co.uk

CASTLE HOTEL, PORLOCK TA24 8PY (01643 862504). Fully licensed, family-run hotel in centre of lovely Exmoor village. 13 en suite bedrooms, all with colour TV. Pool, darts & skittles. Bar snacks and meals. Well-behaved children and pets welcome. Five acres of fields for exercising dogs. [🐕]

When making enquiries or bookings, a stamped addressed envelope is always appreciated

Quantock Hills

Granite and limestone ridge running north-west and south-east from Quantoxhead and Kingston.

THE OLD CIDER HOUSE, 25 CASTLE STREET, NETHER STOWEY, SOMERSET TA5 1LN (01278 732228). Set in picturesque and historic village of Nether Stowey, in the Quantock Hills. Guesthouse all en suite, licensed dining, non-smoking. ◆◆◆◆. Two bedroomed cottage, fully-equipped kitchen, CD, DVD, Video, non-smoking. [Pets £15.50 per week]
e-mail: info@theoldciderhouse.co.uk website: www.theoldciderhouse.co.uk

Watchet

Small port and resort with rocks and sands. Good centre for Exmoor and the Quantocks. Bathing, boating, fishing, rambling. Tiverton 24 miles, Bridgwater 19, Taunton 17, Dunster 6.

SUNNY BANK HOLIDAY CARAVANS, DONIFORD, WATCHET TA23 0UD (01984 632237). Small picturesque family-run park overlooking sea. All caravans with mains services. Colour TV. Heated swimming pool. Shop. Launderette. ETC ★★★★★. Also caravans for sale. Brochure. [Pets £2 per night, £14 per week.]
website: www.sunnybankcp.co.uk

MRS K. MUSGRAVE, CROFT HOLIDAY COTTAGES, THE CROFT, ANCHOR STREET, WATCHET TA23 0BY (01984 631121; Fax: 01984 631134). Courtyard of six cottages/bungalows situated in a quiet backwater of the small harbour town of Watchet. Parking, central heating. TV, washing machine, fridge/freezer, microwave. Use of heated indoor pool. Sleeps 2-8 persons. £130-£580 per property per week. ETC ★★★★ [🐕]
e-mail: croftcottages@talk21.com website: www.cottagessomerset.com

Wells

England's smallest city. West front of Cathedral built around 1230, shows superb collection of statuary.

INFIELD HOUSE, 36 PORTWAY, WELLS BA5 2BN (01749 670989; UK Local Rate 0845 1304645). Richard and Heather invite you and your dog (if older than one year) to visit England's smallest city. Wonderful walks on Mendip Hills. No smoking. Bountiful breakfasts, dinners by arrangement. AA ◆◆◆◆ [🐕]
website: www.infieldhouse.co.uk

Weston-Super-Mare

Popular resort on the Bristol Channel with a wide range of entertainments and leisure facilities. An ideal base for touring the West Country.

MR AND MRS C. G. THOMAS, ARDNAVE HOLIDAY PARK, KEWSTOKE, WESTON-SUPER-MARE BS22 9XJ (01934 622319). Caravans - De luxe. 2-3 bedrooms, shower, toilet, colour TVs, all bedding included. Parking. Dogs welcome. Graded ★★★. [🐕 pw!]

BRAESIDE HOTEL, 2 VICTORIA PARK, WESTON-SUPER-MARE BS23 2HZ (Tel & Fax: 01934 626642). Delightful, family-run Hotel, close to shops and sea front. All rooms en suite, colour TV, tea/coffee making. November to April (excl Easter weekend)THIRD NIGHT FREE. See display advertisement. ETC/AA ◆◆◆◆ [🐕]
e-mail: braeside@tesco.net website: www.braesidehotel.co.uk

Wiveliscombe

Small town 9 miles west of Taunton.

JENNY COPE, NORTH DOWN FARM, PYNCOMBE LANE, WIVELISCOMBE, TAUNTON TA4 2BL (Tel & Fax: 01984 623730). Traditional working farm. All rooms en suite, furnished to high standard. Log fires. Central heating. B&B £25pppn. Weekly and 3-day break rates available for BB&EM. Dogs welcome. [🐕]
e-mail: jennycope@tiscali.co.uk website: www.north-down-farm.co.uk

Marl Flat Farm • Newtown • Staffordshire Moorlands

10-acre farm quietly located close to Rudyard Lake with hiking and biking trails and superb moorland walks. Visit the famous Potteries and stately homes and gardens nearby, then relax by a real fire with fine home-cooked fare, before enjoying the comfort of our well-appointed balcony rooms with en suite facilities, TV, tea/coffee.

•Dogs most welcome. •Holiday with your horse. •Excellent Stabling and Kennel.

01782 379145 Prices from £19pppn. ***Self-catering apartment available.***

Barn Conversion Units. Full self-catering. Facilities situated next to medieval castle and tourist village. Spectacular views. Near Alton Towers and other theme parks. Ample parking. Please phone for brochure.

Park Lane, Tutbury, Near Burton-on-Trent, Staffordshire DE13 9JQ
Tel & Fax: 01283 812654 • Mobile: 07884 343460

Biddulph

Located 2 miles north east of Biddulph town, 7 miles north of Stoke-on-Trent.

MARL FLAT FARM, NEWTOWN, BIDDULPH MOOR ST8 7SW (01782 379145). 10-acre farm with superb moorland walks. Rooms with en suite facilities, TV, tea/coffee. Dogs most welcome; holiday with your horse. Terms from £19pppn. [pw! 🐕 ⌂]

Leek

Village 10 miles from Stoke-on-Trent.

EDITH & ALWYN MYCOCK, 'ROSEWOOD COTTAGE and ROSEWOOD FLAT', LOWER BERKHAMSYTCH FARM, BOTTOM HOUSE, NEAR LEEK ST13 7QP (Tel & Fax: 01538 308213). One cosy three bedroomed cottage with four-poster. Also delightful flat which sleeps up to six. Both fully equipped and carpeted throughout. Electricity and linen inclusive, laundry room. Ideal base for Alton Towers, Potteries and Peak District. Terms £160 to £315. [Pets £5]

Tutbury

Village 4 miles north west of Burton-upon-Trent. Ruins of 14th century castle.

LITTLE PARK HOLIDAY HOMES, PARK LANE, TUTBURY, NEAR BURTON-ON-TRENT DE13 9JQ (Tel & Fax: 01283 812654; Mobile: 07884 343460). Barn Conversion Units. Full self-catering. Facilities situated next to medieval castle and tourist village. Spectacular views. Near Alton Towers and other theme parks. Ample parking. Please phone for brochure. [Pets £1 per night, £5 per week]

Aldeburgh, Diss, Dunwich

FREE or REDUCED RATE entry to Holiday Visits and Attractions – see our READERS' OFFER VOUCHERS on pages 101-116

KNIGHTS HOLIDAY HOMES • KESSINGLAND

Quality **SEASIDE BUNGALOWS**. Open all year, central heating, colour TV, parking, bed linen, heating and lighting included. Sleep 1/6 persons. Direct access to award-winning beach.

BROCHURE ◆ CALENDAR ◆ OFFER LETTER ◆ BOOKING FORM

KNIGHTS HOLIDAY HOMES, 198 CHURCH ROAD, KESSINGLAND, SUFFOLK NR33 7SF

Tel: 01502 588533

CHILDREN AND PETS WELCOME

Freephone: 0800 269067

SHORT BREAK SPECIALS

See also Colour Advertisement on page 53

AA ★★★ 77% 2 Rosettes ✦ ***IVY HOUSE COUNTRY HOTEL*** ✦ ETC ★★★ Silver Award

We are tucked away down a leafy driveway on the south-western shores of Oulton Broad. Standing in 40 acres of country gardens, lily ponds and grazing meadows it is an ideal base from which to explore the Suffolk Heritage Coast, the Norfolk Broads and the Waveney Valley. Super accommodation for you and your four-legged friend(s)! Delicious cuisine is served in the beamed, thatched Crooked Barn. We have 2 AA Rosettes for cuisine and are wheel-chair accessible too.

Ivy House Country Hotel, Ivy Lane, Oulton Broad, Lowestoft, Suffolk NR33 8HY

Tel: 01502 501353 • Fax: 01502 501539 • www.ivyhousefarm.co.uk • pets@ivyhousefarm.co.uk

See also Colour Advertisement on page 54

Set in 22 acres of the rolling countryside typical of the Stour Valley, made famous by John Constable, Gladwins Farm offers a selection of high quality accommodation. Guests in our 5★ or 4★ self-catering cottages, most of which accept pets, or farmhouse B&B, can use the heated indoor pool and sauna, the hard tennis court and children's play area. Our cottages sleep from 2 to 8 people. There's a well-stocked fishing lake with trout and coarse fish, plus farm animals to entertain the children. We can offer you stabling for horses, an outdoor ménage and loads of space to walk your dogs. *Winners, Regional Self-Catering Holiday of the Year 2003*

Call Pauline or Robert Dossor on 01206 262261 and arrange a memorable stay. Colour brochure.

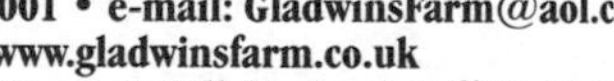

Fax: 01206 263001 • e-mail: GladwinsFarm@aol.com

www.gladwinsfarm.co.uk

Gladwins Farm, Harper's Hill, Nayland, Suffolk CO6 4NU

See also Colour Advertisement on page 53

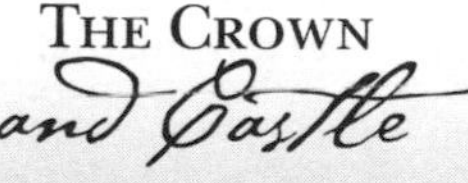

Suffolk Heritage Coast

Now owned by the ex-proprietors of Hintlesham Hall, this comfortable and very dog-friendly hotel is situated close to the 12th century castle in this historic and unspoilt village. Honest good food served in the acclaimed award-winning Trinity Restaurant.

Orford, Woodbridge, Suffolk IP12 2LJ

Tel: 01394 450205

e-mail: info@crownandcastle.co.uk

website: www.crownandcastle.co.uk

See also Colour Advertisement on page 54

FHG PUBLICATIONS

publish a large range of well-known accommodation guides. We will be happy to send you details or you can use the order form at the back of this book.

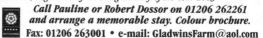

SUFFOLK COUNTRY COTTAGES (01603 873378). Suffolk's No. 1 holiday cottage letting agency. A fine choice of individually selected cottages now available. We are a friendly, local and independent firm.
website: www.suffolkcountrycottages.co.uk

Aldeburgh

Coastal town 6 miles south-east of Saxmundham. Annual music festival at Snape Maltings.

WENTWORTH HOTEL, ALDEBURGH IP15 5BD (01728 452312). Country House Hotel overlooking the sea. Immediate access to the beach and walks. Two comfortable lounges with log fires and antique furniture. Refurbished bedrooms with all facilities and many with sea views. Restaurant specialises in fresh produce and sea food. ETC Silver Award. AA ★★★ One Rosette. [Pets £2 per day]
e-mail: stay@wentworth-aldeburgh.co.uk website: www.wentworth-aldeburgh.com

Bury St Edmunds

This prosperous market town on the River Lark lies 28 miles east of Cambridge.

RAVENWOOD HALL COUNTRY HOUSE HOTEL AND RESTAURANT, ROUGHAM, BURY ST EDMUNDS IP30 9JA (01359 270345; Fax: 01359 270788). 16th century heavily beamed Tudor Hall set in seven acres of perfect dog walks. Individually furnished en suite bedrooms; renowned restaurant; relaxing inglenook fires. AA ★★★, AA Rosette. [🐕 pw!]
e-mail: enquiries@ravenwoodhall.co.uk website: www.ravenwoodhall.co.uk

Diss

Small market town on the River Waveney 19 miles south west of Norwich.

PAUL AND YOLANDA DAVEY, STRENNETH, AIRFIELD ROAD, FERSFIELD, DISS IP22 2BP (01379 688182; Fax 01379 688260). Family-run, fully renovated period property with two cottages. All rooms en suite, colour TVs, hospitality trays. Ground floor rooms. Non-smoking. Extensive breakfast menu. Licensed. Bed and Breakfast from £25. ETC ◆◆◆◆. [🐕]
e-mail: pdavey@strenneth.co.uk website: www.strenneth.co.uk

Dunwich

Small village on coast, 4 miles south west of Southwold.

MR & MRS COLE, THE CLOSE, MIDDLEGATE BARN, DUNWICH IP17 3DP (01728 648741). Situated in a quiet, private road 200 yards from the sea. Furnished and equipped to a high standard. Centrally heated; available all year. [🐕]

Kessingland

Little seaside place with expansive beach, safe bathing, wildlife park, lake fishing. To the south is Benacre Broad, a beauty spot. Norwich 26 miles, Adleburgh 23, Lowestoft 5.

Comfortable well-equipped bungalow on lawned site overlooking beach, next to Heritage Coast. Panoramic sea views. Easy beach access. Unspoiled walking area. ETC ★★ MR AND MRS J. SAUNDERS, 159 THE STREET, ROCKLAND ST MARY, NORWICH NR14 7HL (01508 538340). [Pets £10 per week].

Quality seaside bungalows in lawned surrounds overlooking the sea. Open all year, central heating, colour TV, parking, bed-linen, microwave, video recorder, heat and light included. Sleep 1/6. Direct access to award winning beach. Pets very welcome. APPLY– KNIGHTS HOLIDAY HOMES, 198 CHURCH ROAD, KESSINGLAND, SUFFOLK NR33 7SF (FREEPHONE 0800 269067).

Long Melford

Small town 3 miles north of Sudbury. Melford Hall and Kentwell Hall of interest.

BLACK LION HOTEL & RESTAURANT, THE GREEN, LONG MELFORD CO10 9DN (01787 312356; Fax: 01787 374557). 17th Century hotel opposite The Green. Leave your car and walk the dog. Contemporary restaurant, bar meals. Stylish en suite bedrooms, cosy lounge. Short breaks available. AA ★★★ 1 Rosette for Food [🐕 pw!]
e-mail: enquiries@blacklionhotel.net website: www.blacklionhotel.net

Lowestoft

Holiday resort and fishing port. Britain's most easterly point. Maritime museum traces seafaring history.

IVY HOUSE COUNTRY HOTEL, IVY LANE, OULTON BROAD, LOWESTOFT NR33 8HY (01502 501353/588144; Fax: 01502 501539). A relaxing, tranquil location with walks from your bedroom door. "Oulton Broad's hidden oasis". ETC ★★★ Silver Award, AA ★★★ 77% and 2 Rosettes. See our full colour advert under Suffolk. [Pets £5 per stay].
e-mail: pets@ivyhousefarm.co.uk website: www.ivyhousefarm.co.uk

Middleton

Small village 3 miles from the coast.

MILL BARN COTTAGES (01728 648377). Two fully equipped cottages, each sleeps two adults, situated in quiet village in good walking area. Coast three miles. Terms from £175 to £195 weekly. Pets free. Open all year. [🐕]

Nayland

Small town 6 miles north of Colchester. Many old houses. Church contains painting by Constable.

MR & MRS R. DOSSOR, GLADWINS FARM, HARPER'S HILL, NAYLAND CO6 4NU (01206 262261; Fax: 01206 263001). Set in 22 acres of rolling countryside, self-catering cottages (sleep 2-8), most of which accept pets. Use of indoor heated pool, sauna, tennis, fishing. Stabling, outdoor menage. ETC ★★★★/★★★★★ [Pets £20 per week, £13 for 3/4 nights].
e-mail: GladwinsFarm@aol.com website: www.gladwinsfarm.co.uk

Sudbury

Birthplace of Thomas Gainsborough, with a museum illustrating his career. Colchester 13 miles.

Situated in small, picturesque village within 15 miles of Sudbury, Newmarket Racecourse and historic Bury St Edmunds. Bungalow well equipped to accommodate 4 people. All facilities. Car essential, parking. Children and pets welcome. Terms from £63 to £125 per week. For further details send SAE to MRS M. WINCH, PLOUGH HOUSE, STANSFIELD, SUDBURY CO10 8LT (01284 789253). [🐕]

Woodbridge

Town on River Deben, 8 miles east of Ipswich.

THE CROWN AND CASTLE, ORFORD, WOODBRIDGE IP12 2LJ (01394 450205). Comfortable and very dog-friendly hotel situated close to 12th century castle in historic and unspoilt village of Orford. Honest good food served in award-winning Trinity Restaurant. [🐕]
e-mail: info@crownandcastle.co.uk website: www.crownandcastle.co.uk

Chase Lodge Hotel

An Award Winning Hotel

with style & elegance, set in tranquil surroundings at affordable prices.

10 Park Road Hampton Wick Kingston-Upon-Thames KT1 4AS

Pets welcome

Tel: 020 8943 1862 . Fax: 020 8943 9363

E-mail: info@chaselodgehotel.com Web: www.chaselodgehotel.com & www.surreyhotels.com

Quality en suite bedrooms
Close to Bushy Park
Full English Breakfast
A la carte menu
Licensed bar
Wedding Receptions
Honeymoon suite
available with jacuzzi & steam area
20 minutes from Heathrow Airport
Close to Kingston town centre & all major transport links.

AA * * * Les Routiers RAC * * *

All Major Credit Cards Accepted

See also Colour Advertisement on page 54

Kingston-upon-Thames

Market town, Royal borough and administrative centre of Surrey. Kingston is ideally placed for London and environs.

CHASE LODGE HOTEL, 10 PARK ROAD, HAMPTON WICK, KINGSTON-UPON-THAMES KT1 4AS (020 8943 1862; Fax: 020 8943 9363). Award-winning hotel offering quality en suite bedrooms. Easy access to town centre and major transport links. A la carte menu, licensed bar. ETC/AA/RAC ★★★ [🐂]

e-mail: info@chaselodgehotel.com websites: www.chaselodgehotel.com & www.surreyhotels.com

Other specialised

FHG PUBLICATIONS

Published annually: available in all good bookshops or direct from the publisher.

- **Recommended COUNTRY HOTELS OF BRITAIN £7.99**
- **Recommended SHORT BREAK HOLIDAYS IN BRITAIN £7.99**
- **Recommended COUNTRY INNS & PUBS OF BRITAIN £7.99**
- **BED AND BREAKFAST STOPS £6.99**
- **THE GOLF GUIDE Where to Play / Where to Stay £9.99**

FHG PUBLICATIONS LTD
Abbey Mill Business Centre,
Seedhill, Paisley, Renfrewshire PAI ITJ

Tel: 0141-887 0428 • Fax: 0141-889 7204
e-mail: fhg@ipcmedia.com • website: www.holidayguides.com

Fairhaven Holiday Cottages

Fairhaven offers a wide selection of holiday homes as well as comprehensive local knowledge and a friendly service. We specialise in Kent and Sussex but also offer two cottages on a Wiltshire farm. Our directors personally visit all of our properties to ensure quality and up-to-date information. Pets are welcome in many properties and short breaks are available out of season. For full details of all our properties visit our website **www.fairhaven-holidays.co.uk**
Alternatively request a colour brochure by telephone, fax or e-mail:
Tel: 08452 304334 • Fax: 01634 570157 • E-mail: enquiries@fairhaven-holidays.co.uk

See also Colour Advertisement on page 45

Battle, Brighton, Camber, Chiddingly

Little Hemingfold Hotel, Battle

TELHAM, BATTLE, EAST SUSSEX TN33 0TT

Tel: 01424 774338 • Fax: 01424 775351

Email: littlehemingfoldhote@tiscali.co.uk • Web: www.littlehemingfoldhotel.co.uk

Relax and enjoy the friendly, tranquil atmosphere of our part 17th century and early Victorian farmhouse.
Treat your pets to one of our courtyard garden rooms, all en suite and some with log-burning stoves
Fish, row and swim in our two-acre trout lake or play on our grass tennis court.
Special breaks available all year including Christmas and New Year. 2 days DB&B £64 pppn

Discounts for children and FREE accommodation for pets.

Special Places to Stay ETC ◆◆◆ Charming Small Hotels

See also Colour Advertisement on page 55

• Brighton & Hove
• Eastbourne • Lewes
• Worthing • Seaford
• Alfriston • Arundel
• Chichester

A very good selection of houses, flats, apartments and cottages.

Town Centre, Seafront & Countryside locations - many taking pets (Pets £15/£20 per week)

Camber Sands Holiday Park

ETC ★★★★

Camber, Nr Rye, East Sussex TN31 7RT

Lively park opposite award winning blue flag beach. Great range of hire caravans. 4 Indoor fun pools, sauna, spa, solarium, outdoor play area, and a choice of bars and entertainment venues. Explore the local area and visitor attractions. Tourers and Tents welcome.

www.gbholidayparks.co.uk Call **0870 442 9284** for brochure

Chiddingly, East Sussex

Adorable, small, well-equipped cottage in grounds of Tudor Manor

• Full central heating • Two bedrooms • Colour TV
• Fridge/freezer, microwave, dishwasher, laundry facilities,
• Telephone • Use of indoor heated swimming pool, sauna/jacuzzi, tennis and badminton court • Large safe garden

From £385 – £685 per week inclusive. Pets and children welcome

Breaks available £230 – £315 **ETC ★★★**

Apply: Eva Morris, "Pekes", 124 Elm Park Mansions, Park Walk, London SW10 0AR
Tel: 020-7352 8088 Fax: 020-7352 8125 e-mail: pekes.afa@virgin.net web:www.pekesmanor.com

FAIRLIGHT COTTAGE *Tel: 01424 812545*

Warren Road (via Coastguard Lane), Fairlight, East Sussex TN35 4AG

Country house in idyllic location with clifftop walks and panoramic views from balcony. Centrally heated en suite rooms, with beverage trays and colour TV. Comfortable guest lounge. Delicious home cooking, generous breakfasts. ETC ◆◆◆◆ No smoking. Ample parking. Dogs stay with owners.

See also Colour Advertisement on page 56

LITTLE OAKS, FARLEY WAY, FAIRLIGHT ETC ★★★★ *Tel & Fax: 01424 812545*

Luxury bungalow, on one level, set in quiet coastal village with clifftop parklands, close to ancient towns of Rye, Battle and Hastings. Furnished to a very high standard, the spacious accommodation comprises double bedroom with en suite shower, twin bedroom, lounge with TV, dining room, fully equipped kitchen/diner, bathroom, conservatory and balcony overlooking beautiful secluded garden, garage. No smoking in bungalow. Pets welcome. Rates from £275 per week to include central heating, electric and linen.

Contact: Ray and Janet Adams, Fairlight Cottage, Warren Road, Fairlight, East Sussex TN35 4AG

See also Colour Advertisement on page 55

BEAUPORT PARK HOTEL ETC/AA ★★★

A Georgian Country House Hotel set amid 33 acres of formal gardens and woodland. All rooms have private bath, satellite colour TV, trouser press, hairdryer and auto-dial telephone with modem. Outdoor Swimming Pool, Tennis, Squash, Badminton, Outdoor Chess, French Boules, Croquet Lawn, Putting, Golf and Riding School. Own woodland walks. Special Country House Breaks available all year. Please telephone for Brochure and Tariff.

BEAUPORT PARK HOTEL
Battle Road, Hastings TN38 8EA
Tel: Hastings (01424) 851222

e-mail: reservations@beauportparkhotel.co.uk • website: www.beauportparkhotel.co.uk

Cadborough Farm **Udimore Road, Rye, East Sussex TN31 6AA**

Tel: 01797 225426; Fax: 01797 224097

Five newly converted individual cottages. Each sleeps two, some with own courtyards. Direct access to '1066' country walks and cliff track with sea views to Rye (1 mile). Full GCH & CTV and CD player. Rates from £165 - £395 per week. Double and Twin available. Minimum two day lets from £55/night. Linen, towels, gas and electricity inclusive. One small well-behaved dog welcome. Non-smoking. Sorry no children.

website: www.cadborough.co.uk e-mail: info@cadborough.co.uk ETC ★★★★

JEAKE'S HOUSE

Mermaid Street, Rye, East Sussex TN31 7ET
Telephone: 01797 222828 Fax: 01797 222623
E-mail: stay@jeakeshouse.com
Website: www.jeakeshouse.com

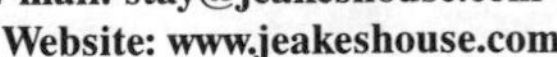

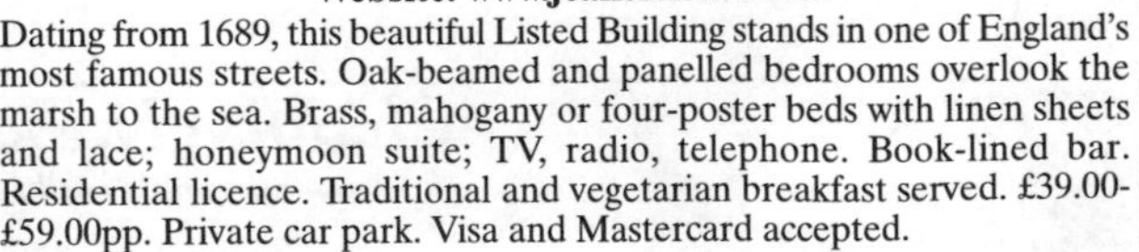

Dating from 1689, this beautiful Listed Building stands in one of England's most famous streets. Oak-beamed and panelled bedrooms overlook the marsh to the sea. Brass, mahogany or four-poster beds with linen sheets and lace; honeymoon suite; TV, radio, telephone. Book-lined bar. Residential licence. Traditional and vegetarian breakfast served. £39.00-£59.00pp. Private car park. Visa and Mastercard accepted.

AA PREMIER SELECTED ◆◆◆◆◆ RAC SPARKLING DIAMOND ◆◆◆◆◆ & WARM WELCOME AWARD **Good Hotel Guide** César Award

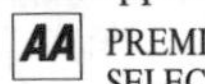

See colour advertisement on page 55

BEACH COTTAGES, CLAREMONT ROAD, SEAFORD BN25 2QQ

Well-equipped, three-bedroomed terraced cottage on seafront. CH, open fire and woodburner. South-facing patio overlooking sea. Downland walks (wonderful for dogs), fishing, golf, wind-surfing, etc.

Details from: Julia Lewis, 47 Wandle Bank, London SW19 1DW

Tel: 020 8542 5073 • e-mail: julialewis@beachcottages.info • website: www.beachcottages.info

FAIRHAVEN HOLIDAY COTTAGES. (08452 304334; Fax: 01634 570157) Fairhaven offers a wide selection of holiday homes in Kent and Sussex but also offer two cottages on a Wiltshire farm. Pets are welcome in many properties and short breaks are available out of season. Please visit our website or request a colour brochure.
e-mail: enquiries@fairhaven-holidays.co.uk website: www.fairhaven-holidays.co.uk

Battle

Site of the famous victory of William the Conqueror; remains of an abbey mark the spot where Harold fell.

FOX HOLE FARM, KANE HYTHE ROAD, BATTLE TN33 9QU (Tel & Fax: 01424 772053). Beautiful secluded 18th century woodcutter's cottage, nestling in over 40 acres of its own rolling, lush East Sussex land. Surrounded by Forestry Commission woodland. AA ◆◆◆◆ [🐕]

LITTLE HEMINGFOLD HOTEL, TELHAM, BATTLE TN33 0TT (01424 774338; Fax: 01424 775351). In the heart of 1066 Country, 40 acres of bliss for you and your pets. Farmhouse hotel, all facilities. Fishing, boating, swimming, tennis. Special Breaks all year. Discounts for children 7-14 years old. FREE accommodation for pets. ETC ◆◆◆ [pw! 🐕]
e-mail: littlehemingfoldhote@tiscali.co.uk website: www.littlehemingfoldhotel.co.uk

Brighton

Famous resort with shingle beach and sand at low tide. Varied entertainment and nightlife; excellent shops and restaurants. Portsmouth 48 miles, Hastings 37, Newhaven 9.

BEST OF BRIGHTON & SUSSEX COTTAGES has available a very good selection of houses, flats, apartments and cottages in Brighton and Hove as well as East and West Sussex from Eastbourne to Chichester. Town centre/seaside and countryside locations – many taking pets. (01273 308779; Fax: 01273 390211). [Pets £15/£20 per week.]
website: www.bestofbrighton.co.uk

Camber

Seaside resort on Rye Bay, 3 miles east of Rye.

CAMBER SANDS HOLIDAY PARK, CAMBER, NEAR RYE TN31 7RT. Lively park opposite award-winning blue flag beach. Great range of hire caravans. Four indoor fun pools; outdoor play area; choice of bar and entertainment venues. Tourers and tents welcome. Call 0870 442 9284 for brochure. ETC★★★★
website: www.gbholidayparks.co.uk

Chiddlingly

Charming village, 4 miles north-west of Hailsham. Off the A22 London-Eastbourne road.

Adorable, small, well-equipped cottage in grounds of Tudor Manor. Two bedrooms. Full central heating. Colour TV. Fridge/freezer, laundry facilities. Large safe garden. Use indoor heated swimming pool, sauna/jacuzzi and tennis. From £385 to £685 per week inclusive. ETC ★★★. Contact: EVA MORRIS, "PEKES", 124 ELM PARK MANSIONS, PARK WALK, LONDON SW10 0AR (020 7352 8088; Fax: 020 7352 8125). [2 dogs free, extra dog £5 (max. 4) pw!].
e-mail: pekes.afa@virgin.net website: www.pekesmanor.com

Fairlight

Village 3 miles east of Hastings.

JANET & RAY ADAMS, FAIRLIGHT COTTAGE, WARREN ROAD, FAIRLIGHT TN35 4AG (01424 812545). Country house in idyllic location with clifftop walks. Tasteful en suite rooms, comfortable guest lounge. Delicious breakfasts. No smoking. Dogs stay with owners. ETC ◆◆◆◆ [🐕]

LITTLE OAKS, FARLEY WAY, FAIRLIGHT. Luxury bungalow set in quiet coastal village close to Rye, Hastings and Battle. Beautiful secluded garden, balcony and conservatory. No smoking. ETC ★★★★ Contact: RAY & JANET ADAMS, FAIRLIGHT COTTAGE, WARREN ROAD, FAIRLIGHT, EAST SUSSEX TN35 4AG (Tel & Fax: 01424 812545).[🐕]

Hastings

Seaside resort with a famous past - the ruins of William the Conqueror's castle lie above the Old Town. Many places of historic interest in the area, plus entertainments for all the family.

BEAUPORT PARK HOTEL, BATTLE ROAD, HASTINGS TN38 8EA (01424 851222). Georgian country mansion in 33 acres. All rooms private bath, colour television, trouser press, hairdryer, telephone with modem. Country house breaks available all year. ETC/AA ★★★ [pw! 🐕]
e-mail: reservations@beauportparkhotel.co.uk website: www.beauportparkhotel.co.uk

Polegate

Quiet position, 5 miles from the popular seaside resort of Eastbourne. London 58 miles, Lewes 12.

MRS M. FIELD, 20 ST JOHN'S ROAD, POLEGATE BN26 5BP (01323 482691). Homely private house. Quiet location; large enclosed garden. Parking space. Ideally situated for walking on South Downs and Forestry Commission land. All rooms, washbasins and tea/coffee making facilities. Bed and Breakfast. Pets very welcome. [pw!]

Rye

Picturesque hill town with steep cobbled streets. Many fine buildings of historic interest. Hastings 12 miles, Tunbridge Wells 28.

FLACKLEY ASH HOTEL, PEASMARSH, RYE TN31 6YH (01797 230651). Georgian Country House Hotel in beautiful grounds. Indoor swimming pool and Leisure Centre. Beauty and massage. Visit Rye and the castles and gardens of East Sussex and Kent. AA/RAC ★★★ [Pets £7.50 per night]
website: www.flackleyashhotel.co.uk

CADBOROUGH FARM, UDIMORE ROAD, RYE TN31 6AA (01797 225426; Fax: 01797 224097). Five newly converted individual cottages. Each sleeps two, some with own courtyards. Double and Twin available. One small well-behaved dog welcome. Non-smoking. Sorry, no children. ETC ★★★★ [🐕].
e-mail: info@cadborough.co.uk website: www.cadborough.co.uk

JEAKE'S HOUSE, MERMAID STREET, RYE TN31 7ET (01797 222828; Fax: 01797 222623). Dating from 1689, this Listed Building has oak-beamed and panelled bedrooms overlooking the marsh. TV, radio, telephone. Book-lined bar. £39.00-£59.00 per person. ETC/AA/RAC ◆◆◆◆◆ [Pets £5 per night]
e-mail: stay@jeakeshouse.com website: www.jeakeshouse.com

Seaford

On the coast midway between Newhaven and Beachy Head.

BEACH COTTAGES, CLAREMONT ROAD, SEAFORD. Well-equipped, three-bedroomed terraced cottage on seafront. CH, open fire and woodburner. South-facing patio overlooking sea. Downland walks (wonderful for dogs), fishing, golf, wind-surfing, etc. Details from JULIA LEWIS, 47 WANDLE BANK, LONDON SW19 1DW (020 8542 5073). [pw! 🐕]
e-mail: julialewis@beachcottages.info website: www.beachcottages.info

THE SILVERDALE, 21 SUTTON PARK ROAD, SEAFORD BN25 IRH (01323 491849). We don't just accept dogs, we welcome them. Only a few minutes from seafront and parks. Delightful small diningroom and bar. All rooms individually decorated. SEEDA award winner 2003, Clean Catering Award winner for 10 years. ETC/AA ◆◆◆◆
e-mail: silverdale@mistral.co.uk website: www.mistral.co.uk/silverdale

Wandleys Caravan Park

Eastergate, West Sussex PO20 6SE
Telephone: 01243 543235
or 01243 543384 (evenings/weekends)

You will find peace, tranquillity and relaxation in one of our comfortable holiday caravans. All have internal WC and shower. Dogs welcome. The Sussex Downs, Chichester, Bognor Regis, Arundel, Littlehampton – all these historic and interesting places are only 15 minutes from our beautiful, small and quiet country park. SAE please for brochure.

CHEQUERS HOTEL

Old Rectory Lane, Pulborough,
West Sussex RH20 1AD
Tel: 01798 872486
e-mail: chequershotel@btinternet.com
www.thechequers-hotel.co.uk

Delightful small Queen Anne Hotel on the edge of the village, overlooking the Arun Valley towards the South Downs. All bedrooms with private bathrooms, plus colour TV, telephone, trouser press, hairdryer and tea/coffee making facilities. Restaurant serves fresh market produce from daily changing menu. Garden Conservatory and Coffee Shop. Car park. Superb centre for walking or touring, with safe walks for your dog available directly from the hotel in our 9-acre meadow.

Walk for miles along the South Downs Way, or along the banks of the River Arun, or visit one of the many local places of interest such as Parham House and Gardens, Petworth House and Park, Goodwood, Arundel, or the Weald and Downland Open Air Museum.

Children are also very welcome. Major Credit Cards accepted. BARGAIN BREAKS all through the year from £49.50 per person for Dinner, Bed and Breakfast. Reduced rates for longer stays. Winter Bargain - any 3 nights DB&B from £140.
AA ★★★, AA Rosettes for Good Food.

No charge for dogs belonging to readers of Pets Welcome!

St. Andrews Lodge

ETC/AA ◆◆◆◆

ST ANDREWS LODGE

Chichester Road, Selsey, West Sussex PO20 0LX
Tel: 01243 606899 • Fax: 01243 607826
e-mail: info@standrewslodge.co.uk
web: www.standrewslodge.co.uk

Welcoming, family-run hotel with a reputation for an excellent hearty breakfast. Situated on the Manhood peninsula just south of Chichester, close to unspoilt beaches and countryside. Ten bedrooms, all en suite, with direct-dial telephones, TV, fridge and tea-making facilities; some on ground floor. Spacious lounges with log fire; licensed bar for residents only. Wheelchair accessible room. Large car park. Dogs welcome in rooms overlooking large garden. Bed & Breakfast from £30 pppn. Apply for brochure, prices and details of special winter offers October to February.

See also colour advertisement on page 56

Eastergate

Village between the sea and South Downs. Fontwell Park nearby. Bognor Regis 5 miles south.

WANDLEYS CARAVAN PARK, EASTERGATE PO20 6SE (01243 543235 or 01243 543384 evenings/weekends). You will find peace, tranquillity and relaxation in one of our comfortable holiday caravans. All have internal WC and shower. Dogs welcome. Many historic and interesting places nearby. SAE for brochure. [🐕]

Pulborough

Popular fishing centre on the River Arun. South Downs Way nearby; Arundel 8 miles.

CHEQUERS HOTEL, PULBOROUGH RH20 1AD (01798 872486). Lovely Queen Anne house in village overlooking Arun Valley. Excellent food. Children and dogs welcome. No charge for dogs belonging to readers of Pets Welcome! ETC ★★★ Silver Award, AA ★★★ [pw! 🐕]
e-mail: chequershotel@btinternet.com website: www.thechequers-hotel.co.uk

Selsey

Seaside resort 8 miles south of Chichester. Selsey Bill is headland extending into the English Channel.

ST ANDREWS LODGE HOTEL, CHICHESTER ROAD, SELSEY PO20 0LX (01243 606899; Fax: 01243 607826). 10 bedrooms, all en suite, with direct dial telephones and modem point, some on ground floor. Spacious lounges with log fire; licensed bar for residents only. Wheelchair accessible room. Dogs welcome in rooms overlooking large garden. Apply for brochure and prices. ETC/AA ◆◆◆◆ [🐕]
e-mail: info@standrewslodge.co.uk website: www.standrewslodge.co.uk

Worthing

Residential town and seaside resort with 5 miles seafront. Situated 10 miles west of Brighton.

CAVENDISH HOTEL, 115 MARINE PARADE, WORTHING BN11 3QG (01903 236767; Fax: 01903 823840). Ideal base for touring Sussex villages and the rolling South Downs. All rooms are en suite, have TV, direct-dial telephone and tea/coffee facilities. No charge for dogs belonging to readers of Pets Welcome! AA/RAC ★★ [🐕].
e-mail: cavendishworthing@btinternet.com website: www.cavendishworthing.co.uk

SYMBOLS

🐕 **Indicates that pets are welcome free of charge.**
£ **Indicates that a charge is made for pets: nightly or weekly.**
pw! **Shows some special provision for pets; exercise facility, feeding or accommodation arrangement.**
⌂ **Indicates separate pets accommodation.**

TYNE & WEAR

Whitley Bay Holiday Park ETC ★★★★

The Links, Whitley Bay, Tyne & Wear NE26 4RR

Whitley Bay is a popular 4 star park on the edge of a lively seaside resort. Well equipped caravans for hire. Indoor heated pool, family and adult bars, entertainment, kid's club and multi sports court. Lovely walks along the beach.

www.gbholidayparks.co.uk

Call 0870 442 9282 for brochure

Whitley Bay

North Sea coast resort 2 miles north of Tynemouth. Extensive sands to the north.

WHITLEY BAY HOLIDAY PARK, THE LINK, WHITLEY BAY NE26 4RR. Popular park with well equipped caravans for hire. Indoor heated pool, multi-sports court, kids' club, lovely beach walks. Family and adult bars, entertainment. Call 0870 442 9282 for brochure. ETC★★★★
website: www.gbholidayparks.co.uk

WARWICKSHIRE

Stratford-upon-Avon

Stratford-upon-Avon

RIVERSIDE CARAVAN PARK – ON THE BANKS OF THE RIVER AVON

Features at a Glance:
- Pets Welcome
- River Taxi to and from Town Centre
- Club House • Shop & Café
- Bowling Green
- Kids Playground
- Snooker Table
- 1½ miles of Free Fishing
- Only 1 mile to Town Centre

Riverside Park is ideally placed for visiting all Shakespearian attractions and the beautiful Cotswolds. In Stratford itself there is everything you could wish for: shops, pubs, restaurants, swimming pool, sports centre, The Royal Shakespeare Theatre, and a generous helping of history and the Bard! The luxury 12ft wide Caravan Holiday Homes accommodate up to 6 persons in comfort. All have kitchen with cooker and fridge, bathroom with shower/washbasin/WC, two bedrooms, one double bedded, one with two single beds, (cots available), lounge, eating area, electric fire, colour TV, carpeted throughout. Also available, TWO COTTAGES, "Sleepy Hollow" and "Kingfisher Cottage", both with modern facilities set on the river bank.

Riverside Caravan Park, Tiddington Road,
Stratford-upon-Avon, Warwickshire CV37 7BE
Telephone: 01789 292312 **www.stratfordcaravans.co.uk**

GREEN HAVEN ETC◆◆◆◆

Bed & Breakfast • Private Car Park • Ideal for theatre and town centre
Centrally heated • Close to Warwick and Cotswolds • All rooms en suite
Non – smoking • Competitive rates • Private parking • Pets £5.00.

217 Evesham Road, Stratford-upon-Avon CV37 9AS
Tel: 01789 297874 • Fax: 01789 550487
e-mail: information@green-haven.co.uk • website: www.green-haven.co.uk

Mrs Hazel Mellor
ARRANDALE
208 Evesham Road,
Stratford-upon-Avon CV37 9AS

Comfortable family Guest House situated at the town end of Evesham Road on the B439 (Bidford). 10 minutes' walk to River Avon, Shakespearean properties, theatre. One hour's drive to Cotswolds. Tea-making facilities and TV in bedrooms; centrally heated. Pets in room. Parking, though car not essential. Lift from bus or train station by arrangement.

Bed and Breakfast: room with shower, washbasin £17.50 per person; en suite toilet, shower, washbasin £20 per person. Weekly terms £115-£130. Evening Meals £8.00 extra. Single person supplement £10 pppn.

Tel: (01789) 267112 • website: www.arrandale.netfirms.com

THE CROFT **ETC/AA ◆◆◆◆**

Haseley Knob, Warwick CV35 7NL Tel & Fax: 01926 484447

- Friendly family country guesthouse • non-smoking • TV
- All rooms en suite or private bathroom, hairdryer, tea/coffee
- Central location for Warwick, Stratford, Coventry and NEC.

e-mail: david@croftguesthouse.co.uk **website: www.croftguesthouse.co.uk**

Stratford-upon-Avon

Historic town famous as Shakespeare's birthplace and home. Birmingham 24, Warwick 8.

RIVERSIDE CARAVAN PARK, TIDDINGTON ROAD, STRATFORD-UPON-AVON CV37 7BE (01789 292312). Luxury Caravans, sleep 6. Fully equipped kitchens, bathroom/ shower/WC. Also two riverside Cottages, all modern facilities to first-class standards. Private fishing. On banks of River Avon. [Pets £15 weekly.]
website: www.stratfordcaravans.co.uk

MRS H. J. MELLOR, ARRANDALE, 208 EVESHAM ROAD, STRATFORD-UPON-AVON CV37 9AS (01789 267112). Guest House situated near River Avon, theatre, Shakespeare properties. Washbasins, tea making, TV, central heating, en suite available. Children, pets welcome. Parking. Bed and Breakfast £17.50-£20. Weekly terms £115-£130. Evening Meal £8.00. [🐕]
website: www.arrandale.netfirms.com

DEREK & SUSAN LEARMOUNT, GREEN HAVEN, 217 EVESHAM ROAD, STRATFORD-UPON-AVON CV37 9AS (01789 297874; Fax: 01789 550487). Cosy, pretty, refurbished guest house. Central heating, colour TV, courtesy trays. All en suite. Private parking. Easily accessible to Cotswolds and Warwick. Non-smoking. Pets by arrangement only. ETC ◆◆◆◆ [Pets £5.00 one-off charge]
e-mail: susanlearmount@green-haven.co.uk OR information@green-haven.co.uk
website: www.green-haven.co.uk

Warwick

Town on the River Avon, 9 miles south-west of Coventry, with medieval castle and many fine old buildings.

DOREEN BROMILOW, "WAVERLEY", WOLVERTON FIELDS, NORTON LINDSEY, WARWICK CV35 8JN (01926 842446) Overlooking beautiful countryside, near Warwick. All rooms en suite, TV, tea/coffee making. Ground floor double room. Large paddock, ideal for dogs. Non-smoking. Private car park.

DAVID & PATRICIA CLAPP, CROFT GUESTHOUSE, HASELEY KNOB, WARWICK CV35 7NL (Tel & Fax: 01926 484447). All bedrooms en suite or with private bathroom, some ground floor. Non-smoking. Picturesque rural setting. Central for NEC, Warwick, Stratford, Stoneleigh and Coventry. B&B single £35, double/twin £52. ETC/AA ◆◆◆◆ [Dogs £3]
e-mail: david@croftguesthouse.co.uk website: www.croftguesthouse.co.uk

Devizes

Market town 10 miles south-east of Chippenham on Kennet and Avon Canals.

LONGWATER FARM GUEST HOUSE, ERLESTOKE, DEVIZES SN10 5UE (Tel & Fax: 01380 830095). Good old-fashioned hospitality with all the facilities of a modern home. Twin, double and family rooms, all en suite; ground floor rooms. Wheelchair-friendly. Pets welcome. Brochure on request. ETC ◆◆◆ [🐕]

Malmesbury

Country town on River Avon with a late medieval market cross. Remains of medieval abbey.

JOHN AND EDNA EDWARDS, STONEHILL FARM, CHARLTON, MALMESBURY SN16 9DY (01666 823310). Family-run dairy farm, ideal for touring. 3 comfortable rooms, one en suite. Also 2 fully equipped bungalow-style barns, each sleeps 2/3 plus cot, self catering. ETC ★★★ [Pets £5 per week].
e-mail: johnedna@stonehillfarm.fsnet.co.uk
website: www.SmoothHound.co.uk/hotels/stonehill.html

Salisbury

13th century cathedral city, with England's highest spire at 404ft. Many fine buildings.

MR A. SHERING, SWAYNES FIRS FARM, GRIMSDYKE, COOMBE BISSETT, SALISBURY SP5 5RF (01725 519240). Small working farm with horses, poultry, geese and duck ponds. Spacious rooms, all en suite with colour TV. Ideal for visiting the many historic sites in the area. ETC ◆◆◆ [🐕]
e-mail: swaynes.firs@virgin.net website: www.swaynesfirs.co.uk

The 17th-century Dormy House Hotel is set high in the rolling Cotswold countryside between the picturesque villages of Broadway and Chipping Campden, with Stratford-upon-Avon only a short drive away. Adjacent to Broadway Golf Course, it is a really lovely place in which to relax with your dog(s) and enjoy a one night stay or Classic Dormy Break. **Telephone: 01386 852711 for brochure/booking.**

Willersey Hill, Broadway, Worcestershire WR12 7LF
Telephone: (01386) 852711 Fax: (01386) 858636
E-Mail: reservations@dormyhouse. co.uk • Web: www.dormyhouse.co.uk

Quality of food

See also Colour Advertisement on page 56

Traditional 18th century country house surrounded by peaceful and picturesque gardens. All rooms en suite with colour TV, generous beverage tray, hairdryer, radio alarm and more. Children welcome. Babysitting service. Dogs and cats by arrangement. Worcester 10 minutes, Stratford-upon-Avon, Warwick, Cotswolds, Birmingham and Wales all within one hour. M5 motorway six minutes. Single from £30, double from £50.

Mrs Salli Harrison, Middleton Grange, Salwarpe, Droitwich Spa WR9 0AH
Tel: 01905 451678 Fax: 01905 453978 ETC ◆◆◆◆ SILVER AWARD
e-mail: salli@middletongrange.com • website: www.middletongrange.com

Croft Guest House, Bransford, Worcester WR6 5JD

16th-18th Century country house, 10 minutes from Worcester, Malvern and M5. Three en suite rooms (two double, one family) and two with washbasins available. All bedrooms non-smoking, with tea/coffee tray, colour TV and radio alarm. Dogs welcome by arrangement. Bed & Breakfast from £26 to £35 single, £44 to £60 double.

Ann & Brian Porter • Tel: 01886 832227 • Fax: 01886 830037 AA ◆◆◆
e-mail: hols@crofthousewr6.fsnet.co.uk • www.croftguesthouse.com

See also Colour Advertisement on page 56

WHITEWELLS FARM COTTAGES

ETC ★★★★

Ridgeway Cross, Near Malvern, Worcestershire WR13 5JR • www.whitewellsfarm.co.uk
Tel: 01886 880607 • Fax: 01886 880360 • e-mail: info@whitewellsfarm.co.uk

Seven well-established cottages converted from old farm buildings and a hop kiln, full of charm and character with original exposed timbering. These award-winning cottages are exceptionally clean and comfortable and equipped to the highest standards. One cottage suitable for the disabled with full wheelchair access. Idyllically set around a duckpond with two and a half acres of the property being a fully-fenced woodland plantation, ideal for exercising dogs, on or off the lead.

Set in unspoilt countryside with outstanding views of the **Malvern Hills** on the **Herefordshire/Worcestershire border. Ideal base for touring Worcestershire, Herefordshire, the Malverns, Gloucestershire, Welsh mountains, Cotswolds and Shakespeare country**. Electricity and linen included in price. Short breaks and long lets, suitable for relocation. Children and pets welcome. Open all year.

Colour brochure available from: Kate and Denis Kavanagh.

Moseley Farm Bed and Breakfast

Moseley Road, Hallow, Worcester WR2 6NL
Tel: 01905 641343 www.moseleyfarmbandb.co.uk

Spacious 17th Century former farmhouse with large garden and views over Worcestershire. Rural location, 3 miles from Worcester. Severn Way and Wychavon Way nearby. En suite or standard rooms with colour TV, radio alarm clocks and tea/coffee making facilities. From £25 pppn.

FHG PUBLICATIONS LIMITED

publish a large range of well-known accommodation guides. We will be happy to send you details or you can use the order form at the back of this book.

Broadway

Small town below escarpment of Cotswold Hills, 5 miles south-east of Evesham.

DORMY HOUSE, WILLERSEY HILL, BROADWAY WR12 7LF (01386 852711; Fax: 01386 858636). The 17th-century Dormy House Hotel is set high in the rolling Cotswold countryside. Adjacent to Broadway Golf Course, it is a really lovely place in which to relax with your dog(s) and enjoy a one night stay or Classic Dormy Break. AA/RAC ★★★ [Pets £5 per dog per night]
e-mail: reservations@dormyhouse.co.uk website: www.dormyhouse.co.uk

Droitwich

Town 6 miles north-east of Worcester. Former spa status due to saline springs.

MRS SALLI HARRISON, MIDDLETON GRANGE, SALWARPE, DROITWICH SPA WR9 0AH (01905 451678; Fax: 01905 453978). Traditional 18th century country house surrounded by picturesque gardens. Children welcome. Babysitting service. Dogs and cats by arrangement. All rooms en suite. M5 motorway six minutes. Worcester 10 minutes. ETC ◆◆◆◆ *SILVER AWARD.* [🐕]

Great Malvern

Fashionable spa town in last century with echoes of that period.

ANN AND BRIAN PORTER, CROFT GUEST HOUSE, BRANSFORD, WORCESTER WR6 5JD (01886 832227; Fax: 01886 830037). 16th-18th century country house. 10 minutes from Worcester, Malvern and M5. All bedrooms non-smoking; colour TV, tea/coffee tray; central heating. Three en suite. Dinners available; residential licence. Dogs by arrangement. AA ◆◆◆ [🐕]
e-mail: hols@crofthousewr6.fsnet.co.uk website: www.croftguesthouse.com

KATE AND DENIS KAVANAGH, WHITEWELLS FARM COTTAGES, RIDGEWAY CROSS, NEAR MALVERN WR13 5JR (01886 880607; Fax: 01886 880360). Charming converted Cottages, sleep 2–6. Fully equipped with colour TV, microwave, barbecue, fridge, iron, etc. Linen, towels also supplied. One cottage suitable for the disabled with full wheelchair access. Short breaks, long lets, large groups. ETC ★★★★ [pw! Pets £10 per week.] Also see Display Advert..
e-mail: info@whitewellsfarm.co.uk website: www.whitewellsfarm.co.uk

Worcester

Cathedral city on River Severn, 24 miles south-west of Birmingham.

MOSELEY FARM BED & BREAKFAST, MOSELEY ROAD, HALLOW, WORCESTER WR2 6NL (01905 641343). Spacious 17th Century former farmhouse with large garden and views over Worcestershire. En suite or standard rooms with colour TV, radio alarm clocks and tea/coffee making facilities. Worcester three miles. ETC ◆◆◆ [Pets £5 per week]
website: www.moseleyfarmbandb.co.uk

PLEASE NOTE

All the information in this book is given in good faith in the belief that it is correct. However, the publishers cannot guarantee the facts given in these pages, neither are they responsible for changes in policy, ownership or terms that may take place after the date of going to press. Readers should always satisfy themselves that the facilities they require are available and that the terms, if quoted, still apply.

Barmby Moor

Village 2 miles west of Pocklington.

MR AND MRS THORPE, PARKLANDS, YORK ROAD, BARMBY MOOR, YORK YO42 4HT (Tel & Fax: 01759 380260). Tastefully converted stables in private grounds. Ideally placed for wolds, moors, coast. Self-contained, self-catering, sleeps 2/6. Full central heating. No smoking. Pets welcome. [pw! 🐕]

Bridlington

Traditional family resort with picturesque harbour and a wide range of entertainments and leisure facilities. Ideal for exploring the Heritage coastline and the Wolds.

CHRIS & JACKY SHORT, HEATHFIELD GUEST HOUSE, 34 TENNYSON AVENUE, BRIDLINGTON YO15 2EP ((01262 672594). Easy walking to beach and all amenities. En suite rooms available. B&B from £16pppn. TV, tea and coffee in all rooms. Non-smoking. Dogs welcome free of charge. ETC ◆◆◆ [🐕]
e-mail: Chris.Jacky@tiscali.co.uk

Driffield

Town 11 miles south west of Bridlington.

MRS TIFFY HOPPER, KELLEYTHORPE FARM, DRIFFIELD YO25 9DW (01377 252297). Lovely Georgian farmhouse overlooking small lake. Friendly atmosphere, attractive bedrooms. Aberdeen Angus herd with beef sold in shop. Children welcome. B&B from £22. Evening Meal by prior arrangement.[🐕]

SYMBOLS

- 🐕 **Indicates that pets are welcome free of charge.**
- £ **Indicates that a charge is made for pets: nightly or weekly.**
- pw! **Shows some special provision for pets; exercise facility, feeding or accommodation arrangement.**
- ⌂ **Indicates separate pets accommodation.**

Flamborough

Village 4 miles north-east of Bridlington.

THORNWICK & SEA FARM HOLIDAY CENTRE, NORTH MARINE ROAD, FLAMBOROUGH YO15 1AV (01262 850369; Fax: 01262 851550) Set on the spectacular Heritage Coast with unrivalled coastal scenery. Six-berth caravans and chalets for hire. Tents and tourers welcome. Bars, entertainment, shop, pool and gym on site. [Pets £5 per week.] ETC ★★★★.
e-mail: enquiries@thornwickbay.co.uk website: www.thornwickbay.co.uk

Kilnwick Percy

Located 2 miles east of Pocklington

PAWS-A-WHILE, KILNWICK PERCY, POCKLINGTON YO42 1UF (01759 301168; Mobile: 07711 866869). Small family B & B set in forty acres of parkland twixt York and Beverley. Golf, sauna, walking, riding. Pets and horses most welcome. Brochure available. ETC ◆◆◆◆ [pw! 🐕]
e-mail: paws.a.while@lineone.net website: www.pawsawhile.net

Withernsea

Coastal resort 15 miles east of Hull.

WITHERNSEA HOLIDAY PARK, NORTH ROAD, WITHERNSEA HU19 2BS. Total relaxation on the rugged Yorkshire coast. Well equipped caravans. Licensed club, entertainment, play area, beach access, takeaway. Ideal for walking. Call 0870 442 9313 for brochure.
website: www.gbholidayparks.co.uk

•• *Some Useful Guidance for Guests and Hosts* ••

Every year literally thousands of holidays, short breaks and overnight stops are arranged through our guides, the vast majority without any problems at all. In a handful of cases, however, difficulties do arise about bookings, which often could have been prevented from the outset.
It is important to remember that when accommodation has been booked, both parties – guests and hosts – have entered into a form of contract. We hope that the following points will provide helpful guidance.

GUESTS:

- When enquiring about accommodation, be as precise as possible. Give exact dates, numbers in your party and the ages of any children.
- State the number and type of rooms wanted and also what catering you require – bed and breakfast, full board etc. Make sure that the position about evening meals is clear – and about pets, reductions for children or any other special points.
- Read our reviews carefully to ensure that the proprietors you are going to contact can supply what you want. Ask for a letter confirming all arrangements, if possible.
- If you have to cancel, do so as soon as possible. Proprietors do have the right to retain deposits and under certain circumstances to charge for cancelled holidays if adequate notice is not given and they cannot re-let the accommodation.

HOSTS:

- Give details about your facilities and about any special conditions. Explain your deposit system clearly and arrangements for cancellations, charges etc. and whether or not your terms include VAT.
- If for any reason you are unable to fulfil an agreed booking without adequate notice, you may be under an obligation to arrange suitable alternative accommodation or to make some form of compensation.

While every effort is made to ensure accuracy, we regret that FHG Publications cannot accept responsibility for errors, omissions or misrepresentations in our entries or any consequences thereof. Prices in particular should be checked because we go to press early. We will follow up complaints but cannot act as arbiters or agents for either party.

See also Colour Advertisement on page 9

Clapham, Danby

See also Colour Advertisement on page 6

Readers are requested to mention this guidebook when seeking accommodation (and please enclose a stamped addressed envelope).

Garbutts Ghyll, Thornton Hill, Easingwold YO61 3PZ

Garbutts Ghyll is a working farm situated in its own wooded valley on the edge of the North York Moors National Park. Relax and unwind in our friendly, non-smoking home which has traditional furnishings. Children welcome; babysitting available. Stabling for horses/dogs. One double/family bedroom, one twin bedroom; both en suite.

Tel: 01347 868644

"SEA CABIN" 16 Gap Road, Hunmanby Gap, Near Filey YO14 9QP

Warm and friendly hospitality plus good food at our well-appointed twin-bedroomed Granny annexe. En suite, own private lounge. Located on the cliff top, with easy access to the golden sands of Filey Bay. Private parking, quiet location, five minutes' drive from Filey town. Full English Breakfast. Bookings for B&B plus optional Evening Meal. Pet friendly beach and area.

for brochure & terms:
Leonard & Diane Hunter Tel: 01723 891368 **Dogs come free of charge!**

JERRY AND BEN'S HOLIDAY COTTAGES

Seven comfortable properties on a private estate near Grassington in the Yorkshire Dales National Park, with wooded mountain becks, waterfalls, rocky crags and surrounded by accessible hill and footpath walking. £134 to £425. Brochure from:

Mrs J. M. Joy, Jerry and Ben's Holiday Cottages, Hebden, Skipton, North Yorkshire BD23 5DL. Tel: 01756 752369; Fax: 01756 753370
e-mail: dawjoy@aol.com website: www.yorkshirenet.co.uk/stayat/jerryandbens

The Foresters Arms

MAIN STREET, GRASSINGTON, SKIPTON
NORTH YORKSHIRE BD23 5AA
Tel: 01756 752349 • Fax: 01756 753633

The Foresters Arms, Grassington, once an old coaching inn, situated in the heart of the Yorkshire Dales. An ideal centre for walking or touring. A family-run business for over 35 years. Serving hand-pulled traditional ales. Bar meals served lunchtime and evenings. All bedrooms are en suite and have satellite TVs and tea/coffee making facilities. Prices £30 single; £60 double.

Proprietor: Rita Richardson

Grassington House Hotel & Restaurant

AA ★★ ETC ★★ *HOTEL*

The Square, Grassington, Skipton
North Yorkshire BD23 5AQ
Tel: 01756 752406 Fax: 01756 752135

The hotel is situated in the quaint cobbled square and is renowned for its atmosphere of warmth and friendliness. Our restaurant, serving à la carte, is very popular for its good food where we use produce from local suppliers. We also serve a large selection of meals and snacks in the bar and conservatory. The hotel is well situated for walking in the beautiful dales or touring. Large private car park.

The Courtyard at Duke's Place

Bishop Thornton, Near Harrogate HG3 3JY

Tel: 01765 620229 • Fax: 01765 620454

e-mail: jakimoorhouse@onetel.net.uk

ETC ★★★/★★★★

In the heart of Nidderdale, in beautiful surroundings, a group of well-maintained and equipped holiday cottages adjoining Georgian farmhouse. Sleep two to six; linen, fully equipped kitchens and colour TV. Laundry and payphone, barbecue and woodland garden. Riding stables on site. Excellent walking. Pets and children most welcome.

LUXURY COTTAGES AND TIMBER LODGES IN BEAUTIFUL SURROUNDINGS

FOLLIFOOT, HARROGATE HG3 1JH

TEL: 01423 870439
FAX: 01423 870859

e-mail:holiday-park@ruddingpark.com
www.ruddingpark.com

- Deer House family pub
- Children's adventure playground
- Pets welcome
- Heated outdoor swimming pool and paddling pool
- Games room
- 18 hole pay & play golf course plus floodlit driving range

RELAX IN THE HEART OF YORKSHIRE

See also Colour Advertisement on page 58

STONE HOUSE HOTEL

Licensed Country House Hotel & Restaurant overlooking Magnificent Wensleydale

~ 23 Quality En Suite Bedrooms ~

(some with private conservatories opening onto Gardens)

~ Delicious Food & Fine Wines ~

The Perfect Venue for a relaxing break deep in the heart of the Yorkshire Dales.

Dogs genuinely welcome – Short Breaks available now

Sedbusk, Hawes, North Yorkshire DL8 3PT
Tel: 01969 667571 • Fax: 01969 667720
website: www.stonehousehotel.com

See also Colour Advertisement on page 57

COUNTRY COTTAGE HOLIDAYS

DRYDEN HOUSE ◆ MARKET PLACE ◆ HAWES ◆ N. YORKS DL8 3RA

100 Cottages in the lovely Yorkshire Dales. Our Cottages feature colour TV, central heating, open fires, superb views, gardens, private parking and many allow pets. Sleep 1-10. Short breaks throughout the year. Rents from £155 per week. Brochure / Booking Line open 9.00am - 7.00pm daily (Answer machine out of hours).

Browse/book our properties on www.countrycottageholidays.co.uk

Telephone **WENSLEYDALE (01 969) 667 654**

Experience the Unique Atmosphere and Traditional Hospitality at

SIMONSTONE HALL COUNTRY HOUSE HOTEL

Hawes, Wensleydale, North Yorkshire DL8 3LY
Tel: 01969 667255 Fax: 01969 667741

Outstanding Bar Meals and Sunday Lunches served in the Game Tavern. Our restaurant provides an elegant setting for our wide selection of fine food and wines. Set in magnificent countryside near the market town of Hawes, Simonstone Hall is a beautifully restored Country House hotel with spectacular views over the Dale and surrounding Fell. An excellent base for walking and exploring the Dales. Pets welcome in most rooms. Kennels provided if required. A relaxed friendly establishment with open fires, Four-Poster Beds and experienced staff to look after all your needs. AA ★★

e-mail: information@simonstonehall.demon.co.uk **website: www.simonstonehall.co.uk**

See also Colour Advertisement on page 58

1637 **OVER 350** **2005**

YEARS OF GOOD SERVICE

Formerly a Posting House in coaching days, and full of character, a convenient centre for the North Yorkshire Moors and east coast, with Castle Howard and Rievaulx and Byland Abbeys within easy distance. 12 en suite rooms, all with colour TV, tea and coffee facilities, radio, and direct-dial telephone. One private lounge. Jacobean dining room offering traditional country-style cooking, with many choices. Special Breaks all year. Dogs welcome (no charge). Under the same ownership for 46 years. Brochure sent on request.

Dinner, Bed and Breakfast from £45.00.

AA/RAC ★★

THE CROWN HOTEL

Helmsley, North Yorkshire YO62 5BJ Tel: Helmsley (01439) 770297

★★ HOTEL

THE NEW INN MOTEL

AA ◆◆◆ *GUEST ACCOMMODATION*

MAIN STREET, HUBY, YORK YO61 1HQ Tel: (01347) 810219

The village of Huby, 'twixt York and Easingwold, is situated 9 miles north of York between the A19 and B1363 near Easingwold. Ideal base for a day here and a day there in York, Dales, Moors, coast and Herriot Country. COUNTRY WALKS FOR DOGS. Bed and Breakfast from £26 pppn (Evening Meal available). Special 3 and 4 Day Breaks. Rooms en suite, colour TV, tea/coffee making facilities. ***Telephone for brochure.***

Malham - Miresfield Farm

In beautiful gardens bordering village green and stream. Well known for excellent food. 11 bedrooms, all with private facilities. Full central heating. Two well-furnished lounges and conservatory for guests' use. 3 Diamonds Commended. B&B from £24pppn.

Mr. C. Sharp, Miresfield Farm, Malham, Skipton BD23 4DA Tel: 01729 830414

HELME PASTURE LODGES AND COTTAGES • Old Spring Wood

FREEDOM HOLIDAYS

Ideal for Discriminating Dogs

Rosemary Helme,
Helme Pasture,
Hartwith Bank, Summerbridge,
Harrogate, N. Yorks HG3 4DR

See also Colour Advertisement on page 57

- Great sniffing trails, highest paw category walks in the heart of unspoilt Nidderdale.
- Renowned snooze spots while owners explore.
- Central for Harrogate, York, Herriot and Brontë Country. National Trust area; outstanding natural beauty.
- After your hard day, stretch out and watch woodland wildlife from the luxurious comfort of your Scandinavian lodge or converted Yorkshire Dales barn.
- David Bellamy Gold Conservation Award
- ETC Welcome Host Award.
- ETC Category 1 for Disabled Access.

Tel: 01423 780279 Fax: 01423 780994
E-mail: info@helmepasture.co.uk
Website: www.helmepasture.co.uk

The White Swan at Pickering

Market Place, Pickering, North Yorkshire YO18 7AA
Tel: 01751 472288 Fax: 01751 475554
e-mail: welcome@white-swan.co.uk Website: www.white-swan.co.uk

AA Rosette since 1996; Yorkshire Post Top Ten Yorkshire Eateries
NOW TOTALLY REFURBISHED - E.T.C.★★ Silver Award

Family-run inn, with a buzz. Relaxed and informal atmosphere with friendly and professional staff. A passion for good food, fine wine and people, Rooms and Suites beyond expectation but affordably priced. The surrounding countryside offers a thousand and one things to do and places to visit. Hospitality that you will want to recommend in one of the most beautiful and undiscovered parts of the country.

Hotel of the Year 2000 - *Yorkshire Tourist Board*

"the best of North Yorkshire – Coast and Countryside..."

Coronation Cottage Pickering, York

Luxurious, newly refurbished, family cottage in historic village of Old Malton on River Derwent. Sleeps 2-8 + cot in 4 bedrooms. 2 bathrooms. Great days out - close to Whitby, York, Scarborough, Heartbeat and Herriot country. Secluded patio/garden with gas BBQ. Non-smoking. Pets welcome. Private parking. Open all year. ETC ★★★★

Contact David & Jane Beeley Tel: 01653 698251

e-mail: enquiries@forgevalleycottages.co.uk
website: www.forgevalleycottages.co.uk

See also Colour Advertisement on page 57

BANAVIE ETC ◆◆◆◆

Mrs Ella Bowes, Banavie, Roxby Road, Thornton-le-Dale, Pickering YO18 7SX * Tel: 01751 474616

Large stone-built semi-detached house set in Thornton-le-Dale. Ideal for touring. One family bedroom and two double bedrooms, all en suite. All with TV, shaver points, central heating and tea-making facilities. Open all year. Car park, cycle shed. B&B from £22pppn. Hygiene Certificate held. Your pets are very welcome.

website: www.banavie.uk.com **e-mail: ella@banavie.fsbusiness.co.uk**

NORTH YORKSHIRE MOORS NATIONAL PARK

Stone Cottage with log fire in North York Moors National Park. Sleeps 4. Near Cleveland coastal footpath, sea view. Non-smoking. Whitby 9 miles. Brochure available.

Mrs J. Hiley, 3 Valley Gardens, Stockton-On-Tees, Teesside TS19 8BE.
Tel & Fax: 01642 613888 E-mail: comesatime.cottage@ntlworld.com

HARMONY COUNTRY LODGE

ETC ◆◆◆◆

Limestone Road, Burniston, Scarborough YO13 0DG. (Non-Smoking)

Unique octagonal peaceful retreat in own grounds with superb 360º views of National Park and sea. Two miles from Scarborough. Parking facilities and fully licensed. Fragrant massage available. B&B £22.50 to £32.50. Five-berth caravan available for self-catering.from £100 to £315. Local dog walks. Pets welcome.

Sue & Tony Hewitt • Tel: 0800 2985840 • website: www.harmonylodge.net

Wayside Farm

ETC ★★ - ★★★

Whitby Road, Cloughton, Scarborough YO13 0DX
Tel: 01723 870519 www.waysidefarm.co.uk

Excellent cottages, ideally situated between Whitby and Scarborough. Within North York Moors National Park. Good for walking and visiting picturesque villages and fishing ports close by. Tariff from £150 - £469.

• Ground floor bedrooms • Central Heating • TV • Linen provided • Laundry facilities • Parking • Children and pets welcome • Sleep 2-6 • Golf & horse riding nearby

'The Anchor'

Highly recommended hotel. Situated opposite beautiful Peasholm Park where dogs can be walked on the lead, and approximately 350 yards from dog friendly beach. On-site car park. Non-smoking. *'Fresh local produce cooked to perfection'.*

Please phone 01723 364518 for full details

Open all year

En suite B&B from £20 per person per night.

61 Northstead Manor Drive, Scarborough YO12 6AF.

CHERRY TREES HOLIDAY FLATS

72 NORTH MARINE ROAD, SCARBOROUGH YO12 7PE • 01723 501433

Comfortable, well-equipped flats. • Close to all attractions, town and beach. • Part weeks available from October to June. • Senior citizens' discount October/June. • Trained pets welcome. • Free street parking. • Stamp for brochure giving dates, number in party. • Terms from £20-£40 daily, weekly from £90-£250 per flat.

Resident Proprietor: Helen Sanderson

"the best of North Yorkshire – Coast and Countryside..."

Luxurious, newly refurbished stone cottage in lovely village of East Ayton on River Derwent. Scarborough 4 miles. Sleeps 2-5 + cot in 2 bedrooms. Great days out – close to Whitby, York, Heartbeat and Herriot country. Non-smoking. Pets welcome. Private parking. Open all year. ETC ★★★★

Contact David & Jane Beeley Tel: 01653 698251

e-mail: enquiries@forgevalleycottages.co.uk
website: www.forgevalleycottages.co.uk

Honeysuckle Cottage
East Ayton, Scarborough

See also Colour Advertisement on page 58

Over 200 super self-catering cottages
IN THE YORKSHIRE DALES, YORK, COAST, MOORS, LANCS COAST, PEAK and LAKE DISTRICT

Fully illustrated brochure 01756 700872 • e-mail: p@holidaycotts.co.uk
Holiday Cottages Yorkshire Ltd., Water St, Skipton (18), North Yorkshire BD23 1PB

THE CONISTON HOTEL

Coniston Cold, Skipton, North Yorkshire BD23 4EB
Tel: 01756 748080 • Fax: 01756 749487 • e-mail: info@theconistonhotel.com
website: www.theconistonhotel.com

Set in a 1200 acre estate, the Hotel provides an ideal base for business or leisure guests looking for peace and relaxation. There are 40 en suite bedrooms with full facilities. Special rates are available for leisure breaks and family rooms. *ETC ★★★ Silver Award • AA ★★★ and Rosette.*

See also Colour Advertisement on page 59

Foxhills Hideaways *Felixkirk, Thirsk. YO7 2DS*

Quiet, no hassle holidays in cosy Scandinavian log cabins. Secluded garden setting. Central for the Moors, Dales, York and the coast. Village pub round the corner. Fully inclusive prices (£200 to £340 per week). Open all year.

Out of season short breaks from £100 inclusive.
Please write or phone for a brochure

TELEPHONE 01845 537575

Golden Fleece

Market Square, Thirsk,
North Yorkshire YO7 1LL
Tel: 01845 523108
Fax: 01845 523996

This Characterful old Coaching Inn offers good food and up to date facilities. All rooms have new bathrooms, satellite TV, phone, trouser press, hairdryer. On site parking. Perfect for Dales and Moors touring and walking or shopping in York or Harrogate.

ETC ★★ Silver Award AA ★★ 69%

e-mail: goldenfleece@bestwestern.co.uk www.goldenfleecehotel.com

---

Terms quoted in this publication may be subject to increase if rises in costs necessitate

---

Panoramic views, waterfalls, wild birds and tranquillity

See also Colour Advertisement on page 58

Stone farmhouse with panoramic views, high in the Yorkshire Dales National Park (Herriot family's house in 'All Creatures Great and Small' on TV). Three bedrooms (sleeps 6-8), sitting and dining rooms with wood-burning stoves, kitchen, bathroom, WC. House has electric storage heating, cooker, microwave, fridge, washing machine, colour TV, telephone. Garden, large barn, stables. Access from lane, private parking, no through traffic. Excellent walking from front door, near Wensleydale. Pets welcome. Self-catering from £400 per week.

Allaker in Coverdale, West Scrafton,
Leyburn, North Yorkshire DL8 4RM
For bookings telephone 020 8567 4862
e-mail: ac@adriancave.com • website: www.adriancave.com/allaker

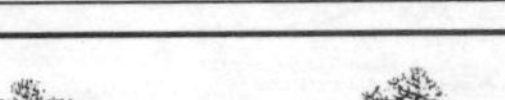

PARTRIDGE NEST FARM

Eskdaleside, Sleights, Whitby YO22 5ES Tel: 01947 810450

Six caravans on secluded site, five miles from Whitby and sea. Ideal touring centre.
All have mains electricity, colour TV, fridge, gas cooker. Also cottages to let.

e-mail: barbara@partridgenestfarm.com web: www.partridgenestfarm.com

The Seacliffe Hotel

12 North Promenade, West Cliff, Whitby YO21 3JX

Friendly family-run hotel overlooking the sea. Licensed à la carte restaurant specialising in fresh local seafoods, steaks and vegetarian dishes. Open all year.

Freephone 0800 0191747 www.seacliffe.co.uk ETC/AA ◆◆◆◆

For brochure & further details get in touch with Sally Robinson, at
Valley View Farm, Old Byland, Helmsley, York YO6 5LG Tel: 01439 798221
E-mail: sally@valleyviewfarm.com Website: www.valleyviewfarm.com

YORK LAKESIDE LODGES

Moor Lane, York YO24 2QU
Tel: 01904 702346 • Fax: 01904 701631
E-mail: neil@yorklakesidelodges.co.uk

Unique in a city! Luxurious Scandinavian lodges, and cottages in mature parkland overlooking large private fishing lake. Nearby superstore with coach to centre every 10 minutes. Easy access to ring road for touring. Open year round.

YORKSHIRE & HUMBERSIDE TOURIST BOARD WHITE ROSE AWARDS FOR TOURISM
WINNER

Award – British Holiday Home Parks Association

4-5 STARS SELF-CATERING **Website: www.yorklakesidelodges.co.uk**

HIGH BELTHORPE

Set on an ancient moated site at the foot of the Yorkshire Wolds, this comfortable Victorian farmhouse offers huge breakfasts, private fishing and fabulous walks. With York only 13 miles away, it is a peaceful rural idyll that both dogs and owners will love. Open all year except Christmas. From £20 + VAT.

Bishop Wilton, York YO42 1SB
Tel: 01759 368238; Mobile: 07786 923330

ASCOT HOUSE, 80 East Parade, York YO31 7YH • Tel: 01904 426826
Fax: 01904 431077 • ETC/AA/RAC ♦♦♦♦ • ETC SILVER AWARD

An attractive Victorian villa with easy access to the historic city centre by walking or by public transport. Most rooms have four-poster or canopy beds, and family and double rooms are en suite. All rooms have central heating, colour TV and tea/coffee facilities. Sauna available to hire by the hour. Singles from £28 to £56, doubles £60 to £68 including Traditional English Breakfast and VAT.

e-mail: admin@ascothouseyork.com • website: www.ascothouseyork.com

WOLDS VIEW HOLIDAY COTTAGES ~ 12 miles from York

GRANVILLE LODGE (Sleeps 6-8) newly built, 1 twin/double, 1 king-size, bed settee in TV room, lounge, dining room, very modern kitchen. PARLOUR (Sleeps 6) 1 double, 2 twin rooms, large kitchen/diner, lounge, bathroom, 1 en suite. BARN (sleeps 4) kitchen, hall/diner, lounge, 1 king-size and one double bedroom (1 with shower & vanity unit and 1 bathroom) Downstairs wash hand basin and WC. STABLES (Sleeps 3) 1 double, 1 single bedroom, lounge, dining room, bathroom. COURTYARD (Sleeps 4) 2 double bedrooms (1 with shower) 1 bathroom, kitchen/diner/lounge.

Mrs M. S. A. Woodliffe, Mill Farm, Yapham, Pocklington, York YO42 1PH Tel: 01759 302172

PLEASE MENTION THIS GUIDE WHEN YOU WRITE OR PHONE TO ENQUIRE ABOUT ACCOMMODATION.

IF YOU ARE WRITING, A STAMPED, ADDRESSED ENVELOPE IS ALWAYS APPRECIATED.

DALES HOLIDAY COTTAGES offer a choice of over 350 superb, personally inspected holiday properties, in beautiful rural and coastal locations. Including Calendar Girls and Bronte, Herriot and Heartbeat country. Cosy cottages to country houses, many welcome pets, and short breaks are available. FREE brochure. DALES HOLIDAY COTTAGES, CARLETON BUSINESS PARK, SKIPTON, NORTH YORKSHIRE BD23 2AA (0870 909 9500).
website: www.dales-holiday-cottages.com

Bentham

Quiet village amidst the fells. Good centre for rambling and fishing. Ingleton 5 miles north-east.

MRS L. J. STORY, HOLMES FARM, LOW BENTHAM, LANCASTER LA2 7DE (015242 61198). Cottage conversion in easy reach of Dales, Lake District and coast. Central heating, fridge, TV, washer, games room. ★★★★. [ ]

Clapham

Attractive village with caves and pot-holes in vicinity, including Gaping Ghyll. Nearby lofty peaks include Ingleborough (2,373ft.) to the north. Kendal 24 miles, Settle 6.

DAVID & JACKIE KINGSLEY, ARBUTUS GUEST HOUSE, RIVERSIDE, CLAPHAM (NEAR SETTLE) LA2 8DS (015242 51240). Restored Georgian vicarage in a delightful setting. All rooms en suite, or private facilities. TV, tea/coffee. Central heating. Open all year round. Pets welcome. ETC ◆◆◆◆ [ ]
e-mail: info@arbutus.co.uk website: www.arbutus.co.uk

NEW INN HOTEL, CLAPHAM, NEAR INGLETON, NORTH YORKSHIRE LA2 8HH (015242 51203; Fax: 015242 51496). 'Jewel of the Dales'. A comfortable hotel in the Yorkshire Dales National Park. The ideal holiday destination for your pet, be assured of a warm and friendly reception, sit back, close your eyes and soak up the history and atmosphere.
e-mail: info@newinn-clapham.co.uk website: www.newinn-clapham.co.uk

Coverdale

Small village set in Yorkshire Dales, in heart of Herriot Country.

MRS JULIE CLARKE, MIDDLE FARM, WOODALE, COVERDALE, LEYBURN DL8 4TY (01969 640271). Peacefully situated farmhouse away from the madding crowd. B&B with optional Evening Meal. Home cooking. Pets sleep where you prefer. Ideally positioned for exploring the beautiful Yorkshire Dales. [pw!]
e-mail: julie-clarke@amserve.com

Danby

Village on River Esk 12 miles west of Whitby.

THE FOX & HOUNDS INN, AINTHORPE, DANBY YO21 2LD (01287 660218; Fax: 01287 660030). Residential 16th Century Coaching Inn. Comfortable en suite bedrooms available. Enjoy our real ales or quality wines. Special mid-week breaks available Oct - May. Open all year. ETC ◆◆◆◆ [Pets £1.50 per night.]

Easingwold

Small market town with cobbled streets where weathered red brick dwellings are grouped around a large green. 12 miles north-west of York.

GARBUTTS GHYLL, THORNTON HILL, EASINGWOLD YO61 3PZ (01347 868644). Working farm on edge of North York Moors National Park. Friendly, non-smoking home; children welcome; babysitting available. Stabling for horses/dogs. One double/family, one twin room; both en suite. [ ]

Terms quoted in this publication may be subject to increase if rises in costs necessitate

Filey

Well-known resort with sandy beach. Off-shore is Filey Brig. Hull 40 miles, Bridlington 11, Scarborough 7.

LEONARD & DIANE HUNTER, "SEA CABIN", 16 GAP ROAD, HUNMANBY GAP, NEAR FILEY YO14 9QP (01723 891368). En suite, twin-bedroomed Granny annexe with private lounge. Full English breakfast. Vegetarians catered for. B&B plus optional Evening Meal. Open all year. Pet friendly beach. [🐕 pw!]

Grassington

Wharfedale village in attractive moorland setting. Ripon 22 miles, Skipton 9.

JERRY AND BEN'S HOLIDAY COTTAGES. Seven comfortable properties on private estate near Grassington in Yorkshire Dales National Park. Wooded mountain becks, waterfalls, rocky crags and accessible hill and footpath walking. Brochure from: MRS J. M.JOY, JERRY AND BEN'S HOLIDAY COTTAGES, HEBDEN, SKIPTON BD23 5DL (01756 752369; Fax: 01756 753370). [pw! one pet free, subsequent pets £5 per week] [🐕]
e-mail: dawjoy@aol.com website: www.yorkshirenet.co.uk/stayat/jerryandbens

FORESTERS ARMS, MAIN STREET, GRASSINGTON, SKIPTON BD23 5AA (01756 752349; Fax: 01756 753633). The Foresters Arms is situated in the heart of the Yorkshire Dales and provides an ideal centre for walking or touring. Within easy reach of York and Harrogate. ETC ◆◆◆ [🐕]

GRASSINGTON HOUSE HOTEL, THE SQUARE, GRASSINGTON BD23 5AQ (01756 752406; Fax: 01756 752135). A small hotel with a big reputation. All rooms en suite, colour TV, tea making. Parking. Ideal for walking or touring. AA/ETC ★★, [🐕]

Harrogate

Charming and elegant spa town set amid some of Britain's most scenic countryside. Ideal for exploring Herriot Country and the moors and dales. York 22 miles, Bradford 19, Leeds 16.

THE COURTYARD AT DUKE'S PLACE, BISHOP THORNTON, NEAR HARROGATE HG3 3JY (01765 620229; Fax: 01765 620454). In the heart of Nidderdale, group of well maintained and equipped holiday cottages. Sleep 2/6; linen, fully equipped kitchens. Riding stables on site. Pets and children most welcome. ETC ★★★/★★★★ [🐕]
e-mail: jakimoorhouse@onetel.net.uk

RUDDING HOLIDAY PARK, FOLLIFOOT, HARROGATE HG3 1JH (01423 870439; Fax: 01423 870859). Luxury cottages and lodges sleeping two to seven people. All equipped to a high standard. Pool, licensed bar, golf and children's playground in the Parkland. Illustrated brochure available. ETC ★★★. [🐕]
e-mail: holiday-park@ruddingpark.com website: www.ruddingpark.com

Hawes (near Mallerstang)

12 miles north-west on the Hawes to Kirkby Stephen road.

COCKLAKE HOUSE, MALLERSTANG CA17 4JT (017683 72080). Charming, High Pennine Country House B&B in unique position above Pendragon Castle in Upper Mallerstang Dale, offering good food and exceptional comfort to a small number of guests. Two double rooms with large private bathrooms. Three acres riverside grounds. Dogs welcome.

STONE HOUSE HOTEL, SEDBUSK, HAWES DL8 3PT (01969 667571; Fax: 01969 667720). This fine Edwardian country house has spectacular views and serves delicious Yorkshire cooking with fine wines. Comfortable en suite bedrooms, some ground floor. Phone for details. [🐕]
website: www.stonehousehotel.com

SIMONSTONE HALL, HAWES, WENSLEYDALE DL8 3LY (01969 667255; Fax: 01969 667741). Facing south across picturesque Wensleydale. All rooms en suite with colour TV. Fine cuisine. Extensive wine list. Friendly personal attention. A relaxing break away from it all. AA ★★. [🐕 ⌂]
e-mail: information@simonstonehall.demon.co.uk website: www.simonstonehall.co.uk

COUNTRY COTTAGE HOLIDAYS, DRYDEN HOUSE, MARKET PLACE, HAWES DL8 3RA (01969 667654). 100 cottages in the lovely Yorkshire Dales. Colour TV, central heating, open fires. Gardens, private parking. Many allow pets. Rents from £155 per week. Sleep 1-10.
website: www.countrycottageholidays.co.uk

Helmsley

A delightful stone-built town on River Rye with a large cobbled square. Thirsk 12 miles.

CROWN HOTEL, MARKET SQUARE, HELMSLEY YO62 5BJ (01439 770297). Fully residential old coaching inn. Bedrooms are very well appointed, all have tea and coffee-making facilities, colour TV, radio and telephones. Traditional country cooking. ETC/AA/RAC ★★. [🐕]

MRS JENNIFER PILLING, SHAW MOOR HOUSE, HAROMEHEADS LANE, HAROME YO62 5HZ (01439 771804). Quiet rural location, 3 miles from Helmsley, 1 mile Harome, which has pub and corner shop. Courtyard suite sleeps 2-4. Shower, kitchen, sittingroom, woodburner, TV etc. Ideal for families. Views to Howardian hills. Good walking country. Open all year. £30 pp. [🐕]
e-mail: jenniferpilling@btopenworld.com

Huby

Small village 9 miles north of York. Ideal as base for exploring Dales, Moors and coast.

THE NEW INN MOTEL, MAIN STREET, HUBY, YORK YO61 1HQ (01347 810219). Ideal base for Yorkshire attractions. Ground floor rooms, en suite, colour TVs etc. Bed and Breakfast from £26 pppn (Evening Meal available). Pets welcome; maximum 2. Special 3 & 4 day breaks. Telephone for brochure. AA ◆◆◆ [🐕].

Leeming Bar

Small, pretty village two miles north-east of Bedale.

THE WHITE ROSE HOTEL, LEEMING BAR, NORTHALLERTON DL7 9AY (01677 422707/424941; Fax: 01677 425123). Ideally situated for touring the spectacular scenery of two National Parks,Yorkshire Dales, coastal resorts, Herriot & Heartbeat Country. 18 rooms, all private bathroom, colour TV/radio, tea & coffee, hair dryer, trouser press and telephone. B&B £49 single, £63 double/twin, £69 family room all including breakfast. RAC ★★ [🐕]
e-mail: john@whiterosehotel.co.uk website: www.whiterosehotel.co.uk

Leyburn

Small market town, 8 miles south-west of Richmond, standing above the River Ure in Wensleydale.

BARBARA & BARRIE MARTIN, THE OLD STAR, WEST WITTON, LEYBURN DL8 4LU (01969 622949). Former 17th century Coaching Inn now run as a guest house. Oak beams, log fire, home cooking. En suite B&B from £23 pppn. ETC ◆◆◆. [🐕]

Malham

In picturesque Craven District with spectacular Malham Cove (300ft.) and Gordale Scar with waterfalls. Malham Tarn (N T.) is 4 miles north, Skipton 12 miles.

MR C. SHARP, MIRESFIELD FARM, MALHAM, SKIPTON BD23 4DA (01729 830414). In beautiful gardens bordering village green and stream. Excellent food. 11 bedrooms, all with private facilities. Full central heating. Two well-furnished lounges and conservatory. B&B from £24pppn. ETC ◆◆◆ [🐕 pw!]

Pateley Bridge

Small town in Nidderdale, 11m north-west of harrogate.

ROSEMARY HELME, HELME PASTURE LODGES & COTTAGES, OLD SPRING WOOD, HARTWITH BANK, SUMMERBRIDGE, HARROGATE HG3 4DR (01423 780279, Fax: 01423 780994). Country accommodation for dogs and numerous walks in unspoilt Nidderdale. Central for Harrogate, York, Herriot and Bronte country. National Trust area. ETC ★★★★, ETC Category 1 for Disabled Access. [pw! Pets £5 per night, £25 per week.]
e-mail: info@helmepasture.co.uk website: www..helmepasture.co.uk

Pickering

Pleasant market town on southern fringe of North Yorkshire Moors National Park with Moated Norman Castle. Bridlington 31 miles, Whitby 20, Scarborough 16, Helmsley 13, Malton 3.

MRS S. M. PICKERING, 'NABGATE', WILTON ROAD, THORNTON-LE-DALE, PICKERING YO18 7QP (01751 474279). All rooms en suite. TV, courtesy trays, central heating. Good food and a very warm welcome for pets and owners. Central for coast, steam railway, moors. Nearby walks for dogs. Own keys. Car park. Hygiene and Welcome Host Certificates. Open all year. Bed and Breakfast from £22. Also Self-Catering Cottage available. ETC ◆◆◆◆ [🐕]
e-mail: enquire@nabgateguesthouse.co.uk website: www.nabgateguesthouse.co.uk

THE WHITE SWAN AT PICKERING, YORKSHIRE HOTEL OF THE YEAR 2000 (01751 472288). One of only a handful of inns with the Silver Quality award. Dog friendly with excellent: service, rooms, food and wine. "...consistently brilliant.." Please phone or visit our website for a brochure. [Pets £7.50 per visit].
website: www.white-swan.co.uk

CORONATION COTTAGE (01653 698251). Luxurious family cottage in conservation village, sleeps 2-8 + cot in four bedrooms. Patio with gas barbecue; parking. Pets welcome. Non-smoking. Open all year. ETC 4 Star. Contact DAVID AND JANE BEELEY. [🐕]
e-mail: enquiries@forgevalleycottages.co.uk website: www.forgevalleycottages.co.uk

MRS ELLA BOWES, BANAVIE, ROXBY ROAD, THORNTON-LE-DALE, PICKERING YO18 7SX (01751 474616). Large stone-built semi-detached house set in Thornton-le-Dale. Ideal for touring. One family bedroom and two double bedrooms, all en suite. All with TV, shaver points, central heating and tea-making facilities. Open all year. Car park, cycle shed. B&B from £22pppn. Welcome Host and Hygiene Certificate held. ETC ◆◆◆◆ [🐕]
e-mail: ella@banavie.fsbusiness.co.uk website: www.banavie.uk.com

Port Mulgrave

Located 1km north of Hinderwell.

NORTH YORK MOORS NATIONAL PARK. Stone Cottage (sleeps) 4 in North York Moors National Park. Sea view, near Cleveland coastal footpath. Log fire, non-smoking. Whitby 9 miles. Brochure available (Tel & Fax: 01642 613888). [🐕]
e-mail: comesatime.cottage@ntlworld.com

Scarborough

Very popular family resort with good sands. York 41 miles, Whitby 20, Bridlington 17, Filey 7.

HARMONY GUEST HOUSE, PRINCESS ROYAL TERRACE, SCARBOROUGH YO11 2RP (01723 373562). Friendly guest house, near South Bay attractions. We offer quality en suite and four-poster rooms. Excellent food. Brochure on request. Five bedrooms B&B £22pppn, DB&B £30pppn. Open all year. ◆◆◆ [🐕].

SUE AND TONY HEWITT, HARMONY COUNTRY LODGE, LIMESTONE ROAD, BURNISTON, SCARBOROUGH YO13 0DG (0800 2985840). A peaceful retreat set in two acres of private grounds with 360° panoramic views of the National Park and sea. An ideal centre for walking or touring. En suite centrally heated rooms with superb views. Fragrant massage available. Non-smoking, licensed, private parking facilities. B&B from £22.50 to £32.50. ETC ◆◆◆◆
website: www.harmonylodge.net

WAYSIDE FARM, WHITBY ROAD, CLOUGHTON, SCARBOROUGH YO13 0DX (01723 870519). Excellent cottages, ideally situated between Whitby and Scarborough. Within North York Moors National Park. Good for walking and visiting picturesque villages and fishing ports close by. ETC ★★ - ★★★
website: www.waysidefarm.co.uk

'THE ANCHOR', 61 NORTHSTEAD MANOR DRIVE, SCARBOROUGH YO12 6AF (01723 364518). Pets are welcome at this detached hotel overlooking Peasholm Park. Close to beach and swimming pools. Single, double, twin and family en suite rooms available. TV, tea making facilities. Car parking. Non-smoking. [🐕]
See page 320 for more details.

CHERRY TREES HOLIDAY FLATS, 72 NORTH MARINE ROAD, SCARBOROUGH YO12 7PE (01723 501433). Comfortable, well-equipped flats, close to attractions, town and beach. Part weeks and senior citizen discounts available October - June. Free street parking. Trained pets welcome. Stamp for brochure, giving dates and number in party. Contact resident proprietor: HELEN SANDERSON.

HONEYSUCKLE COTTAGE (01653 698251). Luxury cottage in lovely village, four miles from Scarborough. Sleeps 2-5 + cot in 2 bedrooms. Private parking. Pets welcome. Non-smoking. Open all year. ETC ★★★★. Contact DAVID AND JANE BEELEY. [🐕]
e-mail: enquiries@forgevalleycottages.co.uk website: www.forgevalleycottages.co.uk

Skipton

Airedale market town, centre for picturesque Craven district. Fine Castle (14th cent). York 43 miles, Manchester 42, Leeds 26, Harrogate 22, Settle 16.

Over 200 super self-catering Cottages, throughout the Yorkshire Dales, York, Moors, Lancs Coast, Peak and Lake District. For our fully illustrated brochure apply: HOLIDAY COTTAGES (YORKSHIRE) LTD, WATER STREET, SKIPTON (18) BD23 1PB (01756 700872). [🐕]
e-mail: p@holidaycotts.co.uk website: www.holidaycotts.co.uk

THE CONISTON HOTEL, CONISTON COLD, SKIPTON BD23 4EB (01756 748080; Fax: 01756 749487). Set in a 1200 acre estate, an ideal base for business or leisure guests. 40 en suite bedrooms with full facilities. Special rates for leisure breaks and family rooms. ETC ★★★ Silver Award, AA ★★★ & Rosette. [pw! Pets £5 per night]
e-mail: info@theconistonhotel.com website: www.theconistonhotel.com

Staithes

Fishing village surrounded by high cliffs on North Sea coast 9 miles north west of Whitby.

MS M.J. HEALD, BROOKLYN, BROWN'S TERRACE, STAITHES, SALTBURN-BY-THE-SEA TS13 5BG (01947 841396). Sea captain's house in quiet location in old part of this picturesque, historic fishing village. Views across rooftops to Cowbar Cliffs. Pets and children welcome. [🐕]

Thirsk

Market town with attractive square. Excellent touring area. Northallerton 3 miles.

FOXHILLS HIDEAWAYS, FELIXKIRK, THIRSK YO7 2DS (01845 537575). Scandinavian log cabins, heated throughout, linen provided. A supremely relaxed atmosphere on the edge of the North Yorkshire Moors National Park. Open all year. Village pub round the corner. [🐕]

GOLDEN FLEECE HOTEL, MARKET SQUARE, THIRSK YO7 1LL (01845 523108; Fax: 01845 523996). Characterful Coaching Inn offering good food and up to date facilities. All rooms have new bathrooms, satellite TV, phone, trouser press, hairdryer. ETC/AA ★★, [🐕]
e-mail: goldenfleece@bestwestern.co.uk website: www.goldenfleecehotel.com

West Scrafton

Village 3 miles south of Wensley

ALLAKER IN COVERDALE, WEST SCRAFTON, NEAR LEYBURN DL8 4RM (020 8567 4862 for bookings). Stone farmhouse with panoramic views. Three bedrooms sleeping 6-8. Well-equipped with electric storage heating and woodburning stoves. Garden, barn, stables. Ideal for families/walkers. Self-catering from £400 per week. [pw 🐕]
e-mail: ac@adriancave.com website: www.adriancave.com/allaker

SYMBOLS

🐕 Indicates that pets are welcome free of charge.
£ Indicates that a charge is made for pets: nightly or weekly.
pw! Shows some special provision for pets; exercise facility, feeding or accommodation arrangement.
⌂ Indicates separate pets accommodation.

Whitby

Charming resort with harbour and sands. Of note is the 13th century ruined Abbey. Stockton-on-Tees 34 miles, Scarborough 20, Saltburn-by-the-Sea 19.

MRS JILL McNEIL, SWALLOW HOLIDAY COTTAGES, LONG LEAS FARM, HAWSKER, WHITBY YO22 4LA (01947 603790). Discover historic Whitby, pretty fishing villages, countryside with way-marked walks. Four cottages, two or three bedrooms. Private parking. Children and dogs welcome. Private parking. Children and dogs welcome. Weekly rates from £195 to £500. Please phone or write for a brochure. ETC ★★★★ [🐕]

WHITE ROSE HOLIDAY COTTAGES, NEAR WHITBY. Superior centrally heated village cottages and bungalows, also apartments in Whitby. Available all year. Ideal for coast and country. Up to ETC ★★★★. APPLY: MRS J. ROBERTS (PW), 5 BROOK PARK, SLEIGHTS, NEAR WHITBY YO21 1RT (01947 810763) [£5 per week, pw!]
e-mail: enquiries@whiterosecottages.co.uk website: www.whiterosecottages.co.uk

PARTRIDGE NEST FARM, ESKDALESIDE, SLEIGHTS, WHITBY YO22 5ES (01947 810450). Six caravans on secluded site, five miles from Whitby and sea. Ideal touring centre. All have mains electricity, colour TV, fridge, gas cooker. Also cottages to let. [Dogs £10 per week]
e-mail: barbara@partridgenestfarm.com website: www.partridgenestfarm.com

THE SEACLIFFE HOTEL, WEST CLIFF, WHITBY Y021 3JX (Freephone 0800 0191747). Friendly family-run hotel overlooking the sea. Licensed à la carte restaurant specialising in fresh local seafoods, steaks and vegetarian dishes. Tel & Fax: 01947 603139. ETC/AA ◆◆◆◆. [🐕]
website: www.seacliffe.co.uk

York

Historic cathedral city and former Roman Station on River Ouse. Magnificent Minster and 3 miles of ancient walls. Facilities for a wide range of sports and entertainments. Horse-racing on Knavesmire. Bridlington 41 miles, Filey 41, Leeds 24, Harrogate 22.

ST GEORGE'S HOUSE HOTEL, 6 ST GEORGE'S PLACE, YORK YO24 1DR (01904 625056). Family-run Hotel in quiet cul-de-sac near racecourse. All rooms en suite with colour TV, tea/coffee making facilities. Private parking. Pets welcome. ETC/RAC/AA ◆◆◆ [🐕]
e-mail: sixstgeorg@aol.com website: http://members.aol.com/sixstgeorg/

MRS SALLY ROBINSON, VALLEY VIEW FARM, OLD BYLAND, HELMSLEY, YORK YO6 5LG (01439 798221). B&B £30. BB&D £43.50 Working farm, home cooking, table licence, private parking, full central heating, colour TV. Self catering cottages. Kennel and run available. Pets Welcome. [🐕] ETC ◆◆◆◆
e-mail: sally@valleyviewfarm.com website: www.valleyviewfarm.com

YORK LAKESIDE LODGES, MOOR LANE, YORK YO24 2QU (01904 702346; Fax: 01904 701631). Self-catering pine lodges. Mature parkland setting. Large fishing lake. Nearby superstore with coach to centre every 10 mins. ETC ★★★★/★★★★★ [pw! Pets £18 per week]
e-mail:neil@yorklakesidelodges.co.uk website: www.lakesidelodges.co.uk

HIGH BELTHORPE, BISHOP WILTON, YORK YO42 1SB (01759 368238; Mobile: 07786 923330). Set on an ancient moated site at the foot of the Yorkshire Wolds, this comfortable Victorian farmhouse offers huge breakfasts, private fishing and fabulous walks. Dogs and owners will love it! Open all year except Christmas. Prices from £20 +VAT. ETC ◆◆◆ [pw! 🐕]

ASCOT HOUSE, 80 EAST PARADE, YORK YO31 7YH (01904 426826; Fax: 01904 431077). Attractive Victorian villa with easy access to city centre. Family and double rooms en suite. Comfortable residents' lounge, dining room. Sauna. Single room £28-£56, double room £60-£68. ETC/AA/RAC ◆◆◆◆, ETC Silver Award. [🐕]
e-mail: admin@ascothouseyork.com website: www.ascothouseyork.com

MRS M. S. A. WOODLIFFE, MILL FARM, YAPHAM, POCKLINGTON, YORK YO42 1PH (01759 302172). WOLDS VIEW HOLIDAY COTTAGES. Granville Lodge (sleeps 6-8), Parlour (sleeps 6), Barn (sleeps 4), Stables (sleeps 3) and Courtyard (sleeps 4). Full details on request.

See also Colour Advertisement on page 59

Bingley

Town on River Aire 5 miles north-west of Bradford.

THE FIVE RISE LOCKS HOTEL & RESTAURANT, BECK LANE, BINGLEY BD16 4DD (01274 565296). Large Victorian house tucked away in tranquil area, but close main roads, tourist sites, cities. Good views, individual decor, informal style. Comfy sofas, interesting artworks. Antidote to chain hotels. Historic canal locks and excellent walking (dogs and humans) close by. AA/RAC/VisitBritain ◆◆◆◆, RAC DIning Award.
e-mail: info@five-rise-locks.co.uk website: www.five-rise-locks.co.uk

Holmfirth

Town on the River Holme, 5 miles south of Huddersfield.

SUMMERWINE COTTAGES. Close to 'Last of the Summer Wine' country, three comfortable, well-equipped cottages, each with French doors leading into a beautiful walled garden. Set within six acres; indoor heated swimming pool. Cats and dogs welcome; DIY livery available. ETC ★★★ CONTACT: MR & MRS HALSTEAD, WEST ROYD FARM, MARSH LANE, SHEPLEY, NEAR HOLMFIRTH, HUDDERSFIELD HD8 8AY (01484 602147; Fax: 01484 609427).
e-mail: summerwinecottages@lineone.net website: www.summerwinecottages.co.uk

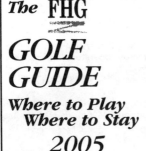

When making enquiries or bookings, a stamped addressed envelope is always appreciated

See also Colour Advertisement on page 9

See also Colour Advertisement on page 61

ISLANDS & HIGHLANDS COTTAGES, BRIDGE ROAD, PORTREE, ISLE OF SKYE IV51 9ER (01478 612123 ; Fax: 01478 612709). We specialise in self-catering holiday accommodation on and around the Isle of Skye and the South-West Scottish Highlands. Relax in the luxury of one of our holiday homes situated at the side of a loch. Dogs welcome in many properties.
e-mail: sales@islands-and-highlands.co.uk website: www.islands-and-highlands.co.uk

FHG PUBLICATIONS

publish a large range of well-known accommodation guides. We will be happy to send you details or you can use the order form at the back of this book.

FREE or REDUCED RATE entry to Holiday Visits and Attractions – see our READERS' OFFER VOUCHERS on pages 101-116

See also Colour Advertisement on page 61

See also Colour Advertisement on page 62

Banchory

Small town on River Dee 11 miles north-west of Stonehaven.

RAEMOIR HOUSE HOTEL & RESTAURANT, RAEMOIR, BANCHORY AB31 4ED (01330 824884; Fax: 01330 822171). Elegant hotel set in 3,500 acres of parkland with many beautiful walks, 9-hole golf course, tennis. 20 bedrooms. Ideal for visiting Aberdeen and many castles in the area. [🐕]
e-mail: enquiries@raemoir.com website: www.raemoir.com

Grantown-on-Spey

Market town 19 miles south of Forres.

MR AND MRS J. R. TAYLOR, MILTON OF CROMDALE, GRANTOWN-ON-SPEY PH26 3PH (01479 872415). Fully modernised Cottage with large garden and views of River Spey and Cromdale Hills. Golf, tennis and trekking within easy reach. Fully equipped except linen. Two double bedrooms. Shower, refrigerator, electric cooker, colour television. Car desirable. Open March to October. £120 per week. Children and pets welcome. [🐕]

Methlick

Village 9 miles from Ellon and 7 miles from Fyvie, between Haddo House and Fyvie Castle.

MRS CHRISTINE STAFF, SUNNYBRAE FARM, GIGHT, METHLICK, ELLON AB41 7JA (Tel & Fax: 01651 806456). Comfortable accommodation on a working farm situated in a quiet, peaceful location with superb views. Centrally situated for many places of interest. Double, twin, single rooms, some en suite. Open all year. Dogs and owners most welcome. STB ★★. [🐕]
e-mail: sunnybrae-farm@talk21.com

Rattray Head

Fishing port on the north east coast 27 miles north of Aberdeen. The most easterly town on the Scottish mainland. Arbuthnot Museum features displays on local history.

SAND DUNES & SECLUDED 10 MILE BEACH. Homely, relaxed non-smoking B&B for cyclists, walkers, carnivores, vegetarians and pets (even giant dogs). Wet/dry room for washing and drying clothes, pets etc. Breakfast available all morning. Hot and cold drinks available 24/7. ROB & VAL, LIGHTHOUSE COTTAGES, RATTRAY HEAD, PETERHEAD AB42 3HB (01346 532236). [🐕, pw!]
website: www.rattrayhead.net

Stonehaven

Fishing port of east coast, 13 miles south of Aberdeen.

MRS AILEEN PATON, 'WOODSIDE OF GLASSLAW', STONEHAVEN AB39 3XQ (01569 763799). Modern bungalow with six centrally heated en suite bedrooms with colour TV and hospitality trays. Stonehaven two miles. Accessible for disabled guests.

Tomintoul

Village and resort in elevated position between River Avon and Conglass Water. 10 mile south-east of Grantown-on-Spey..

LIN FORRESTER, ARGYLE HOUSE, 7 MAIN STREET, TOMINTOUL, BALLINDALLOCH AB37 9EX (01807 580766). Small family-run guesthouse. Five rooms, most with own bathroom. Library with books to borrow, good breakfasts in diningroom, and a genuine welcome from the friendly owner. Lots to do nearby. Dogs welcome in bedrooms.[🐕]

Turriff

Small town in agricultural area, 9 miles south of Banff.

MRS P E. BATES, COUNTRY COTTAGES, FORGLEN ESTATE, TURRIFF AB53 4JP (01888 562918/ 562518; Fax 01888 562 252). Estate on the beautiful Deveron River. Sea only nine miles away, Turriff two miles. 10 cottages sleeping 6–9. From £169 weekly. Special Winter lets. Children and reasonable dogs welcome. [🐕]
website: www.forglen.co.uk

HOUSE IN THE WOOD HOLIDAYS

Glenachulish, Ballachulish, Argyll PH49 4JZ Telephone: 01855 811379

Cottage and Chalets in Natural Woodland sleeping two to six people.
From £155–£270.

GOOD AREA FOR WALKING – AND NATURE LOVERS

PETS WELCOME *BROCHURE AVAILABLE* *NO VAT* *REGRET NO SMOKERS*

Cairndow, Argyll PA26 8BN

Tel: 01499 600286 • Fax: 01499 600220

HALF PRICE GOLF AT INVERARAY GOLF CLUB (9 MILES), THE MOST INTERESTING AND TESTING 9-HOLE COURSE IN ARGYLL

SPECIAL RATES AT COWAL GOLF CLUB, DUNOON

Historic Coaching Inn on Loch Fyne ★ 14 well-appointed en suite bedrooms ★ Excellent cuisine in Stables Restaurant and lounge meals all day ★ Two de luxe bedrooms with two-person spa baths. ★ Amenities include lochside beer garden, sauna, multi-gym and solarium.

Scottish Tourist Board ★★★ INN

AT THE HEAD OF LOCH FYNE. Two comfortable holiday cottages at the head of the longest sea loch in Scotland. INVERFYNE, a very spacious cottage with 4 twin-bedded rooms and BRIDGE COTTAGE, sleeps four. Linen and electricity are included. Achadunan Estate is set amidst lovely walking country. Golden eagles and deer are your neighbours. Achadunan is home to Fyne Ales micro brewery.

Brochures available from Mrs Delap, Achadunan, Cairndow, Argyll PA26 8BJ.
Tel & Fax: 01499 600238 website: www.argyllholidaycottages.com

Scottish Tourist Board ★★★ SELF CATERING

See also Colour Advertisement on page 63

Rockhill Waterside Country House

Est 1960

Ardbrecknish, By Dalmally, Argyll PA33 1BH Tel: 01866 833218

17th century guest house in spectacular waterside setting on Loch Awe with breathtaking views to Ben Cruachan, where comfort, peace and tranquillity reign supreme. Small private Highland estate breeding Hanoverian competition horses. 1200 metres free trout fishing. Five delightful rooms with all modern facilities. First-class highly acclaimed home cooking with much home-grown produce. Wonderful area for touring the Western Highlands, Glencoe, the Trossachs and Kintyre. Ideal for climbing, walking, bird and animal watching. Boat trips locally and from Oban (30 miles) to Mull, Iona, Fingal's Cave and other islands. Dogs' Paradise!

Also Self-Catering Cottages.

ABBOT'S BRAE HOTEL West Bay, Dunoon, Argyll PA23 7QJ

Tel: 01369 705021 • Fax: 01369 701191

e-mail: info@abbotsbrae.co.uk • website: www.abbotsbrae.co.uk

Award-winning, small Country House Hotel set in its own secluded woodland garden with breathtaking views of the sea and hills. Spacious en suite bedrooms. Welcoming, homely atmosphere, peaceful surroundings. Pets stay free. Ideal base to explore the Western Highlands. For further details contact either Helen or Gavin.

See also Colour Advertisement on page 63

Gigha Hotel

Situated in the Inner Hebrides, the community owned Isle of Gigha (God's Island) is surely one of Scotland's most beautiful and tranquil islands. Explore the white sandy bays and lochs. Easy walking, bike hire, birds, wildlife and wild flowers. Home to the famous Achamore Gardens with rhododendrons, azaleas and semi-tropical plants. Grass Airstrip, 9-hole golf course and regular ferry service (only 20 minutes from the mainland). We are dog-friendly. Holiday cottages also available.

Scottish Tourist Board ★★★ Small Hotel

Isle of Gigha PA41 7AA

Tel: 01583 505254 • Fax: 01583 505244 • website: www.isle-of-gigha.co.uk

MACDONALD — HOTEL —

FORT WILLIAM ROAD, KINLOCHLEVEN PH50 4QL

TEL: 01855 831539
FAX: 01855 831416

Ideally located midway between Glencoe and Ben Nevis, at the foot of the Mamore Mountains. The hotel has 10 bedrooms, all en suite, with TV and tea/coffee making facilities. Ideal for touring/walking - guests have use of outside drying room shared with campsite. 'Bothy Bar' with over 40 malt whiskies, and restaurant serving fresh local produce.

Scottish Tourist Board ★★★ Hotel

Walkers Welcome

E-mail: availability@macdonaldhotel.co.uk Web: www.macdonaldhotel.co.uk

Darroch Mhor Chalets

Carrick Castle, Loch Goil, Argyll PA24 8AF

Chill out in Scotland's first national park. Five self catering chalets nestling on the shores of Loch Goil, each with superb lochside views and offering a peaceful and relaxing holiday in the heart of Argyll Forest Park. Each chalet has two bedrooms, living room with colour TV, fitted kitchen with fridge, freezer, microwave, toaster etc. and bathroom with bath and overhead shower. Car parking by each chalet. Great hill walking. Ideal for pets, genuinely pet friendly.

Open all year – weekly rates £120-£295.

Weekend & short breaks available all year round from £70, reductions for two persons. One pet free.

Tel: 01301 703249 • Fax: 01301 703348

ARDUAINE COTTAGES, Arduaine, near Kilmelford

Bring your easel and your paints and capture the sparkling water, the bright white yachts and an archipelago of low-slung small islands - a memorable location, even by west coast terms. *The Chalet* sleeps 2, plus 2 - open plan sitting room/kitchen with double sofa bed, separate twin bedrooms. *The Post House Cottage* has a large kitchen/diner and sleeps up to 5 in two bedrooms - one king sized double, the other one double, one single. Both cottages have garden frontage overlooking stunning panoramic views to sea. TV, video and stereo. Pets welcome. Linen and towels included. Terms from £175. Please contact for further details.

Contact: Julie Rowden, Arduaine Cottages, Arduaine, Argyll PA34 4XQ

Tel: 01852 200216 • mobile: 07767 695088 • e-mail: arduainecottages@aol.com

MELFORT PIER & HARBOUR

KILMELFORD, BY OBAN PA34 4XD

Tel: 01852 200333; Fax: 01852 200329

"A Luxury Dog's Life!". Private beach, Hillwalking, Underfloor heating. Dog sitter. Superb Lochside Houses, each with Sauna, Spabath, Satellite TV, Telephone, E-mail hook-up, right on the shores of Loch Melfort. Close by restaurants/bars. Excellent base for touring Argyll and the Isles. From £80 to £205 per house/night. Sleep 2/6. Min 2 nights, start any day of the week. 2 pets welcome. Mention Pets Welcome and 1 pet stays FREE! STB ★★★★★ Self-Catering.

E-mail: melharbour@aol.com Website: www.mellowmelfort.com

See also Colour Advertisement on page 62

Colin and Jo Mossman, Lerags, Oban, Argyll PA34 4SE

• Tel: 01631 562746 • Fax: 01631 570225

• E-mail: lagnakeil@aol.com • Website: www.lagnakeil.co.uk

Our timber lodges and three cottages are set in a tranquil, scenic wooded glen overlooking Loch Feochan, only 3 miles from the picturesque harbour town of Oban **"Gateway to the Isles"**, offering a wonderful holiday at any time of the year. Free loch fishing. Pets welcome. O.A.P. discount. Sleep 2-10 comfortably. *Mini breaks from £43 per lodge per night, weekly from £220. ASSC Member.* **visitscotland ★★★/★★★★** *Self Catering*

See also Colour Advertisement on page 62

COLOGIN COUNTRY CHALETS Oban

Our cosy holiday chalets, set on an old farm in a peaceful private glen, can sleep from two to six people in comfort. They all have adjacent parking, heating, colour TV and bed linen. Pets welcome. Open all year round. Call now for colour brochure and find out more: **Mrs Linda Battison, Cologin Farmhouse, Lerags Glen, By Oban, Argyll PA34 4SE • 01631 564501 • Fax: 01631 566925 • www.west-highland-holidays.co.uk e-mail: cologin@west-highland-holidays.co.uk** **STB ★★★ / ★★★★ Self-Catering**

See also Colour Advertisement on page 62

"The finest location on the West Coast"

Loch Melfort Hotel & Restaurant

Enjoy stunning views down the Sound of Jura to the Islands. Located between Inveraray and Oban, beside the famous Arduaine Gardens. Join our regular guests and relax with excellent award-winning cuisine, comfortable accommodation, and friendly and attentive service. The perfect place for a relaxing holiday or short break.

Arduaine, By Oban, Argyll PA34 4XG Tel: 01852 200233
Fax: 01852 200214 • www.lochmelfort.co.uk

ELERAIG HIGHLAND CHALETS

Near OBAN, ARGYLL

Gateway to the Highlands and Islands

Well-equipped Norwegian chalets on secluded Eleraig Estate 12 miles from Oban.

PERFECT FOR PETS

In the breathtaking scenery of a private glen within 1800-acre working sheep farm. The chalets are ideal for a holiday with dogs. Widely spaced, sleeping four to seven. Parking by each chalet. Cots and high chairs available. By Loch Tralaig. Free fishing and boating. Peace and tranquillity are features of this walkers' and birdwatchers' paradise. Riding, golf, watersports and evening entertainment available locally. Open March to November.

From £205 weekly per chalet,
including electricity & bed linen.
Colour brochure from resident owners:

Anne and Robin Grey,
Eleraig Highland Chalets,
Kilninver, by Oban, Argyll PA34 4UX.
Tel/Fax: 01852 200225
Website: www.scotland2000.com/eleraig
E-mail: robingrey@eleraig.co.uk

Scottish Tourist Board ★★ Self Catering / Scottish Tourist Board ★★★ Self Catering

STB ★★★★ **WILLOWBURN HOTEL** AA ★★

Clachan Seil, By Oban, Argyll PA34 4TJ Tel: 01852 300276

Peaceful, relaxing, informal and addictive. Superb setting overlooking the Sound of Seil. Walk, fish, birdwatch or simply just laze. Completely non-smoking. Tempted? Bring your owners too! **www.willowburn.co.uk**

See also Colour Advertisement on page 64

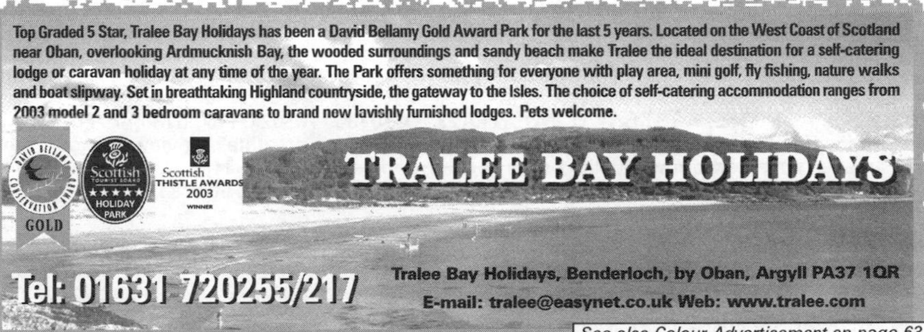

Top Graded 5 Star, Tralee Bay Holidays has been a David Bellamy Gold Award Park for the last 5 years. Located on the West Coast of Scotland near Oban, overlooking Ardmucknish Bay, the wooded surroundings and sandy beach make Tralee the ideal destination for a self-catering lodge or caravan holiday at any time of the year. The Park offers something for everyone with play area, mini golf, fly fishing, nature walks and boat slipway. Set in breathtaking Highland countryside, the gateway to the Isles. The choice of self-catering accommodation ranges from 2003 model 2 and 3 bedroom caravans to brand new lavishly furnished lodges. Pets welcome.
GOLD
Scottish
★★★★★
HOLIDAY PARK
Scottish
THISTLE AWARDS
2003
TRALEE BAY HOLIDAYS
Tel: 01631 720255/217
Tralee Bay Holidays, Benderloch, by Oban, Argyll PA37 1QR
E-mail: tralee@easynet.co.uk Web: www.tralee.com

See also Colour Advertisement on page 63

SKIPNESS ESTATE, By Tarbert, Argyll PA29 6XU Tel: 01880 760207; Fax: 01880 760208

This unspoilt, peaceful, West Highland estate with its own historic castle, mediaeval chapel and way-marked walks has traditional cottages to let all year round. Each cottage has an open fire and television; some cottages have a rowing dinghy in summer. Laundry facilities are available alongside the Seafood Cabin at Skipness Castle. Properties sleep 4 – 10. All cottages have magnificent views and beautiful surrounding countryside and coastline. Safe, sandy beaches can be enjoyed on the estate, with fishing, pony trekking and golf nearby. Local ferries to Arran, Gigha, Islay, and Jura. PETS WELCOME. Apply for rates and further details: Sophie James.

FARM HOLIDAY GUIDE DIPLOMA; STB★★/★★★ SELF-CATERING e-mail: sophie@skipness.freeserve.co.uk

See also Colour Advertisement on page 63

Appin

Mountainous area bounded by Loch Linnhe, Glen Creran and Glencoe.

MRS J PERY, ARDTUR, APPIN PA38 4DD (01631 730223 or 01626 834172). Two adjacent cottages in secluded surroundings. Ideal for hill walking, climbing, pony trekking, boating and fly fishing. Shop one mile; sea 200 yards; car essential; pets allowed.
e-mail: pery@eurobell.co.uk

Ballachulish

Impressively placed village at entrance to Glencoe and on Loch Leven. Magnificent mountain scenery including Sgorr Dhearg (3362ft). Good centre for boating, climbing and sailing. Glasgow 89 miles, Oban 38, Fort William 14, Kinlochleven 9.

Cottages and Chalets in Natural Woodland sleeping two to six people. The Glencoe area is lovely for walking and perfect for nature lovers too. Regret no smokers. No VAT. Brochure available. APPLY: HOUSE IN THE WOOD HOLIDAYS, GLENACHULISH, BALLACHULISH PH49 4JZ (01855 811379). Pets welcome. [🐕]

Cairndow

Village at mouth of Kinglas Water on Loch Fyne in Argyll, near head of Loch.

CAIRNDOW STAGECOACH INN, CAIRNDOW PA26 8BN (01499 600286; Fax: 01499 600220). 14 well-appointed en suite bedrooms. Excellent cuisine in Stables Restaurant and lounge meals all day. Amenities include lochside beer garden, sauna, multi-gym and solarium. STB ★★★ Inn.

Two comfortable holiday cottages at the head of the longest sea loch in Scotland, in lovely walking country. Sleep four and eight. Linen and electricity included. STB ★★★ Self Catering.MRS DELAP, ACHADUNAN, CAIRNDOW, ARGYLL PA26 8BJ (Tel & Fax: 01499 600238).
website: www.argyllholidaycottages.com

Dalmally

Small town in Glen Orchy to the south-west of Loch Awe, with romantic Kilchurn Castle (14th century). Edinburgh 98 miles, Glasgow 69, Ardrishaig 42, Oban 25, Inveraray 16.

ROCKHILL WATERSIDE COUNTRY HOUSE, ARDBRECKNISH, BY DALMALLY PA33 1BH (01866 833218). 17th century guest house on waterside with spectacular views over Loch Awe. Five delightful rooms with all modern facilities. First-class home cooking with much home-grown produce.

Dunoon

Lively resort reached by car ferry from Gourock. Cowal Highland Gathering held at end of August.

ABBOTS BRAE HOTEL, WEST BAY, DUNOON PA23 7QJ (01369 705021; Fax: 01369 701191). Small welcoming hotel at the gateway to the Western Highlands with breathtaking views. Comfortable, spacious, en suite bedrooms, quality home cooking and select wines. [🐕]
e-mail: info@abbotsbrae.co.uk website: www.abbotsbrae.co.uk

Isle of gigha

A tranquil island, one of the Inner Hebrides just of the west coast of Scotland. A haven for birds and wildlife.

GIGHA HOTEL, ISLE OF GIGHA PA41 7AA (01583 505254; Fax: 01583 505244). Beautiful, tranquil island. Explore the white sandy bays and lochs; famous Achamore Gardens. Easy walking, bike hire, birds, wildlife and wild flowers. Dog-friendly. Holiday cottages also available.
website: www.isle-of-gigha.co.uk

Kinlochleven

At the eastern end of Loch Leven, seven miles east of Glencoe.

MACDONALD HOTEL, FORT WILLIAM ROAD, KINLOCHLEVEN PH50 4QL (01855 831539; Fax: 01855 831416). Ideally located midway between Glencoe and Ben Nevis, adjacent West Highland Way. 10 bedrooms, all en suite, 'Bothy Bar' and restaurant. Campsite. Drying room. **STB ★★★**
e-mail: availability@macdonaldhotel.co.uk website: www.macdonaldhotel.co.uk

Loch Goil

Six-mile long loch stretching from Lochgoilhead to Loch Long.

DARROCH MHOR, CARRICK CASTLE, LOCH GOIL PA24 8AF (01301 703249; Fax: 01301 703348). Five self-catering Chalets on the shores of Loch Goil in the heart of Argyll Forest Park. Fully equipped except linen. Colour TV, fitted kitchen, carpeted. Pets very welcome. Open all year. [🐕]

Oban

Popular Highland resort and port, yachting centre, ferry services to Inner and Outer Hebrides. Sandy bathing beach at Ganavan Bay. McCaig's Tower above town is Colosseum replica built in 1890's.

MRS STEWART, GLENVIEW, SOROBA ROAD, OBAN PA34 4JF (01631 562267). Small family-run guest house, 10 minutes' walk from train, boat and bus terminal. A warm welcome awaits you all year round. [🐕]

JULIE ROWDEN, ARDUAINE COTTAGES, ARDUAINE PA34 4XQ (01852 200216; mobile: 07767 695088). Two self-catering properties in magnificent location sleeping 2 to 5. Garden, TV, video and stereo. Beautiful panoramic views to sea. Linen and towels included. Terms from £175 per week. STB ★★ Self- Catering. [Pets £20 per week]
e-mail: arduainecottages@aol.com

MELFORT PIER AND HARBOUR, KILMELFORD, BY OBAN PA34 4XD (01852 200333; Fax: 01852 200329). Superb Lochside houses each with Sauna, Spabath, Satellite TV, Telephone, E-mail hook-up, on the shores of Loch Melfort. Excellent base for touring Argyll and the Isles. From £80 to £205 per house/night. Minimum stay 2 nights. 2 pets welcome.STB ★★★★★ Self Catering. [Pets £10 each per stay]
e-mail: melharbour@aol.com. website: www.mellowmelfort.com

LAGNAKEIL HIGHLAND LODGES, LERAGS, OBAN, ARGYLL PA34 4SE (01631 562746; Fax: 01631 570225). Our Timber Lodges and three cottages are set in a tranquil, scenic wooded glen overlooking Loch Feochan, only 3 miles from the picturesque harbour town of Oban: "Gateway to the Isles". Fully equipped Lodges to a high standard, including linen and towels, country pub a short walk. O.A.P. discount. Free loch fishing. Special Breaks from £43 per lodge per night, weekly from £220 Sleep 2-10 comfortably. Our colour brochure will tell lots more. STB ★★★/★★★★ self-catering. [Pets £10 per week].
e-mail: lagnakeil@aol.com website: www.lagnakeil.co.uk

MRS LINDA BATTISON, COLOGIN COUNTRY CHALETS, LERAGS GLEN, BY OBAN PA34 4SE (01631 564501; Fax: 01631 566925). Cosy timber chalets, sleep two to six, all conveniences. Situated on farm, wildlife abundant. Games room, launderette, licensed bar serving home-cooked food. Free fishing. Playpark. Live entertainment. STB ★★★/★★★★ Self-Catering [pw! Pets £15 per week.]
e-mail: cologin@west-highland-holidays.co.uk website: www.west-highland-holidays.co.uk

LOCH MELFORT HOTEL & RESTAURANT, ARDUAINE, BY OBAN PA34 4XG (01852 200233; Fax: 01852 200214). Stunning views down the Sound of Jura to the Islands. Located between Inveraray and Oban, beside the famous Arduaine Gardens. Excellent award-winning cuisine, comfortable accommodation, and friendly and attentive service. [🐕]
website: www.lochmelfort.co.uk

Well-equipped Scandinavian chalets in breathtaking scenery near Oban. Chalets sleep 4–7, are widely spaced and close to Loch Tralaig. Car parking. From £205 per week per chalet. Available March to November. STB ★★ & ★★★ Self Catering. APPLY – ANNE & ROBIN GREY, ELERAIG HIGHLAND CHALETS, KILNINVER, BY OBAN PA34 4UX (01852 200225) [🐕]
e-mail: robingrey@eleraig.co.uk website: www.scotland2000.com/eleraig

WILLOWBURN HOTEL, CLACHAN SEIL, BY OBAN PA34 4TJ (01852 300276). Peaceful, relaxing, informal and addictive. Superb setting overlooking the Sound of Seil. Walk, fish, birdwatch or simply just laze. Completely non-smoking. Tempted? Bring your owners too! STB ★★★★ Small Hotel, AA ★★ [🐕]
website: www.willowburn.co.uk

TRALEE BAY HOLIDAYS, BENDERLOCH, BY OBAN PA37 1QR (01631 720255/217). Overlooking Ardmucknish Bay. The wooded surroundings and sandy beaches make Tralee the ideal destination for a self-catering lodge or caravan holiday anytime of the year. STB ★★★★★.
e-mail: tralee@easynet.co.uk website: www.tralee.com

Tarbert

Fishing port on isthmus connecting Kintyre to the mainland.

Peaceful, unspoilt West Highland estate. Traditional cottages, with open fires; some with a dinghy in summer. Sleep 4–10. Pets welcome. Walks, pony trekking, golf nearby. APPLY SOPHIE JAMES, SKIPNESS CASTLE, BY TARBERT PA29 6XU (01880 760207; Fax: 01880 760208). STB ★★/★★★[🐕]
e-mail: sophie@skipness.freeserve.co.uk

ISLE OF ARRAN

Catacol

Ayr

Popular family holiday resort with sandy beaches. Excellent shopping, theatre, racecourse.

HORIZON HOTEL, ESPLANADE, AYR KA7 1DT (01292 264383; Fax: 01292 264011). Highly recommended for golf breaks; special midweek rates. Coach parties welcome. Lunches, dinners and bar suppers served. Phone now for free colour brochure. [🐕]
e-mail: mail@horizonhotel.com website: www.horizonhotel.com

Ballantrae

Small fishing port 12 miles south-west of Girvan.

ROGER AND MARILYN BOURNE, LAGGAN HOUSE LEISURE PARK, BALLANTRAE KA26 0LL (01465 831229; Fax: 01465 831511). Luxury caravans and chalets for hire. Overlooking secluded countryside and sea. Heated indoor pool, sauna, bar, children's playground. Short Breaks available. STB ★★★★ [£2 per night, £12 per week]
website: www.lagganhouse.com

Saltcoats

Town and resort on Firth of Clyde adjoining Ardrossan to south east.

SANDYLANDS HOLIDAY PARK, AUCHENHARVIE PARK, SALTCOATS KA21 5JN. Park on edge of Saltcoats. Access to beach. Indoor pool, 3 clubrooms, kids' club, mini market. Tourers and tents welcome. Ferry trips to Arran. Delightful coastal walks. Call 0870 442 9312 for brochure.
website: www.gbholidayparks.co.uk

Catacol (Isle of Arran)

Location on north side of Catacol Bay on north-west coast of Arran.

CATACOL BAY HOTEL, CATACOL, LOCHRANZA KA27 8HN (01770 830231 or 0870 908 9303; Fax: 01770 830350). Comfortable, friendly, small country house hotel where good cooking is our speciality. Extensive bar menu, meals are served from noon until 10pm. Centrally heated. Open all year. Details of Special Breaks and brochure on request. Children and pets welcome. [🐕]
e-mail: davecatbay@lineone.net website: www.catacol.co.uk

SYMBOLS

- 🐕 **Indicates that pets are welcome free of charge.**
- £ **Indicates that a charge is made for pets: nightly or weekly.**
- pw! **Shows some special provision for pets; exercise facility, feeding or accommodation arrangement.**
- ⌂ **Indicates separate pets accommodation.**

FREE or REDUCED RATE entry to Holiday Visits and Attractions – see our READERS' OFFER VOUCHERS on pages 101-116

We are 10 Yorkshire Terrier "ladies" and would love you to come and spend a few days or longer in our former farmhouse home. We live in the heart of the Scottish Border country among rolling hills and green valleys. Our people would like to meet your people, as long as they are well behaved. We all look forward to seeing you. Love from ***Fudge, Buttons, Poppy, Amber, Joy, Debbie, Penny, Skye, Sophie and Willow.***

WILLIAMHOPE HOUSE, OLD PEEL, CLOVENFORDS, NEAR GALASHIELS TD1 3LL
TEL: 01896 850243

Scottish Tourist Board ★★★ B&B

Glenbank House Hotel

Castlegate, Jedburgh TD8 6BD

Tel: 01835 862258

e-mail: enquiries@glenbankhotel.co.uk
website: www.glenbankhotel.co.uk

Set in its own grounds with ample private parking and beer garden. Licensed restaurant and bar with an extensive wine list and selection of malt whiskies. All rooms are en suite with TV. Open to non-residents. Reduced rates for children. Pets Welcome.

Westwood House – Kelso **Overlooking Scotland's famous River Tweed**

TOTAL "OFF LEAD" FREEDOM FOR DOGS IN ENCLOSED AND SECLUDED GROUNDS

Renovated riverside cottage with 12 acres of paths, through walled gardens and on own private island.
4 bedrooms sleeping 2 - 8 (+ child), 2 bathrooms, period features, cosy log fire and centrally heated.
• ½ mile Kelso town • one hour Edinburgh/Newcastle • ½ hour Berwick (station) and Northumberland coast

DOGS WELCOME FREE

For Brochure and tariff, from £325 per week fully inclusive of all linen and towels, electricity and heating.
2-person discounts available. Trout fishing also included.

Debbie Crawford, Tel: 07788 134 832
Pippin Heath Farm, Holt, Norfolk NR25 6SS
e-mail: westwood.house@btinternet.com

ACHIEVING GOLD IN GREEN TOURISM AND 'HIGHLY COMMENDED' IN SCOTTISH THISTLE AWARDS

See also Colour Advertisement on page 64

The Crook Inn

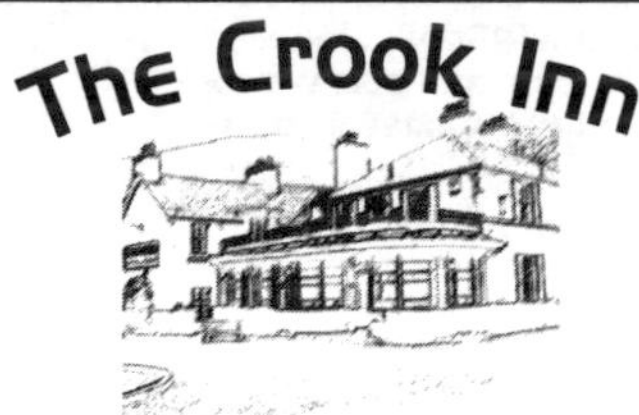

Tweedsmuir,
Scottish Borders, ML12 6QN

Tel: 01899 880272 • Fax: 01899 880294
e-mail: thecrookinn@btinternet.com
website: www.crookinn.co.uk

This comfortable, family-run hotel is set in the Upper Tweed Valley 35 miles south of Edinburgh. The Crook is the oldest licensed inn in Scotland and retains many notable and historic features. The 17th century bar where Robert Burns wrote 'Willie Wastle's Wife' is a real time capsule. In the 1930s the hotel was refurbished in the Art Deco style and many of these features have been retained. Meals both in the bar and the restaurant are prepared to order with as much fresh local ingredients as possible. Step back in time at The Crook – an ideal base for touring the Borders, hillwalking or just relaxing.

THE GARDEN HOUSE

Whitmuir, Selkirk TD7 4PZ
Tel: 01750 721728
Fax: 01750 720379
E-mail: hilary.dunlop@virgin.net
www.whitmuirfarm.co.uk

Warm, modern farmhouse B&B set in delightful walled garden in the heart of the Scottish Borders. Spacious bedrooms with private bathrooms. Good home cooking using local produce. Loch fishing; grazing for horses; ideal for walking, cycling and horse riding. Well behaved pets welcome. Open all year

---

Terms quoted in this publication may be subject to increase if rises in costs necessitate

See also Colour Advertisement on page 64

Galashiels

Town on Gala Water, 14 miles north of Hawick.

WILLIAMHOPE HOUSE, OLD PEEL, CLOVENFORDS, NEAR GALASHIELS TD1 3LL (01896 850243). Fudge, Buttons, Poppy, Amber, Joy, Debbie, Penny, Skye, Sophie and Willow. (Yorkshire Terriers) invite you to spend a few days in their former farmhouse home in the heart of the Scottish Borders, among rolling hills and green valleys. STB ★★★ B&B.[🐕]

Jedburgh

Small town on Jed water, 10 miles north-east of Hawick. Ruins of abbey founded in 1138.

ALAN & CHRISTINE SWANSTON, FERNIEHIRST MILL LODGE, JEDBURGH TD8 6PQ (01835 863279). A chalet style guest house set in grounds of 25 acres. All rooms en suite with tea/coffee making facilities. Licensed for residents. Well behaved pets (including horses) welcome by arrangement. STB, AA, RAC. [🐕]
e-mail: ferniehirstmill@aol.com website: www.ferniehirstmill.co.uk

GLENBANK HOUSE HOTEL, CASTLEGATE, JEDBURGH TD8 6BD (01835 862258). Set in its own grounds with ample private parking and beer garden. Licensed restaurant and bar. All rooms en suite with TV. Open to non-residents. Reduced rates for children. [🐕]
e-mail: enquiries@glenbankhotel.co.uk website: www.glenbankhotel.co.uk

PLEASE MENTION THIS GUIDE WHEN YOU WRITE OR PHONE TO ENQUIRE ABOUT ACCOMMODATION. IF YOU ARE WRITING, A STAMPED, ADDRESSED ENVELOPE IS ALWAYS APPRECIATED.

Kelso

Market town 18 miles north-west of Hawick and 20 miles south-west of Berwick-upon-Tweed.

WESTWOOD HOUSE, OVERLOOKING SCOTLAND'S FAMOUS RIVER TWEED. Enclosed and secluded riverside cottage with walled gardens and own private island. Sleep 2-8 persons plus child, from £325 per week. 2 person discounts. STB ★★★ Self-catering. For brochure contact: DEBBIE CRAWFORD, PIPPIN HEATH FARM, HOLT, NORFOLK NR25 6SS (07788 134832). [🐕]
e-mail: westwood.house@btinternet.com

Peebles

On the River Tweed, famous for tweeds and knitwear.

MS S. BELL, THE CROOK INN, TWEEDSMUIR, SCOTTISH BORDERS ML12 6QN (01899 880272; Fax: 01899 880294). All rooms en suite. Full breakfast included in charge. Bar meals always available as well as dining-room menu in evenings. Children and pets welcome.
e-mail: thecrookinn@btinternet.com website: www.crookinn.co.uk

Selkirk

Town in the Scottish Borders, site of the first Border Abbey where William Wallace, "Braveheart", was declared guardian of Scotland.

THE GARDEN HOUSE, WHITMUIR, SELKIRK TD7 4PZ (01750 721728; Fax: 01750 720379). Comfortable, warm modern farm house B&B. Spacious bedrooms, private bathrooms. Good home cooking. Fishing, walking, cycling and horse riding nearby. Grazing available. Open all year. [🐕]
e-mail: hilary.dunlop@virgin.net website: www.whitmuirfarm.co.uk

West Linton

Village on east side of Pentland hills, 7 miles south-west of Penicuick. Edinburgh 18 miles.

MRS C. M. KILPATRICK, SLIPPERFIELD HOUSE, WEST LINTON EH46 7AA (Tel & Fax: 01968 660401). Two well-equipped converted cottages set in 100 acres of lochs and woodlands. Sleep 4/6. Available all year. Central Heating. Car essential. Self Catering. Ideal, dog-friendly location. STB ★★★/★★★★ [🐕]
e-mail: cottages@slipperfield.com website: www.slipperfield.com

PLEASE NOTE

All the information in this book is given in good faith in the belief that it is correct. However, the publishers cannot guarantee the facts given in these pages, neither are they responsible for changes in policy, ownership or terms that may take place after the date of going to press. Readers should always satisfy themselves that the facilities they require are available and that the terms, if quoted, still apply.

Twin bedroom in comfortable bungalow with magnificent country and sea views. Dedicated dogs' garden. Good long and short walks, lots of beaches. Ten minutes by car from Kirkcudbright.

Balmangan Beag **By Borgue, Kirkcudbright DG6 4TR**

❖ ❖ Tel: 01557 870 499 ❖ ❖

Craigadam Working organic sheep farm. Family-run 18th century farmhouse. All bedrooms en suite. Billiard room. Lovely oak-panelled dining room offering Cordon Bleu cooking using local produce such as venison, pheasant and salmon. Trout fishing, walking, and golfing available.

THE TASTE OF SCOTLAND

Tel & Fax: 01556 650233 • Mrs C. Pickup, Craigadam, Castle Douglas DG7 3HU • www.craigadam.com

STB ★★★★ B&B • **RAC** ◆◆◆◆◆ & Little Gem Award • **AA** ◆◆◆◆◆ Premier Award • Winner Macallan Taste of Scotland 2001.

THE *Urr Valley* HOTEL

A privately owned hotel set in 14 acres of mature woodland and gardens in Galloway, one of the most beautiful and diverse areas of countryside in Britain - 17 en suite rooms, wood panelling, log fires and cosy bar. Pets welcome. **AA** ★★

Ernespie Rd, Castle Douglas, Dumfries & Galloway DG7 3JG Tel: 01556 502188 Fax: 01556 504055
E-mail: info@urrvalleyhotel.co.uk Website: www.urrvalleyhotel.co.uk

See also Colour Advertisement on page 64

DAVID & GILL STEWART

AE FOREST COTTAGES

GUBHILL FARM DUMFRIES DG1 1RL
TEL: 01387 860648

Modern accommodation in old stone buildings on a traditional farm, overlooking a peaceful valley, surrounded by hills and forests. Beautiful views, plentiful wildlife and endless paths on the doorstep. A great country retreat between Dumfries, Moffat and Thornhill.

E-mail: gill@gubhill.co.uk **STB★★★ SELF CATERING**

Beautiful, spacious farmhouse and charming, cosy cottages set amid stunning Scottish scenery near beaches (dogs allowed), hills, forests, castles, gardens and golf course. Loch and river fishing with tuition, free tennis, wonderful walking, cycling and riding country.

Sleep 2-12 • Rates £189- £1155 • Short breaks available

Pets, including horses, welcome.

info@ruskoholidays.co.uk • www.ruskoholidays.co.uk

Scottish Tourist Board ★★ Self Catering · Scottish Tourist Board ★★★★ Self Catering · Green Tourism Business Scheme Silver · Walkers Welcome · Cyclists Welcome

Rusko Holidays

Gatehouse of Fleet, Castle Douglas DG7 2BS
Tel: 01557 814215 • Fax: 01557 814679

See also Colour Advertisement on page 65

AA ◆◆◆ **BARNHILL SPRINGS** *STB* ★★ *Guest House*

Country Guest House, Moffat, Dumfriesshire DG10 9QS Tel: 01683 220580

Early Victorian country house overlooking some of the finest views of Upper Annandale. Comfortable accommodation, residents' lounge with open fire. Ideal centre for touring South-West Scotland and the Borders, or for an overnight stop. Situated on the Southern Upland Way half-a-mile from A74/M74 Moffat Junction. Pets free of charge. Bed & Breakfast from £22; Evening Meal (optional) from £15.

Annandale Arms Hotel *A warm welcome is offered at the Annandale Arms Hotel to dogs with well-mannered and house-trained owners. There are all the comforts and facilities that owners enjoy such as an excellent restaurant and a relaxing panelled bar. The Hotel has a large private parking area at the rear full of the most exquisite sniffs. £75 per room for dogs travelling with two owners; £47.50 per room for dogs travelling with one owner.*

High Street, Moffat DG10 9HF Tel: 01683 220013 Fax: 01683 221395

MORLICH HOUSE Ballplay Road, Moffat DG10 9JU

In beautiful 'Burns Country', this superb Victorian country house is set in quiet elevated grounds overlooking the town and surrounding hills. Just 5 minutes' walk from town centre. Rooms are en suite with colour TV, radio alarm, tea/coffee, four poster available. Private car park. B&B from £22pp. Weekly terms. Well behaved dogs welcome. Open all year.

Tel: 01683 220589
e-mail: info@morlichhouse.co.uk **www.morlichhouse.co.uk** **Fax: 01683 220887**

Buccleuch Arms Hotel *We are genuinely dog friendly, not just dog tolerant.*

Add to this the best food and service available in Southern Scotland. Shortlisted "Best New Restaurant 2004" by the Scottish Chefs Association. **High Street, Moffat DG10 9ET (01683 220003)**

Fax: 01683 221291 • enquiries@buccleucharmshotel.com • www.buccleucharmshotel.com

The Buccleuch Team welcomes you – Wine, Dine and Explore *STB ★★★ Hotel*

See also Colour Advertisement on page 65

THE TASTE OF SCOTLAND

Nether Barr Steading & The Black Sheep Inn

• Luxury Self Catering Lodges • Taste of Scotland Licensed Restaurant

A fine stone-built courtyard steading sensitively converted into six individually designed lodges, accommodating 2 to 6 guests. Fully equipped lounge/dining area/kitchen/ bathroom. The Black Sheep Inn, a licensed restaurant serving high quality Taste of Scotland cuisine using the best local produce.

Nether Barr Farm, Newton Stewart DG8 6AU (Winner of Galloway Preservation Society Award 2000)

Tel: 01671 404326 • Fax: 01671 404860 • E-mail: info@netherbarr.co.uk • Web: www.netherbarr.co.uk

Hope Cottage, Thornhill, Dumfriesshire DG3 5BD.

Pretty stone cottage in the peaceful conservation village of Durisdeer. Well-equipped self-catering cottage with large secluded garden. Sleeps 6. Towels, linen, heating and electricity included. Pets Welcome.

For brochure telephone:
Mrs S Stannett Tel: 01848 500228 Fax: 01848 500337
e-mail: a.stann@btinternet.com website: www.hopecottage.co.uk STB ★★★★

Borgue

Village south west of Kirkcudbright, setting for Robert Louis Stevenson's "Master of Ballantrae".

MRS MILLARD BARNES, BALMANGAN BEAG, BY BORGUE, KIRKCUDBRIGHT DG6 4TR. (01557 870 499). Twin bedroom in comfortable bungalow with magnificent country and sea views. Dedicated dogs' garden. Good long and short walks, lots of beaches. Ten minutes by car from Kirkcudbright.

Castle Douglas

Old market town at the northern end of Carlingwalk Loch, good touring centre for Galloway

MRS CELIA PICKUP, "CRAIGADAM", CASTLE DOUGLAS DG7 3HU (Tel & Fax: 01556 650233). Family-run 18th century famhouse. All bedrooms en suite. Billiard room. Lovely oak-panelled dining room offering Cordon Bleu cooking using local produce such as venison, pheasant and salmon. Trout fishing, walking and golfing available. STB ★★★★ Hotel, RAC ◆◆◆◆◆ & Little Gem Award, AA ◆◆◆◆ Premier Collection. [🐕]
website: www.craigadam.com

URR VALLEY HOTEL, ERNESPIE ROAD, CASTLE DOUGLAS, DUMFRIES & GALLOWAY DG7 3JG (01556 502188; Fax: 01556 504055). Hotel within easy walking distance of Castle Douglas. Sandy beaches, grouse moors, harbour villages and forest walks. Log fires, Sportsman's bar, 17 en suite rooms, colour TV, tea/coffee making facilities, and direct dial telephones. AA ★★ [🐕]
e-mail: info@urrvalleyhotel.co.uk website: www.urrvalleyhotel.co.uk

PLEASE SEND A STAMPED ADDRESSED ENVELOPE WITH ENQUIRIES

Dumfries

County town of Dumfries-shire and a former seaport. Dumfries contains many interesting buildings including an 18th century windmill containing a camera obscura. Robert Burns lived in the town before his death in 1796.

DAVID & GILL STEWART, AE FOREST COTTAGES, GUBHILL FARM, DUMFRIES DG1 1RL (01387 860648). Modern accommodation in old stone buildings on a traditional farm, overlooking a peaceful valley. Beautiful views, plentiful wildlife and endless paths on the doorstep. Between Dumfries, Moffat and Thornhill. STB ★★★ SELF CATERING, CATEGORY ONE DISABILITY. [🐕]
e-mail: gill@gubhill.co.uk

Gatehouse of Fleet

Small town near mouth of Water of Fleet, 6 miles north-west of Kirkcudbright.

RUSKO HOLIDAYS, GATEHOUSE OF FLEET, CASTLE DOUGLAS DG7 2BS (01557 814215; Fax: 01557 814679). Spacious farmhouse and charming, cosy cottages near beaches, hills, gardens, castles and golf course. Walking, fishing, tennis. Pets, including horses, welcome. Sleep 2-12. Rates £189-£1155. STB ★★ to ★★★★ Self-Catering. Disabled Awards. [🐕]
email: info@ruskoholidays.co.uk website: www.ruskoholidays.co.uk

Kirkcudbright

Small town on River Dee estuary 10 miles south of Castle Douglas.

GORDON HOUSE HOTEL, 116 HIGH STREET, KIRKCUDBRIGHT DG6 4JQ (Tel & Fax: 01557 330670/331041). 8 en suite bedrooms with TV, tea/coffee, radio alarm and central heating. Restaurant - Scottish cuisine. Lounge and public bar. Garden. Dogs welcome! STB ★★★ Hotel.
e-mail: mail@gordon-house-hotel.co.uk website: www.Gordon-House-hotel.co.uk

Moffat

At head of lovely Annandale, grand mountain scenery. Good centre for rambling, climbing, angling and golf. The 'Devil's Beef Tub' is 5 miles, Edinburgh 52, Peebles 33, Dumfries 21.

BARNHILL SPRINGS COUNTRY GUEST HOUSE, MOFFAT DG10 9QS (01683 220580). Early Victorian country house overlooking some of the finest views of Upper Annandale. Comfortable accommodation, residents' lounge with open fire. Situated on the Southern Upland Way half-a-mile from A74/M74 Moffat Junction. Pets free of charge. Bed & Breakfast from £22; Evening Meal (optional) from £15. STB ★★ Guest House. AA ◆◆◆. [pw! 🐕]

ANNANDALE ARMS HOTEL, HIGH STREET, MOFFAT DG1O 9HF (01683 220013; Fax: 01683 221395). A warm welcome is offered at the Annandale Arms to dogs with well-mannered and house-trained owners. Excellent restaurant and a relaxing panelled bar. Large private parking area. £75 per room for two; £47.50 per room for one. [pw! 🐕]

MORLICH GUEST HOUSE, BALLPLAY ROAD, MOFFAT DG10 9JU (01683 220589; Fax: 01683 220887). Set in beautiful 'Burns Country' Morlich House is a superb Victorian country house. Rooms are en suite with TV, radio alarm, tea/coffee, four-poster available. Private car park. B&B from £22pp. Weekly terms. Open all year. [🐕]
e-mail: info@morlichhouse.co.uk website: www.morlichhouse.co.uk

BUCCLEUCH ARMS HOTEL, HIGH STREET, MOFFAT DG10 9ET (01683 220003; Fax: 01683 221291). We are genuinely dog friendly, not just dog tolerant. Add to this the best food and service available in Southern Scotland. The Buccleuch Team welcomes you – wine, dine and explore. STB ★★★ [Pets £5 per night, £30 per week]
e-mail: enquiries@buccleucharmshotel.com website: www.buccleucharmshotel.com

Newton Stewart

Town on the edge of the Galloway Forest Park. Central for touring south west Scotland.

NETHER BARR STEADING & BLACK SHEEP INN, NETHER BARR FARM, NEWTON STEWART DG8 6AU (01671 404326; Fax: 01671 404860) Stone-built courtyard steading converted into six individually designed lodges, accommodating 2 to 6 guests. Fully equipped. The Black Sheep Inn, licensed restaurant serving high quality Taste of Scotland cuisine.
e-mail: info@netherbarr.co.uk website: www.netherbarr.co.uk

Thornhill

Small town on River Nith 13 miles north-west of Dumfries. Site of Roman signal station lies to the south.

MRS S. STANNETT, HOPE COTTAGE, HOLESTANE FARM, THORNHILL, DUMFRIESSHIRE DG3 5BD (01848 500228; Fax: 01848 500337). Pretty stone cottage in the peaceful conservation village of Durisdeer. Well-equipped self-catering cottage with large secluded garden. Sleeps 6. Towels, linen, heating and electricity included. Self-catering. Phone for brochure. STB ★★★★ [🐕]
e-mail: a.stann@btinternet.com website: www.hopecottage.co.uk

DUNBARTONSHIRE

Drymen

Village 7 miles north-east of Balloch. To the west is the site of Buchanan Castle, formerly the Seat of the Duke of Montrose.

CROFTBURN BED & BREAKFAST, CROFTAMIE, DRYMEN, LOCH LOMOND G63 0HA (01360 660796; Fax: 01360 661005). Rural location set in one acre of gardens with views of the Campsie Fells and the Strathendrick Valley. Excellent base for walking, touring etc. Pets welcome. STB★★★, AA ◆◆◆◆. [🐕]
e-mail: johnreid@croftburn.fsnet.co.uk
website: www.dellta.org/croftburn or www.croftburn.co.uk

Loch Lomond

Largest stretch of inland water in Britain. Extends from Ardlui in the north to Balloch in the south.

MRS SALLY MACDONELL, MARDELLA FARMHOUSE, OLD SCHOOL ROAD, GARTOCHARN, LOCH LOMOND G83 8SD (01389 830428). Situated on a quiet country lane, surrounded by fields and hills, with lovely walks and exciting smells for your four-legged friends. Relax with your dogs for they are truly loved here.

EDINBURGH & LOTHIANS

Edinburgh

Scotland's capital with magnificent castle overlooking "The Athens of the North".

PETER FRASER, RIMSWELL HOUSE HOTEL, 33 MAYFIELD GARDENS, EDINBURGH EH9 2BX (Tel & Fax: 0131 667 5851). A convenient and comfortable private hotel. 9 bedrooms, most en suite with TV and tea/coffee facilities. Private off-road parking. Bed and full Scottish Breakfast from £20 to £35 per person.
e-mail: reception@rimswellhouse.co.uk website: www.rimswellhouse.co.uk

St Andrews

Home of golf - British Golf Museum has memorabilia dating back to the origins of the game. Remains of castle and cathedral. Sealife Centre and beach Leisure Centre. Excellent sands. Ideal base for exploring the picturesque East Neuk.

MR & MRS PATRICK WEDDERBURN, ST ANDREWS COUNTRY COTTAGES, MOUNTQUHANIE ESTATE, FREEPOST, CUPAR KY15 4BR (01382 330318; Fax: 01382 330480). Quality self-catering houses and cottages in St Andrews and on a tranquil Country Estate. Central heating, TV, phone. Enclosed gardens. STB ★★★ to ★★★★★ Self Catering. [pw! Dogs £10 per week, Cats F.O.C.].
e-mail: enquiries@standrews-cottages.com website: www.standrews-cottages.com

•• *Some Useful Guidance for Guests and Hosts* ••

Every year literally thousands of holidays, short breaks and ovemight stops are arranged through our guides, the vast majority without any problems at all. In a handful of cases, however, difficulties do arise about bookings, which often could have been prevented from the outset.

It is important to remember that when accommodation has been booked, both parties – guests and hosts – have entered into a form of contract. We hope that the following points will provide helpful guidance.

GUESTS:

- When enquiring about accommodation, be as precise as possible. Give exact dates, numbers in your party and the ages of any children.
- State the number and type of rooms wanted and also what catering you require – bed and breakfast, full board etc. Make sure that the position about evening meals is clear – and about pets, reductions for children or any other special points.
- Read our reviews carefully to ensure that the proprietors you are going to contact can supply what you want. Ask for a letter confirming all arrangements, if possible.
- If you have to cancel, do so as soon as possible. Proprietors do have the right to retain deposits and under certain circumstances to charge for cancelled holidays if adequate notice is not given and they cannot re-let the accommodation.

HOSTS:

- Give details about your facilities and about any special conditions. Explain your deposit system clearly and arrangements for cancellations, charges etc. and whether or not your terms include VAT.
- If for any reason you are unable to fulfil an agreed booking without adequate notice, you may be under an obligation to arrange suitable alternative accommodation or to make some form of compensation.

While every effort is made to ensure accuracy, we regret that FHG Publications cannot accept responsibility for errors, omissions or misrepresentations in our entries or any consequences thereof. Prices in particular should be checked because we go to press early. We will follow up complaints but cannot act as arbiters or agents for either party.

COVE VIEW 36 Mellon Charles, Aultbea IV22 2JL

Wester Ross is ideal for a quiet restful holiday. Detached chalet has two small bedrooms, sitting area with mini kitchen, bathroom with shower. Ideal for two persons. Terms from £150 to £200 per week.

Your dog is welcome free. Open April to October. Tel: 01445 731351

Cairngorm Highland Bungalows STB ★★★/★★★★

Glen Einich, 29 Grampian View, Aviemore, Inverness-shire PH22 1TF
Tel: 01479 810653 Fax: 01479 810262

Beautifully furnished and well-equipped bungalows ranging from one to four bedrooms. All have colour TV, video, microwave, cooker, washer-dryer, fridge and patio furniture. Log fires. Children and pets welcome. Ideally situated for outdoor activities and touring. Golf, leisure club. Phone for colour brochure. Open all year.

E-mail: linda.murray@virgin.net Website: www.cairngorm-bungalows.co.uk

See also Colour Advertisement on page 65

CULLIGRAN COTTAGES
GLEN STRATHFARRAR

Pure magic! Come for a spell in a chalet or cottage and this glen will cast one over you! Nature Reserve with native woodlands and wildlife. Fifteen miles of private road. Bikes for hire. Fly fishing (salmon and trout) on the rivers Farrar and Glass. Watch the wild deer from your window. Feed the farm deer. Brochure. (March - November).

FRANK & JULIET SPENCER-NAIRN : STRUY : NR. BEAULY : INVERNESS-SHIRE : IV4 7JX
Tel/Fax: 01463 761285 : E-mail: juliet@culligran.demon.co.uk

An individual hotel for individual guests.
Award-winning cuisine. Pets welcome.
The Boat, Boat of Garten, Inverness-shire
Telephone: (01479) 831258
Fax: (01479) 831414
www.boathotel.co.uk

GLENURQUHART
LODGES

Situated between Loch Ness and Glen Affric in a spectacular setting ideal for walking, touring or just relaxing in this tranquil location. Four spacious chalets all fully equipped for six people, set in wooded grounds. Owner's hotel adjacent where guests are most welcome in the restaurant and bar.

NEAR DRUMNADROCHIT, INVERNESS IV3 6TJ
Tel: 01456 476234
Fax: 01456 476286

The Clan MacDuff Hotel

Achintore, Fort William, Inverness-shire PH33 6RW.
Tel: (01397) 702341 Fax: (01397) 706174

Small, well behaved pets are always welcome at the Clan MacDuff. This family-run hotel overlooks Loch Linnhe, two miles south of Fort William. Situated in its own grounds in a quiet and peaceful location with a large car park, the hotel is in an excellent location for touring and experiencing the rugged mountains and enchanting coastline of the West Highlands. All bedrooms have colour TV, hair dryer and hospitality tray, all with private facilities. The hotel offers great value hospitality, Bed and Breakfast in an en suite room from £25.50 per person per night. Three nights Dinner, Bed & Breakfast from £105. Spring and Autumn Special Offer. Please phone or write for our colour brochure & tariff.

Website: www.clanmacduff.co.uk STB ★★★ Hotel

LOCH LEVEN HOTEL

11 en suite rooms with great views. The Public Bar has a real fire and lots of atmosphere! Enjoy a meal of freshly prepared Scottish produce. Secluded garden. Safe, private parking in our extensive grounds. Great walks. We welcome dogs. B&B from £25-£50 pppn.

Onich, By Fort William PH33 6SA • Tel: 01855 821236 • Fax: 01855 821550
e-mail: reception@lochlevenhotel.co.uk • website: www.lochlevenhotel.co.uk

Nether Lochaber Hotel

Onich, Fort William, Inverness-shire PH33 6SE
Tel: 01855 821235; Fax: 01855 821545

An ideal centre from which to explore Lochaber, the Ardnamurchan Peninsula and Glencoe. Traditional home cooking goes hand in hand with homely service, comfortable accommodation and private facilities. The inn stands on the shores of beautiful Loch Linnhe at Corran Ferry, 8 miles south of Fort William.

Terms from £25-£35 per person Bed and Breakfast. Children and Pets Welcome!

Inchbae Lodge Hotel *by Garve, Ross-shire IV23 2PH*

Situated six miles west of Garve, this old hunting lodge nestles on the bank of the River Blackwater. Ideal location for bird watching, hunting, fishing and walking. There are 16 bedrooms, all with en-suite bathrooms or shower rooms. The warm and friendly atmosphere is felt in all the reception rooms - the home from home feel of the lounge, the cosy bar and the elegant diningroom.

Tel: 01997 455269 • Fax: 01997 455207
e-mail: stay@inchbae.com • website: www.inchbae.com

INVERGARRY HOTEL INVERGARRY, INVERNESS-SHIRE PH35 4HJ

Set in a small village amidst the beautiful scenery of the Scottish Highlands, The Invergarry Hotel has ten comfortable en suite rooms in a distinctive Victorian building. The restaurant features fine Scottish produce and the well-stocked bar has a range of over 30 malts.

Telephone: 01809 501206 • Fax: 01809 501400
e-mail: hotel@invergarry.net • website: www.invergarry.net/hotel

Our views are breathtaking – from both the hotel and the numerous miles of wonderful walks around us. "Hamish", our lovable labrador (together with owners, Ann and Martyn), looks forward to welcoming you and your dog(s) to their lovely home. You'll enjoy good "Taste of Scotland" food, log fires and a well-equipped bedroom in which you are as welcome as your dog!

Coul House Hotel

Contin, By Strathpeffer, Ross-shire IV14 9ES
Tel: 01997 421487; Fax: 01997 421945
e-mail: coulhouse@bestwestern.co.uk
website: www.milford.co.uk/go/coulhouse

STB ★★★★ Hotel

When making enquiries or bookings, a stamped addressed envelope is always appreciated

COLUMBA HOUSE
HOTEL & GARDEN RESTAURANT

In an area of oustanding natural beauty. An Oasis amidst the magnificent scenery, stunning landscapes and tranquillity, in the foothills of snow-capped peaks of the Cairngorm and Monadhliath mountains. Quiet Highland retreat, nestling among tall Scots Pines and Beech trees, in a secluded, landscaped, walled garden with patio for summer time dining. Offering the highest standards of welcoming hospitality, accommodation and customer care, friendly atmosphere. Rooms with their own front doors, perfect for doggie holidays. Candlelit Garden Restaurant, renowned for excellent cuisine and attentive service. Homely, enchanting lounge and cosy bar, offering modern facilities while retaining their original charm. Free Leisure Club facilities.

AA ◆◆◆◆ • Bed and Breakfast from £35 • STB ★★★ Small Hotel

Manse Road, Kingussie PH21 1JF • Tel: 01540 661402 • Fax: 01540 661652

e-mail: pets@columbahousehotel.com • www.columbahousehotel.com

THE NIP INN HOTEL Main St, Lairg, Sutherland IV27 4DB

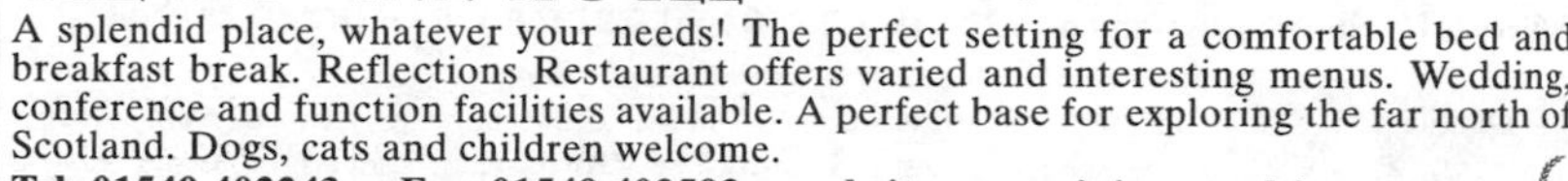

A splendid place, whatever your needs! The perfect setting for a comfortable bed and breakfast break. Reflections Restaurant offers varied and interesting menus. Wedding, conference and function facilities available. A perfect base for exploring the far north of Scotland. Dogs, cats and children welcome.

Tel: 01549 402243 Fax: 01549 402593 website: www.nipinn.co.uk/

• LOCH NESS • STB Self Catering ★★★★

Exceptional riverside lodges close to the spectacular Loch Ness. Mountains, lochs, waterfalls and wildlife abound.

• Charming riverside lodges with private lawns, some with log fires, up to 6 persons. • Cosy studio lodges just for two. • All enjoy magnificent views. • Quiet location with excellent walks from your lodge. • Heating, linen and towels included. • Short Breaks welcome. • Pets welcome. • Free Fishing. • Country pub and restaurant nearby. • Colour brochure/website. **Wildside, Whitebridge, Inverness IV2 6UN**

Tel: 01456 486 373 • Fax: 01456 486 371 • e-mail: info@wildsidelodges.com • website: www.wildsidelodges.com

See also Colour Advertisement on page 65

WILDERNESS COTTAGES, LOCH NESS/WEST COAST - SELF-CATERING

Open all year - Sleeps 2-12 - Pets welcome

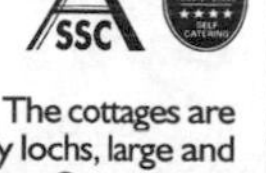

Wilderness Cottages have self-catering cottages all around Loch Ness. The cottages are set in the spectacular countryside of forests and mountains, with many lochs, large and small, dotted around the area like jewels in this undiscovered landscape. Our cottages provide privacy, perfect peace and some have the most breathtaking views of Loch Ness and miles of forest walks, which start at your back door. For dog owners, this is definitely the place to bring 'man's best friend'.

We have a selection of 4 star quality self-catering cottages in the area that welcome you and your pets, we also have a small selection of West coast properties. Please see our website for full details, or send for a brochure.

Contact: **Gordon & Corinne Roberts, Roebuck Cottage, Errogie, Stratherrick, Inverness-shire IV2 6UH • Tel & Fax: 01456 486358**

e-mail: corinne@wildernesscottages.co.uk • website: www.wildernesscottages.co.uk

Crubenbeg Holiday Cottages

Newtonmore, Inverness-shire PH20 1BE

Tel: 01540 673566 • Fax: 01540 673509
E-mail: enquiry@crubenbeg.com
Website: www.crubenbeg.com

Comfortable 4 Star country cottages in idyllic surroundings in the Cairngorm National Park as well as 'Monarch of the Glen' country. Lots of lovely walks, loads of sporting activities or simply relax and spot the wildlife around you. PETS WELCOME. Prices start at £235 per week for a one bedroom cottage.

Readers are requested to mention this guidebook when seeking accommodation (and please enclose a stamped addressed envelope).

Aultbea (Ross-shire)

Village on east shore of Loch Ewe, 5 miles north of Poolewe.

COVE VIEW, 36 MELLON CHARLES, AULTBEA IV22 2JL (01445 731351). Wester Ross is ideal for hill walking or a quiet restful holiday. Detached chalet with two small bedrooms, sitting area with mini kitchen, bathroom with shower. From £150 to £200 per week. A warm welcome awaits you and your pet. [🐕]

Aviemore (Inverness-shire)

Scotland's leading ski resort in Spey valley with superb sport and entertainment facilities. All-weather holiday centre with accommodation to suit all pockets. Excellent fishing. Centre for exploring Cairngorms. Edinburgh 129 miles, Grantown-on-Spey 14, Kingussie 12. Carrbridge 7.

SILVERGLADES HOLIDAY HOMES. Stylish bungalows, sleep 2-10. TV, video, CD player and Sky pack. Garden and barbecue. Some with sauna and wood burning stove. Pets welcome. Short breaks from £235. Brochure available (01479 810165). [Pets £10 per week]
website: www.silverglades.co.uk

CAIRNGORM HIGHLAND BUNGALOWS, GLEN EINICH, 29 GRAMPIAN VIEW, AVIEMORE, INVERNESS-SHIRE PH22 1TF. (01479 810653, Fax: 01479 810262). Well equipped bungalows ranging from one to four bedrooms. Open all year. Leisure facilities nearby. Children and pets welcome. Phone for brochure. [🐕]
e-mail: linda.murray@virgin.net website: www.cairngorm-bungalows.co.uk

Beauly (Inverness-shire)

Town at head of Beauly Firth, 11 miles west of inverness.

FRANK & JULIET SPENCER-NAIRN, CULLIGRAN COTTAGES, GLEN STRATHFARRAR, STRUY, NEAR BEAULY IV4 7JX (Tel & Fax: 01463 761285). Pure magic! Come for a spell in a chalet or cottage and this glen will cast one over on you! Nature Reserve with native woodlands and wildlife. Brochure. (March - November).
e-mail: juliet@culligran.demon.co.uk

Boat of Garten (Inverness-shire)

Village on Speyside 5 miles from Aviemore.

THE BOAT, BOAT OF GARTEN PH24 3BH (01479 831258; Fax: 01479 831414). An individual hotel for individual guests. Award-winning cuisine. Pets welcome. STB ★★★★, AA ★★★ and Two Rosettes. [Pets £5 per night.]
website: www.boathotel.co.uk

Carrbridge (Inverness-shire)

Village on River Dulnain, 7 miles north of Aviemore. Landmark Visitor Centre has exhibition explaining history of local environment.

THE PINES COUNTRY GUESTHOUSE, DUTHIL, CARRBRIDGE PH23 3ND (FREEPHONE: 0800 9701763). Relax and enjoy our Highland hospitality, woodland setting; all rooms en suite. Traditional or vegetarian home cooking. B&B £22.50 daily; DB&B £211 weekly. Children and pets welcome. AA ◆◆◆ [🐕]
website: www.thepines-duthil.fsnet.co.uk

Drumnadrochit (Inverness-shire)

Village on the shores of Loch Ness with "Monster" visitor centre. Sonar scanning cruises.

CAROL HUGHES, GLENURQUHART LODGES, BY DRUMNADROCHIT IV3 6TJ (01456 476234; Fax: 01456 476286). Situated between Loch Ness and Glen Affric in a spectacular setting ideal for walking, touring or just relaxing in this tranquil location. Four spacious chalets all fully equipped for six people, set in wooded grounds. Owner's hotel adjacent where guests are most welcome in the restaurant and bar. [Pets £10 per week.]

Fort William (Inverness-shire)

Small town at foot of Ben Nevis, ideal base for climbers and hillwalkers.

LOCH LEVEN HOTEL, ONICH, BY FORT WILLIAM PH33 6SA (01855 821236; Fax: 01855 821550). 11 en suite rooms with lovely views. Meals using freshly prepared Scottish produce. Secluded garden. Safe, private parking. Extensive grounds. Great walks. [pw! 🐕]
e-mail: reception@lochlevenhotel.co.uk website: www.lochlevenhotel.co.uk

THE CLAN MACDUFF HOTEL, ACHINTORE, FORT WILLIAM PH33 6RW (01397 702341; Fax: 01397 706174). This family-run hotel overlooks Loch Linnhe, two miles south of Fort William, excellent for touring the rugged mountains of the West Highlands. All rooms have TV, hair dryer and hospitality tray; all with private facilities. Three nights DB&B from £105 pppn. STB ★★★ Hotel. Phone or write for colour brochure and tariff. [🐕]
website: www.clanmacduff.co.uk

NETHER LOCHABER HOTEL, ONICH, FORT WILLIAM PH33 6SE (01855 821235; 01855 821545). Traditional home cooking goes hand in hand with homely service, comfortable accommodation and private facilities on the shores of beautiful Loch Linnhe. B&B from £25-£35 per person. [🐕]

ISLES OF GLENCOE HOTEL AND LEISURE CENTRE, BALLACHULISH, NEAR FORT WILLIAM PH49 4HL (0871 222 3415; Fax: 0871 222 3416). Almost afloat, this stylish, modern Hotel nestles on the lochside. Spacious bedrooms offer a commanding panorama of sky, mountain and loch. Delicious cuisine in Conservatory Restaurant. Heated pool and Leisure Centre. STB ★★★★ [pw! £10 per night]
e-mail: reservations@freedomglen.co.uk website: www.freedomglen.co.uk

THE BALLACHULISH HOTEL, BALLACHULISH, NEAR FORT WILLIAM PH49 4JY (0871 222 3415; Fax: 0871 222 3416) Glide through the dramatic pass of Glencoe and the mountains divide to reveal this breathtaking lochside setting. Fulfil your dream of the perfect historic Highland Hotel by staying here amongst the turrets. STB ★★★★. [Pets £10 per night].
e-mail: reservations@freedomglen.co.uk website: www.freedomglen.co.uk

THE LODGE ON THE LOCH, CREAG DHU, ONICH, BY FORT WILLIAM PH33 6RY (0871 222 3415; Fax: 0871 222 3416). Discover seclusion and serenity - enjoy one of the West Coast's finest panoramas. Choice of individual luxury rooms with many personal touches. Taste of Scotland. STB ★★★★, AA ★★★. [Pets £10 per night].
e-mail: reservations@freedomglen.co.uk website: www.freedomglen.co.uk/ll

When making enquiries please mention FHG Publications

Garve (Ross-shire)

Locality in Ross and Cromarty District, 10 miles west of Dingwall.

INCHBAE LODGE HOTEL, BY GARVE IV23 2PH (01997 455269; Fax: 01997 455207). In outstanding mountain scenery between Inverness and Ullapool. Family-run Victorian hunting lodge in riverside eight acres. Good Scottish food. Real ale. Ideal centre for all outdoor activities. Bargain Breaks eg: three nights DB&B £190 per dog, owner free. STB ★★★. [pw!]
e-mail: stay@inchbae.com website: www.inchbae.com

Invergarry

Village south of Fort Augustus on the shore of Loch Oich.

INVERGARRY HOTEL, INVERGARRY PH35 4HJ (01809 501206; Fax: 01809 501400). Fine Scottish produce and a well-stocked bar in a distinctive Victorian building, amidst the beautiful scenery of the Scottish Highlands. Ten comfortable en suite rooms. [ ]
e-mail: hotel@invergarry.net website: www.invergarry.net/hotel

Inverness

Capital of the Highlands. Lively tourist centre and good base for visiting local attractions.

COUL HOUSE HOTEL, CONTIN, BY STRATHPEFFER IV14 9ES (01997 421487; Fax: 01997 421945). Hamish, our lovable labrador looks forward to welcoming you. "Taste of Scotland" food, log fires, well-equipped bedrooms. Miles of wonderful walks. STB ★★★★ Hotel. [pw!]
e-mail: coulhouse@bestwestern.co.uk website: www.milford.co.uk/go/coulhouse

Kincraig (Inverness-shire)

Attractive Highland village close to Loch Insh and Glenfeshie, midway between Aviemore and Kingussie.

NICK & PATSY THOMPSON, INSH HOUSE GUESTHOUSE AND SELF-CATERING COTTAGES, KINCRAIG, NEAR KINGUSSIE PH21 1NU (01540 651377). B&B in 1827 Telford Manse and two timber s/c cottages in superb rural location. Ideal for many outdoor activities and good touring base. Dogs and children welcome. STB ★★★. [ ]
e-mail: inshhouse@btinternet.com website: www.kincraig.com/inshhouse

Kingussie (Inverness-shire)

Tourist centre on the River Spey 28 miles south of Inverness.

COLUMBA HOUSE HOTEL AND GARDEN RESTAURANT, MANSE ROAD, KINGUSSIE PH21 1JF (01540 661402; Fax: 01540 661652). Quiet Highland retreat offering highest standards of hospitality, care and accommodation. Candlelit Garden Restaurant. Ground-floor rooms with own front doors, perfect for doggie holidays. AA ◆◆◆◆, STB ★★★. [pw! Pets £5 per night, £15 per week]
e-mail: pets@columbahousehotel.com website: www.columbahousehotel.com

FREE or REDUCED RATE entry to Holiday Visits and Attractions — see our READERS' OFFER VOUCHERS on pages 101-116

Lairg (Sutherland)

Resort and salmon fishing village at south east end of Loch Shin in Sutherland district. 17 miles west of Golspie on the east coast. Many ancient sites to be seen in surrounding hills.

THE NIP INN HOTEL, MAIN ST, LAIRG IV27 4DB (01549 402243: Fax: 01549 402593). The perfect setting for a comfortable bed and breakfast break. Reflections Restaurant offers varied and interesting menus. Wedding, conference and function facilities available. A perfect base for exploring the far north of Scotland. STB ★★★ [🐕]
website: www.nipinn.co.uk/

Lochcarron (Ross-shire)

Village on north shore of Loch Carron 2 miles below the head of the loch. Known for its ties and tartans.

THE COTTAGE, STROMECARRONACH, LOCHCARRON WEST, STRATHCARRON. Small, stone-built Highland cottage, double bedroom, shower room, open plan kitchen/living room, fully equipped. Panoramic views over Loch Carron and the mountains. For further details please phone. MRS A.G. MACKENZIE, STROMECARRONACH, LOCHCARRON WEST, STRATHCARRON IV54 8YH (01520 722284) [🐕]
website: www.lochcarron.org

Loch Ness (Inverness-shire)

Home of 'Nessie', extending for 23 miles from Fort Agustus to south of Inverness.

DAVID AND PATRICIA ALLEN, WILDSIDE HIGHLAND LODGES, WILDSIDE, WHITEBRIDGE, INVERNESS IV2 6UN. (01456 486373; Fax: 01456 486371). Self-Catering. Cosy studio units built for two. Exceptional riverside lodges for up to six. Some with log fires. Open all year round, with free central heating. Mini-breaks available and pets welcome. See our colour brochure or visit our website. STB ★★★★ Self-catering. [Pets £15 per booking].
e-mail: info@wildsidelodges.com website: www.wildsidelodges.com

Self-catering cottages all around Loch Ness plus small selection of West coast properties. Pets welcome. Please see website for details or for a brochure contact: GORDON & CORINNE ROBERTS, ROEBUCK COTTAGE, ERROGIE, STRATHERRICK, INVERNESS-SHIRE IV2 6UH (Tel & Fax: 01456 486358). [1 dog free, extra dogs £10 each per week]
e-mail: corinne@wildernesscottages.co.uk website: www.wildernesscottages.co.uk

Nethy Bridge (Inverness-shire)

Popular Strathspey resort on River Nethy with extensive Abernethy Forest to the south. Impressive mountain scenery. Grantown-on-Spey 5 miles.

MONDHUIE CHALETS & B&B, NETHY BRIDGE, INVERNESS-SHIRE PH25 3DF (Tel & Fax: 01479 821062). Situated in the country between Aviemore and Grantown-on-Spey, two comfortable, self-catering chalets, or you can have Dinner, B&B in the house. A warm welcome awaits you. Pets welcome. [🐕]
e-mail: david@mondhuie.com website: www.mondhuie.com

Newtonmore (Inverness-shire)

Village on River Spey. 3 miles west of Kingussie. Holiday and ski centre. Clan Macpherson Museum..

CRUBENBEG FARM HOLIDAY COTTAGES, NEWTONMORE PH20 1BE (01540 673566; Fax: 01540 673509). Comfortable 4 Star country cottages in idyllic surroundings in the Cairngorm National Park. Lots of lovely walks, loads of sporting activities or simply relax and spot the wildlife around you. STB ★★★★ [Pets £15 per week]
e-mail: enquiry@crubenbeg.com website: www.crubenbeg.com

Onich

On shores of Loch Linnhe. Good boating, fishing. Fort William 10 miles.

INCHREE HOLIDAY CENTRE, ONICH, FORT WILLIAM PH33 6SE (Tel & Fax: 01855 821287). Between Ben Nevis and Glencoe. 8 self-catering chalets, 4 or 6 berth. Bistro and bar on site. 10% discount for couples. Short-stay breaks available most of the year. [Pets £20 per week]
e-mail: enquiry@inchreecentre.co.uk website: www.inchreecentre.co.uk

Poolewe (Ross-shire)

Village lying between Lochs Ewe and Maree with the river Ewe flowing through.

MR A. URQHART, CROFTERS COTTAGES, 15 CROFT, POOLEWE IV22 2JY (01445 781 268; Fax: 01445 781704). Three traditional cottages situated in a scenic and tranquil area, ideal for a "get away from it all" holiday. Comfortably furnished with all mod cons. [🐕]
e-mail: croftcottages@btopenworld.com website: www.croftcottages.btinternet.co.uk

Rhiconich (Sutherland)

Locality at the head of Loch Inchard on west coast of Sutherland District.

LYNN & GRAHAM, GULL COTTAGE, ACHRIESGILL, RHICONICH, SUTHERLAND IV27 4RJ (01971 521717). High quality accommodation on the wild and unspoilt west coast. Superb scenery and excellent walks on mountains, moors and beaches. Pets welcome under firm control. STB ★★★ Self-Catering. Also B&B available. [🐕]

RHICONICH HOTEL, SUTHERLAND, N. W. HIGHLANDS IV27 4RN (01971 521224; Fax: 01971 521732). She's your best friend so why leave her at home, bring her to Rhiconich Hotel, she'll be made equally as welcome as you will. A place where we put service, hospitality and really fresh food as a priority, but why don't you come and see for yourself? For further details contact Jasmine Campbell. STB ★★★ [🐕]
e-mail: rhiconichhotel@aol.com website: www.rhiconichhotel.co.uk

Spean Bridge (Inverness-shire)

Village on River Spean at foot of Loch Lochy. Site of WWII Commando Memorial.

RIVERSIDE LODGES, INVERGLOY, SPEAN BRIDGE PH34 4DY (01397 712684). Peace and quiet. Three lodges, each sleep 6 in 12 acres of woodland garden on Loch Lochy. Free fishing. Open all year. Pets welcome. Brochure on request. [🐕]
e-mail: enquiries@riversidelodge.org.uk website: www.riversidelodge.org.uk

Tain (Ross-shire)

Small town in Ross & Cromarty district on south shore of Dornoch Firth. Invergordon 10 miles..

CALEDONIAN HOTEL, BEACH FRONT, PORTMAHOMACK, BY TAIN, ROSS-SHIRE IV20 1YS (01862 871345; Fax: 01862 871757). Family-run hotel overlooking sandy beach. Magnificent views across Dornoch Firth. Watersports, golf close by. Regular live music. Children welcome. Horse riding available for experienced riders. STB ★★★ Hotel.
e-mail: info@caleyhotel.co.uk website: www.caleyhotel.co.uk

Tongue (Sutherland)

Village near north coast of Caithness District on east side of Kyle of Tongue.

BORGIE LODGE HOTEL, SKERRAY, TONGUE KW14 7TH (Tel & Fax: 01641 521332). Set in a secluded Highland glen lies Borgie Lodge. Try pony trekking, cycling and fishing. Sammy and Susie, Borgie Lodge pets, would like to make new friends. STB ★★★★ [🐕]
e-mail: info@borgielodgehotel.co.uk website: www.borgielodgehotel.co.uk

LANARKSHIRE

CARMICHAEL COUNTRY COTTAGES ★★ – ★★★★ *SELF-CATERING*

CARMICHAEL ESTATE, BY BIGGAR, LANARKSHIRE ML12 6PG

Tel: 01899 308336 • Fax: 01899 308481

website: www.carmichael.co.uk/cottages • e-mail:chiefcarm@aol.com

Our Stone Cottages nestle in the woods and fields of our Historic Family-run Estate. Ideal homes for families, pets and particularly dogs. Walking trails, private tennis, fishing, restaurant/farm shop. 15 cottages, 32 bedrooms. Open all year. Central location. £180 to £550 per week.

Blair Mains Farm, Harthill ML7 5TJ Tel: 01501 751278

Attractive farmhouse on small farm of 72 acres. Immediately adjacent to Junction 5 of M8 motorway. Ideal centre for touring, with Edinburgh, Glasgow, Stirling 30 minutes' drive. One double, three twin, one single (three en suite); bathroom; sittingroom, diningroom; sun porch. Central heating. Children welcome. Pets welcome. Ample grounds for walking. Car essential – parking. Bed and Breakfast from £18; weekly rates available. Reduced rates for children. Open all year.

e-mail: heather@blairmains.freeserve.co.uk **website: www.blairmains.co.uk**

Biggar

Small town set round broad main street. Gasworks museum, puppet theatre seating 100, street museum displaying old shop fronts and interiors. Peebles 13 miles.

CARMICHAEL COUNTRY COTTAGES, CARMICHAEL ESTATE, BY BIGGAR ML12 6PG (01899 308336; Fax: 01899 308481). Our stone cottages nestle in the woods and fields of our historic family-run estate. Ideal homes for families, pets and dogs. 15 cottages, 32 bedrooms. STB ★★/★★★★ Self catering. Open all year. £180 to £550 per week. [pw! 🐕]
e-mail: chiefcarm@aol.com website: www.carmichael.co.uk/cottages

Harthill

Village 5 miles south-west of Bathgate.

MRS STEPHENS, BLAIR MAINS FARM, HARTHILL ML7 5TJ (01501 751278; Fax: 01501 753383). Attractive farmhouse on small farm. Ideal for touring. Children welcome. Bed and Breakfast from £18; weekly rates available. Reduced rates for children. Open all year. [🐕]
e-mail: heather@blairmains.freeserve.co.uk website: www.blairmains.co.uk

Readers are requested to mention this guidebook when seeking accommodation (and please enclose a stamped addressed envelope).

Loch Tay Lodges
PERTHSHIRE

STB ★★★★ Self Catering **Acharn, By Aberfeldy**

Escape the rat race in comfort, peace and tranquillity. Loch, woodlands and mountains on the doorstep. £210-£520 per house per week.

Tel: 01887 830209 • Fax: 01887 830802

e-mail: remony@btinternet.com • www.lochtaylodges.co.uk

PERTHSHIRE AND CENTRAL HIGHLANDS

★ A choice of 1-3 bedroom self-catering Scandinavian-style chalets in 2 acres parkland, only 5 minutes' walk from shops and town centre.★ OPEN ALL YEAR. Spring/Autumn Short Breaks welcome in warm, fully equipped, comfortable accommodation. Colour TV, Tennis, Children's amenities on site. ★ Ideal centre for touring in all directions. Golf (40 courses within an hour's drive), walking and fishing holidays. ★ Credit cards accepted. ★ Pets £1.80 per night, ★ Senior Citizen offers ★ Children half price.

For detailed brochure and bookings, please write or telephone:

ALTAMOUNT CHALETS, BLAIRGOWRIE, PERTHSHIRE PH10 6JN

Tel: (01250) 873324 website: www.altamountchalets.co.uk

The Highland House Hotel **South Church Street, Callander FK17 8BN**

Tel: 01877 330269 • Fax: 01877 339004 • E-mail: highland.house.hotel@lineone.net

This Georgian town house built around 1790 is now a private hotel run under the personal supervision of Lorna and Robert Leckie. All our nine bedrooms have en suite facilities and are tastefully decorated. Each room benefits from colour TV, hospitality trays and full central heating. Relax in our comfortable lounge, enjoy evening meals and why not sample a wee dram in our cosy intimate bar. Whatever your choice you will be assured of a friendly atmosphere and a warm welcome. B&B £20-£25pp; Room only £17-£20pp. • **www.highlandhouseincallander.co.uk**

Lynne and Alistair Ferguson, 43 Fingal Road, Killin, Perthshire FK21 8XA

Tel: 01877 330638 • e-mail: alifer@msn.com • ***'Good Walkies Area'***

Situated in a quiet cul-de-sac, but only a few minutes' stroll to the village, the park and the hills. Killin is a small, tranquil village in the heart of Highland Perthshire. It is surrounded by mountains and glens, rivers and lochs. Gateway to the Loch Lomond and Trossachs National Park, Killin is famous for the Falls of Dochart, Loch Tay and Ben Lawers. We offer a varied Scottish Breakfast. We have one double, one twin, and one family room, all with central heating, a tea/coffee maker and en suite or private bathroom. Bed and Breakfast from £22 per person per night; single use of rooms from £27 per person per night. Details on request. Ideal touring base, with walking, climbing, cycling, fishing, sailing, golfing, tennis, touring and sightseeing all nearby. (Until 2004 we owned Roslin Cottage in Callander, so if you tried us there, then come and see us in our new home).

Your dogs can sleep in your room, and are welcome in the sitting room and garden.

REDUCED RATES for 3+ days **DOGS ESPECIALLY WELCOME** *(and stay free)*

Wester Lix, near Killin, Perthshire, five cottages for groups of four to ten. Family-run. Remote location set in nine acres with private Lochan. Excellent base for walking, hill climbing, mountain biking, and water sports, or touring and sight seeing. Sky TV in four cottages. Sauna in Steading. Private decking area on two cottages. STB ★★★ ASSC Member

Gill & Dave Hunt, Wester Lix, Killin, Perthshire FK21 8RD

Tel: 01567 820 990 or 07747 862641 • Fax: 01567 820093 • E-mail: gill@westerlix.co.uk • Website: www.westerlix.co.uk

Terms quoted in this publication may be subject to increase if rises in costs necessitate

The Luggie *Kirkmichael.* Well-equipped two-bedroom mid-terrace cottage with enclosed garden and small private terrace with barbecue and garden furniture. Full central heating throughout. Pets welcome. Golf and fishing trips can be arranged and horse riding is available locally.

Scottish Tourist Board ★★★ Self Catering

Contact: **George and Andrea Hay, 3 Rosemount Place, Perth PH2 7EH**
Telephone & Fax: 01738 625240 • Mobile: 07968 059669
e-mail: andrea.hay@blueyonder.co.uk • website: www.assc.co.uk/luggie

STUNNINGLY BEAUTIFUL SCOTTISH MOUNTAIN AND LOCH SCENERY AT ITS VERY BEST – ALL AT ONCE

Situated halfway along the side of Loch Tay between Killin and Kenmore, just an hour north of Perth or Stirling, The Ben Lawers Hotel is an ideal base for exploring Scotland's dramatic Central Highlands and the beautiful East and West coasts, Glen Coe, Aviemore, Oban and more. A small rural hotel (5 en suite rooms) with a good local and tourist trade for quality food and drink, and important factors such as a welcoming and friendly atmosphere for everybody, including families, pets and real ale drinkers! (always one or two real ales). The hotel has been in the current owners' hands for 8 years now, and is continually being upgraded. Please visit our website or telephone/e-mail. Terms £27.50pp. Pets no charge.

BEN LAWERS HOTEL, LAWERS, ABERFELDY/KILLIN PH15 2PA
Tel: 01567 820436 • Fax: 0870 7065828
e-mail: petswelcome@benlawershotel.co.uk • www.tayside-inn.co.uk

---

Balrobin Hotel

STB ★★★ Hotel

Pitlochry PH16 5HT • Tel: 01796 472901 • Fax: 01796 474200 • www.balrobin.co.uk

AA & RAC ★★ Scottish Country House Hotel. 15 en suite rooms, most with panoramic views, yet close to the town centre. Non-smoking. Owned and run by the Hohman family at value-for-money prices. Ideal for short or longer breaks. **e-mail:info@balrobin.co.uk**

The finest lochside location in the Southern Highlands
Meall Reamhar Restaurant for fine dining and Tarken Room

offer imaginative modern European cuisine using only the best fresh Scottish produce.

Well placed to enjoy many excellent days out within the area or further afield.

Hey, Sham here, now into the second year at the hotel, and I am getting a bit better at this advertising thing. The dictation is easy. My thoughts flow, of course, along the walking and food line. I have taken Andrew (and Mary) for many a wonderful walk, there is so much choice in our great outdoors. My chef has this year introduced a new menu for dog guests, and though the AA inspectors would not give it the two Red Rosettes, I am told that it is excellent and freshly prepared. We (both) offer you a warm welcome and friendly service.

The Four Seasons Hotel
St Fillans, Perthshire PH6 2NF
Tel: 01764 685333 e-mail: sham@thefourseasonshotel.co.uk

See also Colour Advert on page 66

Aberfeldy

Small town standing on both sides of Uriar Burn near its confluence with the River Tay. Pitlochry 8 miles.

LOCH TAY LODGES, REMONY, ACHARN, ABERFELDY PH15 2HR (01887 830209). Enjoy hill walking, golf, sailing or touring. Salmon and trout fishing available. Log fires. Pets welcome. Walks along loch shore from house. STB ★★★★ SELF CATERING in village close to Loch. For brochure, contact MRS P. W. DUNCAN MILLAR at above address. [🐕]
e-mail: remony@btinternet.com website: www.lochtaylodges.co.uk

Blairgowrie

Town on the River Ericht 17 miles north west of Dundee.

ALTAMOUNT CHALETS, COUPAR ANGUS ROAD, BLAIRGOWRIE PH10 6JN (01250 873324; Fax: 01250 872464). Modern, fully equipped 1, 2 and 3 bedroom Scandinavian-style Chalets. Colour television. Centrally situated for touring Highlands. Children's amenities on site. Pets welcome. [Pets £1.80 per night].
e-mail: alastair@altamountchalets.co.uk website: www.altamountchalets.co.uk

Callander

Good base for walks and drives around the Trossachs and Loch Katrine. Stirling 14 miles.

LORNA AND ROBERT LECKIE, THE HIGHLAND HOUSE HOTEL, SOUTH CHURCH STREET, CALLANDER FK17 8BN (01877 330269; Fax: 01877 339004). Georgian town house built around 1790. Nine en suite bedrooms with colour TV, hospitality trays and full central heating. Comfortable lounge, evening meals, residents bar. B&B £20-£25 pp; Room only £17-£20 pp. [🐕]
e-mail: highland.house.hotel@lineone.net website: www.highlandhouseincallander.co.uk

Killin

Village at confluence of Rivers Dochart and Lochay at head of Loch Tay.

GILL & DAVE HUNT, WESTER LIX HOLIDAY COTTAGES, WESTER LIX, KILLIN FK21 8RD (01567 820 990 & 07747 862641; Fax: 01567 820093). All cottages are decorated and equipped to a high standard. All cottages have washing machines, freezers, oven, four have sky TV etc. Well behaved pets welcome by arrangement. STB ★★★ SELF-CATERING. ASSC Member. [Pets £15 per week for first pet, then £5 per pet for others]
e-mail: gill@westerlix.co.uk website: www.westerlix.co.uk

LYNNE AND ALISTAIR FERGUSON, 43 FINGAL ROAD, KILLIN FK21 8XA (01877 330638). Bed and varied Scottish Breakfast in small, tranquil village in the heart of Highland Perthshire. Ideal touring base. "Good walkies area" – dogs are especially welcome and stay free. [🐕 pw!]
e-mail: alifer@msn.com

Kinloch Rannoch

Village at foot of Loch Rannoch.

KILVRECHT CAMP SITE, KINLOCH RANNOCH, PERTHSHIRE (01350 727284; Fax: 01350 727811). Secluded campsite on a level open area in quiet, secluded woodland setting. Fishing available for brown trout on Loch Rannoch. Several trails begin from campsite. Please write, fax or telephone for further information. [🐕]
e-mail: hamish.murray@forestry.gsi.gov.uk

Kirkmichael

A village situated between Glenshee and Blairgorie, 9 miles east of Pitlochry. Settlements here believed to date from 200 BC.

THE LUGGIE, KIRKMICHAEL. Well-equipped mid-terrace cottage. One double and one twin bedroom. Full central heating. Enclosed garden. Golf, fishing trips, horse riding available locally. STB ★★★ Self-catering. Contact: GEORGE AND ANDREA HAY, 3 ROSEMOUNT PLACE, PERTH PH2 7EH (Tel & Fax: 01738 625240; Mobile: 07968 059669) [🐕]
e-mail: andrea.hay@blueyonder.co.uk website: www.assc.co.uk/luggie

Loch Tay

15 miles long loch stretching from Killin in the south west to Kenmore in the north east.

BEN LAWERS HOTEL, LAWERS, ABERFELDY/KILLIN PH15 2PA (01567 820436). Welcoming and friendly hotel between mountain and loch in beautiful area. Good reputation for food, licensed bar with real ales. Central location. Well-behaved dogs welcome. [🐕]
e-mail: petswelcome@benlawershotel.co.uk website: www.tayside-inn.co.uk

Pitlochry

Popular resort on River Tummel in beautiful Perthshire Highlands. Excellent golf, loch and river fishing. Famous for summer Festival Theatre; distillery, Highland Games.

JACKY & MALCOLM CATTERALL, "TULLOCH", ENOCHDHU, BY KIRKMICHAEL, PITLOCHRY PH10 7PW (01250 881404; Fax: 01250 881304). Former farmhouse offers comfortable accommodation and good food. One family room with washbasin, one twin with washbasin; one en suite double room. All have tea/coffee making facilities and face open country to mountains beyond. Peace and quiet guaranteed. B&B from £20; Dinner if required from £10. Haven for wildlife and dogs. STB ★★★. [🐕]
e-mail: maljac@tulloch83.freeserve.co.uk website: www.maljac.com

BALROBIN HOTEL, HIGHER OAKFIELD, PITLOCHRY PH16 5HT (01796 472901; Fax: 01796 474200). Scottish Country House Hotel. 15 en suite rooms, most with panoramic views, yet close to the town centre. Non-smoking. Owned and run by the Hohman family at value-for-money prices. [🐕]
e-mail: info@balrobin.co.uk website: www.balrobin.co.uk

St Fillans

Village at foot of Lochearn, 5 miles west of Comrie.

THE FOUR SEASONS HOTEL, ST FILLANS PH6 2NF (01764 685333). Ideal holiday venue for pets and their owners. Spectacular Highland scenery, walking, fishing, watersports. Wonderful food. Full details on request. STB ★★★ Hotel, AA ★★★ and 2 Red Rosettes, RAC ★★★ Highly Recommended, Which? Hotel Guide, Good Hotel Guide, Johansens, Best Loved Hotels. [🐕]
e-mail: sham@thefourseasonshotel.co.uk website: www.thefourseasonshotel.co.uk

Strathyre

Village set in middle of Strathyre Forest, just off A84 north of Callander. Information centre and picnic area.

ARDOCH LODGE, STRATHYRE (01877 384666). Log cabins and cottage in wonderful mountain scenery. Comfortably furnished and fully equipped. Country house accommodation also available. Phone for brochure. Open all year. Pets most welcome. STB ★★★★ [pw! 🐕]

MUNRO INN, STRATHYRE FK18 8NA (01877 384333). Jules (and her pal Jess) warmly welcome doggy friends to the Munro Inn in beautiful Highland Perthshire. Perfect base for walking, cycling, climbing, watersports, fishing and relaxing! [🐕]
website: www.munro-inn.com

FREE or REDUCED RATE entry to Holiday Visits and Attractions — see our READERS' OFFER VOUCHERS on pages 101-116

When making enquiries or bookings, a stamped addressed envelope is always appreciated

Gruline

"Torlochan" • Isle of Mull A small croft in the centre of the Isle of Mull, with panoramic views over Loch na Keal. An ideal place where you can relax and enjoy our variety of animals. We have two comfortable and spacious log cabins which are well fitted. They can sleep 4-6 people. We also have a smaller log cabin for bed and breakfast brought to your door. Self catering from £330 per week. Short breaks from £45 per night off season. B&B £21 per person. PETS FREE OF CHARGE.

Mrs Emily van Rhyn, "Torlochan", Gruline, Isle of Mull, Argyll PA71 6HR • Tel/Fax: 01680 300380
e-mail: torlochan@btopenworld.com • website: www.torlochan.com

See also Colour Advertisement on page 66

Gruline

Locality at the head of Loch na Keal, 3 miles south-west of Salen.

TORLOCHAN, GRULINE, ISLE OF MULL PA71 6HR (Tel & Fax: 01680 300380). Situated in centre of Mull. Panoramic views over Loch na Keal. Working croft of 33 acres, Two Log Cabins for self-catering and en suite Bed & Breakfast. Friendly welcome awaits. Pets free of charge.[🐕]
e-mail: torlochan@btopenworld.com website: www.torlochan.com

ISLE OF SKYE

Breakish, Portree

Tigh Holm Cottages, *Sculamus Moss, Breakish IV42 8QB*
Furnished to a very high standard, the location and comfort make these cottages ideal for exploring the Misty Isle. Open plan spacious ground floor with all modern appliances, upper level comprises bathroom with shower, one twin and one double bedroom. Restaurants and bars within walking distance. Terms from £195 - £395.
Telephone: 01471 822848 • Fax: 01471 822328 • e-mail: info@tigh-holm-cottages.com

Trotternish
Isle of Skye IV51 9UF

tel: 01470 552213 • e-mail: info@duntulmcastle.co.uk • www.duntulmcastle.co.uk

excellent value hotel accommodation

Duntulm Castle Hotel offers comfortable yet excellent value accommodation which includes a generous full Scottish breakfast. Single, double, twin and family bedrooms available.

• Many rooms with sea view • Tea/coffee making facilities, colour TV • Bar and conservatory meals • Fully licensed with Skye real ales • Children welcome

See also Colour Advertisement on page 66

Breakish

Location 2 miles east of Broadford on the Isle of Skye

TIGH HOLM COTTAGES, SCULAMUS MOSS, BREAKISH IV42 8QB (01471 822848; Fax: 01471 822328). Open plan spacious ground floor with all modern appliances. Upper level comprises bathroom with shower, one twin and one double bedroom. All bedding and linen supplied, electricity included. [🐕]
e-mail: info@tigh-holm-cottages.com

Portree

Port and chief town on the Isle of Skye.

DUNTULM CASTLE HOTEL, TROTTERNISH IV51 9UF (01470 552213). Comfortable, excellent value accommodation; many rooms with sea view. Fully licensed; bar and conservatory meals. Children welcome. STB ★ Hotel.
e-mail: info@duntulmcastle.co.uk website: www.duntulmcastle.co.uk

Staffin

Crofting and fishing village on rocky coast around Staffin bay, 12 miles north of Portree.

IAN STRATTON & DOREEN HARBEN, GLENVIEW HOTEL, CULNACNOC, STAFFIN IV51 9JH (01470 562248; Fax: 01470 562211). Traditional island house, ideally situated for exploring North East Skye. Comfortable en suite bedrooms. Restaurant renowned for fresh seafood and traditional home cooking. Dogs most welcome. WHICH? Best B&B. [🐕]
e-mail: enquiries@glenviewskye.co.uk website: www.glenviewskye.co.uk

• • *Some Useful Guidance for Guests and Hosts* • •

Every year literally thousands of holidays, short breaks and overnight stops are arranged through our guides, the vast majority without any problems at all. In a handful of cases, however, difficulties do arise about bookings, which often could have been prevented from the outset.
It is important to remember that when accommodation has been booked, both parties – guests and hosts – have entered into a form of contract. We hope that the following points will provide helpful guidance.

GUESTS:

- When enquiring about accommodation, be as precise as possible. Give exact dates, numbers in your party and the ages of any children.
- State the number and type of rooms wanted and also what catering you require – bed and breakfast, full board etc. Make sure that the position about evening meals is clear – and about pets, reductions for children or any other special points.
- Read our reviews carefully to ensure that the proprietors you are going to contact can supply what you want. Ask for a letter confirming all arrangements, if possible.
- If you have to cancel, do so as soon as possible. Proprietors do have the right to retain deposits and under certain circumstances to charge for cancelled holidays if adequate notice is not given and they cannot re-let the accommodation.

HOSTS:

- Give details about your facilities and about any special conditions. Explain your deposit system clearly and arrangements for cancellations, charges etc. and whether or not your terms include VAT.
- If for any reason you are unable to fulfil an agreed booking without adequate notice, you may be under an obligation to arrange suitable alternative accommodation or to make some form of compensation.

While every effort is made to ensure accuracy, we regret that FHG Publications cannot accept responsibility for errors, omissions or misrepresentations in our entries or any consequences thereof. Prices in particular should be checked because we go to press early. We will follow up complaints but cannot act as arbiters or agents for either party.

Ratings You Can Trust

ENGLAND

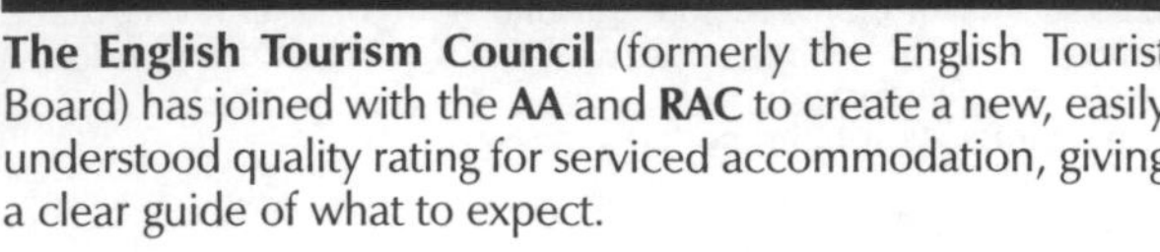

The English Tourism Council (formerly the English Tourist Board) has joined with the **AA** and **RAC** to create a new, easily understood quality rating for serviced accommodation, giving a clear guide of what to expect.

HOTELS are given a rating from One to Five **Stars** – the more Stars, the higher the quality and the greater the range of facilities and level of services provided.

GUEST ACCOMMODATION, which includes guest houses, bed and breakfasts, inns and farmhouses, is rated from One to Five **Diamonds**. Progressively higher levels of quality and customer care must be provided for each one of the One to Five Diamond ratings.

HOLIDAY PARKS, TOURING PARKS and CAMPING PARKS are now also assessed using **Stars**. Standards of quality range from a One Star (acceptable) to a Five Star (exceptional) park.

Look out also for the new **SELF-CATERING** Star ratings. The more **Stars** (from One to Five) awarded to an establishment, the higher the levels of quality you can expect. Establishments at higher rating levels also have to meet some additional requirements for facilities.

SCOTLAND

Star Quality Grades will reflect the most important aspects of a visit, such as the warmth of welcome, efficiency and friendliness of service, the quality of the food and the cleanliness and condition of the furnishings, fittings and decor.

THE MORE STARS, THE HIGHER THE STANDARDS.

The description, such as Hotel, Guest House, Bed and Breakfast, Lodge, Holiday Park, Self-catering etc tells you the type of property and style of operation.

WALES

Places which score highly will have an especially welcoming atmosphere and pleasing ambience, high levels of comfort and guest care, and attractive surroundings enhanced by thoughtful design and attention to detail

STAR QUALITY GUIDE FOR

HOTELS, GUEST HOUSES AND FARMHOUSES

SELF-CATERING ACCOMMODATION
(Cottages, Apartments, Houses)

CARAVAN HOLIDAY HOME PARKS
(Holiday Parks, Touring Parks, Camping Parks)

★★★★★ *Exceptional quality*
★★★★ *Excellent quality*
★★★ *Very good quality*
★★ *Good quality*
★ *Fair to good quality*

In England, Scotland and Wales, all graded properties are inspected annually by Tourist Authority trained Assessors.

1st Choice

Selected cottages throughout Wales, Shropshire, Cotswolds & Peak District

Pets Welcome • Low Prices

free brochure **08700 718 718**

recommended-cottages.co.uk

MR P.W. REES, "QUALITY COTTAGES', CERBID, SOLVA, HAVERFORDWEST, PEMBROKESHIRE SA62 6YE (01348 837871). Cottages set in all coastal areas, unashamed luxury, highest residential standards. Dishwashers, microwaves, washing machines. Log fires. Linen supplied. Pets welcome. [pw! 🐕]
website: www.qualitycottages.co.uk

RECOMMENDED COTTAGE HOLIDAYS. 1st Choice for dream cottages at very competitive prices in all holiday regions of beautiful Britain. Pets welcome. All properties inspected. For a brochure call: 08700 718718.
website: www.recommended-cottages.co.uk

ANGLESEY & GWYNEDD

Aberdovey, Caernarfon, Criccieth

Aberdovey Hillside Village
Tel: 01654 767522
Fax: 01654 767069
www.hillsidevillage.co.uk
info@hillsidevillage.co.uk

A cluster of specially designed houses and apartments overlooking Aberdovey. Shops and beaches are within 300 yards. Properties sleep 4/6/8.

• Short breaks available • Dogs welcome • Ideal for family holidays
• Terms inclusive of heating (Oct - June) and electricity - no coin meters.

Colour Brochure from Aberdovey Hillside Village, Aberdovey, Gwynedd LL35 0ND

See also Colour Advertisement on page 67

Plas-Y-Bryn Chalet Park Bontnewydd, Near Caernarfon LL54 7YE (01286 672811)

Our small park is situated two miles from the historic town of Caernarfon. Set into a walled garden it offers safety, seclusion and beautiful views of Snowdonia. It is ideally positioned for touring the area. Shop and village pub nearby. A selection of chalets and caravans available at prices from £110 (low season) to £390 (high season) per week for the caravans and £110 (low season) to £295 (high season) per week for the chalets. Well behaved pets always welcome.

WTB ★★★★ **website: www.plasybrynholidayscaernarfon.co.uk**

Rhos Country Cottages

Quality self-catering. Traditional cosy cottages in an idyllic setting which enjoy their very own quiet seclusion away from the crowds. 4½ miles from Criccieth and the beach.

Olde Worlde Charm and Character with oak beams, inglenook fireplace, log fires, antiques and lovely country furnishings. Some have four-poster beds, own snooker table, sauna or jacuzzi. Open all year. Always warm and inviting with home from home comforts.

Rhos Country Cottages, Ynys, Criccieth, Gwynedd LL52 0PB
Telephone & Fax: 01758 720047 E-mail: cottages@rhos.freeserve.co.uk
Website: www.rhos-cottages.co.uk **WTB★★★★★**

Tai Gwyliau DWYFACH Country Cottages

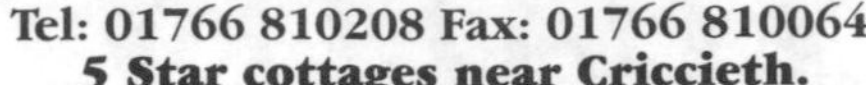

Tel: 01766 810208 Fax: 01766 810064

5 Star cottages near Criccieth.

Our luxury cottages are set in peaceful, beautiful countryside with stunning views of Cardigan Bay and Snowdonia. They are superbly equipped with dishwasher, microwave, washer/dryer, C/H, linen and barbecue. With numerous attractions, country walks, leisure centres, fishing and beaches nearby this is the ideal place to unwind and relax. Special rates off season. Exciting choice of eating places. Enquiries and brochure:

S. Edwards, Pen-y-Bryn, Chwilog, Pwllheli, Gwynedd LL53 6SX

e-mail: llyredwards@ukonline.co.uk

website: www.dwyfach.co.uk

PARC WERNOL PARK **Chwilog, Pwllheli, Gwynedd LL53 6SW (01766 810506)**

• Panoramic views • Peaceful and quiet • Ideal for touring Lleyn and Snowdonia • 4 miles Criccieth and Pwllheli • 3 miles beach • Cycle route • Free coarse fishing lake • Safe children's play area • Games room • Footpaths • Dog exercise field • Self-catering holidays • 3 bedroom farmhouse • 2 and 3 bedroom caravans and chalets • Colour brochure • Personal attention at all times • A truly Welsh welcome. **www.wernol.com**

See also Colour Advertisement on page 00

Gwesty Minffordd Hotel

Talyllyn LL36 9AJ

Tel: 01654 761665 Fax: 01654 761517

E-mail: hotel@minffordd.com; Website: www.minffordd.com

Small 17th century Drovers' Inn at the base of Cader Idris, ideal for 'walkies' or as a centre for touring. For the two-legged guest enjoy a Minffordd dinner, cooked on an Aga using local Welsh produce, organic vegetables, Welsh flavouring. Residential and restaurant licence; seven bedrooms all en suite, two ground floor.

Non-smoking. Pets welcome. No children under 12. Dolgellau six miles, Machynlleth eight miles, Cader Idris 2,697 ft. Hosts: **Gordon & Michelle Holt.**

WTB ★★★ AA ★★ • Founder Member Taste of Wales • Good Food Guide 2000

COASTAL HOUSE
TYWYN
GWYNEDD

Three bedrooms
Sleeps five
£179-£229
per week

- ❋ Two minutes' walk to sandy beach
- ❋ Two minutes' walk to pub/bar meals
- ❋ Fully equipped as own home
- ❋ Garden front and rear ❋ Garage
- ❋ Scenic and pleasant walking areas nearby
- ❋ Tal-y-Llyn Steam Railway walking distance
- ❋ Pets welcome FREE OF CHARGE

Enquiries: **Mr Ian Weston, 18 Elizabeth Road, Basingstoke, Hampshire RG22 6AX Tel: 01256 352364; 01256 412233 (evenings)**

e-mail: i.weston1@ntlworld.com

MR P.W. REES, "QUALITY COTTAGES', CERBID, SOLVA, HAVERFORDWEST, PEMBROKESHIRE SA62 6YE (01348 837871). Cottages set in all coastal areas, unashamed luxury, highest residential standards. Dishwashers, microwaves, washing machines. Log fires. Linen supplied. Pets welcome. [pw! 🐕]
website: www.qualitycottages.co.uk

Aberdovey

Small resort on north shore of River Dovey estuary, 9 miles west of Machynlleth.

ABERDOVEY HILLSIDE VILLAGE, ABERDOVEY LL35 0ND (01654 767522; Fax: 01654 767069). Houses and apartments (sleep 4/6/8) overlooking Aberdovey. Shops and beaches within 300 yards. Dogs welcome. Ideal for family holidays. No coin meters. Brochure.
e-mail: info@hillsidevillage.co.uk website: www.hillsidevillage.co.uk

Bala

Natural touring centre for Snowdonia. Narrow gauge railway runs along side of Bala lake, the largest natural lake in Wales. Golf, sailing, fishing, canoeing.

TALYBONT ISA - Self-catering twin-bedded studio-type annexe with bathroom with shower, colour TV, etc. TY GWYN - two-bedroomed luxury caravan in private grounds. Both situated just two miles from Bala in beautiful country area, ideal for walking, sailing, fishing and canoeing. Only 30 miles from seaside. Contact: MRS A. SKINNER, TY GWYN, RHYDUCHAF, BALA LL23 7SD(01678 521267 or 520234). [🐕]

Barmouth

Modern seaside resort with two miles of sandy beaches. Surrounding hills full of interesting archaeological remains.

LAWRENNY LODGE HOTEL, BARMOUTH LL42 1SU (01341 280466; Fax: 01341 281551). Quiet, family-run hotel overlooking harbour and estuary but only 5 minutes from town. Most rooms en suite, all with TV, tea/coffee making facilities and clock radio alarms. Restaurant menu includes vegetarian dishes. Residential licence. Large car park. WTB ★★ Hotel [🐕]

Beaumaris

Elegant little town dominated by castle built by Edward I in 13th century. Museum of Childhood has Victorian toys and music boxes.

MR P. W. REES, "QUALITY COTTAGES", CERBID, SOLVA, HAVERFORDWEST, PEMBROKESHIRE SA62 6YE (01348 837871). Cottages set in all coastal areas, unashamed luxury, highest residential standards. Dishwashers, microwaves, washing machines. Log fires. Linen supplied. Pets welcome. [pw! 🐕]
website: www.qualitycottages.co.uk

Bodorgan

A rural area in South West Anglesey.

MRS J. GUNDRY, FARMYARD LODGE, BODORGAN, ANGLESEY LL62 5LW (01407 840977). Comfortable three-bedroomed house. Enclosed garden. Near beaches, common, forest. Fully equipped, bedding and electricity inclusive. Colour TV/video, microwave. Dogs and children welcome. WTB ★★★★ [🐕]

Caernarfon

Historic walled town and resort, ideal for touring Snowdonia. Museums, Segontium Roman Fort, magnificent 13th century castle. Old harbour, sailing trips.

PLAS-Y-BRYN CHALET PARK, BONTNEWYDD, NEAR CAERNARFON LL54 7YE (01286 672811). Two miles from Caernarfon. It offers safety, seclusion and beautiful views of Snowdonia. Ideally positioned for touring. Well behaved pets always welcome. WTB ★★★★ [Pets £10 per week].
website: www.plasybrynholidayscaernarfon.co.uk

Criccieth

Popular family resort with safe beaches divided by ruins of 13th century castle. Salmon and sea trout fishing. Festival of Music and Arts in the summer.

MR P. W. REES, "QUALITY COTTAGES", CERBID, SOLVA, HAVERFORDWEST, PEMBROKESHIRE SA62 6YE (01348 837871). Cottages set in all coastal areas, unashamed luxury, highest residential standards. Dishwashers, microwaves, washing machines. Log fires. Linen supplied. Pets welcome. [pw! 🐕]
website: www.qualitycottages.co.uk

A warm welcome awaits you in comfortable self-catering cottages. Easily accessible to numerous attractions, or enjoy tranquillity of countryside. Short breaks available. Pets welcome. MRS M. WILLIAMS, GAERWEN FARM, YNYS, CRICCIETH, GWYNEDD LL52 0NU (01766 810324).
e-mail: gaerwen@btopenworld.com

MRS LENA HUGHES JONES, TYDDYN HEILYN, CHWILOG, CRICCIETH LL53 6SW (01766 810441). Cosy, comfortably renovated Welshstone country cottage with historic features, double glazing and centrally heated. Ramped french window entrance to en suite bedroom. Cardigan Bay sea views and mild Gulf Stream climate. Suitable parking and spacious garden, ideal for dogs. Three miles South Criccieth, on Llyn Peninsula and edge Snowdonia. Beautiful river walks amid wildlife, tree lined walks through farmland. Also Norwegian home to let, furnished. Open all year. [🐕]

MRS A. M. JONES, RHOS COUNTRY COTTAGES, YNYS, CRICCIETH LL52 0PB (Tel & Fax: 01758 720047/01766 810295). Quality self-catering, traditional cosy cottages in an idyllic setting with oak beams, inglenook fireplace, log fires, antiques and lovely country furnishings. Some have four-poster beds, own snooker table, sauna or jacuzzi. WTB★★★★★ [🐕]
e-mail: cottages@rhos.freeserve.co.uk website: www.rhos-cottages.co.uk

DWYFACH COUNTRY COTTAGES, NEAR CRICCIETH (01766 810208; Fax: 01766 810064). Five Star luxury cottages in the countryside with stunning views of Cardigan Bay and Snowdonia. Numerous attractions. Enquiries and brochure: S EDWARDS, PEN-Y-BRYN, CHWILOG, PWLLHELI, GWYNEDD LL53 6SX. [🐕]
e-mail: llyredwards@ukonline.co.uk website: www.dwyfach.co.uk

PARC WERNOL PARK, CHWILOG, PWLLHELI LL53 6SW (01766 810506). Peaceful and quiet, ideal for touring. Self-catering holidays – 3-bedroom farmhouse, 2 and 3 bedroom caravans and chalets. Colour brochure. [Pets £10 per week.]
website: www.wernol.com

Dulas Bay

On north-east coast of Anglesey, between Amlwch and Moelfre.

MRS G. McCREADIE, DERI ISAF, DULAS BAY LL70 9DX (01248 410536; Mobile: 077 21 374471). Beautiful Victorian Country House standing in 20 acres of woodland, gardens and fields. High standard of accommodation in two family rooms and one double all en suite. Pets welcome. Stabling/grazing available. ★★★★ [Pets £2 per night, £10 per week]
e-mail: mccreadie@deriisaf.freeserve.co.uk website: www.angleseyfarms.com

Dwyran

Village on Anglesey 2 miles east of Newborough.

JUDY HUTCHINGS, TAL-Y-FOEL STUD FARM AND RIDING CENTRE, DWYRAN, ANGLESEY LL61 6LQ (Tel & Fax: 01248 430377) Rural waterfront location with spectacular views of Snowdonia. Luxury en suite rooms with whirlpool baths and many facilities. Walking, birdwatching, fishing, riding and horse livery. Brochure on application. WTB ★★★★ FARM [🐕]
e-mail: enquiry@tal-y-foel.co.uk website: www.tal-y-foel.co.uk

Ffestiniog

Village 9 miles east of Porthmadog.

NEIL & MOIRA RICHARDS, SNOWDONIA HOLIDAYS LTD, PLAS BLAENDDOL, LLAN FFESTINIOG LL41 4PH (01766 762786; Fax: 01766 762796) Self-catering in beautiful Victorian manor house in the heart of Snowdonia. In nine acres of woodland, lake and gardens. Free booking service for a wide range of activities - quad biking, white water rafting, mountain biking, etc. Brochure on request. [Pets £18 per week]
e-mail: pw@snowdonia-holidays.co.uk website: www.snowdonia-holidays.co.uk

Harlech

Small stone-built town dominated by remains of 13th century castle. Golf, theatre, swimming pool, fine stretch of sands.

MR P. W. REES, "QUALITY COTTAGES", CERBID, SOLVA, HAVERFORDWEST, PEMBROKESHIRE SA62 6YE (01348 837871). Cottages set in all coastal areas, unashamed luxury, highest residential standards. Dishwashers, microwaves, washing machines. Log fires. Linen supplied. Pets welcome. [pw!]
website: www.qualitycottages.co.uk

Llanddona

Village on Anglesey 3 miles north west of Beaumaris.

MR P. W. REES, "QUALITY COTTAGES", CERBID, SOLVA, HAVERFORDWEST, PEMBROKESHIRE SA62 6YE (01348 837871). Cottages set in all coastal areas, unashamed luxury, highest residential standards. Dishwashers, microwaves, washing machines. Log fires. Linen supplied. Pets welcome. [pw!]
website: www.qualitycottages.co.uk

Llithfaen

Village 4 miles north-east of Nefyn.

LLITHFAEN. Traditional cottage set in picturesque rural area. Ideal base for walking or sightseeing. Open fire, garden, panoramic views. No smoking. Sleeps 4. Contact: MRS J. CHARLES (01723 363845). [ ]

Morfa Nefyn

Picturesque village 2 miles west of Nefyn.

MR P. W. REES, "QUALITY COTTAGES", CERBID, SOLVA, HAVERFORDWEST, PEMBROKESHIRE SA62 6YE (01348 837871). Cottages set in all coastal areas, unashamed luxury, highest residential standards. Dishwashers, microwaves, washing machines. Log fires. Linen supplied. Pets welcome. [pw!]
website: www.qualitycottages.co.uk

Porthmadog

Harbour town with mile-long Cob embankment, along which runs Ffestiniog Narrow Gauge Steam Railway to Blaenau Ffestiniog. Pottery, maritime museum, car museum. Good beaches nearby.

MR P. W. REES, "QUALITY COTTAGES", CERBID, SOLVA, HAVERFORDWEST, PEMBROKESHIRE SA62 6YE (01348 837871). Cottages set in all coastal areas, unashamed luxury, highest residential standards. Dishwashers, microwaves, washing machines. Log fires. Linen supplied. Pets welcome. [pw!]
website: www.qualitycottages.co.uk

Porth Neigel

Bay on south side of Lleyn peninsula, also known as Hell's Mouth.

Attractive cottage set in meadow near beach, quiet rural area. Sleeps 6, open fire, all comforts. Local carer. Near Abersoch. Details from MRS E.M. COOPER, 18 ST MARY'S LANE, LOUTH, LINCOLNSHIRE LN11 0DT (01507 604408 or 01507 354892).

Red Wharf Bay

Deep curving bay with vast expanse of sand, very popular for sailing and swimming.

MR P. W. REES, "QUALITY COTTAGES", CERBID, SOLVA, HAVERFORDWEST, PEMBROKESHIRE SA62 6YE (01348 837871). Cottages set in all coastal areas, unashamed luxury, highest residential standards. Dishwashers, microwaves, washing machines. Log fires. Linen supplied. Pets welcome. [pw! 🐕]
website: www.qualitycottages.co.uk

Talyllyn

Lake in course of River Dysynni, 2 miles south of summit of Cader Idris.

GWESTY MINFFORDD HOTEL, TALYLLYN LL36 9AJ (01654 761665; Fax: 01654 761517). Small 17th century Drovers' Inn at the base of Cader Idris, ideal for 'walkies' or as a centre for touring. Residential and restaurant licence; seven en suite bedrooms. WTB ★★★, AA ★★, Founder Member Taste of Wales, Good Food Guide 2000. [pw! £5 per night, £35 per week]
e-mail: hotel@minffordd.com website: www.minffordd.com

Tywyn

Pleasant seaside resort, start of Talyllyn Narrow Gauge Railway. Sea and river fishing, golf.

Fully equipped coastal house, close to sandy beach. 3 bedrooms, sleeps five. Gardens; garage. Pets welcome free of charge. APPLY – MR IAN WESTON, 18 ELIZABETH ROAD, BASINGSTOKE, HAMPSHIRE RG22 6AX (01256 352364; 01256 412233 evenings).[🐕]
e-mail: i.weston1@ntlworld.com

MR P. W. REES, "QUALITY COTTAGES", CERBID, SOLVA, HAVERFORDWEST, PEMBROKESHIRE SA62 6YE (01348 837871). Cottages set in all coastal areas, unashamed luxury, highest residential standards. Dishwashers, microwaves, washing machines. Log fires. Linen supplied. Pets welcome. [pw! 🐕]
website: www.qualitycottages.co.uk

PLEASE NOTE

All the information in this book is given in good faith in the belief that it is correct. However, the publishers cannot guarantee the facts given in these pages, neither are they responsible for changes in policy, ownership or terms that may take place after the date of going to press. Readers should always satisfy themselves that the facilities they require are available and that the terms, if quoted, still apply.

Seaside Cottages

In Idyllic North Wales

We have a large selection of self-catering seaside and country cottages, bungalows, farmhouses, caravans etc. offering superb, reasonably priced accommodation for owners and their pets. Our brochures contain details of all you need for a wonderful holiday - please telephone for your FREE copies now.

Mann's Holidays, Shaw's Holidays & Snowdonia Tourist Services

01758 701 702 (24 hrs)

www.manns-holidays.com www.shaws-holidays.co.uk www.snowdoniatourist.com

Colwyn Bay, Conwy

NORTH WALES HOLIDAYS

WTB ★★★ ★★★★ ★★★★★

Cedarwood Chalets Cottages Coach House

High quality chalets, cottages and coach house for 2-9, overlooking sea at Bron-Y-Wendon or in picturesque valley at Nant-Y-Glyn. Wide range of facilities with many leisure activities nearby. Short breaks all year. Pets Welcome.

For colour brochures telephone: 01492 512903/512282

or visit our website at www.northwales-holidays.co.uk

Bron-Y-Wendon & Nant-Y-Glyn Holiday Parks, Wern Road, Llanddulas, Colwyn Bay LL22 8HG

e-mail: bron-y-wendon@northwales-holidays.co.uk

BRONGAIN

TY'N-Y-GROES
CONWY NORTH WALES LL32 8TJ

Centrally heated Victorian cottage. Mountain views, enclosed garden, parking. Enjoy mountains, beaches, walking, bird watching. Good local food and pubs. £155 - £310.

Contact: Mrs G. M. Simpole, 105 Hay Green Road, Terrington St Clement, Kings Lynn, Norfolk PE34 4PU Tel: 01553 828897 Mobile: 0798 9080665

FREE or REDUCED RATE entry to Holiday Visits and Attractions — see our READERS' OFFER VOUCHERS on pages 101-116

When making enquiries or bookings, a stamped addressed envelope is always appreciated

Sychnant Pass House

Sychnant Pass Road, Conwy LL32 8BJ
Telephone: 01492 596868
e-mail: bresykes@sychnant-pass-house.co.uk
website: www.sychnant-pass-house.co.uk

Nellie and Molly, our lovely collies, would love to welcome your four-legged friends to their home in the hills above Conwy. Sychnant Pass House is a lovely Victorian House set in two acres with a little pond and stream running through it. Step out of our garden and straight onto Snowdonia National Park land where you can walk for miles with your dogs. Just over two miles from the beach and one-and-a-half miles from Conwy, it is an ideal base from which to tour Wales. All our rooms are en suite, our garden rooms have French windows opening into the garden which are ideal for pets. We have a lovely sitting room that you can share with your best friends after dinner which is served in our informal, friendly restaurant, doggie bags are always available.
Your four- legged friends and their folk are most welcome here.

AA Best Guest Accommodation 2004
Great Little Places & AA & RAC 5 Diamonds
Bed & Breakfast from £35 pp
"Booker Prize for Excellence 2002"
RAC Little Gem Award 2004

Bre & Graham C. Sykes (FHG Diploma Winner)

TREFRIW • CONWY VALLEY • SNOWDONIA

Secluded cottages, log fire and beams
Dogs will love it – a place of their dreams
Plenty of walks around mountains and lakes
Cosy and tranquil – it's got what it takes.
It's really a perfect holiday let
For up to 2-7 people, plus their pet(s).

Apply: Mrs Williams
Tel: 01724 733990 or 07711 217 448 (week lets only)

DEVA & SILVERDALE APARTMENTS & PINE COTTAGE

c/o Mrs E. A. Williams, Ty Heddwch, Maesdu Ave, Llandudno LL30 1NR

Self-catering accommodation up to the top grade. (Pine Cottage WTB ★★★★★). Central locations with car parking. 1-6 persons. Short breaks early and late season. Well behaved dogs welcome. Telephone, e-mail or send SAE. Specify type of accommodation, number in party and dates.

01492 581789 • e-mail: melvin.williams@btopenworld.com • www.llandudnoholidayflats-cottages.co.uk

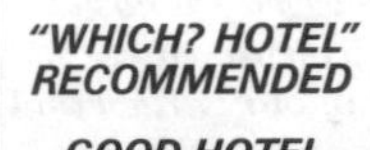

GOOD HOTEL GUIDE
Country Hotel of the Year 2003

ETC
★★★
(Silver Award)

★★★ 77%

Food Award

Pen-y-Dyffryn Country Hotel

RHYDYCROESAU, NEAR OSWESTRY, SHROPSHIRE SY10 7JD

This silver stone former Georgian Rectory, set almost a thousand feet up in the Shropshire/Welsh hills, is in a dream situation for both pets and their owners. Informal atmosphere, no traffic, just buzzards, badgers and beautiful country walks, yet Shrewsbury, Chester, Powis Castle & Lake Vyrnwy are all close by. The well-stocked bar and licensed restaurant are always welcoming at the end of another hard day's relaxing. All bedrooms en suite etc; four have private patios, ideal for pets; several have spa baths. Short breaks available from £75 pppd, Dinner, B&B. Pets free.

TEL: 01691 653700

E-MAIL: stay@peny.co.uk WEBSITE: www.peny.co.uk

Situated in the heart of the Ceiriog Valley, one of the most picturesque in North Wales.

THE GOLDEN PHEASANT *Country* Hotel & Inn

This 18th century hotel offers peace and tranquillity. All rooms en suite, some with whirlpool baths and four-poster beds. Excellent restaurant and bar meals, old world charm bar with open fire, comfortable lounges, garden, patios and large car park. Pets welcome in all rooms except restaurants and lounge. Pets from £5 per night. 2 nights Dinner, Bed & Breakfast from £120pp. Bed & Breakfast from £85, two sharing.

Llwynmawr, Glyn Ceiriog, Near Llangollen LL20 7BB
Tel: 01691 718281 • Fax: 01691 718479
e-mail: goldenpheasant@micro-plus-web.net
website: www.goldenpheasanthotel.co.uk

See also Colour Advertisement on page 67

A useful Index of Towns/Villages and Counties appears on page 426 – please also refer to Contents Page 3.

SEASIDE COTTAGES. MANN'S, SHAW'S AND SNOWDONIA TOURIST SERVICES (01758 701 702). Large selection of self-catering seaside and country cottages, bungalows, farmhouses, caravans etc. offering superb, reasonably priced accommodation for owners and their pets. Please telephone for brochure.
websites: www.manns-holidays.com www.shaws-holidays.co.uk www.snowdoniatourist.com

MR P.W. REES, "QUALITY COTTAGES', CERBID, SOLVA, HAVERFORDWEST, PEMBROKESHIRE SA62 6YE (01348 837871). Cottages set in all coastal areas, unashamed luxury, highest residential standards. Dishwashers, microwaves, washing machines. Log fires. Linen supplied. Pets welcome. [pw! 🐕]
website: www.qualitycottages.co.uk

Betws-y-Coed

Popular mountain resort in picturesque setting where three rivers meet. Trout fishing, craft shops, golf, railway and motor museums, Snowdonia National Park Visitor Centre. Nearby Swallow Falls are famous beauty spot.

MRS MORRIS, TY COCH FARM-TREKKING CENTRE, PENMACHNO, BETWS-Y-COED LL25 0HJ (01690 760248). Hill farm in Wales. TV, teamaking, en suite. Set in National Park/Snowdonia. Very quiet and well off the beaten track. A great welcome and good food. Many return visits. £19 B&B. [🐕]
e-mail: tycoch@amserve.net

SUMMER HILL NON-SMOKERS' GUEST HOUSE, BETWS-Y-COED LL24 0BL (01690 710306). Quiet location, overlooking river. 150 yards from main road and shops. En suite and standard rooms, teamaking facilities. Residents' lounge. TV. Ideal for walkers. B&B from £18 - £25. [Pets £1.50 per night.]

Colwyn Bay

Lively seaside resort with promenade amusements. Attractions include Mountain Zoo, Eirias Park; golf, tennis, riding and other sports. Good touring centre for Snowdonia. The quieter resort of Rhos-on-Sea lies at the western end of the bay.

NORTH WALES HOLIDAYS, BRON-Y-WENDON AND NANT-Y-GLYN HOLIDAY PARKS, WERN ROAD, LLANDDULAS, COLWYN BAY LL22 8HG (01492 512903/512282). Cottages with sea views at Bron-Y-Wendon or chalets, cottages and coach house in picturesque valley at Nant-Y-Glyn. WTB ★★★/★★★★/★★★★★ [Pets £10 per week].
e-mail: bron-y-wendon@northwales-holidays.co.uk website: www.northwales-holidays.co.uk

Conwy

One of the best preserved medieval fortified towns in Britain on dramatic estuary setting. Telford Suspension Bridge, many historic buildings, lively quayside (site of smallest house in Britain). Golf, pony trekking, pleasure cruises.

BRONGAIN, TY'N-Y-GROES, CONWY. Homely Victorian stone cottage, picturesque Conwy Valley. Snowdonia Mountain views. Enjoy lakes, mountains, walking, bird watching, beaches, Bodnant, RSPB, Conwy Castle. £155-£310. Contact: MRS G. M. SIMPOLE, 105 HAYGREEN ROAD, TERRINGTON ST CLEMENT, KINGS LYNN, NORFOLK PE34 4PU (01553 828897; Mobile: 0798 9080 665) [pw! 🐕]

SYCHNANT PASS HOUSE, SYCHNANT PASS ROAD, CONWY LL32 8BJ (01492 596868). Sychnant Pass House is a lovely Victorian House set in two acres with a little pond and stream running through it. Step out of our garden and straight onto Snowdonia National Park land where you can walk for miles with your dogs. All rooms en suite. AA/RAC ◆◆◆◆◆ [🐕]
e-mail: bresykes@sychnant-pass-house.co.uk website: www.sychnant-pass-house.co.uk

Conwy Valley

Fertile valley with wood and moor rising on both sides. Many places of interest in the area.

Secluded cottages with log fire and beams. Dogs will love it. Plenty of walks around mountains and lakes. For 2 - 7 people plus their pet(s). MRS WILLIAMS (01724 733990 or 07711 217 448) week lets only. [🐕]

Llandudno

Premier holiday resort of North Wales coast flanked by Great Orme and Little Orme headlands. Wide promenade, pier, two beaches; water ski-ing, sailing, fishing trips from jetty. Excellent sports facilities: golf, indoor pool, tennis, pony trekking, Leisure Centre. Summer variety shows, Alice In Wonderland Visitor Centre.

CLIFFBURY HOTEL, 34 ST DAVID'S ROAD, LLANDUDNO LL30 2UH (Tel & Fax: 01492 877224). Pets and well-behaved owners very welcome at our non-smoking hotel situated in a quiet area close to town centre and both beaches. Car park. En suite rooms with TV and beverage making facilities. Please contact John or Rita for brochure. WTB ★★ Hotel. [🐕]
e-mail: info@cliffburyhotel.co.uk website: www.cliffburyhotel.co.uk

MRS E.A. WILLIAMS, DEVA & SILVERDALE APARTMENTS & PINE COTTAGE, TY HEDDWCH, MAESDU AVE, LLANDUDNO LL30 1NR (01492 581789). Top grade self-catering accommodation for 1-6 people. Central location. Car parking on premises. Short breaks early and late season. Well behaved dogs welcome. [Pets £10 per week]
e-mail: melvin.williams@btopenworld.com website: www.llandudnoholidayflats-cottages.co.uk

Llangollen

Famous for International Music Eisteddfod held in July. Plas Newydd, Valle Crucis Abbey nearby. Standard gauge steam railway; canal cruises; ideal for golf and walking.

PEN-Y-DYFFRYN COUNTRY HOUSE HOTEL, NEAR RHYDYCROESAU, OSWESTRY SY10 7JD (01691 653700). Picturesque Georgian Rectory quietly set in Shropshire/ Welsh Hills. 12 en suite bedrooms, four with private patios. 5-acre grounds. No passing traffic. Johansens recommended. Dinner, Bed and Breakfast from £75.00 per person per day. AA/ETC ★★★. [🐕 pw!]
e-mail: stay@peny.co.uk website: www.peny.co.uk

GOLDEN PHEASANT COUNTRY HOTEL, GLYN CEIRIOG, NEAR LLANGOLLEN LL20 7BB (01691 718281; Fax: 01691 718479). Situated in the beautiful Ceiriog Valley. All 19 rooms en suite, colour TV and tea/coffee making facilities. Pets welcome in all rooms (except restaurant and lounge). WTB/AA ★★★ [pw! £5 per night per pet]
e-mail: goldenpheasant@micro-plus-web.net website: www.goldenpheasanthotel.co.uk

Porthmadog (near)

Resort on the Glaslyn estuary, 12 miles east of Pwllheli.

Old, detached, stone cottage. Fully modernised, with three bedrooms. Ample parking, enclosed garden. Open all year. Lovely walks to nearby estuary and lake. Send SAE or ring CAROL SIMKINS, TAN DDERWEN, TALSARNAU, GWYNEDD LL47 6YG (01766 771352). [Pets £1.50 per night]

Rhos-on-Sea

Popular resort at east end of Penrhyn Bay, adjoining Colwyn Bay to the north-west.

SUNNYDOWNS HOTEL, 66 ABBEY ROAD, RHOS-ON-SEA, CONWY LL28 4NU (01492 544256; Fax: 01492 543223). A 3 star luxury family hotel just two minutes' walk to beach and shops. All rooms en suite with colour TV, video & satellite channels, tea/coffee facilities and central heating. Hotel has bar, pool room and car park. [pets £1.50 per night]
e-mail: sunnydowns-hotel@tinyworld.co.uk website: www.hotelnorthwales.co.uk

Trefriw

Hillside village, popular as spa in Victorian times. Local beauty spots at Llyn Crafnant and Llyn Geironnydd. Woollen mill demonstrating traditional techniques.

MRS B. COLE, GLANDWR, TREFRIW, NEAR LLANRWST LL27 0JP (01492 640431). Large Country House on outskirts of Trefriw village. Good touring area with Llanrwst, Betws-y-Coed and Swallow Falls five miles away. Fishing, walking, golf, pony trekking close by. Comfortable bedrooms, lounge with TV, diningroom. Good home cooking. Parking. B&B from £25.

SYMBOLS

- 🐕 **Indicates that pets are welcome free of charge.**
- £ **Indicates that a charge is made for pets: nightly or weekly.**
- pw! **Shows some special provision for pets: exercise facility, feeding or accommodation arrangement.**
- ⌂ **Indicates separate pets accommodation.**

Llanelli

Village on the River Taf estuary, 10 mile north-west of Swansea.

THE DIPLOMAT HOTEL, FELINFOEL ROAD, AELYBRYN, LLANELLI SA15 3PJ (01554 756156; Fax: 01554 751649). Privately owned and operated with warmth and generous hospitality. The Diplomat Hotel offers a rare combination of charm and character with excellent well appointed facilities to ensure your comfort and convenience. WTB/AA ★★★ [Pets £5 per night]
e-mail: reservations@diplomat-hotel-wales.com website: www.diplomat-hotel-wales.com

The Old Castle, Laugharne

ON THE COAST MID-WAY BETWEEN NEW QUAY & ABERAERON

Gilfach Holiday Village

Self Catering Holidays Overlooking the Sea

HORSE & PONY RIDING: PETS WELCOME

Gilfach is set in lovely unspoilt countryside on the coast midway between the resorts of New Quay and Aberaeron, not far from Aberystwyth, Devil's Bridge and other attractions. There is a a choice of modern bungalows, accommodating up to 6 persons or luxury 2/3 person apartments set in 36 acres of grounds. Horse riding is available in the Village to suit all ages. Enjoy sea fishing trips or fish from the beach. River fishing is also available nearby. The Village has its own licensed bar, food is available with weekly BBQ and Sunday lunches. There is also an en tout cas all-weather tennis court. The children have a den and playground and pets are welcome. All the accommodation is fully equipped and includes colour TV, and bed linen is available. For our colour brochure pack write or call the manager at:

GILFACH HOLIDAY VILLAGE

Llwyncelyn, Nr. Aberaeron, Ceredigion SA46 0HN Telephone: (01545) 580 288
www.stratfordcaravans.co.uk email: info@stratfordcaravans.co.uk

See also Colour Advertisement on Inside Back Cover

TYGLYN HOLIDAY ESTATE

A chance to spend a relaxing time amidst beautiful, unspoilt Welsh countryside yet within easy reach of the renowned coastal towns and beaches of New Quay and Aberystwyth. Set in 17 acres of the awe-inspiring Aeron valley, home to Buzzards, Kestrels and Red Kites, with fishing available on the River Aeron.

• Semi detached self-catering bungalows, sleep four to six. • Bar and Restaurant adjoining • Horseriding • Golf • Tennis • Bowls • Walking • Swimming • Ten-Pin Bowling • Cycling • Quad Biking • Leisure Centres- all nearby • Full Colour Brochure.

Tyglyn Holiday Estate, Ciliau Aeron, Lampeter, Ceredigion SA48 8DD
Tel: 01570 470625 • Fax: 01570 471435 • www.tyglyn.com
E-mail: look@tyglyn.com

See also Colour Advertisement on page 68

MR P.W. REES, "QUALITY COTTAGES", CERBID, SOLVA, HAVERFORDWEST, PEMBROKESHIRE SA62 6YE (01348 837871). Cottages set in all coastal areas, unashamed luxury, highest residential standards. Dishwashers, microwaves, washing machines. Log fires. Linen supplied. Pets welcome. [pw! 🐕]
website: www.qualitycottages.co.uk

Aberaeron

Attractive little town on Cardigan Bay, good touring centre for coast and inland. The Aeron Express Aerial ferry offers an exciting trip across the harbour. Marine aquarium; Aberarth Leisure Park nearby.

GILFACH HOLIDAY VILLAGE, LLWYNCELYN, NEAR ABERAERON SA46 OHN (01545 580288). Choice of modern Bungalows (up to 6 persons) or luxury 2/3 person apartments. Fully equipped, linen available, colour TV. Horse and pony riding. Tennis. Write or phone for brochure pack to the Manager. [Pets £15 per week.]
e-mail: info@stratfordcaravans.co.uk website: www.stratfordcaravans.co.uk

TYGLYN HOLIDAY ESTATE, CILIAU AERON, LAMPETER, CEREDIGION SA48 8DD (01570 470625; Fax: 01570 471435) Semi-detached self-catering bungalows, sleep 4-6. Bar and restaurant adjoining. Horseriding, golf, tennis, bowls, walking, swimming, ten-pin bowling, cycling, quad-biking and leisure centres - all nearby. [pw! Pets £12 per week]
e-mail: look@tyglyn.com website: www.tyglyn.com

Aberporth

Popular seaside village offering safe swimming and good sea fishing. Good base for exploring Cardigan Bay coastline.

MR P. W. REES, "QUALITY COTTAGES", CERBID, SOLVA, HAVERFORDWEST, PEMBROKESHIRE SA62 6YE (01348 837871). Cottages set in all coastal areas, unashamed luxury, highest residential standards. Dishwashers, microwaves, washing machines. Log fires. Linen supplied. Pets welcome. [pw! 🐕]
website: www.qualitycottages.co.uk

Ciliau Aeron

Village in undulating country just inland from the charming Cardigan Bay resorts of New Quay and Aberaeron. New Quay 12 miles, Aberaeron 6.

MR P. W. REES, "QUALITY COTTAGES", CERBID, SOLVA, HAVERFORDWEST, PEMBROKESHIRE SA62 6YE (01348 837871). Cottages set in all coastal areas, unashamed luxury, highest residential standards. Dishwashers, microwaves, washing machines. Log fires. Linen supplied. Pets welcome. [pw! 🐕]
website: www.qualitycottages.co.uk

PLEASE NOTE

All the information in this book is given in good faith in the belief that it is correct. However, the publishers cannot guarantee the facts given in these pages, neither are they responsible for changes in policy, ownership or terms that may take place after the date of going to press. Readers should always satisfy themselves that the facilities they require are available and that the terms, if quoted, still apply.

Llangrannog

Pretty little seaside village overlooking a sandy beach. Superb cliff walk to NT Ynys Lochtyn, a secluded promontory.

MR P. W. REES, "QUALITY COTTAGES", CERBID, SOLVA, HAVERFORDWEST, PEMBROKESHIRE SA62 6YE (01348 837871). Cottages set in all coastal areas, unashamed luxury, highest residential standards. Dishwashers, microwaves, washing machines. Log fires. Linen supplied. Pets welcome. [pw! 🐕]
website: www.qualitycottages.co.uk

Parcllyn

Located 1 mile north of Aberporth.

MR & MRS MILLAR, PARC NEWYDD FACH, PARCLLYN, ABERPORTH, CARDIGAN SA43 2DR (01239 811325). Quality self-contained cottage, stunning views over Cardigan Bay, peaceful location, garden, close to dog friendly beach. Parking. Sleeps 4. Pets welcome. Terms from £195 to £400 per week. [🐕]

MONMOUTHSHIRE

Raglan

Raglan

Village 7 miles south-west of Monmouth. Remains of 15th century castle lie to the north.

MRS J.E.THOM, THE GRANGE, PENRHOS, RAGLAN, MONMOUTHSHIRE NP15 2LQ (01600 780202). Organic mixed farm (115 acres). Local golf and fishing, or simply sit and enjoy the views. On the Offa's Dyke footpath. Bring dogs and horses! En suite rooms. Bed and Breakfast from £23 pp. WTB ★★★ [pw!🐕]

Readers are requested to mention this guidebook when seeking accommodation (and please enclose a stamped addressed envelope).

Welcome to Ivybridge, where your pet is as welcome as you are!

• Situated down a leafy lane, Ivybridge is a modern guesthouse. • All rooms en suite with TV/hot drinks tray. • Swim in our indoor pool, relax in our lounge/bar.• Good home cooking. • Ample off-road parking. • Close by are quiet walks to the sea which you and your pet will enjoy.

Ivybridge, Drim Mill, Dyffryn, Goodwick, Pembrokeshire SA64 0FT • 01348 875366 • Fax: 01348 872338
e-mail: ivybridge@cwcom.net • website: www.ivybridge.cwc.net

See also Colour Advertisement on page 69

Scamford Caravan Park

Peaceful family-run park

Close to the coastal path and lovely sandy beaches. 25 luxurious caravans with Dragon Awards for excellence. Five touring pitches. Super playground. Pets welcome.

Richard & Christine White.
Tel/Fax: 01437 710304
e-mail:holidays@scamford.com
Scamford Caravan Park, Keeston, Haverford West, Pembrokeshire, SA62 6HN

Dragon Award

www.scamford.com

NOLTON HAVEN QUALITY COTTAGES

All the **WTB 3,4 & 5 Star cottages** with a sea view in Nolton Haven are on our books. Ideal for out of season breaks, with full central heating and open log/coal fires. Two to five bedrooms sleeping 2 to 14 guests. Some are situated just 30 yards from the beach. Children and pets welcome. The Coastal Path passes through the village. Good cliff walks, safe, sandy beach. Choice of accommodation from two-bedroomed chalets to a five-bedroomed Georgian mansion. Pub in village.

Nolton Haven Farmhouse B&B - situated beside the beach, this family home offers an ideal situation from which to explore the Pembrokeshire National Park. Seven bedrooms, some en suite.

Contact: Jim & Joyce Canton,
Nolton Haven Farmhouse,
Nolton Haven, Haverfordwest
SA62 6NH (01437 710263)
e-mail: PW5@noltonhaven.com
www.noltonhaven.com

Nolton Cross Caravan Park WTB ★★★

British Holiday Home Parks Association

Small quiet family park, set in open countryside overlooking St Brides Bay. Ideal base for touring Pembrokeshire. Luxury caravans for hire, short breaks available. 15 touring pitches. Open March to November.

Contact Philip and Helen Thomas, Nolton Cross Caravan Park, Nolton, Haverfordwest, Pembrokeshire SA62 3NP
Tel: 01437 710701 Fax: 01437 710329
E-mail: noltoncross@nolton.fsnet.co.uk Website: www.noltoncross-holidays.co.uk

Nolton Haven Farm Cottages • **Nolton Haven, Haverfordwest, Pembrokeshire SA62 3NH**
Tel: 01437 710200 • e-mail: info@havencottages.co.uk • www.havencottages.co.uk

Sympathetically converted cottages situated on a grass bank overlooking Nolton Haven's sandy beach.
• *Primrose Cottage sleeps 5* • *Bluebell Cottage sleeps 6* • *Thrift Cottage sleeps 2+2* • *Honeysuckle & Buttercup Cottages sleep 5* • *Rose Cottage sleeps 6.* All are fully equipped, with colour TV, fridge/freezer, microwave etc. Duvets supplied, but no linen. Coin meters for cooking and hot water. Children and pets welcome.

See also Colour Advertisement on page 71

LLANTEGLOS ESTATE

Charming self-contained Woodland Lodges in quiet estate. Wonderful views of coast and country. Safe children's play area. Fully licensed clubhouse. Miles of sandy beaches. Attractions for all ages and interests. For further details/ colour brochure: **(01834) 831677/ 831739**

TONY & JANE BARON, LLANTEGLOS ESTATE, LLANTEG, NEAR AMROTH, PEMBROKESHIRE SA67 8PU
e-mail: llanteglosestate@supanet.com • website: www.llanteglos-estate.com

Scamford Holidays

Richard & Christine White
Scamford Holidays Keeston
Haverfordwest Pembrokeshire SA62 6HN
Tel: 01437 710304
Email:holidays@scamford.com
Web Page www.stdavids.co.uk/folkeston/

Folkeston Hill Holiday Bungalows

A small group of bungalows in a sheltered valley which winds down to the sea at Nolton Haven. WTB Graded. Pets welcome (no charge)

Cosy cottages and farmhouses near superb beaches and coastal path, around beautiful St Brides Bay in Pembrokeshire. WTB graded. Sleep 2-11. Pet welcome.

Tel: 0870 7572270

See also Colour Advertisement on page 69

FFYNNON DDOFN

Luxury cottage in quiet lane between St Davids and Fishguard, with panoramic views over spectacular coastline. Ideal for walking; rocky coves and safe, sandy beaches nearby. The cottage is fully carpeted, warm, comfortable and very well-equipped, sleeping six in three bedrooms, plus cot. Washing machine, tumble dryer, freezer, microwave and video. Large games room, children's toys, pleasant secure garden. Perfect for early or late holidays, with central heating and double glazing. Parking. Shop one mile. Footpath to beach. Open all year. Terms from £260, including heating and electricity. Brochure on request.

Mrs B. Rees White, Brickhouse Farm, Burnham Road,Woodham Mortimer, Maldon, Essex CM9 6SR (01245 224611)

CARNE MOUNTAIN FARM

Saundersfoot, Reynalton, Kilgetty SA68 OPD Tel & Fax: 01834 860 546

Mrs Joy Holgate WORKING FARM

A warm welcome awaits you at our lovely 200-year-old farmhouse, set amidst the peace and tranquillity of the beautiful Pembrokeshire countryside, 3½ miles Saundersfoot. Pretty, picturesque south facing bedrooms with TV, washbasins, tea/coffee tray and central heating. Attractive beamed sitting room with TV, books, maps and guides. Vegetarians very welcome. Bed and Breakfast from £20.00. Welcome Host and Farmhouse Awards. SAE please. First dog free, second £1 per night.

Conveniently situated on outskirts of picturesque coastal village with shops, beaches and restaurants. We have large gardens and paddock for pets, and owners' relaxation and exercise. Private parking for guests. Warm hospitality in relaxed atmosphere. Non-smoking throughout. All rooms en suite with central heating, clock-radio, colour TV, hairdryer and hospitality tray. Children 6 to 16 years, half price when sharing with two adults. £1 per day per dog. Brochure and pet guidelines on request.

VINE COTTAGE

GUEST HOUSE

Telephone: 01834 814422

E-mail: enquiries@vinecottageguesthouse.co.uk

Website: www.vinecottageguesthouse.co.uk

David & Helen Trimmings
The Ridgeway, Saundersfoot
Pembrokeshire SA69 9LA

AA ♦♦♦♦

See also Colour Advertisement on page 69

Mrs M. Jones

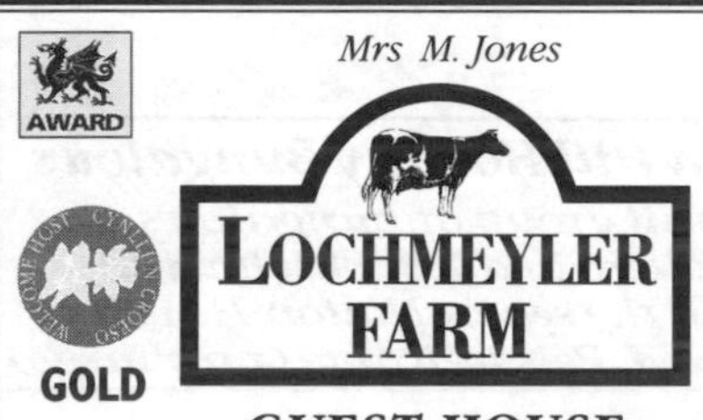

GUEST HOUSE

WTB ★★★★★ Farm AA/RAC ♦♦♦♦♦ Award

A warm Welsh welcome awaits you at Lochmeyler, a dairy farm at the centre of the St David's Peninsula. Luxury facilities including some four-poster beds for those romantic breaks. Vegetarian and traditional Pembrokeshire farmhouse fare served using home cooked local produce. Children welcome – with play area. Smoking and non-smoking lounges – no smoking in bedrooms. National Park Activity Packs provided to help you to explore our beautiful coastline and countryside. Well behaved dogs welcome but are not permitted to be left unattended in the rooms. Credit cards accepted. For information pack and brochure please let us have your address. Closed Christmas and New Year.

Llandeloy, Pen-y-Cwm, Near Solva,
St Davids, Pembrokeshire SA62 6LL
Tel: 01348 837724 • Fax: 01348 837622
Website: www.lochmeyler.co.uk
E-mail: stay@lochmeyler.co.uk

B&B from £25–£30pp.
Dinner £15 pp.
Children half-price when sharing with 2 adults.
10% discount on B&B and Dinner bookings of 7 nights or more.

See also Colour Advertisement on page 70

Gwarmacwydd is a country estate of over 450 acres, including two miles of riverbank. See a real farm in action, the hustle and bustle of harvest, newborn calves and lambs. Children are welcomed. On the estate are six character stone cottages. Each cottage has been lovingly converted from traditional farm buildings, parts of which are over 200 years old. Each cottage is fully furnished and equipped. All electricity and linen included. All cottages are heated for year-round use. Colour brochure available.

Tel: 01437 563260 • Fax: 01437 563839 • e-mail: info@a-farm-holiday.org
website: www.a-farm-holiday.org • Cottages 1-5 WTB ★★★★ SELF CATERING
Mrs Angela Colledge, Gwarmacwydd Farm, Llanfallteg, Whitland, Pembrokeshire SA34 0XH

See also Colour Advertisement on page 69

MR P.W. REES, "QUALITY COTTAGES', CERBID, SOLVA, HAVERFORDWEST, PEMBROKESHIRE SA62 6YE (01348 837871). Cottages set in all coastal areas, unashamed luxury, highest residential standards. Dishwashers, microwaves, washing machines. Log fires. Linen supplied. Pets welcome. [pw! 🐕]
website: www.qualitycottages.co.uk

POWELLS COTTAGE HOLIDAYS, 51 HIGH STREET, SAUNDERSFOOT, PEMBROKESHIRE SA69 9EJ. Many of our top quality holiday properties accept pets. Cottages in Devon, Cornwall, Cotswolds, Pembrokeshire and Heart of England. For colour brochure FREEPHONE 0800 378771 (24 hours). website: www.powells.co.uk

FBM HOLIDAYS, ST JULIAN STREET, TENBY, PEMBROKESHIRE SA70 7AU (01834 844565; Fax: 01834 844525). Over 300 properties achieving 3, 4 and 5 Star Wales Tourist Board Gradings. Character cottages or breathtaking seafront properties. Family accommodation or quiet retreats for couples where your pets are welcome. Call now for our 86 page colour brochure.
e-mail: info@fbmholidays.co.uk website: www.fbmholidays.co.uk

Bosherton

Village 4 miles south of Pembroke, bordered by 3 man-made lakes, a haven for wildlife and covered in water lilies in early summer.

MR P. W. REES, "QUALITY COTTAGES", CERBID, SOLVA, HAVERFORDWEST, PEMBROKESHIRE SA62 6YE (01348 837871). Cottages set in all coastal areas, unashamed luxury, highest residential standards. Dishwashers, microwaves, washing machines. Log fires. Linen supplied. Pets welcome. [pw! 🐕]
website: www.qualitycottages.co.uk

Broad Haven

Attractive little resort on St Bride's Bay in the Pembrokeshire Coast National Park. Superb sandy beach; National Park Information Centre.

PEMBROKESHIRE NATIONAL PARK. Sleeps 6. Three-bedroom fully furnished Holiday House. Walking distance sandy beaches and coastal footpath. £120 to £300 per week. MRS L.P. ASHTON, 10 ST LEONARDS ROAD, THAMES DITTON, SURREY KT7 0RJ (020-8398 6349). [🐕]
e-mail: lejash@aol.com

Croes Goch

Hamlet 6 miles north east of St Davids.

MR P. W. REES, "QUALITY COTTAGES", CERBID, SOLVA, HAVERFORDWEST, PEMBROKESHIRE SA62 6YE (01348 837871). Cottages set in all coastal areas, unashamed luxury, highest residential standards. Dishwashers, microwaves, washing machines. Log fires. Linen supplied. Pets welcome. [pw! 🐕]
website: www.qualitycottages.co.uk

Fishguard

Small town at end of Fishguard Bay

IVYBRIDGE, DRIM MILL, DYFFRYN, GOODWICK SA64 0FT (01348 875366, Fax: 01348 872338). Stay at Ivybridge, swim in our heated pool or relax in our comfortable guest lounge. En suite rooms, home cooking, large off road carpark. Pets welcome! [🐕]
e-mail: ivybridge@cwcom.net website: www.ivybridge.cwc.net

Haverfordwest

Administrative and shopping centre for the area; ideal base for exploring National Park. Historic town of narrow streets; museum in castle grounds; many fine buildings.

SCAMFORD CARAVAN PARK, KEESTON, HAVERFORDWEST SA62 6HN (Tel & Fax: 01437 710304). 25 luxurious caravans (shower, fridge, microwave, colour TV). Peaceful park near lovely sandy beaches. Super playground. Launderette. Five touring pitches, hook-ups. Modern shower block. Pets welcome.
e-mail: holidays@scamford.com website: www.scamford.com

NOLTON HAVEN QUALITY COTTAGES. Sleep 2 to 14. 3,4 & 5 star cottages with sea view, some just 30 yards from the beach. Children and pets welcome. Farmhouse B&B also available - seven bedrooms, some en suite. WTB ★★★/★★★★/★★★★★ Self-Catering. Contact: JIM & JOYCE CANTON, NOLTON HAVEN FARMHOUSE, NOLTON HAVEN, HAVERFORDWEST SA62 3NH (01437 710263).
e-mail: PW5@noltonhaven.com website: www.noltonhaven.com

PHILIP & HELEN THOMAS, NOLTON CROSS CARAVAN PARK, NOLTON, HAVERFORDWEST SA62 3NP (01437 710701; Fax: 01437 710329). Small, quiet, family park set in open countryside overlooking St Brides Bay. Ideal for touring. Luxury caravans for hire; short breaks available. Open March to November. WTB ★★★ Touring and Holiday Park. [🐕]
e-mail: noltoncross@nolton.fsnet.co.uk website: www.noltoncross-holidays.co.uk

NOLTON HAVEN FARM COTTAGES, NOLTON HAVEN, HAVERFORDWEST SA62 3NH (01437 710200). Quality beach front cottages, sleep 2-6, adjacent sandy beach. Well equipped. Open all year. Winter breaks. [Pets £10 per week].
e-mail: info@havencottages.co.uk website: www.havencottages.co.uk

Lawrenny

Village near River Cresswell estuary, 8 miles south-west of Narberth

MRS VIRGINIA LORT PHILLIPS, KNOWLES FARM, LAWRENNY SA68 0PX (01834 891221). Come and relax with us in our lovely south-facing farmhouse. Listen to the silence and spoil yourselves and your dogs whilst discovering the delights of hidden Pembrokeshire. Walk along the shores of the Estuary which surrounds our organic farm. B&B from £26, Dinner on request. WTB ★★★ [First pet free, others £2 per pet per night.]
e-mail: ginilp@lawrenny.org.uk website: www.lawrenny.org.uk

Llanteg

Hamlet 4 miles south of Whitland.

TONY & JANE BARON, LLANTEGLOS ESTATE, LLANTEG, NEAR AMROTH SA67 8PU (01834 831677 / 831739). Self-contained Woodland Lodges. Sleep 6. Children's play area. Licensed bar & entertainment. Visitor attractions. Call for brochure. WTB ★★★★ Self Catering
e-mail: llanteglosestate@supanet.com website: www.llanteglos-estate.com

Manorbier

Unspoiled village on South Pembrokeshire coast near Tenby. Sandy bay and fine coastal walks.

AQUARIUM COTTAGE & THE LOBSTER POT, MANORBIER. Two pleasant country properties. Detached cottage (sleeps 6) and ground floor apartment (sleeps 4). Walk to beach. Pets welcome. Ample parking. Electricity, heating, linen, towels inclusive. Brochure: MRS J. HUGHES, ROSE COTTAGE, MANORBIER, TENBY SA70 7ST (01834 871408).

SYMBOLS

🐕 Indicates that pets are welcome free of charge.
£ Indicates that a charge is made for pets: nightly or weekly.
pw! Shows some special provision for pets; exercise facility, feeding or accommodation arrangement.
☖ Indicates separate pets accommodation.

Newgale

On St Bride's Bay 3 miles east of Solva. Long beach where at exceptionally low tide the stumps of a submerged forest may be seen.

MR P. W. REES, "QUALITY COTTAGES", CERBID, SOLVA, HAVERFORDWEST, PEMBROKESHIRE SA62 6YE (01348 837871). Cottages set in all coastal areas, unashamed luxury, highest residential standards. Dishwashers, microwaves, washing machines. Log fires. Linen supplied. Pets welcome. [pw! 🐕]
website: www.qualitycottages.co.uk

Newport

Small town at mouth of the River Nyfer, 9 miles south west of Cardigan. Remains of 13th-century castle.

MR P. W. REES, "QUALITY COTTAGES", CERBID, SOLVA, HAVERFORDWEST, PEMBROKESHIRE SA62 6YE (01348 837871). Cottages set in all coastal areas, unashamed luxury, highest residential standards. Dishwashers, microwaves, washing machines. Log fires. Linen supplied. Pets welcome. [pw! 🐕]
website: www.qualitycottages.co.uk

Nolton Haven

Hamlet at head of inlet on St Bride's Bay. Fine coastal views.

FOLKESTON HILL HOLIDAY BUNGALOWS. A small group of bungalows in a sheltered valley which winds down to the sea. WTB Graded. Pets welcome – no charge. Brochure from RICHARD & CHRISTINE WHITE, SCAMFORD HOLIDAYS, KEESTON, HAVERFORDWEST SA62 6HN (01437 710304).
e-mail: holidays@scamford.com website: www.stdavids.co.uk/folkeston/

St Brides

Located on St Bride's Bay 7 miles north west of Milford Haven.

ST BRIDE'S BAY COTTAGES (0870 7572270). Cosy cottages and farmhouses near superb beaches and coastal path, around beautiful St Bride's Bay in Pembrokeshire. Sleep 2-11. Pet welcome.WTB graded.
website: www.stbridesbaycottages.com

St Davids

Smallest cathedral city in Britain, shrine of Wales' patron saint. Magnificent ruins of Bishop's Palace. Craft shops, farm parks and museums; boat trips to Ramsey Island.

MR P. W. REES, "QUALITY COTTAGES", CERBID, SOLVA, HAVERFORDWEST, PEMBROKESHIRE SA62 6YE (01348 837871). Cottages set in all coastal areas, unashamed luxury, highest residential standards. Dishwashers, microwaves, washing machines. Log fires. Linen supplied. Pets welcome. [pwl 🐕]
website: www.qualitycottages.co.uk

LOWER MOOR COTTAGES, ST DAVIDS. Beautifully restored stone and slate cottages. Panoramic views over coast and open countryside. Near coastal path and sandy beaches. Dishwashers, TV, games rooms, log fire, gas fired central heating. Open all year. Two to seven bedrooms; sleep two to sixteen. WTB ★★★★★. Correspondence: T. M. HARDMAN, HIGH VIEW, CATHERINE STREET, ST DAVIDS, PEMBROKESHIRE SA62 6RJ. Telephone: THELMA HARDMAN (01437 720616).[Pets £10 per week]
e-mail: enquiries@lowermoorcottages.co.uk website: www.lowermoorcottages.co.uk

FFYNNON DDOFN, LLANON, LLANRHIAN, NEAR ST DAVIDS. Comfortable, well-equipped cottage with panoramic coastal views. Sleeps 6. Fully carpeted with central heating. Large games room. Open all year. Pets welcome free of charge. Brochure on request from: MRS B. REES WHITE, BRICKHOUSE FARM, BURNHAM RD, WOODHAM MORTIMER, MALDON, ESSEX CM9 6SR (01245 224611). [🐕]

Saundersfoot

Popular resort and sailing centre with picturesque harbour and sandy beach. Tenby 3 miles

MRS JOY HOLGATE, CARNE MOUNTAIN FARM, REYNALTON, KILGETTY SA68 0PD (Tel & Fax: 01834 860 546). A warm welcome awaits you at our lovely 200-year-old farmhouse set amidst the peace and tranquillity of the beautiful Pembrokeshire countryside. Bedrooms have TV and all facilities. B&B from £20.00 [One dog free, second pet £1.00 per night.]

VINE COTTAGE, THE RIDGEWAY, SAUNDERSFOOT SA69 9LA (01834 814422). Former Farmhouse close to village and beaches. Central heating, log fires. All rooms en suite. Pets welcome – garden and paddock. Private parking. Non-smoking throughout. AA ◆◆◆◆. WTB ★★★ *GUEST HOUSE*, [pw! Pets £1 per night.]
e-mail: enquiries@vinecottageguesthouse.co.uk website: www.vinecottageguesthouse.co.uk

Solva

Picturesque coastal village with sheltered harbour and excellent craft shops. Sailing and watersports; sea fishing, long sandy beach.

MRS M. JONES, LOCHMEYLER FARM GUEST HOUSE, LLANDELOY, PEN-Y-CWM, NEAR SOLVA, ST DAVIDS, PEMBROKESHIRE SA62 6LL (01348 837724; Fax: 01348 837622). Welcome Host Gold Award. 15 en suite luxury bedrooms, eight in the cottage suites adjacent to the house. All bedrooms non-smoking, with TV, video and refreshment facilities. Children welcome. WTB ★★★★★ *FARM*, AA/RAC ◆◆◆◆◆ [pw! 🐕]

MR P. W. REES, "QUALITY COTTAGES", CERBID, SOLVA, HAVERFORDWEST, PEMBROKESHIRE SA62 6YE (01348 837871). Cottages set in all coastal areas, unashamed luxury, highest residential standards. Dishwashers, microwaves, washing machines. Log fires. Linen supplied. Pets welcome. [pw! 🐕]
website: www.qualitycottages.co.uk

Tenby

Popular resort with two wide beaches. Fishing trips, craft shops, museum. Medieval castle ruins, 13th-century church. Golf, fishing and watersports; boat trips to nearby Caldy Island with monastery and medieval church.

MR P. W. REES, "QUALITY COTTAGES", CERBID, SOLVA, HAVERFORDWEST, PEMBROKESHIRE SA62 6YE (01348 837871). Cottages set in all coastal areas, unashamed luxury, highest residential standards. Dishwashers, microwaves, washing machines. Log fires. Linen supplied. Pets welcome. [pw! 🐕]
website: www.qualitycottages.co.uk

Whitland

Village 6 miles east of Narberth. Whitland Abbey 2 km.

MRS ANGELA COLLEDGE, GWARMACWYDD FARM, LLANFALLTEG, WHITLAND SA34 0XH (01437 563260; Fax: 01437 563839). Country estate with six character stone cottages, fully furnished and equipped. All linen and electricity included; heated for year-round use. Cottages 1-5 WTB ★★★★★ Self-catering. [pw! Pets £10 per week]
e-mail: info@a-farm-holiday.org website: www.a-farm-holiday.org

Readers are requested to mention this guidebook when seeking accommodation (and please enclose a stamped addressed envelope).

FOREST CABIN

BARGAIN BREAKS

ARGUABLY AS LIKE THE CANADIAN ROCKIES AS YOU'LL FIND IN THIS COUNTRY!

As low as £65pp for 3 nights. Includes cabin, breakfast and dinner. Pets welcome.

Ring 02920 754887 **www.business.virgin.net/victoria.wells**

Builth Wells

Caer Beris Manor

Family-owned three star Country House Hotel set in 27 acres of parkland. Free salmon and trout fishing on River Wye (two rods) and on River Irfon. Superb walking and touring. 18 hole Golf Course nearby. Excellent cuisine.
All rooms en suite with telephone, TV and tea making.

DOGS WELCOME!

DB&B £57.50 pppn; £345 weekly; B&B £47.50pp.

Mrs Katharine Smith, Caer Beris Manor, Builth Wells
Powys LD2 3NP Tel: 01982 552601 • Fax: 01982 552586
E-mail: caerberismanor@btinternet.com • Website: www.caerberis.co.uk

FREE or REDUCED RATE entry to Holiday Visits and Attractions – see our READERS' OFFER VOUCHERS on pages 101-116

Penllwyn Lodges

Set in a 30 acre woodland, all our lodges are individually designed and fully fitted throughout, including colour TV, microwave, full kitchen, bath/shower room and includes all bedding. 19 lodges sleeping 2 – 8 people and one cottage which sleeps six. Fishing on the Montgomery canal, River Severn and our own private lake. Quad trekking and pony trekking nearby. Pets welcome.
From £175 to £685 per cabin per week including VAT.
Short Breaks. Open all year round.

Tel/Fax 01686 640269 for a colour brochure
Penllwyn Lodges, Garthmyl, Powys SY15 6SB
www.penllwynlodges.co.uk
e-mail: djones@telco4u.net

See also Colour Advertisement on outside back cover

The Park Motel

Crossgates
Llandrindod Wells
Powys LD1 6RF
Tel: (01597) 851201
WTB ★★★ *Country Lodge*

Set in 3 acres of beautiful Welsh countryside and close to the famous Elan Valley. Accommodation includes static caravans, touring pitches and fully equipped motel units which have either a twin or double bedroom, shower room, and kitchen with a dinette that converts to a double bed. Sleeping up to 4, they can be booked for either self catering or B&B. On-site facilities include restaurant, bar and snug, games room, outdoor swimming pool, kids play area. Well behaved pets are very welcome.

MADOG'S WELLS, Llanfair Caereinion, Welshpool, Powys SY21 0DE

Beautiful, peaceful valley with lots of wildlife. Two bungalows, both wheelchair accessible, plus 4 berth caravan. Free gas, electricity, linen and cot available. Picnic benches, games room and children's play area. Daily rates available out of main school holidays. Three bedroom bungalow (**WTB ★★★★★**) from £140 to £395. Two bedroom bungalow (**WTB ★★★**) £115 to £315. Open all year. Caravan from £130 to £230 pw. Open April to November. Farmhouse B&B at £21 pppn.

Contact Michael & Ann Reed for further details. Tel/Fax: 01938 810446 e-mail: madogswells@btopenworld.com

OAK WOOD LODGES Llwynbaedd, Rhayader, Powys LD6 5NT

Self-catering Log Cabins. Luxurious Norwegian log cabins situated at approximately 1000ft above sea level with spectacular views of the Elan Valley and Cambrian Mountains. Enjoy pursuits such as walking, pony trekking, mountain biking, fishing, and bird watching in the most idyllic of surroundings. Excellent touring centre. Dogs welcome. Short breaks as well as full weeks. Open all year round.
For more information and brochure call 01597 811422

See also Colour Advertisement on page 71

Please mention ***PETS WELCOME*** when making enquiries about accommodation featured in these pages.

FOREST CABIN BARGAIN BREAKS (02920 754887). Arguably as like the Canadian Rockies as you'll find in this country. As low as £65pp for 3 nights. Includes cabin, breakfast and dinner. Pets welcome.
website: www.business.virgin.net/victoria.wells

Brecon

Main touring centre for National Park. Busy market; Jazz Festival in summer. Brecknock Museum, ruined castle, cathedral of interest. Golf, walking, fishing, canal cruising, pony trekking.

GILFACH FARM, SENNYBRIDGE, POWYS LD3 8TY (01874 636818; mobile: 07899 892582). Charming barn conversion offering self-catering accommodation for four on picturesque farm. Fantastic location for walking/riding (Brecon 8 miles). Pets and horses welcome from £2 per night. Linen and fuel included. Open all year. Short Breaks available. From £258 per week.
e-mail: sm@mip.co.uk website: www.breconbeaconsriding.co.uk

ERW YR DANTY, TALYBONT-ON-USK, BRECON LD3 7YN (Tel & Fax: 01874 676498). Attractive village on Taff Trail; ideal location for all outdoor pursuits. Stylish barn conversion with wonderful views. Comfortable accommodation. Bed and Breakfast. Dogs welcome. WTB ★★★. Contact: LAURA KOSTORIS. [Pets £2 per night]
e-mail: kosto@ukonline.co.uk website: www.wiz.to/lifestyle/

Builth Wells

Old country town in lovely setting on River Wye amid beautiful hills. Lively markets; host to Royal Welsh Agricultural Show.

MRS LINDA WILLIAMS, OLD VICARAGE, ERWOOD, BUILTH WELLS LD2 3SZ (01982 560680). Situated in secluded grounds with glorious views of the beautiful Wye Valley. Attractive spacious rooms have double aspects, TV, drinks tray, wash basin. Guests own bathroom, separate WC. Bacon and sausage from local traditionally reared pigs, free range eggs and home made preserves for breakfast. WTB ★★ Farm, FHG Diploma Winner 2004..
e-mail: linda@oldvicwyevalley.co.uk website: www.oldvicwyevalley.co.uk

MRS KATHERINE SMITH, CAER BERIS MANOR, BUILTH WELLS LD2 3NP (01982 552601; Fax: 01982 552586). Family-owned country house hotel set in 27 acres of parkland. Free salmon and trout fishing; golf nearby, superb walking and touring. All rooms en suite. WTB/AA ★★★. [🐕]
e-mail: caerberismanor@btinternet.com website: www.caerberis.co.uk

Garthmyl

Situated on A483 between Welshpool and Newtown in unspoilt countryside.

Self-catering log cabins set in 30 acres of unspoilt woodland teeming with wildlife. Central heating, colour TV, microwave etc. Pets Welcome. From £175 – £685 per cabin per week breaks. Apply PENLLWYN LODGES, GARTHMYL, POWYS SY15 6SB (Tel & Fax: 01686 640269) for colour brochure. [Pets £15 per stay]
e-mail: djones@telco4u.net website: www.penllwynlodges.co.uk

Hay-on-Wye

Small market town at north end of Black Mountains, 15 miles north-east of Brecon.

MRS E. BALLY, LANE FARM, PAINSCASTLE, BUILTH WELLS LD2 3JS (Tel & Fax: 01497 851605). 17th century farm in rural Radnorshire, five miles Hay-on-Wye. Wonderful walking country. Self-catering apartments and Bed and Breakfast accommodation. A warm welcome for you and your pet(s). WTB ★★★★ [🐕]
e-mail: jbally@btclick.com

A useful Index of Towns/Villages and Counties appears on page 426 – please also refer to Contents Page 3.

Llandrindod Wells

Popular inland resort, Victorian spa town, excellent touring centre. Golf, fishing, bowling, boating and tennis. Visitors can still take the waters at Rock Park Gardens.

THE PARK MOTEL, CROSSGATES, LLANDRINDOD WELLS LD1 6RF (01597 851201). In three acres, amidst beautiful countryside near Elan Valley. Static caravans, touring pitches and fully equipped motel units. Licensed restaurant, bar, games room. Swimming pool. Children's play area. Pets welcome. WTB ★★★ [🐕]

Llanfair Caereinion

Small town on River Banwy, 8 miles west of Welshpool.

MRS ANN REED, MADOG'S WELLS, LLANFAIR CAEREINION, WELSHPOOL SY21 0DE (Tel & Fax: 01938 810446). Two self-catering bungalows, both wheelchair accessible, plus 4 berth caravan; farmhouse B&B. Astronomy available. WTB ★★★/★★★★★ *SELF-CATERING*. [🐕]
e-mail: madogswells@btopenworld.com

Llangurig

Village on River Wye, 4 miles south-west of Llanidloes. Ideal walking countryside.

MRS J. BAILEY, GLANGWY, LLANGURIG, LLANIDLOES SY18 6RS (01686 440697). Bed, breakfast and evening meals in the countryside. Plenty of walking locally. Prices on request.

Machynlleth

Small market town and tourist centre on River Dovey Valley. 16 miles north-east of Aberystwyth.

PETS WELCOME at The Wynnstay Hotel in historic Market Town of Machynlleth on the edge of Snowdonia, offering sandy beaches and glorious Welsh Countryside perfect for walking. Award winning food prepared by Chef Gareth Johns. WTB/AA/RAC ★★. Good Food Guide & Good Beer Guide Recommended. (01654 702941). [Pets free in kennels, £5 per night in rooms]
e-mail: info@wynnstay-hotel.com website: www.wynnstay-hotel.com

Presteigne

Attractive old town with half timbered houses. Ideal for hillside rambles and pony trekking.

MRS R. L. JONES, UPPER HOUSE, KINNERTON, NEAR PRESTEIGNE LD8 2PE (01547 560207). Cosy cottage in lovely Border countryside. 2 miles from Offa's Dyke. Central heating, washing machine, microwave, colour TV, inglenook, woodburner, linen included. Sleeps 4 plus cot. Ample parking. Sun-trap garden. On working farm in peaceful hamlet. Children and pets welcome. WTB Grade 4. [🐕].

Rhayader

Small market town on River Wye north of Builth Wells. Popular for angling and pony trekking

OAK WOOD LODGES, LLWYNBAEDD, RHAYADER LD6 5NT (01597 811422). SELF-CATERING LOG CABINS. Luxurious Norwegian log cabins with spectacular views of the Elan Valley and Cambrian Mountains. Walking, pony trekking, mountain biking, fishing and bird watching in idyllic surroundings. WTB ★★★★ Self-catering. [Pets £20 per week].

When making enquiries or bookings, a stamped addressed envelope is always appreciated

See also Colour Advertisement on page 71

Abergavenny

Historic market town at south-eastern gateway to Brecon Beacons National Park. Pony trekking, leisure centre; excellent touring base for Vale of Usk.

CHRISTINE SMITH, THE HALF MOON HOTEL, LLANTHONY, NEAR ABERGAVENNY NP7 7NN (01873 890611). Friendly 17th-Century Hotel. Serves good food and real ale. Enjoy wonderful scenery of Black Mountains. Good base. Walking, pony trekking. B&B accommodation. Dogs welcome. [🐕]
e-mail: halfmoonllanthony@talk21.com

Gower

Britain's first designated Area of Outstanding Natural Beauty with numerous sandy beaches and lovely countryside to explore.

CULVER HOUSE HOTEL, PORT EYNON, GOWER SA3 1NN (01792 390755). Small, friendly Hotel with fabulous food and quality service. Peacefully situated, with superb coast and countryside. En suite, sea views. WTB ★★ Country Hotel. [Pets £2 per night.]
website: www.culverhousehotel.co.uk

Llanmadoc

Village on Gower Peninsula, a secluded area with unspoilt beaches and many bird reserves.

MRS A. MAIN, TALLIZMAND, LLANMADOC, GOWER SA3 1DE (01792 386373). Located near the splendid Gower coastline, surrounded by beautiful countryside. Tallizmand has tastefully furnished en suite bedrooms with tea/coffee facilities. Home cooking, packed lunches. Non-smoking. Pets by arrangement. WTB ★★★ Guest House [🐕].
website: www.tallizmand.co.uk

Mumbles

Seaside resort of Swansea to west and north west of Mumbles Head.

MUMBLES & SWANSEA Holiday Homes, some with sea views. Flat locations. Well equipped, modern conveniences. Convenient for beaches, countryside and town's amenities. Personally supervised. Flexible bookings. WTB ★★★ and ★★★★. MRS JEAN GRIERSON, 112 MUMBLES ROAD, BLACKPILL, SWANSEA SA3 5AS (01792 402278). [🐕]

Porthkerry

Hamlet near the coast 2 miles south-west of Barry.

EGERTON GREY COUNTRY HOUSE HOTEL, PORTHKERRY, BARRY CF62 3BZ (01446 711666; Fax: 01446 711690). Magnificently preserved country house set in seven acres in a secluded valley 10 miles from Cardiff. Ideal for touring South Wales. WTB ★★★★ Hotel, AA ★★★ [🐕]
e-mail: info@egertongrey.co.uk website: www.egertongrey.co.uk

Redbrook on Wye

Village on the River Wye, 3 miles south-east of Monmouth.

OLD BREWERY HOUSE, BREWERY YARD, REDBROOK ON WYE, MONMOUTHSHIRE NP25 4LU (01600 713819). Welcoming en suite accommodation with courtyard garden and private parking. Scenic riverside and off-road walks. Two village pubs serve meals. B&B £55 per room per night. Dogs free. WTB ★★★ [🐕]
e-mail: enquiries@oldbreweryhouse.com website: www.oldbreweryhouse.com

Swansea

Second largest city in Wales with a wide variety of leisure activities and excellent shopping.

BEST WESTERN ABERAVON BEACH HOTEL, NEATH PORT TALBOT, SWANSEA BAY SA12 6QP (01639 884949). Modern seafront hotel. A warm Welsh welcome awaits you and your pets. 2 miles of flat promenade and a pet friendly beach. Pets Paradise!! And for you..... comfortable rooms, fine cuisine, leisure centre and many local attractions. AA/RAC ★★★.[🐕]

Wye Valley

Scenic area, ideal for relaxation.

MR & MRS J. LLEWELLYN, CWRT-Y-GAER, WOLVESNEWTON, CHEPSTOW NP16 6PR (01291 650700). 1, 4 or more dogs welcome free. Self-catering, attractively converted stone buildings of Welsh Longhouse. 20 acres, super views of Usk Vale. Brochure. Three units (one suitable for disabled). WTB ★★★ Welcome Host Gold Award. [pw! 🐕].
e-mail: john.llewellyn11@btinternet.com website: www.cwrt-y-gaer.co.uk

PLEASE MENTION THIS GUIDE WHEN YOU WRITE OR PHONE

TO ENQUIRE ABOUT ACCOMMODATION.

IF YOU ARE WRITING, A STAMPED, ADDRESSED ENVELOPE IS

ALWAYS APPRECIATED.

See also colour Advertisement on page 72

See also colour Advertisement on pages 4 & 5

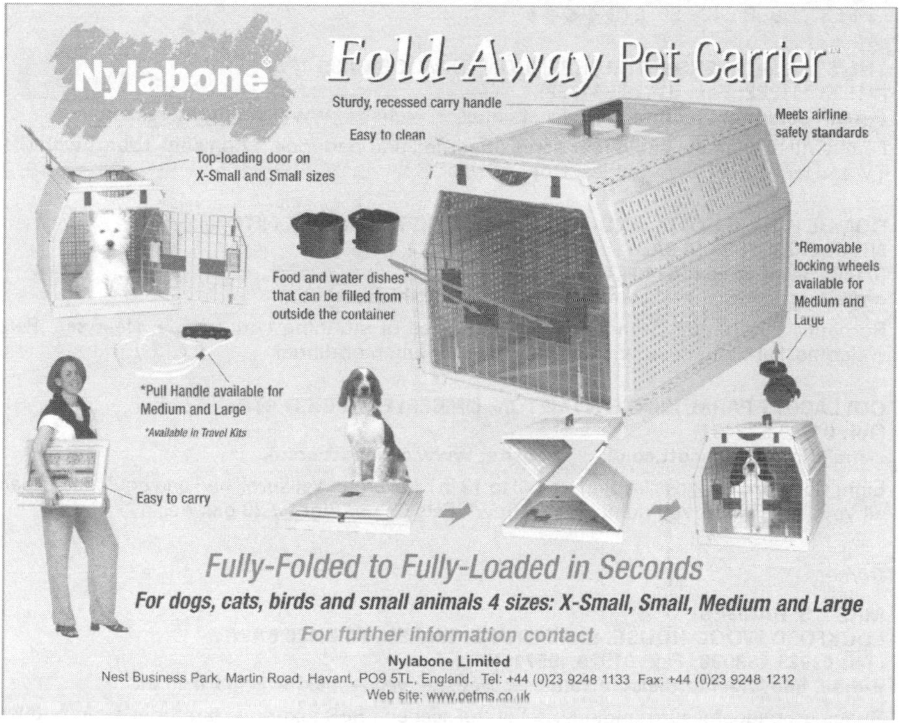

HOLIDAYS WITH HORSES

A selection of accommodation where horse and owner/rider can be put up at the same address – if not actually under the same roof! We would be grateful if readers making enquiries and/or bookings from this supplement would mention *Pets Welcome!*

ENGLAND

Devon

JAYE JONES & HELEN ASHER,
TWITCHEN FARM, CHALLACOMBE, BARNSTAPLE EX31 4TT
(Tel: 01598 763568)
e-mail: holidays@twitchen.co.uk • website: www.twitchen.co.uk

Comfort for country lovers in Exmoor National Park. All rooms en suite with TV. Meals prepared with local and some organic produce. Stabling £50 per week. Dogs no charge. B&B £24-£32, DB&B £42-£50. ETC ◆◆◆◆

THE STAG HUNTERS HOTEL, BRENDON, EXMOOR EX35 1PS
(01598 741222; Fax: 01598 741352)
e-mail: enquiries@staghunters.fsnet.co.uk • website: www.staghunters.com

Family-run village inn set in four acres of garden and paddock. 12 en suite rooms with CH, TV and tea/coffee. Own stables. Open all year.

COMBE HOUSE HOTEL AND RESTAURANT, GITTISHAM, HONITON,
NEAR EXETER EX14 3AD
(01404 540400; Fax: 01404 46004)
e-mail: stay@thishotel.com • website: www.thishotel.com

Romantic Elizabethan Manor set in 3,500 acres of stunning countryside. Near sea. Pets welcome. Fabulous food. Visitors welcome for lunch or dinner.

COLLACOTT FARM, KING'S NYMPTON, UMBERLEIGH EX37 9TP
(Tel: 01769 572491)
e-mail: info@collacott.co.uk • website: www.collacott.co.uk

Eight Country Cottages sleeping from 2 to 12 in rural area. Well furnished and equipped. Open all year. BHS Approved riding school. [pw!, Pets £3 per night, £20 per week]

Dorset

MRS L.S. BARNES
LUCKFORD WOOD HOUSE, EAST STOKE, WAREHAM BH20 6AW
(Tel: 01929 463098; Fax: 01929 405715)
e-mail: info@luckfordleisure.co.uk website: www.luckfordleisure.co.uk

Spacious, peaceful surroundings, delightful scenery. B&B luxurious farmhouse. Farmhouse breakfast served in conservatory or dining room. Camping facilities include showers. [Pets £5 per night, £30 per week].

Durham

MRS P A BOOTH,
IVESLEY EQUESTRIAN CENTRE, IVESLEY, WATERHOUSES DH7 9HB.
(Tel: 0191 373 4324; Fax: 0191 373 4757)
e-mail: ivesley@msn.com • website: ridingholidays-ivesley.co.uk

Beautifully furnished comfortable country house set in 220 acres in Durham but very quiet and rural. Excellent dog exercising facilities. En suite bedrooms. Excellent food. Licensed. Fully equipped Equestrian Centre adjacent.

Gloucestershire

CAROLINE MANN
HARTWELL FARM COTTAGES, NEAR BIBURY GL7 5ND
Tel: 01285 740210
e-mail: cottages@hartwells89.freeserve.co.uk
website: www.selfcateringcotswolds.com

Two comfortable cottages in Cotswolds with country views. Ideally located for touring, horse riding. Stabling available. Children and well-behaved dogs welcome. ETC ★★★★

Hampshire

MRS ADAMS,
THE HIGH CORNER INN, LINWOOD, RINGWOOD, HANTS BH24 3QY
(Tel: 01425 473973; Fax: 01425 483052)

Two en suite bedrooms deep in the heart of The New Forest. Real ales, home-cooked food, Sunday carvery and log fires. Stabling available. Horses and dogs welcome.

Lincolnshire

WEST WOLD FARMHOUSE
DEEPDALE, BARTON-UPON-HUMBER DN18 6ED
(Tel & Fax: 01652 633293)

Friendly, family-run farmhouse with easy access to bridleways and Viking Way. Excellent eating places nearby. Pets welcome, stabling and grazing for horses.

Oxfordshire

JUNE AND GEORGE COLLIER
55 NETHERCOTE ROAD, TACKLEY, KIDLINGTON, OXFORD OX5 3AT
(01869 331255; mobile: 07790 338225; Fax: 01869 331670)
e-mail: colliers.bnb@virgin.net

An ideal base for riding - superb network of Bridleways. Stop-over for Claude Duval route. Close to Blenheim. Regular train and bus service. Local Hostelries serve excellent food. ETC ◆◆◆ [🐕]

Somerset

LEONE & BRIAN MARTIN,
RISCOMBE FARM HOLIDAY COTTAGES, EXFORD,
EXMOOR NATIONAL PARK TA24 7NH
(Tel & Fax: 01643 831480)
website: www.riscombe.co.uk (with up-to-date vacancy info.)

Four self-catering stone cottages in the centre of Exmoor National Park. Excellent walking and riding country. Dogs and horses welcome. Open all year. ETC ★★★★

JANE STYLES
WINTERSHEAD FARM, SIMONSBATH, EXMOOR TA24 7LF
(Tel: 01643 831222)
Website: www.wintershead.co.uk

Five tastefully furnished and well-equipped cottages situated in the midst of beautiful Exmoor. Pets welcome, stables and grazing available. Colour brochure on request. ETC ★★★★ [Dogs and horses £12 per week, DIY Livery]

WESTERCLOSE HOUSE,
WITHYPOOL, EXMOOR NATIONAL PARK TA24 7QR
(Tel: 01643 831302)
website: www.westerclose.co.uk

Moorland cottages including two bungalows in grounds of old hunting lodge overlooking Barle Valley. Dogs and horses welcome. Shop and pub 300 metres. Cosy, quality and peaceful accommodation with excellent riding and superb stables.

East Yorkshire

PAWS-A-WHILE
KILNWICK PERCY, POCKLINGTON YO42 1UF
Tel:01759 301168; Mobile: 07711 866869)
e-mail: paws.a.while@lineone.net • website: www.pawsawhile.net

Small family B & B set in forty acres of parkland twixt York and Beverley. Golf, sauna, walking, riding. Pets and horses most welcome. Brochure available. ETC ◆◆◆◆

North Yorkshire

MEG ABU HAMDAN,
HIGH BELTHORPE, BISHOP WILTON, YORK YO42 1SB
(Tel: 01759 368238; Mobile: 07786 923330)

BHS Approved Livery yard in lovely surroundings. Bring your horse to enjoy the most fabulous hacking over the Yorkshire Wolds, still unspoilt and quiet. Farmhouse B&B. ETC ◆◆◆

West Yorkshire

MR & MRS HALSTEAD,
WEST ROYD FARM, MARSH LANE, SHEPLEY, HOLMFIRTH, HUDDERSFIELD HD8 8AY
(01484 602147; Fax: 01484 609427)
e-mail: summerwinecottages@lineone.net • website: www.summerwinecottages.co.uk

Three comfortable, well-equipped cottages, each with French doors leading into a beautiful walled garden. Set within six acres; indoor heated swimming pool. Cats and dogs welcome; DIY livery for horses available in modern on-site stable yards. ETC ★★★

SCOTLAND

Dumfries & Galloway

RUSKO HOLIDAYS,
GATEHOUSE OF FLEET, CASTLE DOUGLAS DG7 2BS
(Tel: 01557 814215; Fax: 01557 814679)
e-mail: info@ruskoholidays.co.uk • website: www.ruskoholidays.co.uk

Spacious, traditional farmhouse and charming, cosy cottages near beaches, hills and forest park. Lots of off-road riding amid stunning scenery. Stabling and grazing available for your own horse. Beautiful walking and riding country, fishing and tennis. Rates £189 – £1155. STB ★★ to ★★★★

Terms quoted in this publication may be subject to increase if rises in costs necessitate

WALES

Anglesey & Gwynedd

JUDY HUTCHINGS
TAL-Y-FOEL STUD FARM AND RIDING CENTRE
DWYRAN, ANGLESEY LL61 6LQ
(Tel & Fax: 01248 430377)
e-mail: riding@tal-y-foel.co.uk • website: www.tal-y-foel.co.uk

Waterfront location with spectacular views of Snowdonia. Luxury en suite rooms with whirlpool baths. Riding and horse livery, indoor/outdoor arenas, etc. Brochures on application. WTB ★★★★ FARM

Powys

GILFACH EQUITATION & HOLIDAYS
GILFACH FARM, SENNYBRIDGE LD3 8TY
(01874 636818; mobile: 07899 892582)
e-mail: sm@mip.co.uk website: www.breconbeaconsriding.co.uk

Charming self-catering accommodation for four plus grazing/stabling for your horse. Excellent equestrian facilities and instruction available. Fantastic riding country.

MRS E. BALLY
LANE FARM, PAINSCASTLE, BUILTH WELLS LD2 3JS
(Tel & Fax: 01497 851605)
e-mail: jbally@btclick.com

Self-Catering and Bed and Breakfast accommodation. Nine good stables and ample grazing in the heart of rural Radnorshire with wonderful open riding. Some cross-country jumps. WTB ★★★★

• • *Some Useful Guidance for Guests and Hosts* • •

Every year literally thousands of holidays, short breaks and overnight stops are arranged through our guides, the vast majority without any problems at all. In a handful of cases, however, difficulties do arise about bookings, which often could have been prevented from the outset.

It is important to remember that when accommodation has been booked, both parties – guests and hosts – have entered into a form of contract. We hope that the following points will provide helpful guidance.

GUESTS:

- When enquiring about accommodation, be as precise as possible. Give exact dates, numbers in your party and the ages of any children.
- State the number and type of rooms wanted and also what catering you require – bed and breakfast, full board etc. Make sure that the position about evening meals is clear – and about pets, reductions for children or any other special points.
- Read our reviews carefully to ensure that the proprietors you are going to contact can supply what you want. Ask for a letter confirming all arrangements, if possible.
- If you have to cancel, do so as soon as possible. Proprietors do have the right to retain deposits and under certain circumstances to charge for cancelled holidays if adequate notice is not given and they cannot re-let the accommodation.

HOSTS:

- Give details about your facilities and about any special conditions. Explain your deposit system clearly and arrangements for cancellations, charges etc. and whether or not your terms include VAT.
- If for any reason you are unable to fulfil an agreed booking without adequate notice, you may be under an obligation to arrange suitable alternative accommodation or to make some form of compensation.

While every effort is made to ensure accuracy, we regret that FHG Publications cannot accept responsibility for errors, omissions or misrepresentations in our entries or any consequences thereof. Prices in particular should be checked because we go to press early. We will follow up complaints but cannot act as arbiters or agents for either party.

THE FHG DIPLOMA

HELP IMPROVE BRITISH TOURIST STANDARDS

You are choosing holiday accommodation from our very popular FHG Publications. Whether it be a hotel, guest house, farmhouse or self-catering accommodation, we think you will find it hospitable, comfortable and clean, and your host and hostess friendly and helpful.

Why not write and tell us about it?

As a recognition of the generally well-run and excellent holiday accommodation reviewed in our publications, we at FHG Publications Ltd. present a diploma to proprietors who receive the highest recommendation from their guests who are also readers of our Guides. If you care to write to us praising the holiday you have booked through FHG Publications Ltd. – whether this be board, self-catering accommodation, a sporting or a caravan holiday, what you say will be evaluated and the proprietors who reach our final list will be contacted.

The winning proprietor will receive an attractive framed diploma to display on his premises as recognition of a high standard of comfort, amenity and hospitality. FHG Publications Ltd. offer this diploma as a contribution towards the improvement of standards in tourist accommodation in Britain. Help your excellent host or hostess to win it!

FHG DIPLOMA

We nominate ....

....

Because

Name ....

Address ....

....

Telephone No..

A Guide to Pet-Friendly Pubs

ENGLAND

BEDFORDSHIRE

BERKSHIRE

UNCLE TOM'S CABIN
Hills Lane, Cookham Dean, Berkshire (01628 483339).
Dogs allowed throughout.
Pet Regulars: Flossie and Ollie (Old English Sheepdog). Free dog biscuit pub.

THE GREYHOUND (known locally as 'The Dog')
The Walk, Eton Wick, Berkshire (01753 863925).
Dogs allowed throughout the pub.
Pet Regulars: Harvey (Retriever), retrieves anything, including Beer mats. KIA - German Shepherd.

THE SWAN
9 Mill Lane, Clewer, Windsor, Berkshire (01753 862069).
Dogs allowed throughout the pub.
Pet Regulars: Mollie and Lucy (Jack Russells).

THE TWO BREWERS
Park Street, Windsor, Berkshire (01753 855426).
Dogs allowed, public and saloon bars.
Pet Regulars: Harry (Pyrenean) and his mate Molly (Newfoundland) take up the whole bar, 'Bear' (Black Labrador), Tessa (Cocker Spaniel), Rufus (Springer Spaniel), Mr Darcy (Poodle), Mr Darcy (Great Dane), Rosie (Chocolate Labrador), Jessie (Labrador/German Shepherd) and Jemma (Golden Retriever).

Please mention *Pets Welcome*
when enquiring about accommodation featured in these pages.

BUCKINGHAMSHIRE

WHITE HORSE
Village Lane, Hedgerley, Buckinghamshire SL2 3UY (01753 643225).
Dogs allowed at tables on pub frontage, beer garden (on leads), public bar.

FROG AT SKIRMETT
Skirmett, Henley-on-Thames, Buckinghamshire RG9 6TG (01491 638996)
Dogs welcome, pet friendly.
Pet Regular: Resident cat "Cleo".

GEORGE AND DRAGON
High Street, West Wycombe, Buckinghamshire HP14 3AB (01494 464414)
Pet friendly.

CAMBRIDGESHIRE

YE OLD WHITE HART
Main Street, Ufford, Peterborough, Cambridgeshire (01780 740250).
Dogs allowed in non-food areas.

CHESHIRE

THE GROSVENOR ARMS
Chester Road, Aldford, Cheshire CH3 6HJ (01244 620228)
Pet friendly.
Pet Regulars: resident dog "Sadie" (Labrador).

JACKSONS BOAT
Rifle Road, Sale, Cheshire (0161 973 8549).
Dogs allowed throughout on lead.

CORNWALL

DRIFTWOOD SPARS HOTEL
Trevaunance Cove, St Agnes, Cornwall (01872 552428).
Dogs allowed everywhere except the restaurant.
Pet Regulars: Buster (Cornish Labrador cross with a Seal) - devours anything.

JUBILEE INN
Pelynt, Near Looe, Cornwall PL13 2JZ (01503 220312).
Dogs allowed in all areas except restaurant; accommodation for guests with dogs.

THE MILL HOUSE INN
Trebarwith Strand, Tintagel, Cornwall PL34 0HD (01840 770200).
Pet friendly.

THE MOLESWORTH ARMS HOTEL
Molesworth Street, Wadebridge, Cornwall PL27 7DP (01208 812055).
Dogs allowed in all public areas and in hotel rooms.
Pet Regulars: Thomson Cassidy (Black Lab), Ruby Cassidy and Lola (Black Lab).

CUMBRIA

THE BRITANNIA INN
Elterwater, Ambleside, Cumbria LA22 9HP (015394 37210).
Dogs allowed in all areas except dining room and residential lounge.
Pet Friendly.

THE MORTAL MAN HOTEL
Troutbeck, Windermere, Cumbria LA23 lPL (015394 33193).
Pets allowed everywhere except restaurant.

STAG INN
Dufton, Appleby, Cumbria (017683 51608).
Dogs allowed in non-food bar, beer garden, village green plus B&B and cottage.
Pet Regulars: Toffee (cross between Saluki and Golden Setter); Willow (cross between Great Dane and an Old English Sheepdog); Kim (Weimaraner), best bitter drinker; Toffee (cross between Chihuahua and Papillon – likes beef dinner. Seb 'chats up' Toffee.

WATERMILL INN
School Lane, Ings, Near Staveley, Kendal, Cumbria (01539 821309).
Dogs allowed in beer garden, Wrynose bottom bar.
Pet Regulars: Blot (sheepdog) and Scruffy (mongrel). Both enjoy a range of crisps and snacks. Scruffy regularly drinks Cheaston Best Bitter. Pub dog Shelley (German Shepherd). Owners cannot walk dogs past pub, without being dragged in! Biscuits and water provided.

DERBYSHIRE

THE GEORGE HOTEL
Commercial Road, Tideswell, Near Buxton, Derbyshire SK17 8NU (01298 871382).
Dogs allowed in snug and around the bar, water bowls provided.

DOG AND PARTRIDGE COUNTRY INN & MOTEL
Swinscoe, Ashbourne, Derbyshire (01335 343183).
Dogs allowed throughout, except restaurant.
Pet Regulars: Include Mitsy (57); Rusty (Cairn); Spider (Collie/GSD) and Rex (GSD).

DEVONSHIRE ARMS
Peak Forest, Near Buxton, Derbyshire SK17 8EJ (01298 23875)
Dogs allowed in bar.

DEVON

THE SHIP INN
Axmouth, Devon EX12 4AF (01297 21838).
A predominantly catering pub, so dogs on a lead please.
Pet Regulars: Charlie (Labrador), Kym (Boxer), Soxy (cat). Also resident Tawny Owl.

BRENDON HOUSE
Brendon, Lynton, North Devon EX35 6PS (01598 741206).
Dogs very welcome and allowed in tea gardens, guest bedrooms by arrangement.
Owner's dogs - Drummer (Labrador) and Piper (Labrador).

THE BULLERS ARMS
Chagford, Newton Abbot, Devon (01647 432348).
Dogs allowed throughout pub, except dining room/kitchen. "More than welcome".

CROWN AND SCEPTRE
2 Petitor Road, Torquay, Devon TQ1 4QA (01803 328290).
Dogs allowed in non-food bar, family room, lounge. All dogs welcome.
Pet Regulars: Two Jack Russells - Scrappy Doo and Minnie Mouse.

THE JOURNEY'S END INN
Ringmore, Near Kingsbridge, South Devon TQ7 4HL (01548 810205).
Dogs allowed throughout the pub except in the dining room, must be on a lead.

PALK ARMS INN
Hennock, Bovey Tracey, Devon TQ13 9QS (01626 836584).
Pets welcome.

THE ROYAL OAK INN
Dunsford, Near Exeter, Devon EX6 7DA (01647 252256).
Dogs allowed in bars, beer garden, accommodation for guests with dogs.
Pet Regulars: Cleo and Kizi.

THE POLSHAM ARMS
Lower Polsham Road, Paignton, Devon (01803 558360).
Dogs allowed throughout the pub.
Pet Regulars: Stella (German Shepherd), pub dog; C.J. (West Highland Terrier) loves pork scratchings; Patch, owner brings his supply of dog biscuits, and Bracken (German Shepherd).

THE SEA TROUT INN
Staverton, Near Totnes, Devon TQ9 6PA (01803 762274).
Dogs welcome in lounge and public bar, beer garden, owners' rooms (but not on beds).
Pet Regulars: Buster (resident dog) partial to beer drip trays.

THE DEVONSHIRE INN
Sticklepath, Okehampton, Devon EX20 2NW (01837 840626).
Dogs allowed in non-food bar, car park, beer garden, family room and guest rooms.
Pet Regulars: Clarrie and Rosie (Terriers).

THE TROUT & TIPPLE

(A386 - Tavistock to Okehampton Road), Parkwood Road, Tavistock, Devon PL10 0JS (01822 618886)

Dogs welcome at all times in bar, games room and patio.

Pet regulars include: Jet (black Labrador) likes biscuits and his two sons Connor and Fenrhys - sometimes misbehave. Alf (GSD) visits occasionally - but has to stay off the Guinness. Casey (Bronze Springer) - always after food. Border, Chaos and Mischief (Border Collies). Also, our own two dogs Borgia (GBD 57) and Morgan (no brain lurcher).

DORSET

THE ANVIL HOTEL

Sailsbury Road, Pimperne, Blandford, Dorset DT11 8UQ (01258 453431).

Pets allowed in bar, lounge and bedrooms.

THE SQUARE AND COMPASS

Swanage, Dorset BH19 3LF (01929 439229).

Well-behaved dogs allowed - but beware of the chickens!

THE NOTHE TAVERN

Barrack Road, Weymouth, Dorset DT4 8TZ (01305 839255).

Pet friendly - well known for allowing pets.

Pet Regulars: get a warm welcome from the pub Alsatian.

DRUSILLA'S INN

Wigbeth, Horton, Dorset (01258 840297).

Well-behaved dogs welcome.

DURHAM

MOORCOCK INN

Hill Top, Eggleston, Teesdale, County Durham DL12 9AU (01833 650395).

Pet Regulars: Thor, the in-house hound dog, and Raymond, the resident hack, welcome all equine travellers; Gem (Jack Russell); Arnie (Ginger Tom); Poppy (Jack Russell); Haflinger - the horse.

TAP AND SPILE

27 Front Street, Framwellgate Moor, Durham DH1 5EE (0191 386 5451).

Dogs allowed throughout the pub.

THE ROSE TREE

Low Road West, Shincliff, Durham DH1 2LY (0191-386 8512).

Pets allowed in bar area only.

Pet Regulars: "Benson" (Boxer), "Ben" (Miniature White Poodle) and "Oliver" (King Charles).

THE SEVEN STARS

High Street North, Shincliff, Durham (0191-384 8454).

Dogs welcome in bar area only.

ESSEX

WHITE HARTE

The Quay, Burnham-on-Crouch, Essex CM0 8AS (01621 782106).
Pets welcome.
Pet Regulars: Resident dog "Tilly" (Collie).

THE OLD SHIP

Heybridge Basin, Heybridge, Maldon, Essex (01621 854150).
Dogs allowed throughout pub.

GLOUCESTERSHIRE

THE OLD STOCKS HOTEL

The Square, Stow on the Wold, Gloucestershire GL54 1AF (01451 830666).
Dogs allowed in the beer garden, accommodation for dogs and their owners also available.
Pet Regulars: Ben (Labrador) enjoys bitter from the drip trays and Oscar (Doberman) often gets carried out as he refuses to leave.

THE OLD CROWN

The Green, Uley, Gloucestershire GL11 5SN (01453 861070).
Pets allowed throughout the pub.

GREATER LONDON

THE PHOENIX

28 Thames Street, Sunbury on Thames, Middlesex (01932 785358).
Dogs allowed on lead in non-food bar, beer garden, family room. Capability 2 Grading.
Pet Regulars: Sammy (Black Labrador), Billy and Ellie (Lhasa).

THE TIDE END COTTAGE

Ferry Road, Teddington, Middlesex (0208 977 7762).
Dogs allowed throughout the pub.
Pet Regulars: Mimi (Labrador).

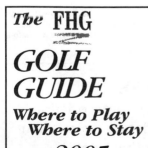

HAMPSHIRE

THE SUN
Sun Hill, Bentworth, Alton, Hampshire GU34 5JT (01420 562338)
Pets welcome throughout the pub.
Pet Regulars: "Rover" (Black Labrador) and "Dilweed" the cat.

HIGH CORNER INN
Linwood, Near Ringwood, Hampshire BH24 3QY (01425 473973).
Dogs, and even horses, are catered for here.

THE CHEQUERS
Ridgeway Lane, Lower Pennington, Lymington, Hants (01590 673415).
Dogs allowed in non-food bar, outdoor barbecue area (away from food).
Pet Regulars: Rusty Boyd - parties held for him. Resident pet - D'for (Labrador).

THE VICTORY
High Street, Hamble-le-Rice, Southampton, Hampshire (023 80 453105).
Dogs allowed.

HERTFORDSHIRE

THE BLACK HORSE
Chorley Wood Common, Dog Kennel Lane, Rickmansworth, Herts (01923 282252).
Dogs very welcome and allowed throughout the pub, on a lead.

THE RED LION
Chenies Village, Rickmansworth, Hertfordshire WD3 6ED (01923 282722).
Pets welcome in bar area only.
Pet Regulars: Resident dog "Bobby" (Terriers mixture), "Moss" and "Luke" (Boxer).

THE ROBIN HOOD AND LITTLE JOHN
Rabley Heath, near Codicote, Hertfordshire (01438 812361).
Dogs allowed in non-food bar, car park tables, beer garden.
Pet Regulars: Bonnie (Labrador), beer-mat catcher. The locals of the pub have close to 50 dogs between them, most of which visit from time to time. The team includes a two Labrador search squad dispatched by one regular's wife to indicate time's up. When they arrive he has five minutes' drinking up time before all three leave together.

KENT

KENTISH HORSE
Cow Lane, Mark Beech, Edenbridge, Kent (01342 850493).
Dogs allowed in reserved area.

THE OLD NEPTUNE
Marine Terrace, Whitstable, Kent CT5 lEJ (01227 272262).
Dogs allowed in beach frontage.

THE SWANN INN
Little Chart, Kent TN27 0QB (01233 840702).
Dogs allowed - everywhere except restaurant.

LANCASHIRE

ASSHETON ARMS
Downham, Clitheroe, Blackburn, Lancashire BB7 4BJ (01200 441227).
Dogs welcome.

MALT'N HOPS
50 Friday Street, Chorley, Lancashire PR6 0AH (01257 260967).
Dogs allowed throughout pub if kept under control.
Pet Regulars: Mork – says please for bag of crisps.

LINCOLNSHIRE

THE HAVEN INN
Ferry Road, Barrow Haven, North Lincolnshire DN19 7EX (01469 530247).
Dogs allowed in the public bar, beer garden, and bedrooms on their own bed/blanket.

THE BLUE DOG INN
Main Street, Sewstern, Grantham, Lincs NG33 5QR (01476 860097).
Dogs allowed.
Pet Regulars: The Guv'nor (Great Dane), best draught-excluder in history; Cassie (Scottie) shares biscuits with pub cats; Nelson – Terrier. Also two cats: Fred and Brahms.

MERSEYSIDE

THE SCOTCH PIPER
Southport Road, Lydiate, Merseyside (0151 526 0503).
Dogs allowed throughout the pub.

MIDLANDS

AWENTSBURY HOTEL
21 Serpentine Road, Selly Park, Birmingham B29 7HU (0121 472 1258).
Dogs allowed.
Pet Regulars: Well-behaved dogs welcome.

NORFOLK

THE OLD RAILWAY TAVERN
Eccles Road, Quidenham, Norwich, Norfolk NR16 2JG (01953 888223).
Dogs allowed, must be on lead.
Pet Regulars: Roscow (Poodle) and pub dogs Flo (Scottish Terrier) and Benji (Jack Russell).

THE HOSTE ARMS
The Green, Burnham Market, King's Lynn, Norfolk PE31 8HD (01328 738777).
Dogs allowed throughout the pub.
Pet Regulars: "Augustus" and "Sweep" (Black Labradors).

THE ROSE AND CROWN
Nethergate Street, Harpley, King's Lynn, Norfolk (01485 520577).
Dogs allowed in non-food bar, car park tables. .

OXFORDSHIRE

THE BELL
Shenington, Banbury, Oxfordshire OX15 6NQ (01295 670274).
Pets allowed throughout.
Pet Regulars: Resident pub dogs "Oliver" (Great Dane) and "Daisy" (Labrador).

THE PLOUGH INN
High Street, Finstock, Chipping Norton, Oxfordshire (01993 868333).
Dogs more than welcome.
Pet Regulars: Resident dogs - "Jodi", "Charlie" and "Rosie" (Poodles); "Henry","Gertie" (Beagles) and "Zac" (Sheepdog) are regular visitors.

THE BELL INN
High Street, Adderbury, Oxon (01295 810338).
Dogs allowed throughout the pub with the exception of the restaurant and letting rooms.
Owner's dog: Elsa (Black Labrador).

FREE or REDUCED RATE entry to Holiday Visits and Attractions – see our READERS' OFFER VOUCHERS on pages 101-116

SHROPSHIRE

THE TRAVELLERS REST INN
Church Stretton, Shropshire (01694 781275).
Well-mannered pets welcome - but beware of the cats!

LONGMYND HOTEL
Cunnery Road, Church Stretton, Shropshire SY6 6AG (01694 722244).
Dogs allowed in owners' hotel bedrooms but not in public areas.
Pet Regulars: Bruno and Frenzie; and owner's dogs, Sam and Sailor.

SOMERSET

CASTLE OF COMFORT HOTEL
Dodington, Nether Stowey, Bridgwater, Somerset TA5 1LE (01278 741264).
Pet friendly.

THE SPARKFORD INN
High Street, Sparkford, Somerset BA22 7JN (01963 440218).
Dogs allowed in bar areas but not in restaurant; safe garden and car park.

THE BUTCHERS ARMS
Carhampton, Somerset (01643 821333).
Dogs allowed in bar. B&B accommodation available.

HOOD ARMS
Kilve, Somerset TA5 1EA (01278 741210)
Pets welcome.

THE SHIP INN
High Street, Porlock, Somerset (01643 862507).
Dogs allowed throughout and in guests' rooms.
Pet Regulars: Include Silver (Jack Russell); Sam (Black Lab) and Max (Staffordshire). Monty (Pug), resident pet.

SUFFOLK

THE KINGS HEAD
High Street, Southwold, Suffolk IP18 6AD (01502 724517).
Well-behaved dogs welcome.

SIX BELLS AT BARDWELL
The Green, Bardwell, Bury St Edmunds, Suffolk IP31 1AW (01359 250820).
Dogs allowed in guest bedrooms but not allowed in bar and restaurant.

SURREY

THE PLOUGH
South Road, Woking, Surrey GU21 4JL (01483 714105).
Pets welcome in restricted areas.

THE SPORTSMAN
Mogador Road, Mogador, Surrey (01737 246655).
Adopted dogs congregate at this pub.
Pet Regulars: "Daisy" (Mongrel) and "Max" (German Shepherd).

THE CRICKETERS
12 Oxenden Road, Tongham, Farnham, Surrey (01252 333262).
Dogs allowed in beer garden on lead.

SUSSEX

THE FORESTERS ARMS
High Street, Fairwarp, Near Uckfield, East Sussex TN22 3BP (01825 712808).
Dogs allowed in the beer garden and at car park tables, also inside.
Dog biscuits always available.

THE PLOUGH
Crowhurst, Near Battle, East Sussex TN33 9AY (01424 830310).
Dogs allowed in non-food bar, car park tables, beer garden. .

QUEENS HEAD
Village Green, Sedlescombe, East Sussex (01424 870228).
Dogs allowed throughout the pub.

THE SLOOP INN
Freshfield Lock, Haywards Heath, West Sussex RH17 7NP (01444 831219).
Dogs allowed in public bar and garden.

THE SMUGGLERS' ROOST

125 Sea Lane, Rustington, West Sussex BN16 2SG (01903 785714).
Dogs allowed in non-food bar, at car park tables, in beer garden, family room.
Pet Regulars: Skip; Malcolm (Bull Mastiff); PJ and Mel (Staffs); Leo (Border Terrier), forms instant affections with anyone who notices him; Tim (King Charles Spaniel), quite prepared to guard his corner when food appears. The landlord owns an Alsatian.

THE SPORTSMAN'S ARMS

Rackham Road, Amberley, Near Arundel, West Sussex BN18 9NR (01798 831787).
Dogs allowed in the bar area.

WILTSHIRE

THE HORSE AND GROOM

The Street, Charlton, Near Malmesbury, Wiltshire (01666 823904).
Dogs welcome in bar.
Pet Regulars: Buster (Basset Hound); Troy (black Labrador).

THE PETERBOROUGH ARMS

Dauntsey Lock, Near Chippenham, Wiltshire SN15 4HD (01249 890409).
All pets welcome in bar.
Resident pets - Poppy, Holly and Lilly (3 generations of Jack Russell).

THE THREE HORSESHOES

High Street, Chapmanslade, Near Westbury, Wiltshire (01373 832280).
Dogs allowed in non-food bar and beer garden.
Resident Pets: Include Oscar (dog) and one cat. Three horses overlooking the beer garden.

YORKSHIRE

BARNES WALLIS INN

North Howden, Howden, East Yorkshire (01430 430639).
Guide dogs only

KINGS HEAD INN

Barmby on the Marsh, East Yorkshire DN14 7HL (01757 630705).
Dogs allowed in non-food bar.
Pet Regulars: Many and varied!

THE FORESTERS ARMS

Kilburn, North Yorkshire YO6 4AH (01347 868386).
Dogs allowed throughout, except restaurant.
Pet Regulars: Ainsley (Black Labrador).

NEW INN HOTEL

Clapham, Near Settle, North Yorkshire LA2 8HH (015242 51203).
Dogs allowed in bar, beer garden, bedrooms.

SIMONSTONE HALL

Hawes, North Yorkshire DL8 3LY (01969 667255).
Dogs allowed except dining area.
Dogs of all shapes, sizes and breeds welcome.

THE SPINNEY

Forest Rise, Balby, Doncaster, South Yorkshire DN4 9HQ (01302 852033).
Dogs allowed throughout the pub.
Pet Regulars: Shamus (Irish Setter), pub thief - fair game includes pool balls, beer mats, crisps, beer, coats, hats - jumped 15 feet off pub roof with no ill effect; Wyn (Labrador) a guide dog and Buster (Staff).

THE ROCKINGHAM ARMS

8 Main Street, Wentworth, Rotherham, South Yorkshire S62 7LO (01226 742075).
Pets welcome.
Pet Regulars: Sheeba (Springer Spaniel), Charlie and Gypsy (Black Labradors), Sally (Alsatian) and Rosie (Jack Russell).

THE GOLDEN FLEECE

Lindley Road, Blackley, near Huddersfield, West Yorkshire (01422 372704).
Dogs allowed in non-food bar.
Pet Regulars: Holly and Honey (Border Collies).

CHANNEL ISLANDS/JERSEY

LA PULENTE INN

La Pulente, St Brelade, Jersey (01534 744487).
Dogs allowed in public bar.

WALES

ANGLESEY & GWYNEDD

THE GRAPES HOTEL

Maentwrog, Blaenau Ffestiniog, Gwynedd LL41 4HN (01766 590365).
Pets allowed in bar area only.

THE BUCKLEY HOTEL

Castle Street, Beaumaris, Isle of Anglesey LL58 8AW (01248 810415).
Dogs allowed throughout the pub, except in the dining room and bistro.
Pet Regulars: Cassie (Springer Spaniel) and Rex (mongrel), dedicated 'companion' dogs, also Charlie (Spaniel).

NORTH WALES

THE WEST ARMS HOTEL

Llanarmon Dyffryn Ceiriog, Llangollen, North Wales LL20 7LD (01691 600665).
Welcome pets.

CARMARTHENSHIRE

PEMBROKESHIRE

THE FARMERS

14-16 Goat Street, St David's, Pembrokeshire (01437 721666).
Pets welcome in the pub area only.

POWYS

SEVERN ARMS HOTEL
Penybont, Llandrindod Wells, Powys LD1 5UA (01597 851224).
Dogs allowed in the bar, but not the restaurant, and in the rooms - but not on the beds.

SCOTLAND

ABERDEEN, BANFF & MORAY

THE CLIFTON BAR
Clifton Road, Lossiemouth, Moray (01343 812100).
Dogs allowed in beer garden only.

ROYAL OAK
Station Road, Urquhart, Elgin, Moray (01343 842607).
Dogs allowed throughout pub.
Pet Regulars: Jack (Collie).

ARGYLL & BUTE

CAIRNDOW STAGECOACH INN
Cairndow, Argyll PA26 8BN (01499 600286).
Pet regulars: Our own dog Rocky is a Golden Labrador.

THE BALLACHULISH HOTEL
Ballachulish, Argyll PA39 4JY (01855 811606).
Dogs allowed in the lounge, beer garden and guests' bedrooms, excluding food areas.

EDINBURGH & LOTHIANS

JOHNSBURN HOUSE
Johnsburn Road, Balerno, Lothians EH14 7BB (0131-449 3847).
Pets welcome in bar area only.
Pet Regulars: Resident dog "Topaz" (Great Dane).

LAIRD & DOG
Lasswade, Midlothian (0131-663 9219).
Dogs allowed in bar.
Pet Regulars: Many pet regulars. Drinking bowls .

PERTH & KINROSS

FOUR SEASONS HOTEL
St Fillans, Perthshire (01764 685333).
Dogs allowed in all non-food areas.

THE MUNRO INN
Main Street, Strathyre, Perthshire FK18 8NA (01877 384333).
Dogs allowed throughout pub, lounge, games room, beer garden and bedrooms (except restaurant).
Pet Regulars: Residents Jess (black mongrel with brown eyes) and Jules (white lurcher with blue eyes) have many local pals who visit including Rory, Cally, Kerry and Robbie. Bring your dog to visit! Water and dog biscuits always available.

Index of Towns and Counties

PLEASE NOTE

Readers are requested to mention this guidebook when seeking accommodation (and please enclose a stamped addressed envelope).

When making enquiries or bookings, a stamped addressed envelope is always appreciated

OTHER FHG TITLES FOR 2005

FHG Publications have a large range of attractive holiday accommodation guides for all kinds of holiday opportunities throughout Britain. They also make useful gifts at any time of year. Our guides are available in most bookshops and larger newsagents but we will be happy to post you a copy direct if you have any difficulty. POST FREE for addresses in the UK. We will also post abroad but have to charge separately for post or freight.

The original
Farm Holiday Guide to COAST & COUNTRY HOLIDAYS in England, Scotland, Wales and Channel Islands. Board, Self-catering, Caravans/Camping, Activity Holidays. ☐

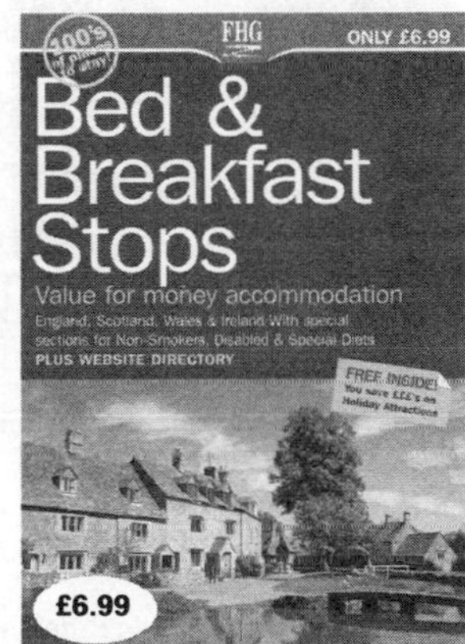

BED AND BREAKFAST STOPS ☐
Over 1000 friendly and comfortable overnight stops. Non-smoking, Disabled and Special Diets Supplements.

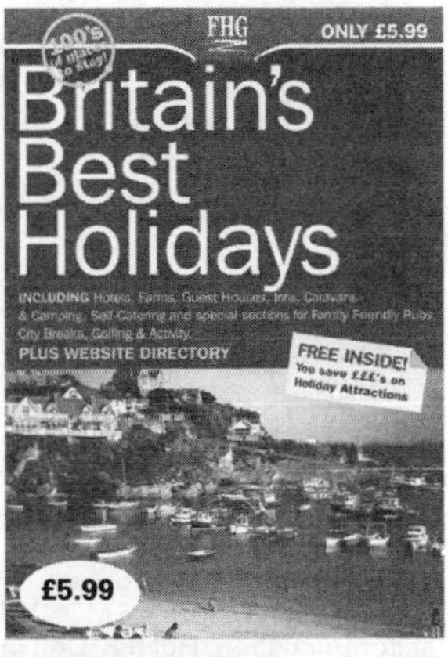

BRITAIN'S BEST HOLIDAYS ☐
A quick-reference general guide for all kinds of holidays.

Recommended ☐
WAYSIDE AND COUNTRY INNS of Britain
Pubs, Inns and small hotels.

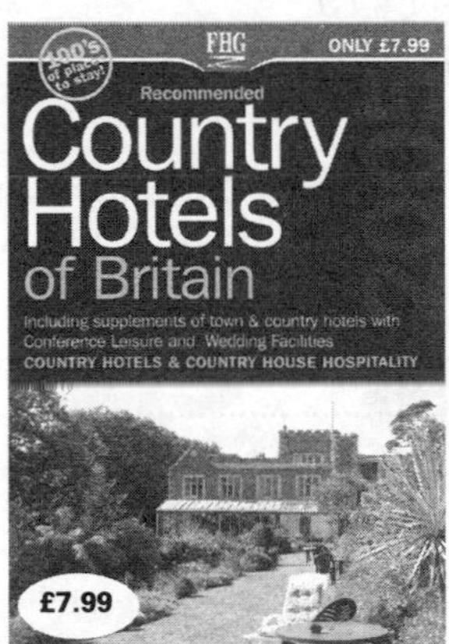

Recommended ☐
COUNTRY HOTELS
of Britain
Including Country Houses, for the discriminating.

Recommended ☐
SHORT BREAK HOLIDAYS IN BRITAIN
"Approved" accommodation for quality bargain breaks.

CHILDREN WELCOME! ☐
Family Holidays and Days Out guide.
Family holidays with details of amenities for children and babies.

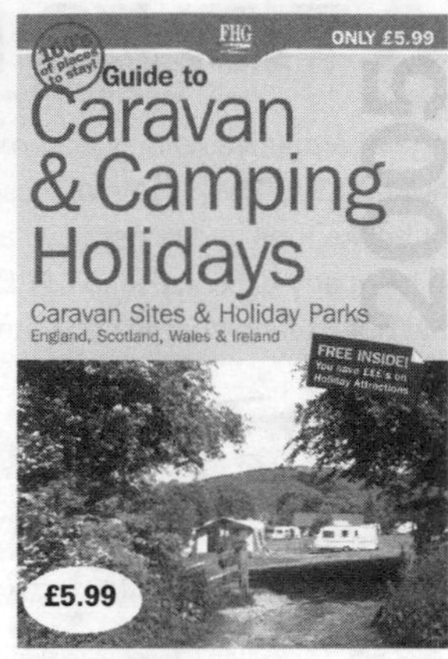

The FHG Guide to **CARAVAN & CAMPING HOLIDAYS,** ☐
Caravans for hire, sites and holiday parks and centres.

SELF-CATERING HOLIDAYS ☐
in Britain
Over 1000 addresses throughout for self-catering and caravans in Britain.

The GOLF GUIDE –
Where to play Where to stay £9.99
In association with GOLF MONTHLY. Over 2800 golf courses in Britain with convenient accommodation. Holiday Golf in France, Portugal, Spain, USA, South Africa and Thailand. ☐

Tick your choice and send your order and payment to

FHG PUBLICATIONS, ABBEY MILL BUSINESS CENTRE, SEEDHILL, PAISLEY PA1 1TJ

TEL: 0141- 887 0428; FAX: 0141- 889 7204

e-mail: fhg@ipcmedia.com

FHG

Deduct 10% for 2/3 titles or copies; 20% for 4 or more.

Send to: NAME ....

ADDRESS ....

....

....

POST CODE ....

I enclose Cheque/Postal Order for £ ....

SIGNATURE ....DATE ....

Please complete the following to help us improve the service we provide. How did you find out about our guides?:

☐Press ☐Magazines ☐TV/Radio ☐Family/Friend ☐Other

Try the fresh new dental chew

For strong teeth and fresh breath

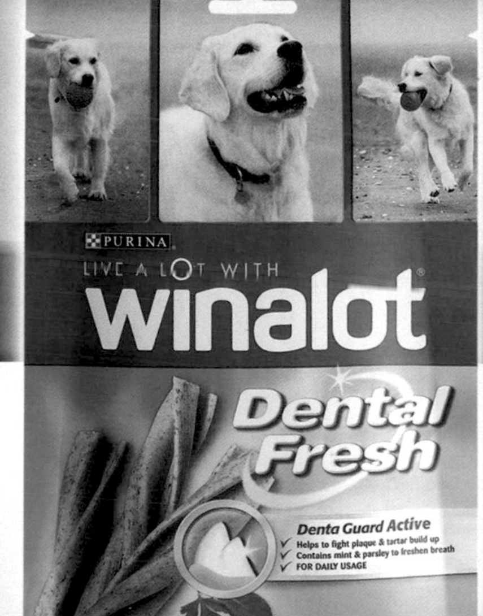

BRITAIN'S BEST-SELLING DOG MAGAZINE
your dog
September 2004
£2.95
20 pages of your questions answered
Clicker training
Coping with adolescence
What makes him so aggressive?
page 54
YOUR DOG ESSENTIALS
page 89
How to...
Make walks interesting
Choose the ideal dog food
Stimulate your dog
DEAF NOT DUMB!
Meet the dogs who live life to the full
THE BIG C
Coping with cancer
DON'T LET HIM SUFFER IN SILENCE
It's Arthritis Awareness Month
BEST OF BRITISH
The Clumber Spaniel
OLDER... AND WISER?
Why mature dogs make great pets
PLUS
How puppies learn in the womb
Training basics – fun and games
Walks in Scotland
The water of life

Your dog-friendly guide to

North Yorkshir

Spring in Yorkshire is the perfect time for visitors to enjoy this delightful county.

Foxup and Cosh, Littondale

by Mary Welsh

This is a glorious walk for a fine spring day, when the pastures of Littondale are spangled with flowers and the air resounds with the calls of curlews. Look for dippers and wagtails as you dawdle by the beck. On a winter's day, the route is dramatic and equally enjoyable, with snow covering the high slopes, the many stone walls cloaked in white.

Walk 1

Route planner

1 From the verge on which you've parked, walk south along the road, in the direction of Stainforth, to take a stile on the left, signposted Nether Hesleden. Follow the footpath, beside a wire fence on the left, and continue where it drops steadily, keeping above the steep slopes of Penyghent Gill to your right. Continue walking, climbing over a stile and walking on again to pass through a gate. Carry on, keeping to the right of the farmhouse, which has a datestone of 1748.

2 After a few metres, take the well-marked stile on your left. From now on it is impossible to get lost. The path is signposted, and several stiles take you through the fields. Pass several barns before coming close to the River Skirfare. Continue on the pleasing way, going through the very narrow, gated step stile on to Halton Bridge. Away to the right lies the hamlet of Halton Gill, nestling below Horse Head Moor. Then go through the stile opposite and follow the stiled pastures to the hamlet of Foxup.

3 Here you may decide to start your return. But if walkers and their dogs wish to extend the walk by going on towards Cosh at the head of the dale, turn right to cross Foxup Bridge and then left. Stroll the track as it leaves the hamlet behind and takes you out into the lower slopes of the wild Great Pasture. Beside you, either in sight or sound, flows Cosh Beck. As you

The dogs will be in their element as they partner you along this walk.

By extending your walk, you'll be able to view remote Cosh Head, and a ruin, once a fine Elizabethan house.

Snowfall turns Foxup into a delightful winter scene.

Potts Moor

2

Littondale

Nether Hesleden

go, look for the tiny arched cobbled bridge over the rushing water. Continue on the gated track as it passes through the lonely moorland. Step across several fords, pass three small enclosed conifer plantations and then go on until you reach the few buildings at Cosh.

4 After a pause here, return by your outward route to cross Foxup Bridge. Just beyond, take the bridleway on the left, signposted Horton-in-Ribblesdale. Go through a gate and climb diagonally right, following a grassy track to a signpost just before the wall. Don't go through the wall, but continue on the delightful path that leads you to a gate in the wall ahead. Stride on the grassy way, with Littondale stretching ahead and Fountains Fell to your far right. Carry on along the lower slopes of Plover Hill. Pass through the next gate and follow the way as it swings right and returns you to the high-level road where you have parked.

A little waterfall which feeds into the River Skirfare.

BRITAIN'S BEST-SELLING DOG MAGAZINE
your dog
DEAF NOT DUMB!
THE BIG C
DON'T LET HIM SUFFER IN SILENCE
BEST OF BRITISH
OLDER... AND WISER?
Why mature dogs make great pets

Fact file

Distance: 4 miles/ 6.5km or 7 miles/ 11.2km.

Time: 2½ hours or 4 hours.

Map: Explorer 30.

Start/parking: One of several verges at Hesleden Bergh; grid reference 878749, marked as a viewpoint on the OS map. This lies on the narrow road from Stainforth just before it begins its descent into Littondale.

Terrain: Generally easy walking; expect plenty of mud and wet paths after heavy rain.

Nearest towns: Kettlewell, Leyburn.

Refreshments: Kettlewell or Leyburn.

Public toilets: Kettlewell or Leyburn.

Public transport: For further information contact Traveline on tel. 0870 608 2608.

Your dog-friendly guide to

Hertfordshire

Bedford
Dunstable
Luton
Aylesbury
Aldbury
Hertford
Amersham
Rickmansworth
Slough
London
Reading

This great walk is easy on the legs and takes in the terrific Grand Union Canal.

Ridgeway path & the Grand Union Canal

by Mary Welsh

Walkers and their dogs will enjoy this ramble. After a visit to the pretty village of Aldbury, the route continues to Pitstone Hill on the Ridgeway path. It then returns over the slopes and fields to join the towpath along the Grand Union Canal.

Northfield Grange
Park Hill Farm
Marsh Croft Farm
Grand Union Canal

Walk 2

Route planner

1 From the car park at Tring station, join the road and walk east. After you have passed the last car park for rail commuters go through the opening in the fence on the south side of the road to join the broad, green path, striking across the field. Ignore where it turns back to the road and continue on along the path across the next field. Soon after crossing the horse galloping lane, take the footpath on the left, running to the outskirts of the picturesque village of Aldbury. Soon you arrive at the Valiant Trooper, a splendid old pub. From here, you might wish to explore the village and, lastly, visit the flintstone church.

2 Walk on past the church, heading west, and take the footpath on the right and running up the side of the graveyard, signposted Pitstone Hill. Head on past the outbuildings of Church Farm, taking in the splendid view of the Bridgewater monument on the hill on your right. Once through a metal gate, pick up the narrow path, hemmed on one side by a hedge. Soon, you come to a crossroads of paths; cut across the bridleway and over a stile to the footpath heading up an incline and through the golf course. Once at the top and through the next stile, go through a gate on the left and carry on along the path, which leads to a small wood where the dog can have some freedom. Follow the waymarks,

Aldbury has a delightful duck pond and stocks in its centre and is worth a visit.

You'll find the route to the Ridgeway path clearly signposted.

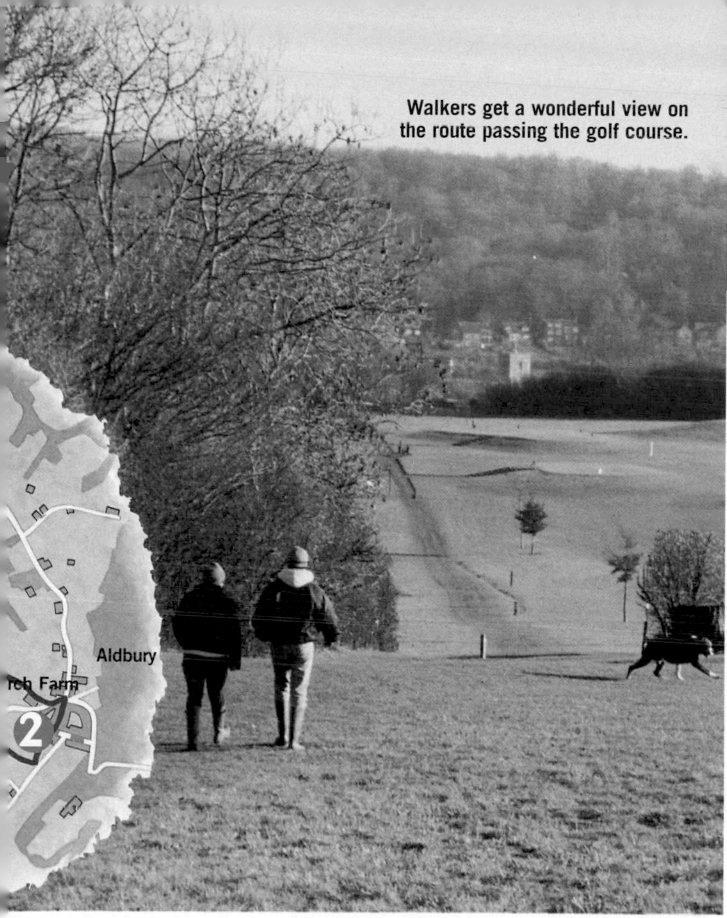

Walkers get a wonderful view on the route passing the golf course.

directing you ahead and then quickly right and left to join the Ridgeway path, which soon winds right, up some log steps.

3 Follow the waymarks through woodland and then on across sheep-cropped downland, with good views north-west and along Grim's Ditch, which was probably Anglo-Saxon boundary earthworks. Go on over Pitstone Hill, and press on to a junction of paths. Here, take the acute left turn to descend the downland slope and then continue on the same contour until you reach a boundary.

4 Turn right here to descend to a lane, where you stroll left. Go past Northfield Grange and on to take a sharp right turn to join a road. Walk on, north, to take the signposted lane on the left to pass close to Park Hill Farm (dogs on the lead). Go over the railway line and pass Marsh Croft Farm to join the towpath of the Grand Union Canal. Dawdle left along the pleasing route and let the dog enjoy lots of free running. Join Station Road and continue to the parking area by the station.

The attractive flintstone church in Aldbury is worth exploring.

Fact file

Distance: 9km/ 5½ miles.

Time: 3 hours.

Map: Explorer 172.

Start/parking: Tring station; grid reference 951122.

Terrain: Easy walking, generally on good paths and tracks.

Nearest town: Tring.

Public toilets: Tring.

Refreshments: The Greyhound pub and the Valiant Trooper, Aldbury, plenty of choice in Tring.

Public transport: Trains from Euston to Tring.

Suitable for: Everyone, but keep dogs under close control where there is livestock.

● There is a shortage of water for dogs on chalk downland, so remember to take some with you.

Your dog-friendly guide to Berkshire

As one of England's classic shires, Berkshire has woodland and parkland stretching in all directions, making this corner of the country an obvious destination for walkers and their four-legged friends.

Sunningdale and Wentworth

by Nick Channer

Despite nearby housing and development, this area along the Surrey border offers an extensive network of attractive woodland paths and peaceful tracks.

Walk 3

Route planner

1 With your back to the Nags Head pub in the centre of Sunningdale, turn left and follow the High Street, keeping the Anglican church on your right and the Baptist church on the left. Pass Church Road and continue along Bedford Lane, crossing a stream. As you reach some bungalows, turn right and follow the path to the A30, where you turn left. Take the main road until you reach a sign on the right for Shrubs Hill Lane and Onslow Road.

2 Stay on the footpath, following it to a junction by a fence — turn right at the waymark. Swing left, heading for a roundabout where you bear left, looking for a path adjacent to a house called Highgate. Follow it through the trees and, when you reach a broader track on a bend, keep left. Skirt the golf course, passing between trees and bracken. As you emerge from the woodland, follow the path across the fairways, keeping left at a junction next to a bunker. Veer left at the first fork, into the trees, and keep going to a junction with an estate drive.

3 Turn left and walk between the imposing detached houses of the exclusive Wentworth Estate. Eventually, you reach the A30. Turn left and follow it down to

Start and finish at the Nags Head.

There is plenty of open space in this area.

Picturesque Coworth Park.

the Berkshire/Surrey border, turning sharp right at a right of way. Follow the shaded path and beyond the wood you reach the buildings of Coworth Park.

4 As you draw level with a bridge, turn left to follow the path across parkland, part of which is used as a polo ground. Cross a track on the far side before walking through the trees and turning left at the road, past some houses. Turn right on reaching a byway, by Sunningdale Bowling Club and a speed restriction sign, following the tarmac drive. Turn left at the next road then, after several paces, swing left at the fork.

From here, it is a short distance back to the start of the walk.

An historic milepost on the A30 illustrates how close you are to London.

Fact file

Distance: 6.5km/ 4 miles.

Time: 1¾ hours.

Map: Explorer 160.

Start/parking: Sunningdale village.

Nearest town: Bracknell.

Refreshments: The Nags Head in Sunningdale serves snacks and meals. Dogs are permitted inside the pub.

Public transport: Contact Traveline, tel. 0870 608 2608.

Stiles: None.

Suitable for: Adults, children and dogs.

Your dog-friendly guide to

Lancashire

Lancaster
Sunderland Point
Fleetwood
Clitheroe
Pendle Hill
Blackpool
Preston
Blackburn
Southport
Bolton

This walk takes you over heather moorland with magnificent views and is guaranteed to delight.

Pendle Hill

by Mary Welsh

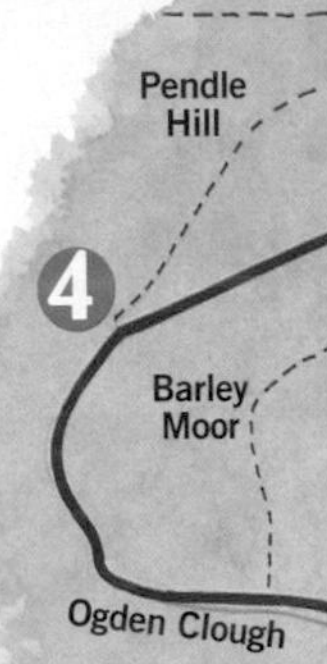

This is an energetic walk to please both walkers and their dogs. It climbs a steepish hill, with magnificent views over Lancashire and then follows good paths over heather moorland and down through a fine valley back to the pretty village of Barley.

Walk 4

Route planner

1 Leave the parking area by a footpath starting from beyond the toilet block. Cross a grassed area and stride a footbridge over the stream. Go on along the footpath to come beside the Barley Mow inn and on past the Tearoom. Then cross the road to take the signed track towards Pendle Hill, with a stream chuckling away beside you and a drink for the dog. Go through a kissing gate and cross a second footbridge. Carry on over a large pasture on the well-signposted Pendle Way, remembering to keep the dog under control. The way soon descends a bank, on the right, crosses the stream and then is signposted left along a surfaced track. Keep to the right, where the way divides, ignore the grassy path and take the metalled way to a group of dwellings. Bear left of a house, following 'path' signs painted on the access track. A short way along, turn right through a metal kissing gate onto a cobbled path, following the sign that says 'This way to Pendle Hill'.

2 Cross a footbridge over the stream, where dippers bob on rocks. Go through a gap stile into pastures, with alders about the stream and the hill towering over you. Here the dog must be on a lead. Carry on through a kissing gate and onto a track. Pass a cottage on your left and go through the next gate to bear right along a farm track. In a few steps, take another gate on the left and press on through two more kissing gates and then another left of Pendle House. Beyond, bear right to a kissing gate in the top right corner to come to the start of the stepped way to the top of the hill.

3 The easy, pitched path, with more freedom for the dog, leads up and up. Pause to catch your breath and savour

Pendle Hill dominates the landscape for miles.

The attractive route up Pendle Hill.

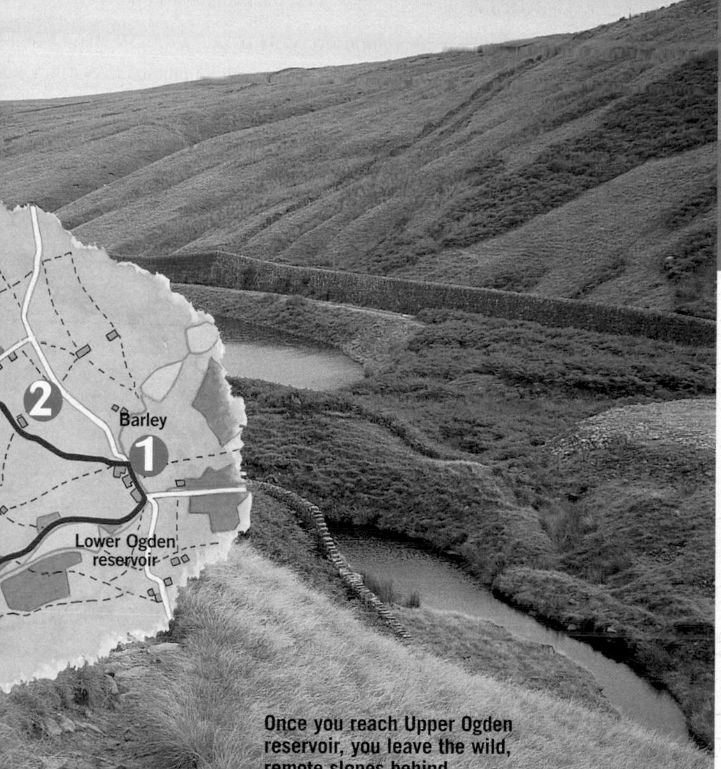

Once you reach Upper Ogden reservoir, you leave the wild, remote slopes behind.

the magnificent views that improve with every step. The stepped way takes you to a stile in the boundary wall, which you ignore. Turn left and follow a worn track across the large, flat summit to the trig point. After another look at the view, continue on to a clear waymarker post for the Pendle Hill circular walk. A few steps on and you stand at the start of the long, paved path across the awesome heather moorland of Pendle Hill. The end of the path brings you to the stream in Ogden Clough, which you step across on stones to join a path going off left.

4 Follow the path as it rises steadily above the stream and carries on along the right side of the steep slopes into the depths of the lonely, treeless hills, with lots of fine sniffs for the dog. When you arrive at a waymark, take the left branch to stroll the narrow path as it winds south through Ogden Clough. It continues high above the stream and then suddenly descends a zig-zagging path down to the side of the stream. Step across on convenient stones, the dog enjoying a good paddle, and join the path on the opposite bank. Turn right to pass through a kissing gate and press on, sometimes through bracken, parallel with the stream and with steep slopes towering up on either side. Just beyond a Pendle Way sign, cross a stream and go on to descend a rough track to a kissing gate.

5 When the Upper Ogden reservoir comes into view, the wild remote slopes are left behind. Scattered trees edge the water and dabchicks dive for food. The path stays high above the reservoir and then passes through a gate to continue along a delightful grassy way to pass the dam. Ignore the path over the dam and descend steeply to a step stile beside a gate. Continue on along the access track, with deciduous woodland to the right and Scots pine to the left. Remain on the wide track to pass through a kissing gate to press on beside the Lower Ogden reservoir. Beyond its dam, descend the narrow lane below beeches and then pass the waterworks building and walk on to the road. Cross, and pass over the road bridge to rejoin the car park on your left.

Fact file

Distance: 9.5km/6 miles.

Time: 3 – 4 hours.

Map: Explorer 41.

Start/parking: Car park in centre of Barley village, grid reference 823404.

Terrain: Clear paths and tracks, well signposted. Steepish ascent to top of hill.

Nearest towns: Barrowford, Clitheroe, Barnoldswick.

Refreshments: Pendle Inn, Barley Mow Inn, the Tearoom — all at Barley.

Public toilets: In car park.

Public transport: Traveline, tel. 0870 608 2608.

Stiles: Two.

Your dog-friendly guide to Ceredigion

Ceredigion (formerly Cardiganshire) should suit you and your dog perfectly, with its gorgeous scenery, fine seascapes, intriguing smells, rich heritage and lots to see – all this and a traditional Welsh welcome too!

Walk 5

Llandysul

by John Needham

This walk never strays very far from historically-interesting Llandysul in its beautiful setting on the River Teifi (pronounced Tie-vey). There is some fairly steep climbing out of the river valley, but you enjoy wonderful views as the reward and a delightful riverside stroll.

Route planner

1 Turn right out of the car park. Walk a short distance and, opposite the church, go up a steep lane between Porth Terrace and Church Street into High Street. Turn right again, cross over and walk past a fine Victorian-fronted draper's shop (Siop y Jones) and a fish and chip shop. Go left up another short lane opposite the Kings Arms and turn right yet again.

2 A few paces along, a lane with a handrail climbs up on the left. Here you have a choice: a direct route uphill to point 4 — if your cardiovascular system is sound — with a wonderful backward view; or a less energetic ascent, but without the view. If taking the first route, turn directly up the lane, crossing a further street and going up a narrow path alongside the playground of an old school. Through a kissing gate into a field, the footpath heads unrelentingly upwards, but you can zigzag to ease the gradient if you like! There may be stock in here, but usually they're in adjoining fields. Resist the temptation to look back. At the top of the field, at a second gate, you can turn and look: take in the glorious view of grey-roofed Llandysul and the sparkling river looping through the valley.
The tree-cloaked slope on the far side is a nature reserve. Continue through the next field and out into a housing estate. Go past garages and along a road to a junction (point 4).

3 If taking the gentler route, continue along the street. Where it curves and drops downhill continue upwards along the right of two parallel access roads (the one you

Llandysul is named after St Tysul's Church.

You'll see these carved chairs along the riverside path

The beautiful River Teifi rushing to the sea.

want has speed bumps). Go past several garages and then bungalows. At a final bungalow, enter a green lane between fields and continue uphill. This is a good spot to let the dog off the lead. Eventually, you reach a wide gate leading into housing. Turn left and follow the road to point 4.

4 Go left along the road out of the estate, skirting a school playing field, until it meets an open road. Almost opposite, go through another kissing gate. Walk down a very narrow path and then a field behind the school. Immediately after, you come to a new leisure centre, which you leave via its main entrance. Across the road opposite is the start of another footpath. Follow this as it drops back down into the valley, with glimpses of distant views. Four-legged friends can be safely off-lead again. A final stepped section and you're beside the foaming, urgent Teifi rushing over its rocky bed.

5 First, turn left along the riverside path to the bridge to read the information board. Then, walk beside the river. Buildings on the opposite bank, many former wool factories, rise directly from the water and look rather Venetian. Continue until the path is barred by a gate and a 'no trespassing' sign. Unfortunately, there's no right of way beyond this point, except to fishermen.

6 Retrace your steps to point 5. Carry on past to the bridge, emerging into the street. Walk up towards the town, past a white chapel, then into a street coming in from the right. A short distance along, go down a metalled path on your right to the recreation fields.

7 Pick up the river again, calm at this point before its frantic rush after the bridge. Dogs have to be on the lead now. Follow the Teifi along its looping course, with Llandysul stacked in layers up the valley side, back to the car park and perhaps a cafe.

Fact file

Distance: 2 – 2½ miles.

Time: 1½ – 2 hours.

Map: Explorer 185.

Start/finish: Llandysul car park.

Terrain: Paths, fields, two shortish sections of street walking, one steep climb (avoidable).

Nearest town: Llandysul.

Refreshments: Several cafes and shops in Llandysul.

Public transport: None to speak of.

Suitable for: Families with older children.

Your dog-friendly guide to West Sussex

Farnham
Crawley
Horsham
Nuthurst
Midhurst
Lavington Common
Worthing
Chichester
Brighton

Experience the beautiful countryside of West Sussex with this walk, suitable for everyone.

Nuthurst

by Sylvie Dobson

Despite its closeness to the bustling market town of Horsham, the village of Nuthurst seems to belong to a bygone age. The surrounding countryside is a delight to explore.

Walk 6

Home Wood
4
Nuthur

Route planner

1 With your back to the church, cross the road and take the drive to Cooks Farm. On your left are the premises of Architectural Plants and, as you walk along, you can get a glimpse of the range of exotic trees and shrubs. Follow the drive around to the left and then fork right to pass a renovated barn and stable block. Now go left away from the main drive to a wide dirt track that soon takes you into the shade of the trees.

2 Maintain direction until you come to a junction of five tracks. Take the second on the right and begin a gentle ascent through the forest. After a short period of level walking, you will start to descend towards a footbridge. Once across, take the right fork and after another gentle climb you will find yourself out in the open on a much narrower path. Follow it through a gap in the hedge and then down to the tiny hamlet of Minks Gate.

3 Walk right — there is a good verge — before turning left in front of the board for the Nuthurst Society. The way ahead appears barred by a metal gate, but, if you look to the right of it, you will find a path that leads up by the side of Keystone Cottage. When you reach the top, go left, disregarding any but the main path, and enjoy a delightful walk through mixed forest. There may be some muddy patches, but these are easily avoided.

4 Eventually, the track becomes an access road and you will pass two cottages. Just beyond the second one, go left on a narrow path that descends through trees. Go over a crossing track and then, with open views ahead, follow

Nuthurst church.

Through the trees.

Bluebells in late spring.

the hedge to the right. Go through one gate and then bear left to another one. Now it's just a case of maintaining direction over open pastureland guided by a succession of gates. There is the possibility of livestock grazing in adjacent fields. You finally join a farm drive where you turn left to Nuthurst, conveniently arriving opposite to the Black Horse Inn. You will find the church along to your right.

The welcoming Black Horse at Nuthurst.

Fact file

Distance: 5.6 km/ 3½ miles.

Time: 1½ hours.

Map: Explorer 134.

Start/parking: Nuthurst village. There is parking on the street in front of the church or school.

Terrain: Lovely woodland paths. Good underfoot except after heavy rain when it can be muddy. Undulating, but not demanding.

Nearest town: Horsham.

Refreshments: The Black Horse Inn at Nuthurst where dogs are allowed. It does not offer all-day opening. Wide choice in nearby Horsham.

Public Transport: Not good. There is a daily post bus from Horsham but times are geared to school hours. You could start at Monks Gate, which has a regular service to Horsham. Contact Traveline, tel. 0870 608 2608.

Stiles: None.

Suitable for: Adults nd children, but especially dogs.

Your dog-friendly guide to Loch Lomondsl

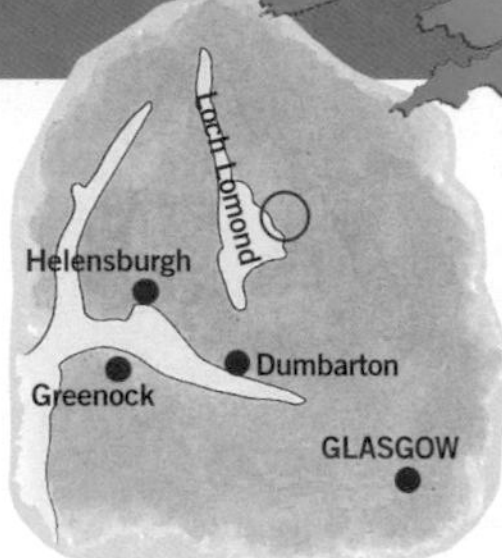

Loch Lomond is the largest fresh water loch in the UK. The area, renowned for its rugged beauty, is also teaming with 200 species of birds and over a quarter of Britain's wild flowers.

Sallochy and the West Highland Way

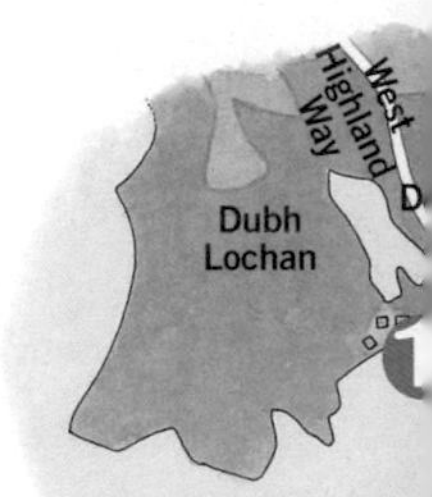

by Mary Welsh

Enjoy this delightful walk through the Sallochy oak woodland, where the dogs can have some freedom. The return is along the east shore of magnificent Loch Lomond.

Route planner

1 Walk back from the shore towards the B-road and take, on the right, the path that cuts off a corner to come to the edge of the road. Cross and walk up the narrow path opposite, which climbs gently through a wide ride in the forest, with conifers to the right and larch set back to the left. Where the path divides, take the unsigned left branch to walk beside a pretty tumbling burn, where dogs can have a swim or a drink, passing through the oaks of this most attractive glen. After passing a blue waymarker, cross a footbridge to the other side of the dancing stream and walk on. At the next waymark, turn left up a short slope, to reach a deer fence adorned with orange netting. Walk right, with the fence to your left and beautiful oak woodland to your right. Follow the blue waymarked path as it winds right into the trees. Go up a slope and wind round, right, again to descend to the next waymark.

2 Turn left and climb a steepish gravel and grass path through more pleasing woodland to join a wide forest road. Look ahead and slightly left to see a shapely conical hill, Dun Maoil. Turn right and descend for nearly a quarter of a

Loch Lomond is a perfect example of the rugged and beautiful landscape visitors can enjoy in Scotland.

A pretty tumbling burn where dogs can enjoy a drink or a quick paddle.

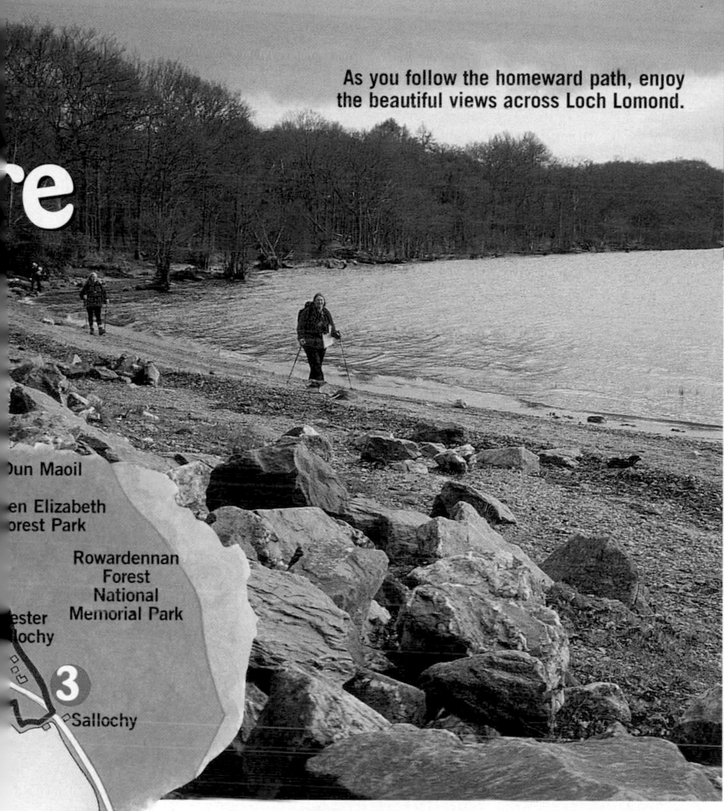

As you follow the homeward path, enjoy the beautiful views across Loch Lomond.

mile. Just after a blue waymark, take a narrow path, left, to walk a short diversion. This leads through an idyllic part of the oak woodland to pass between a small disused slate quarry on the left and two heaps of spoil on the right, with an interesting information board close by. The path then continues, leading you through the woodland to rejoin the forest road. Turn left and descend to the B-road.

3 Here, go left for less than an eigth of a mile to cross the road and take the West Highland Way, which leads off right and heads through oaks towards the shore of Loch Lomond. Follow the delightful path as it takes you on through more glorious oaks. Then, after this very pleasing stretch, the path turns inland and climbs upwards, first by a path and then by steps, beside a huge rock face, to a ridge above. If the trees are not too dense you should, with care, be able to move left to enjoy a fine view of the loch. Having crossed over the large crag, go on down a gravel path, which descends easily almost to the B-road. The path then swings towards the shore once more and leads you out on to the beach at the Sallochy parking area.

The view's great from here, but we're too puffed to look at the moment.

Fact file

Distance: 2½ miles/4km.

Time: 2 hours.

Map: Explorer 364.

Start/parking: Sallochy parking area on the shore of Loch Lomond; grid reference 380958.

Terrain: Easy walking on paths and a forest road.

Nearest town: Dumbarton.

Refreshments: Rowardennan, Milarrochy or Balmaha.

Public toilets: Rowardennan and Milarrochy.

Public transport: Trains from Glasgow to Balloch every 45 minutes (30-minute journey); HAD coaches, tel. 01501 820 598, from Balloch to Balmaha (45-minute journey), followed by two-mile walk on a 'No through road' to Cashel and two miles further on to Sallochy.

Further information: Loch Lomond Shores' tourist information centre, tel. 01301 702260.

Your dog-friendly guide to

Gloucestershire

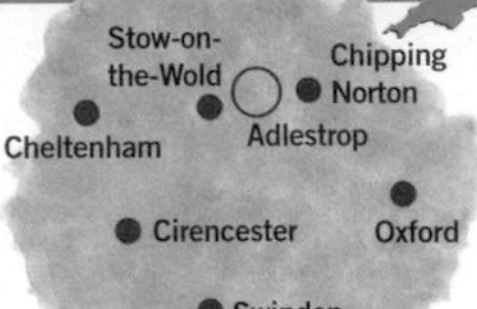

Home to the Cotswolds, the Severn Vale and source of the River Thames, the beautiful county of Gloucestershire boasts a treasure trove of wonderful walks for you and your dog to enjoy.

Adlestrop, Oddington and Daylesford

by Nick Channer

Explore the picturesque village of Adlestrop, made famous by the Edwardian poet Edward Thomas, before crossing rolling Gloucestershire landscape to reach archetypal parkland on this attractive walk which offers something for everyone.

Walk 8

Route planner

1 Keep the famous Adlestrop railway sign on your left and walk through the centre of the village, passing the post office. When the road forks, veer right for the church. Join a track just beyond it and continue down to a lake and kissing gate. Keep the cricket ground on your right and when the track curves left by four trees, pass between them to follow a sunken path across the field to two stiles.

2 Cross over to a lane and turn left to the main road. Turn right and follow the A436. Cross the railway line and look down to the site of Adlestrop's long-vanished station. Continue to the turning for Lower Oddington and follow the road into the village. Pass The Fox pub and walk along to a left turning opposite Forge House.

3 Follow the lane to the church of St Nicholas, keeping it on your left. Avoid a left-hand footpath and take the next left bridleway. Head down through the fields, following the waymarks, and turn right in the bottom corner to reach a footbridge. Cross over to a gate and follow the track over the railway line. Keep alongside the hedge; turn right at the road.

4 Pass New Farm and turn left at the next bridleway sign. Head towards Daylesford House; keep left at the fork and follow the drive between paddocks. Pass the estate

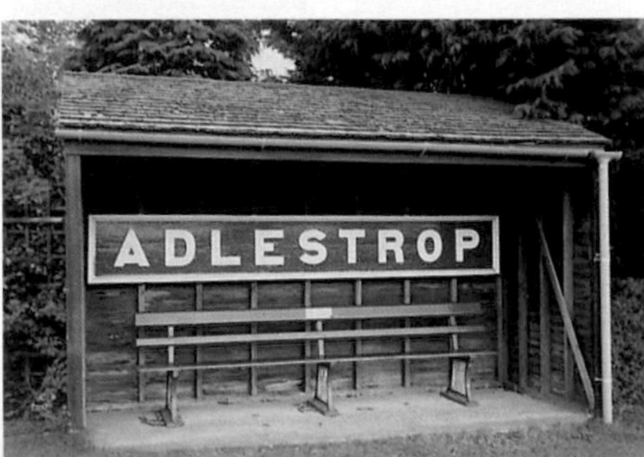

The old station sign at Adlestrop, which caught the attention of Edward Thomas as he arrived there by train.

Picturesque cottages in Lower Oddington; you'll pass through the village on this walk.

Adlestrop Church — note that Queen Victoria's Diamond Jubilee is celebrated in the wrought iron arch.

office and turn left by Hill Farm Cottage. Pass between buildings, cross over at an intersection of tracks and break cover from the trees.

5 Swing right after a couple of hundred yards and follow the waymarks, cutting diagonally right across the paddock to a gate in the corner. Continue ahead through the trees to reach the A436. Turn left, pass a turning to Adlestrop and Evenlode and turn right at a stile. Follow the woodland path as it runs parallel to the road, eventually joining the road and returning to the station sign at Adlestrop.

Sunny glades and woodland drives are revealed as you stroll through Daylesford Park.

Fact file

Distance: 5 miles.

Time: 2 hours.

Map: Explorer OL45.

Start/parking: Adlestrop village centre.

Nearest towns: Moreton-in-Marsh, Chipping Norton.

Refreshments: The Fox at Lower Oddington welcomes well-behaved dogs.

Public transport: Contact Traveline, tel. 0870 608 2608.

Stiles: Three.

Suitable for: Reasonably fit families and dogs.

Your dog-friendly guide to Cumbria

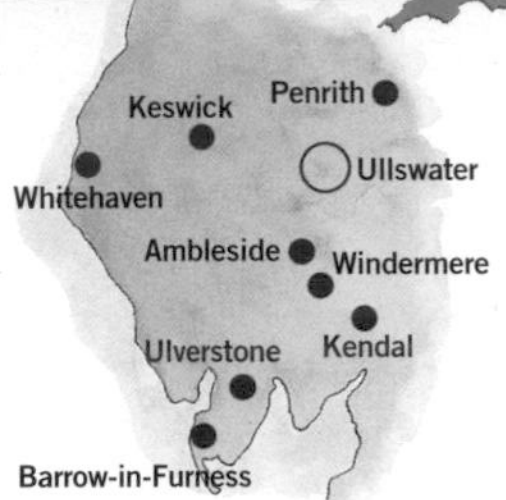

Home to the world-famous Lake District, the northern county of Cumbria boasts spectacular scenery and a wealth of fantastic walks over breathtaking terrain.

Ullswater

by Mary Welsh

A trip on the Ullswater ferry from Glenridding to Howtown provides an exciting start to this walk. Dogs are taken on the trip regularly and they seem quite happy to be on the water. The walk back along the footpath, which is easy to follow, has often been said to be the most delightful in Lakeland.

Walk 9

Route planner

1 From the pier at Howtown walk along the railed jetty. Cross the footbridge on the right, following the signpost directions for Sandwick. Stride the pleasant path and, at the next signpost, follow the directions for Patterdale. Climb the steps and, at the top, walk right along the level path, perhaps to sit on a seat from where you can enjoy the glorious view over the lake; above you is Hallin Fell. Continue on the path over Kailpot Crag and follow the pleasing way through the oaks of Hallinhag Wood, where there are plenty of enticing smells for your dog to enjoy. Go on until you come near to the shore and walk with care over the exposed tree roots.

2 Go on along the path to come to a kissing gate near the shore. Beyond is a delightful shingle reach of the lake where your dog might like a romp in the water. Pass through a kissing gate on your left and then go through two more gates. Turn left to walk below a row of fine larches and beside Sandwick Beck. Cross the hurrying stream by going over the wooden bridge, into the hamlet of Sandwick. Turn left to walk the metalled road and then right beyond Townhead Cottage, the last building on the right. Climb a steep track to where the way levels out and continues beside a wall and a fence on your right. Pass a delightful barn then cross the bridge over Scalehow Beck, where the dog can have a drink and a splash (and children can paddle).

Ullswater is the second largest lake in the Lake District, curving through nearly eight miles of mountain scenery.

Glenridding nestles in the Ullswater valley, next to the great lake thought to be named after an early Viking settler.

Whatever the time of year, the Lake District scenery is stunning; this is the path by Ullswater in winter.

3 Press on along the path as it climbs and then goes on up beside a wall beyond which is Scalehow Wood. Here you might spot Scalehow Force, a fine waterfall, through the trees. Carry on to Long Crag, a high point with a dramatic view. Then, as you descend towards the lake, you pass scree slopes where birches thrive. Go on down the path through scattered birch, juniper and rowans to the slopes below Birkfell Earth. Then the trees cease and you cross a small beck that issues from Silver Crag. Stroll on the clear way with the attractive Silver Bay and its beach to your right, just before Silver Point. Saunter on as the path winds round below Silver Crag and continues uphill towards a walled way through woodland (more dog sniffs here).

4 Go on past a steep-gabled barn and a huge oak tree, and then go on to Side Farm, where you turn right for Glenridding, as directed by the signpost. Stroll the wide track through pastures to cross Goldrill Beck. At the road, put the dog on the lead before you cross to turn right. Pass St Patrick's Church. The pavement runs out here so cross the road again. This area is known as The Butts where archery was practised and the stocks stood. Continue on and take the permitted path through trees until the pavement runs out again. Then cross the road once more, with care, to take another permitted path that goes on through trees, above the road. This returns you to the road. Cross it again to go through a gate in the fence. Stride the track past a small snack bar, with the lake to your right. The track returns you to the car park and the pier.

Fact file

Distance: 7 miles.

Time: 3 hours walking; half an hour on the boat.

Map: Explorer OL5.

Start/parking: Car park at Glenridding pier; grid reference 390169.

Terrain: Distinct path or track, with a few ups and downs; occasionally rough under foot.

Nearest towns: Ambleside, Penrith.

Public toilets: At entrance to car park; toilets on steamers.

Refreshments: Glenridding, Patterdale, Pooley Bridge; hot drinks on boats.

Public transport: Stagecoach Cumberland and Ullswater Rambler 37 from Workington via Keswick. The Patterdale bus 108 provides a long summer service; contact Traveline on tel. 0870 608 2608 for details. Contact Ullswater Steamers on tel. 017684 82229.

Suitable for: All except very young children.

Your dog-friendly guide to

The Isle of Wi

It was Queen Victoria and Prince Albert who made the Isle of Wight fashionable when they built a holiday home at Cowes. Today, the island remains a popular haunt of visitors and walkers, and there are many miles of paths and tracks to enjoy both inland and on the spectacular coast.

Yarmouth and Fort Victoria

by Nick Channer

Start this walk immediately you step off the ferry at Yarmouth, and soon you are leaving the crowds and traffic behind as you follow the tranquil River Yar south towards Freshwater. The walk's return leg flirts with the coast and from here you enjoy stunning views across the Needles Passage to the Hampshire mainland.

Walk 10

Route planner

1 From the ferry terminal, make for the roundabout; keep left towards Newport and pass a car park on the right. Follow the road round to the left, pass the primary school and then turn into Mill Road. Approach a left-hand bend and go straight on along the footpath signposted Freshwater and Broad Lane.

2 Keep the River Yar on your right and follow the path south. Make for a gate; keep right at the junction and follow bridleway Y19. Eventually you reach a bungalow and road. Turn right here and cross the bridge, passing a pillbox as you go. Walk up the lane into Freshwater, keeping the parish church and the Red Lion on your right.

3 Go straight on at the junction, towards Freshwater and Totland, passing the post office on your right. Veer right just beyond it to join path F66 (signposted School Green/Golden Hill). Pass a path to Church Place

Yarmouth harbour marks the start of the walk.

The view across the Needles Passage to Hurst Castle.

The walk follows the picturesque River Yar.

and continue ahead. On reaching a school and bridleway on the left (F18), turn right and climb alongside trees and a bungalow.

4 Pass through woodland, avoid a turning on the left, and continue to Golden Hill. Head down to a junction. On the right is the entrance to the old fort and opposite it is a plaque. Follow the track towards Totland and Yarmouth, passing to the right of industrial buildings. Turn left at the main road and then right into Monks Lane.

5 Pass a sign for Linstone Chine holiday village and go straight on, following the Isle of Wight coast path. Avoid a path to Norton and when you reach the entrance to Cliff End holiday village, go right, still following the coastal trail. Pass a sign for Fort Victoria Country Park, go down some steps and then walk through the woods.

6 Turn left at the sign for toilets and follow the path to Fort Victoria. Pass the building and take the exit road, keeping the Solent and Needles Passage on your left. Rejoin the coast path and follow the road for approximately 80 metres. At a sign 'Danger — bathing prohibited', turn left on to path F6 for Yarmouth. Follow it through the trees to the shore and turn right. Swing right at a sign 'Access by foot to Yarmouth town centre', to reach the road. Turn left and return to the ferry terminal.

Fact file

Distance: 6 miles.

Time: 2¼ hours.

Map: Explorer OL29.

Start: Yarmouth town centre.

Nearest town: Newport.

Refreshments: Pubs and cafes in Yarmouth, the Red Lion at Freshwater (dogs on leads), and the cafe in Fort Victoria Country Park.

Public transport: Contact Traveline on tel. 0870 608 2608. Regular ferry services between Lymington and Yarmouth, Southampton and Cowes, and Portsmouth and Ryde.

Stiles: None.

Suitable for: Adults, children and dogs.

Your dog-friendly guide to Aberdeenshire

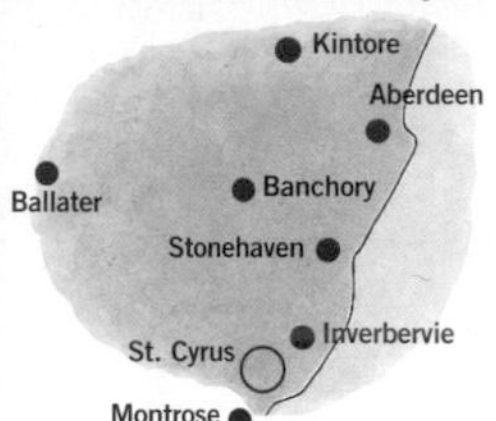

Scotland's wild beauty is just as stunning in the winter months as in summer and offers some wonderful walks to keep out the winter chills.

St Cyrus

by Mary Welsh

When visiting St Cyrus National Nature Reserve in winter choose a day when the North Sea is quiet; you and your dog can enjoy a long walk over the sands and up on the cliffs. In summer you'll find a riot of wild flower colour, from the deep violet of clustered bellflower to the delicate thrift or sea pink.

Route planner

1 Leave the car park, join the railed way and note the request about dog walking. Walk left and then follow the boardwalk across the dune slacks where, in high summer, clustered bellflower, rest harrow and yellow bedstraw grow. Descend to the beach, a wonderful curve of golden sand, stretching south to Montrose and north to Nether Woodston. Turn left and begin your stroll along the sands. Stretching out to the sea from the beach, as they have done since the 13th century, are salmon fishing nets. Offshore you might spot scoters and velvet scoters, the latter with bright white wing patches. To your left, behind the dunes, rear spectacular lava cliffs.

2 As you approach several huge rocky outcrops, take the waymarked route, an attractive flower-lined path that climbs gently up the cliffs to Woodston fishing station. Follow the way as it winds left to join a reinforced track that passes between outbuildings. Go on round with the track from where there is a marvellous view of the bay. Carry on past a house and turn left to walk a path along the cliff top. Soon you can glimpse the spire of the church at St Cyrus. The delightful path leads to a small open area with three seats; the views here are stunning.

Rocky outcrops mark the spot from where the path climbs gently up to the cliffs.

This part of Aberdeenshire is stunning in both summer and winter.

The beach at St Cyrus is stunning in the winter.

Just beyond is a small car park from which a few steps descend to a well-placed seat. From here a path leads down the steep cliffs to the shore. At the time of writing, this was closed because of a recent landslip. If you are unable to descend, return along the cliff top and go down the path taken earlier to the waymark at its foot.

3 Walk a narrow sandy path, right, through the marram grass, passing under the steep cliffs. Go on the wider way behind the fishing huts, with their poles in place for drying the nets. On your right, the track is joined by the paths that you might have used before the landslip. Look for fulmars nesting on the ledges of the cliffs and here you might spot a merlin hurtling across the bay after its prey. Eventually you arrive at the beautifully-maintained Nether Kirkyard. The ancient name of the parish it served was Ecclesgreig and from this the name St Cyrus was derived. There are some interesting plaques to read in the burial ground. Beyond the kirk, pass a huge pasture of barley on the right and the dune slacks to the left as you return to the car park.

The boardwalk crosses the sand dunes which are a mass of colour in summer when the wild flowers are in bloom.

Fact file

Distance: 3 – 4 miles, depending on which path you take to return to the shore from the cliffs.

Time: 1 – 2 hours.

Maps: Explorer 382; Landranger 45.

Start/parking: Car park; grid reference 742635, opposite the small visitor centre. To reach St Cyrus, drive six miles north of Montrose. Leave the A92 immediately north of the viaduct across the River North Esk, to turn right along a narrow lane, signposted 'Beach', and drive on for just over a mile.

Terrain: Easy along the sands; a well-graded path up on to a good path along the cliffs.

Nearest town: Montrose.

Refreshments: St Cyrus and Montrose.

Public toilets: Opposite car park.

Suitable for: All the family. No fresh water along the beach or on the cliff top so remember to take some for your dog.

Publisher's Note

While every effort is made to ensure accuracy, we regret that FHG Publications cannot accept responsibility for errors, omissions or misrepresentations in our entries or any consequences thereof. Prices in particular should be checked because we go to press early. We will follow up complaints but cannot act as arbiters or agents for either party.

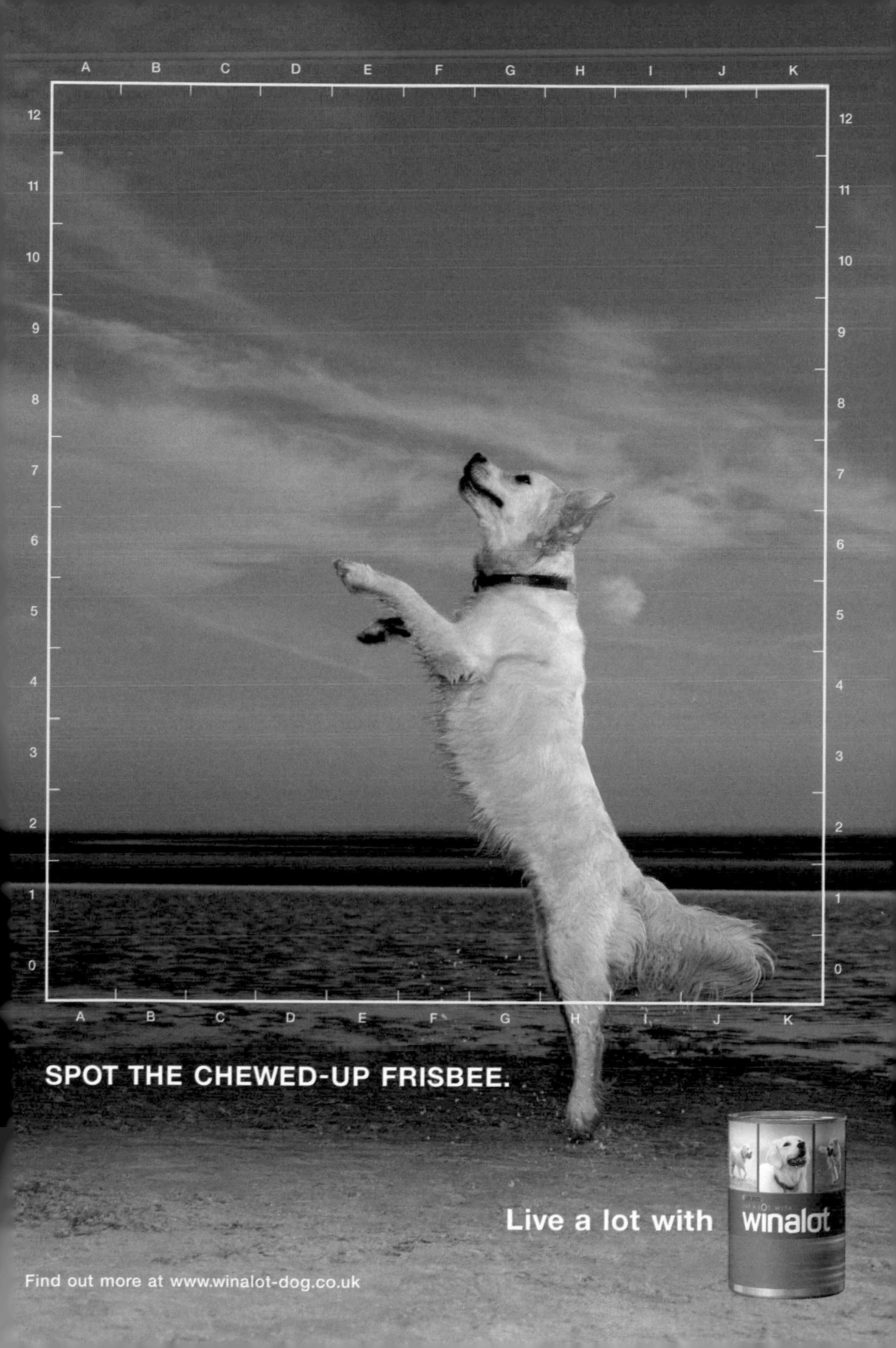

A B C D E F G H I J K
12 11 10 9 8 7 6 5 4 3 2 1 0
SPOT THE CHEWED-UP FRISBEE.
Live a lot with winalot
Find out more at www.winalot-dog.co.uk